# PHYSICAL SCIENCE FOUNDATIONS

## 5TH EDITION

# J. WARD MOODY

## EDITOR

BYU ACADEMIC
PUBLISHING

*Editor*

J. Ward Moody

*Assistant Editor*

M. Jeannette Lawler

*Authors/Contributors*

Scott Bergeson
Juliana Boerio-Goates
David V. Dearden
Eric Hirschmann
Michael D. Joner
Bart J. Kowallis
M. Jeannette Lawler
J. Ward Moody
Steven Nelson
Randy Skinner
R. Steven Turley

*Editors on previous editions*

J. Ward Moody
Scott Bergeson
Eric Hirschmann
B. Kent Harrison

*Managing/Production Editor*

Kent Minson

*Illustrations*

Scott Layton, Kent Minson, Christopher
Henderson, Kelli Rane, Jennifer Berry, Devin
LuBean, Annalee Palowski

*Photography*

Kent Minson, Kelli Rane

*Typesetting*

Kent Minson

*Printer*

BYU Print and Mail Production Center
Doug Maxwell, LaMont Schofield, Ed Godinez

Copyright © 2017
by BYU Academic Publishing and Brigham Young University
ALL RIGHTS RESERVED.
No part of this work covered by the copyright herein may be
reproduced or used in any form or by any means—graphic,
electronic, or mechanical, including photocopying, recording,
taping, web distribution or information storage and retrieval
systems—without the written permission of the publisher.
ISBN: 9781611650242

For more information contact:
BYU Academic Publishing
3995 WSC, Provo, UT 84602
(801) 422–6231
academicpublishing@byu.edu
http://academicpublishing.byu.edu
To report ideas or text corrections email us at:
textideas@byu.edu
For permission to use material from this text or product, contact
us by:
Tel (801) 422–6231 • Fax (801) 422–0070

*Every great advance in science has issued from a new audacity of imagination.*

*John Dewey*

# Contents

*The most exciting phrase to hear in science, the one that heralds new discoveries, is not "Eureka" but "That's funny . . ."*

Isaac Asimov

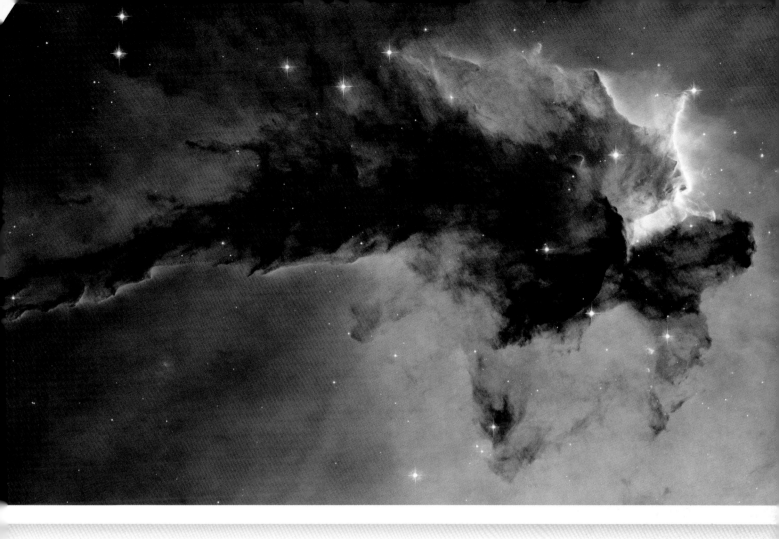

# Preface

*Equipped with his five senses, man explores the universe around him and calls the adventure Science.*

*Edwin Powell Hubble*

To those who anciently understood life through mythology, the world functioned according to the will and whimsy of temperamental gods. Slowly, steadily, this view gave way to the realization that the universe unfolds though processes governed, not by whim, but by law. The practice of discovering, comprehending, and applying these laws is "physical science," and is one of human kind's greatest triumphs.

Knowing laws that govern the world enables us to use them to our benefit. In 1969, when the engines of the Saturn V moon rocket roared to life, it was with the full expectation that, through complicated maneuvers based on immutable laws of motion, men would land on the moon and return safely, which they did. This is but one of countless ways we have harnessed nature's laws to our benefit. Small wonder that science commands near universal respect.

In the development of science, ideas come first, followed by technical detail. Ideas such as *matter is made of molecules, forces cause acceleration,* or *continents drift about on the surface of Earth,* are remarkably simple and straight-forward. We need not understand the details to gain insight into how these fundamental ideas shape our lives. Therefore a goal of this text is to show how a few fundamental concepts can be used as a foundation to understand much of the complexity around us.

Which, of all the ideas from science, are truly most foundational? We chose to emphasize the basic physical and chemical laws and processes that undergird geology and astronomy specifically. Many ideas will be familiar, like Newton's laws of motion or the periodic table of elements. Other ideas, like Archimedes' principle of buoyancy, metallic bonding, the techniques of geological dating, or finding distances to galaxies, may be new. As you read this text, we hope the flow of logic from assumption to conclusion is clear and fills you with the awe and wonder of the logic of it all. We hope this presentation strengthens your reasoning skills and improves your ability to gather and evaluate evidence in *any* field of endeavor.

We especially hope that an increased appreciation of the workings of the physical universe strengthens faith in law, order, and purpose. Those of us who have worked on this presentation are not all of the same faith. But we all believe the physical sciences testify of an ultimate Author of the universe, whom we better understand through learning His work.

We in the College of Physical and Mathematical Sciences at Brigham Young University owe a debt of gratitude to many people who have made this book possible. We are indebted to William Dibble, Jae Ballif, John Merrill, Grant Mason, Kenneth Hamblin, Richard Snow, Dana Griffen, and James Thorne, who all wrote portions of earlier texts from which this one derives. We are grateful to Juliana Boerio-Goates, Bart Kowallis, M. Jeannette Lawler, Michael Joner, Steven Turley, David Dearden, Scott Bergeson, Stephen Nelson, Randy Skinner, and Eric Hirshmann, who contributed much time and effort in writing the current chapters. We are indebted to Kent Minson and Jennifer Berry and their wonderful staff of illustrators, editors and photographers who have made the book presentable and interesting. We are grateful to Deans Earl Woolley and Scott Sommerfeldt and Associate Dean Dana Griffen of the College of Physical and Mathematical Sciences and the chairs and staff of the departments of Physics and Astronomy, Chemistry and Biochemistry, and Geology for continued support and patience throughout many drafts and editions. We especially thank BYU Academic Publishing for investing the resources and talent necessary to make this project a success.

—J. Ward Moody

# Knowledge, Science, and the Universe

*The important thing is not to stop questioning. Curiosity has its own reason for existing. One cannot help but be in awe when he contemplates the mysteries of eternity, of life, of the marvelous structure of reality. It is enough if one tries merely to comprehend a little of this mystery every day. Never lose a holy curiosity.*

*Albert Einstein*

## 1

## LEARN

- To identify and describe the four ways we learn.

- The scientific method and how it generates knowledge.

- Six basic assumptions the scientific method rests upon.

- The four interactions of nature and the scope of their influence.

You are a born explorer. From the cradle your natural curiosity led you to investigate the world around you. As a baby you looked at something you did not understand then instinctively tried to grab it, feel it, touch it, taste it. These experiments taught you that candy tastes good or touching a hot stove is painful! In a remarkably short amount of time you learned and remembered an enormous body of facts about what to embrace and what to avoid. From a young age, and without any training, you have been learning through experimentation.

The process scientists follow to gain knowledge, known formally as the "scientific method," is the same process you followed while experimenting as a toddler. Just as you gained knowledge from your explorations by the sensations they created, scientists gain knowledge from their explorations by the results they observe and measure. The scientific method is not a foreign approach to learning—it is a familiar, natural extension of our ability to scrutinize the world with an inquiring eye.

The scientific method has yielded some of

the greatest ideas ever thought by mankind. These elegant ideas have changed the way people presently look at the world and have shaped expectations for the future. Hopefully these ideas have affected or will affect and shape your thinking as well.

Science proves ideas right or wrong by discovering whether or not predictions match experience. In a careful and deliberate way it leads mankind to truth. Even so, actually knowing what is true is not as straightforward as one might think. So let us first consider how we know what we know.

## 1-1  How We Gain Knowledge

We often assume that we know something without realizing how this knowledge is built from the information presented to us. Information may come to us as signals to our brains from our eyes, ears, hands, etc., while other information comes in less physical ways. Although we all live in the same world, each of us weighs differently the value and validity of the information we receive. This difference in judgment creates a view of the real world that is unique to each of us. In essence, every person is a philosopher, creating his or her own view of the world from shared sources of knowledge.

These "shared sources of knowledge" are **authority**, **intuition**, **reason**, and **sensory data**.

### Authority

Learning through authority means trusting the knowledge possessed by another person or some other source and accepting it as true, even though you yourself have not had the experiences through which your accepted authority gained his or her knowledge. The authority could be a parent, scholar, historian, reporter, leader, scripture, or any of a number of other sources. In cases of conflicting claims of knowledge between competing authorities, we often give precedence to those that come to us from antiquity and thus have been tested by time, or to those that are held to be true by the greatest number and so have been validated by the most witnesses. Perhaps we might give greater weight

**Authority:**
An accepted source of expert information or advice.

**Intuition:**
The act or faculty of knowing or sensing without the use of rational processes; it involves immediate cognition.

**Reason:**
The capacity for logical, rational, and analytic thought—intelligence.

**Sensory Data:**
Knowledge obtained through the senses.

**Figure 1.1**
Much of our learning comes from following authority.

**Figure 1.2**
Intuitive learning is direct and pure but personal. Great moments of learning often come with an intuitive "flash of insight."

to knowledge from a prestigious source, someone with a special perspective, such as an astronomer telling us about the stars. Much, possibly the majority, of our knowledge comes from authority because our own sphere of experience is so limited compared to the world at large.

The strength of this source of knowledge is that it allows us to accept and learn from the experience of others, so that we do not have to experience all things ourselves. Its weakness is that sources of authority may conflict with each other, and we cannot resolve competing claims of truth without reference to one of the other sources. How do we know which sources of authority to trust?

### *Intuition*

We define intuition as knowledge imparted to us through methods outside our five physical senses. Inspiration and revelation are in this category, as are "hunches" or "feelings" or a "belief" that something is correct or true. Because intuitive experiences often come after contemplating questions relating to the meaning and purpose of life, intuition is often regarded as religious knowledge. However, the scientific process benefits from intuition as well. Albert Einstein and other great scientists have freely acknowledged that intuitive thinking was the genesis of many of their ideas. Einstein unashamedly confessed that intuition guided his scientific judgment.

The inner experiences of intuition may be impossible to articulate or quantify scientifically, but nonetheless, they are deeply felt, convinc-

ing, and direct. Individuals who experience this source of knowledge often alter their lives and perform deeds that the other sources of knowledge seldom inspire.

Intuition's greatest strength is that it may be knowledge from the giver of life who knows all things. But it is possible that several individuals may experience a similar intuitive event, yet have an individual interpretation of it that may be difficult to describe to someone else. It is this privateness, this inaccessibility to public scrutiny, that is the weakness of intuitive knowledge. How do we know if our intuition is right or if our interpretation of it is correct and properly communicated?

### *Reason*

Reason is knowledge derived from assumptions and conclusions. An example of reason is the mathematical proof. We begin with basic assumptions, such as Euclid's five postulates of geometry, and proceed to logical, inescapable, and indisputable conclusions. You can write the conclusions down, describe the process by which they are obtained, and subject the argument to public scrutiny. These are the strengths of reason.

The main weakness of reason is the set of assumptions that are the basis for the argument. If the assumptions are reliable, then the conclusions should be reliable. If an assumption is false then some of the reasoning is surely false as well. With limited knowledge, we may not always

**Figure 1.3**
Reason builds conclusions from basic assumptions.

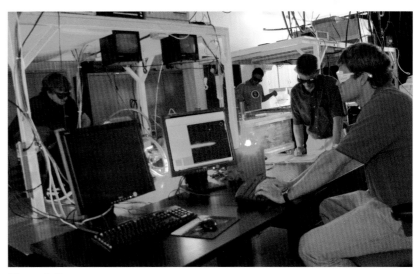

**Figure 1.4**
Sensory data taken under carefully controlled conditions tells us how the universe acts.

choose the best assumption. How do we know our assumptions are valid, and that our reasoning is done correctly?

### Sensory Data

We define sensory data or "sensation" as experience obtained through the five senses of sight, hearing, touch, taste, and smell. Sensation gives us the knowledge of our immediate surroundings necessary to function in everyday life. Sensation's strength is its ability to portray the world accurately. In fact, sensory data is so reliable that we nearly always correctly assume it is true.

We must remember, though, that sensed data represent the *appearance* of things, and from that we infer the reality behind the appearance. Since sensation is filtered through our senses and, in the modern world, may additionally be filtered through instruments like cameras and TV, its information can be altered from reality. Perhaps you have had the delight of being fooled by a magician who showed you empty hands and then immediately produced a bird in them, seemingly from nowhere! Or there are "virtual reality" rooms where individuals can be outfitted with sensors that track their every move. They might wear goggles that tell their eyes and ears they are moving through a jungle or climbing a mountain when it really isn't so.

A weakness, then, of the senses is that they can be tricked or fooled. And their sensitivity

## SCIENCE AND RELIGION

Both science and religion use these shared sources of knowledge. However, their emphases are typically different. Science relies on sensory data; religion depends upon intuition, in the form of inspiration or revelation. Furthermore, their aims differ; religion tells us about life's spiritual journey, while science seeks to describe the physical world around us. (Galileo is supposed to have said that religion teaches us how to go to heaven, while science teaches us how the heavens go.) We hope and expect these two disciplines to be in harmony, but we often see little overlap between them, and sometimes they even appear contradictory. Why?

Differences arise because of the different aims and learning methods, and also because our knowledge is incomplete in both areas. Science is incomplete, as is evidenced by the thousands of new scientific articles written and published every year. Religion is incomplete, as we see from several scriptures which indicate that there is more religious information to come forth. In fact, despite the great amount of knowledge that already exists in both disciplines, there is good reason to believe that there is much, much more to learn. (There are some scientists who think that, at least in some areas, we are approaching completeness. The authors of this book respectfully disagree.) Consequently, it is not surprising that there may be little overlap and some differences.

In view of this situation, humility and patience are required. We must wait for progress in unifying understanding of these areas, be it in this life or the next. We must not try to force a reconciliation of these two areas where it is not yet apparent how to do so. In the meantime, we should be content to allow differences to exist without assuming that either science or religion is wrong.

—B. Kent Harrison

and accuracy can diminish with time or injury. How do we know if what we sense is always accurate?

## 1-2 The Scientific Method

Science uses all four shared sources of knowledge. Authority is very important. Library shelves are filled with technical papers and books reporting research results from scientists all over the world. Scientific exploration begins by reading what others have learned from their experiments and studies. Intuition may be used in choosing which topics to investigate and which assumptions to make in the investigation. Even so, the "scientific method" as it is usually defined relies mostly on the last two ways of obtaining knowledge: reason and sensory data.

*Figure 1.5* illustrates the relation between reason and sensory data. We consider some phenomenon and make an **hypothesis** about why it is that way. An hypothesis is a first guess; a set of assumptions with a reasoned conjecture about what might be happening. It is reasoned from knowledge gleaned from authority, intuition, and the limited sensory data at hand. For example, Albert Einstein began his Special Theory of Relativity by first hypothesizing that the speed of light in empty space is always constant. This assumption was based on experiments and writings from other prominent scientists plus his own inner feelings.

Hypotheses are tested through experimentation. The sensory data obtained is considered against the predictions from the hypothesis and judged to be reasonable or not. If reasonable, the hypothesis and its set of assumptions remain. If not reasonable, the assumptions are modified or replaced and a new hypothesis is formed. The cycle then is repeated: experiment, results, modifications, new hypothesis, experiment, etc. until all results are adequately explained.

A well-tested and refined hypothesis is called a **theory**. The Special Theory of Relativity was considered a viable theory only after Einstein and others made quantitative, verifiable predictions about motion, space, and time from it. While there is no well-defined line between hypotheses and theory, a theory generally possesses a greater level of mature detail than an hypothesis does.

Theories that have been proven accurate are often called **laws**, such as Newton's laws of motion or the law of gravity. They may also be generalized principles such as the law of conservation of momentum. There is no definitive line between a law and a theory and the difference in many cases is just semantics.

Science uses reason based upon its laws, theories, and hypotheses to create **models** of reality. Models are schematic descriptions of physical systems. You will read about many models in this book. Models are often pictorial and may emphasize some concepts while neglecting others. They may sometimes be expressed in terms of mathematics. The predictions of models are tested against the outcome of experiments and models that don't work are revised or rejected.

### Hypothesis:

A tentative explanation for an observation, phenomenon, or scientific problem that can be tested by further investigation.

### Theory:

A set of statements or principles devised to explain a group of facts or phenomena, especially one that has been repeatedly tested or is widely accepted and can be used to make predictions about natural phenomena.

### Law:

A well-tested theory, so firm as to be unquestioned by science.

### Model:

A schematic description of a system, theory, or phenomenon that accounts for its known or inferred properties and may be used for further study of its characteristics.

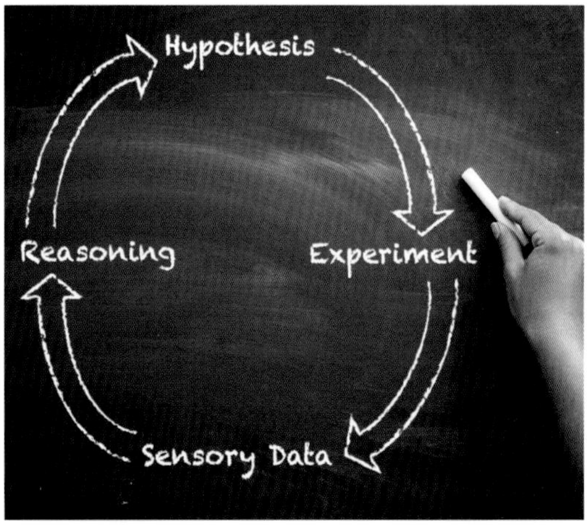

**Figure 1.5**
The scientific method is a refining cycle of hypothesis leading to experiment, experiment leading to sensory data, data leading to better reasoning, and better reasoning leading to a more accurate hypothesis.

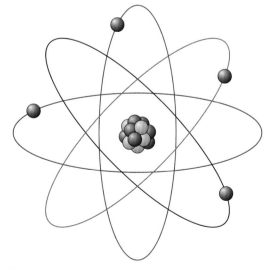

**Figure 1.6**
Models are used to represent reality. Science leads us to truth by building models and refining them through theory and data. This picture of the atom shows electrons orbiting a nucleus. As we will learn later in the book, this model is useful for some things but is not very accurate.

If successful models cannot be built upon the theories, then the theories themselves are called into question. Models that work are kept and tested again. As they pass more tests, trust in their accuracy and truthfulness increases. The cycle is repeated with the trust that the process is progressing toward an enlarged, better understanding of nature's truth.

Scientific research is always a test of an hypothesis, theory, law, or model against the behavior of nature. *This critical feature—consistency with nature—is the hallmark of science.* Any idea that is not or cannot be tested against nature cannot properly be included in scientific knowledge. Some "pseudoscientific" theories claim to be science but fail this test. Ideas rise and fall by this condition, and are always tentative to some degree because there is always some possibility, however small, of disagreement with future experiment.

The scientific method is a priceless tool, which, when powered by curiosity, helps us efficiently comprehend our complex world. It helps our curious minds formulate important "why" and "how" questions. It helps us sift through clouds of variables and possible answers to find the few laws and principles through which a broad range of phenomena can be understood.

## 1-3 Six "Self-Evident" Truths

All reasoning rests upon assumptions. Science as a whole rests upon a set of assumptions so logical and basic that we present them here as six "self-evident" truths or principles.

### 1. Existence

There exists a physical world separate and distinct from our minds that is comprehensible through our senses. This world is governed by certain generalities called the "laws of nature."

Our senses are usually very reliable and give a true picture of the world around us. But as previously stated, they can be deceived. The Chinese philosopher Chuang Tsu illustrated the dilemma with the following story:

> Once upon a time, I, Chuang Tsu, dreamed I was a butterfly, flying happily here and there, enjoying life without knowing who I was. Suddenly I woke up and I was indeed Chuang Tsu.

**Figure 1.7**
Existence: The universe is wonderful and real!

Did Chuang Tsu dream he was a butterfly or did the butterfly dream he was Chuang Tsu?[1]

Perhaps you, too, have had dreams that were so vivid that after awakening you were puzzled for a moment about what was real. In essence the principle of existence asserts that Chuang Tsu is, indeed, a Chinese philosopher and not a butterfly, and the reality around him is the same as the reality that surrounds us. Each of us might see this reality a little differently because of who we are. But regardless of how we understand it, a single, unique, reality is there, existing independent of us.

### 2. Causality

Events in the physical universe have natural causes. Causes precede the events in time and can be explained rationally in terms of the laws of nature.

**Figure 1.8**
Causality: The apple cannot burst before the bullet strikes it.

**Existence:**
The fact or state of having actual or real being.

**Causality:**
Cause must always precede the effect.

---

[1] Chuang Tsu, *Inner Chapters,* p. 48, translated by Gia-Fu Feng and Jane English, Vintage Books, Random House, New York, NY, 1974.

Science has not proven that travel back in time is impossible, but the idea is beset with paradoxes. For example a person traveling to the past could kill their own parents before the traveler was born, negating the cause of their own birth. The principle of causality guides us to reject any hypothesis or theory that leads to the possibility of a result existing in time before its cause does. The cause must always precede the effect. So time travel to the past cannot be possible without constraints that ensure causality is never violated and that paradoxes like the above do not occur.

### 3. Position Symmetry

The laws of nature are the same everywhere in the universe.

The universe is a huge entity. A beam of light takes over 100,000 years to cross the Milky Way Galaxy alone. We have no hope at present of ever traveling to the far side of the Galaxy, conducting experiments, and returning. Even so, we are confident it is reasonable to use the law of gravity to explain how the Galaxy behaves. We therefore assume that the law of gravity—and all laws of nature—hold true for all matter everywhere in the Universe. While this is a general assumption, experiences and observations on Earth and in our solar system provide support for it. The idea of "symmetry" in this context means that the laws of nature remain the same from position to position.

**Figure 1.9**
Position Symmetry: The laws of nature are the same in our galaxy as they are in other galaxies and everywhere in the universe.

**Figure 1.10**
Time Symmetry: The laws of nature as deduced by Galileo in Italy 400 years ago have not changed with time.

### 4. Time Symmetry

The laws of nature have remained the same through time. They are the same now as they were in the distant past, and they will be the same in the future.

In the absence of time travel, we cannot visit past epochs and conduct experiments in those time periods. Even so, we are confident it is reasonable to use the laws of nature to explain the past and predict how nature will unfold in the future. Indeed, science is a means of predicting the future through understanding universal laws. For this to be true, those laws must be eternally true. Here the idea of "symmetry" means that the laws of nature remain the same for all times.

### 5. Principle of Non-contradiction

Of two contradictory propositions, both cannot be true.

When based on different assumptions, reason can lead to different conclusions. When two conclusions contradict each other, at least one conclusion, and possibly both, is wrong. Otherwise logic and reason would not hold true and the basic scientific methodology would be invalid. Apparent contradictions in science therefore indicate a lack of full understanding that must be resolved by further study.

### 6. Occam's Razor

If alternative explanations of any phenomenon are available, where each are logical and

---

**Position Symmetry:**

The laws of the universe are not different at different locations.

**Time Symmetry:**

The laws of the universe do not change with time.

**Principle of Non-contradiction:**

Of two contradictory propositions, both cannot be true.

**Occam's Razor:**

The rule that where two or more explanations exist for the same physical phenomenon, we should choose the simplest one that satisfies all of the observations.

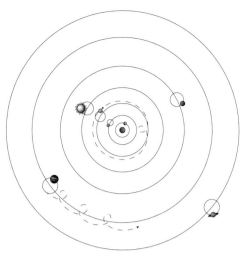

**Ptolemaic Model**

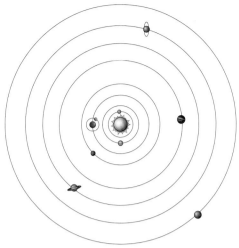

**Copernican Model**

**Figure 1.11**
A drawing of the complex model and the simpler Copernican model. Only one of the competing models of the solar system can be true. The simpler Copernican model is correct.

explain the phenomenon equally well, then the simplest explanation shall be chosen. Explanatory principles or factors are not to be multiplied beyond necessity. On the other hand, explanations cannot be too simple; they must adequately explain the available data.

Of all the self-evident truths, Occam's Razor is perhaps the hardest to quantify, yet it is a bright beacon. Great scientists of antiquity formulated a theory of the universe in which Earth stood motionless in the center and the stars and planets all whirled about it in the heavens. A model based on this theory, called the Ptolemaic cosmology, said the Sun, the Moon, and planets all orbited about Earth on two circles. (See *Figure 1.11*.) This model was accurate for its day in predicting when and where a planet would appear in the sky.

As measurements of planetary positions became more precise, the Ptolemaic model was changed to fit the data by including more circular paths for the planets to move on. Soon the long-accepted Ptolemaic model became an entangled collection of circles connected to circles connected to even more circles that was complex beyond reason. Nicholas Copernicus saw that if the Sun were at the center of the solar system and Earth moved around it, the complex arrangement of circles could be discarded in favor of a simple, single orbital path for each planet.

The simplicity of this new scheme correctly guided mankind to the truth. The incorrect assumption that the Sun and planets orbited about Earth was replaced by the correct and much simpler assumption that Earth and planets orbited about the Sun.

## 1-4 The Universe Around Us

We close this chapter with a brief tour of the Universe. On this tour, we pay attention to the sizes of objects and how they interact. This section may be viewed as a coarse outline of the rest of the book. In later chapters, we look at the specific theories, laws and interactions that govern the objects considered here to understand how these produce the beauty and order of the world around us.

### Interactions and Force

Whether we are looking at microscopic objects nearby, or large bodies halfway across the universe, all things are made of matter and energy organized differently and rather uniquely on different lengths and scales. This organization is governed by the influence of **interactions** that give rise to **forces**.

We know of four interactions in nature: the **strong nuclear**, the **electromagnetic**, the **weak nuclear**, and **gravity**. Matter interacts in accordance with attributes possessed by the matter. The nuclear interactions act only on nucleons and quarks deep inside atoms, the electromagnetic interaction acts on anything that is charged, and gravity acts on anything that has mass. In some structures these four interactions may be at work simultaneously with similar or opposing effects.

The relative strengths of the forces of these interactions are surprisingly diverse. If two protons are placed side by side and the forces on them are measured, the strong nuclear force acting on the protons is 100 times greater than the electromagnetic force, $10^{13}$ times greater

**Interaction:**

Any of four fundamental ways in which elementary particles and bodies can influence each other.

**Force:**

A push or pull on an object.

**Strong Nuclear Interaction:**

The interaction between nucleons that gives rise to the strong force.

**Electromagnetic Interaction:**

The interaction between charged objects that gives rise to the electromagnetic force.

**Weak Nuclear Interaction:**

The interaction between nucleons that gives rise to the weak force.

**Gravity:**

The interaction between anything with mass that gives rise to the gravitational force.

## Table 1.1    The Four Interactions of Nature

| Force | Relative Strength | Range | Acts Upon |
|---|---|---|---|
| Nuclear Strong | $10^{38}$ | Atomic Nuclei $10^{-15}$m | Nucleons |
| Electromagnetic | $10^{36}$ | Earth Diameter $10^7$m | Charged Matter |
| Nuclear Weak | $10^{25}$ | Atomic Nuclei $10^{-15}$m | Nucleons |
| Gravity | 1 | Entire Universe $10^{26}$m | Mass |

Force strength varies with distance. The relative strength listed here is what is felt by two protons sitting side-by-side (approximately 10–15m apart).

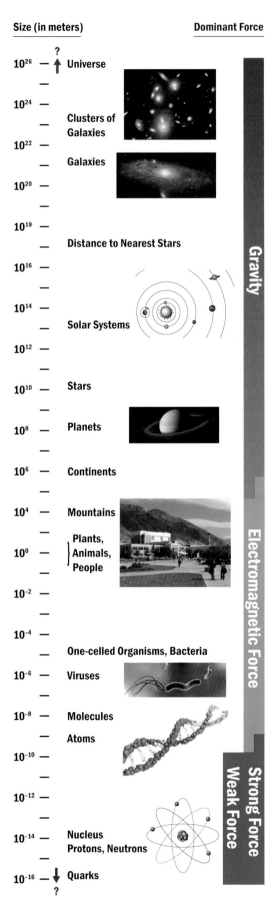

Size (in meters)        Dominant Force

than the nuclear weak force, and $10^{38}$ times greater than the force from gravity (see *Table 1.1*). The strong nuclear force is the most powerful force known, but its range (and that of the weak nuclear force) is so short that the electromagnetic force dominates by the time we have increased in scale to the size of an atom.

The electromagnetic force dominates the world in which we live. Gravity increases slowly and steadily with increasing mass and becomes the dominant force when the sizes we are considering are as large as a planet or larger (see *Figure 1.12).* The nuclear weak force is the only one that does not dominate at any scale length. The realms over which each of these forces dominates is described in the following sections.

### Nuclear Interactions: The Strong and Weak forces

We start at a scale size of approximately $10^{-15}$m. Are there structures smaller than this? Perhaps, but if so, we do not yet have the ability to measure them. **Atomic nuclei** are this size and are comprised of **protons** and **neutrons**, which we together call **nucleons**. Nucleons are so small that it would take one trillion (or $10^{12}$) lined up next to each other to reach across the head of a pin. They are so dense that a pinhead-size ball made of nucleons packed next to each other would weigh about a million tons. No crane could lift it!

A well-tested model theorizes that protons and neutrons are each comprised of more fundamental particles called **quarks**. The strong nuclear force acts on quarks, binding them together into nucleons and also binding the nucleons together into atomic nuclei. The nuclear weak force, on the other hand, attempts to break nuclei apart. Nuclei that are suscepti-

**Atomic Nuclei:**

The positively charged central region of an atom, composed of protons and neutrons.

**Proton:**

A positively charged particle in atomic nuclei made up of three quarks.

**Neutron:**

An uncharged particle in atomic nuclei made up of three quarks.

**Nucleon:**

A generic name for either a proton or a neutron.

**Quark:**

The basic building block of protons and neutrons.

**Figure 1.12**

The organization and character of the universe is determined by forces from the four interactions of nature. Notice the $10^{42}$ change of scale from the small to the large.

## POWERS OF 10 NOTATION

The universe covers a huge range in sizes that are often difficult to represent using ordinary numbers. To overcome this problem, we use a shorthand system called "scientific" or "powers of ten" notation. The cumbersome zeros of a large number are condensed into a "factor of 10," which is 10 raised to an exponent. The exponent indicates how many zeros are needed to properly represent the number. Positive exponents represent places to the left of the decimal while negative exponents represent places to the right. For example:

$10^1$ = 10 (ten)
$10^2$ = 100 (one hundred)
$10^3$ = 1,000 (one thousand)
$10^6$ = 1,000,000 (one million)
$10^9$ = 1,000,000,000 (one billion)
$10^{12}$ = 1,000,000,000,000 (one trillion)
$10^0$ = 1 (one)
$10^{-1}$ = 0.1 (one tenth)
$10^{-6}$ = 0.000001 (one millionth).

These values are read "ten to the first," "ten to the second," on down to "ten to the minus sixth."

Since real values rarely are even powers of ten, we typically must multiply the factor of 10 by a value between 1 and 10 as follows.

$$5 \times 10^5 = 500,000$$
$$1.23456 \times 10^3 = 1,234.56$$
$$9.87 \times 10^{-7} = 0.000000987$$

These would be read "five times ten to the fifth," "one point two three four five six times ten to the third," and "nine point eight seven times ten to the minus seventh," respectively.

ble to being changed or broken apart under the influence of the nuclear weak force are called **radioactive.**

The electromagnetic force is also present in atomic nuclei as a repulsion between positively charged protons. Atomic nuclei do not fly apart only because the strong nuclear force is more powerful than the electromagnetic force. An additional help is that protons alone feel the repulsive electromagnetic force, while both neutrons and protons feel the attractive strong nuclear force.

### The Electromagnetic Interaction

Surrounding atomic nuclei are **electrons** held in place by their electromagnetic attraction to the nuclear protons. Electrons and nuclei bound together constitute **atoms**. The average distance of the outermost electrons from the nucleus is about $10^{-10}$m, meaning an atom is approximately 100,000 times larger than its nucleus and is mostly empty space. If a nucleus were the size of a ballpoint pen tip, its surrounding atom would be the size of a football field! Atoms, in a variety of combinations, make up matter as we know it. The tiniest speck of dust visible to the unaided eye contains about $10^{18}$ atoms. A sample of air the size of a sugar cube contains about this same number of atoms.

The atoms of each of the nearly 100 **elements** found in nature have a unique number of protons and electrons. The lightest element, hydrogen, has one of each. The next lightest element, helium, has two protons, two neutrons and two electrons. The atoms of each successive element increase with each step by one proton, one electron, and usually one or several neutrons.

Atoms join together through the electromagnetic interaction into groups called **molecules**. The common table sugar molecule contains 12 carbon atoms, 22 hydrogen atoms, and 11 oxygen atoms. Some substances, such as nylon, have long molecular chains that may contain a million atoms or more. Molecular sizes vary from $10^{-10}$m to $10^{-8}$m or larger. Even so, the largest molecules are too small to be seen under the most powerful optical microscope.

Objects from $10^{-7}$m to $10^4$m in size are made of large numbers of atoms and molecules mixed together. We will call these arrangements "mixtures." Mixtures can be simple in structure like a shovel full of dirt, in which the individual molecules are just close to each other with little or no atomic-level connection. Other mixtures can be quite complex, such as the human body, where the individual parts interact electromagnetically in a manner so intricate that the absence of a small amount of needed material (proteins, vitamins, etc.) causes other parts of the body to drastically change their functions. The realm of mixtures is the world we live in.

**Radioactive:**
A term referring to atoms whose nuclei can spontaneously change under the influence of the weak nuclear force.

**Electron:**
An elementary particle in atoms having a negative charge. Electrons are located outside atomic nuclei.

**Atom:**
The fundamental unit of an element.

**Element:**
A substance composed entirely of atoms having the same number of protons in their nuclei.

**Molecules:**
The tiniest particles of a substance that retain all the physical properties of that substance. They are usually made up of more than one atom.

### The Realm of the Gravitational Interaction

As molecular assemblies increase in mass, they are eventually held together by gravity instead of electromagnetism. Since gravity always pulls matter inward toward the center of the distribution, objects held together by gravity tend to have a round shape.

Earth has the shape of a ball with a radius of almost 6400 km (4000 miles). This is so large we do not generally notice that the level of a lake curves downward to be about 16 feet lower five miles away than it is at our feet. Earth is a member of the **solar system**, which consists of the Sun, eight planets and their moons, dwarf planets, thousands of asteroids and comets, and an untold number of smaller pieces of rock and ice. The Sun's gravity keeps these bodies orbiting about it in a circular disk. The average distance from the Sun to the farthest planet Neptune is $4.5 \times 10^{12}$m, or the distance light can travel in just over 4 hours.

Like the atom, the solar system is mainly empty space. If the Sun were an orange on the 50-yard line of a football field, Earth would be a BB ten yards away and Neptune would be a marble 300 yards away in the parking lot. On this scale all the material in the entire solar system combined would form a ball smaller than a grapefruit.

As large as the solar system is, it is dwarfed by the enormity of the Milky Way Galaxy in which it resides. This huge structure is a circular disk of over 200 billion stars held together by their mutual gravity. It measures about $10^{21}$m from edge to edge, which is the distance light can travel in 100,000 years. If the entire solar system were a marble on the 50-yard line of a football field in Provo, Utah, then the edge of the galaxy would be about 200 miles away! The nearest stars would be a half-dozen grains of sand spread throughout the football stadium. The vastness and emptiness of it all is staggering. Such distances seem unreal in part because the Milky Way Galaxy seen on a moonless night seems to be crowded with stars. That so many stars are visible attests to their great brightness and prolific abundance.

Finally, we come to the realm of visible galaxies that populate the vastness of the universe itself. The deepest image from the Hubble Space Telescope suggests there are at least 100 billion galaxies averaging over 100 billion stars each. These are spread throughout the $10^{26}$m of visible space in clusters of 10 to 10,000 members or more. Evidence strongly suggests that the universe itself had a beginning about 13.8 billion years ago in an event of nearly incomprehensible magnitude called the "Big Bang."

As you study the realms described above, try to learn not just what they are but *how* we know of them. Distinguish between the well-known parts and those for which our knowledge is more tentative and developing by paying attention to the data, reasoning, and assumptions involved. Let your own intuitive heart guide you through the huge body of authority, evidence, and reason the knowledge is built upon. And do not forget that as you learn more about the world in which we live, you are simply continuing the process of discovery you began as a child.

### Selected Sources of Additional Reading

Bryson, Bill. A Brief History of Nearly Everything.

Trefil, James and Robert M. Hazen. Science Matters.

Weisskopf, Victor. Knowledge and Wonder.

http://www.particleadventure.org/

**Solar System:**
The Sun and all planets, comets, asteroids, and other bodies that orbit about it under the pull of gravity.

# Effective Studying

For many freshmen, adapting to the university's standard of studying is very difficult. Many college students did well in high school without ever really taking notes or studying. Generally, they must develop better study skills to do well at the university level.

There are many resources available to help you develop the necessary learning habits.

## Taking Notes

- Write things down in your own words.
- Review your notes daily.
- Attend class with the mindset that you will ultimately teach someone else the material. Tests are simply a way of teaching the teacher what you have learned.
- Develop a system of abbreviations so you can take notes faster.
- Leave room in your notes, so you can add notes later as you review.
- Rewrite or type your notes each week so you can keep them organized and have an extra chance to review them.

## Reading Texts

- Read assignments before class. This will make lectures easier to understand and, especially, more enjoyable.
- Read through any comprehension questions at the end of chapters in your textbooks to check your understanding.
- Change textbook headings into questions and attempt to answer the questions while reading.
- Read first and highlight later.
- Take reading notes in the margins of your text or in a notebook.

## Study Groups

- Form study groups with classmates from your learning community.
- Prepare beforehand if you are going to participate in a study group.
- Discuss what you are studying with others to sharpen your understanding.
- Try the "round robin" approach. Each person in the group can quiz others on the material. This allows everyone to review by listening and instructing, which helps to commit the material to memory.
- Limit your study groups to four or five people.
- Meet with study groups regularly, not just before tests.
- Find a quiet and convenient place to meet. You can schedule rooms online or at the computers by the library information desk.

## Studying

- Focus your study on what you don't know. An effective way of doing this is to keep an "I don't understand..." note card handy.
- Study for each class every day.
- Find interesting things about what you are learning.
- Study somewhere comfortable for you, but avoid sitting or lying on your bed! Most people like to study somewhere quiet where they can focus and won't be interrupted, such as the library.
- Keep your study area clean and organized.
- Take short breaks during study sessions.

# 1 STUDY GUIDE

## Chapter Framework

### A. Four Ways We Learn
1. Authority
2. Intuition
3. Reason
4. Sensory Data

### B. The Scientific Method
1. Hypothesis > Prediction > Data > Analysis > Hypothesis
2. Theory
3. Laws
4. Models

### C. Six "Self-Evident Truths"
1. Existence
2. Causality
3. Position Symmetry
4. Time Symmetry
5. Principle of Non-contradiction
6. Occam's Razor

### D. The Universe Around Us
1. Four Interactions in Nature
   a. *Strong nuclear*
   b. *Electromagnetic*
   c. *Weak nuclear*
   d. *Gravity*
2. The Realm of Nuclear Forces
   a. *Atomic nuclei—protons, neutrons—and smaller*
3. The Realm of the Electromagnetic Force
   a. *Electrons, protons*
   b. *Atoms*
   c. *Molecules*
   d. *Molecular complexes*
4. The Realm of Gravity
   a. *Earth*
   b. *Solar System*
   c. *Milky Way Galaxy*
   d. *Universe*

## Comprehension

### Matching
a. Time Symmetry
b. Model
c. Reason
d. Interaction
e. Sensory Data
f. Law
g. Position Symmetry
h. Authority
i. Force
j. Causality
k. Element
l. Hypothesis
m. Strong Nuclear Interaction
n. Existence
o. Gravity

1. _____ Cause must always precede the effect.
2. _____ A substance made of atoms, all of which contain the same number of protons.
3. _____ The laws of the universe are not different at different locations.
4. _____ An accepted source of expert information or advice.
5. _____ The force that arises from the interactions of anything with mass.
6. _____ A well-tested theory, so firm as to be unquestioned by science.
7. _____ A push or pull on an object.
8. _____ The assertion that a world separate and distinct from our minds actually exists.
9. _____ Any of four fundamental ways in which elementary particles and bodies can influence each other.

10. _____ A tentative explanation for an observation, phenomenon, or scientific problem that can be tested by further investigation.
11. _____ The capacity for logical, rational, and analytic thought—intelligence.
12. _____ A schematic description of a system, theory, or phenomenon that accounts for its known or inferred properties and may be used for further study of its characteristics.
13. _____ The interaction between nucleons that holds them together.
14. _____ The laws of the universe do not change with time.
15. _____ Knowledge obtained through seeing, hearing, touching, tasting, and smelling.

### True/False
16. _____ Protons and neutrons together form atomic nuclei.
17. _____ Occam's Razor states that complex explanations are more likely to be true than simple explanations.
18. _____ Intuition is the act or faculty of knowing or sensing outside the five physical senses.
19. _____ A law, such as Newton's First Law of Motion, can never be proved wrong.
20. _____ The laws on Mars are slightly different than the laws on Earth due to the differences in each planet's composition.

### Fill in the Blank
1. The Principle of _____ states that of two contradictory propositions, both cannot be true.
2. Electromagnetic Interaction: The interaction between _____ objects that gives rise to the electromagnetic force.
3. Electrons and nuclei together form a(n) _____.
4. A _____ is a set of statements or principles devised from a well-proven hypothesis and used to make predictions about natural phenomenon.
5. Atoms join into groups called _____.

## Analysis

1. Which of the following is not one of the four ways of learning?
   a) Authority
   b) Sensory Data
   c) Discovery
   d) Reason

2. Which of the following forces arises from the electromagnetic interaction?
   a) Weight of a book
   b) The force governing electron motion in an electric circuit

c) Gravitational force of Earth

d) Force keeping the moon in orbit

e) Force keeping the solar system together

3. Some people might say that they "know" the following statements are true. In each case, identify which of the four primary sources of knowledge they base their assertions on and explain your reasoning.

a) The sum of the squared lengths of a right triangle's legs equal the squared length of the hypotenuse (A2 + B2 = C2, the Pythagorean Theorem).

b) God exists.

c) Prescriptions written by doctors cure people because they are experts in medicine.

d) Water is made up of molecules.

e) Earth spins on its axis once every 24 hours.

f) Lowering taxes will stimulate the economy.

g) My great- great- grandfather was a kind man.

4. Which of the 6 "self-evident truths" best applies to each statement? Identify the truth and explain your reasoning.

a) You can vote for a politician who argues for a tax decrease or for one who argues for increasing services in society, but not both— the two ideas oppose one another.

b) You want to know if gravity exists on Pluto.

c) You want to analyze light that left a distant star 100,000 years ago to learn about how the star is today.

d) You must solve a murder based on the details from a crime scene.

e) You are in a comatose state and experience dreams that seem very real.

f) The phone rings before you pick it up and say hello.

5. When Kent got up this morning, he found the refrigerator door open. Use your understanding of Occam's Razor to rank the following explanations from most to least likely, and explain why.

a) A tornado swept through the kitchen at night and pulled open the door.

b) His fridge has suddenly developed a faulty magnetic seal.

c) His roommate, who just left for class, forgot to close it.

d) A goblin lives under the fridge and got hungry during the night. He opened the door, but didn't know how to close the fridge when he was done.

6. The weight of an object on the moon is only one-sixth of its weight on Earth. Why does this not violate position symmetry?

7. If there were different forces present at the beginning of the universe than the ones we observe now, would this violate time symmetry?

8. Describe in your own words what a hypothesis, theory, law, and model are. Give examples of each.

9. Using an analogy or a numerical value, contrast the size of the nucleus and the size of the atom.

10. Using an analogy or a numerical value, contrast the distances between stars, the size of the galaxy, and the distance between galaxies.

11. The four fundamental interactions are each important in different situations. Explain when each of the four fundamental interactions is important.

## Synthesis

1. Describe how scientific methods can be used in the following situations:

a) Building an automobile

b) Dating fossils on the slopes of Mt. Timpanogos

c) Deciding where to build a house

2. Describe six "self- evident truths" and explain what each one means.

3. Pick 5 objects that exemplify different levels of organization observed in the universe. Put the objects in order of size, beginning with the smallest. Explain how each is held together and where it fits into the levels of organization described in the text. Identify the basic forces which dominate in each object.

4. Conspiracy theories are currently fairly common (e.g., the moon landing was a hoax, there are aliens from space hidden in New Mexico, etc.). Explain how you can differentiate between reliable and suspect claims on the basis of how they use scientific methods.

# Laws Governing Motion

*If I have made any valuable discoveries, it has been owing more to patient attention than to any other talent.*

*Isaac Newton*

## LEARN

- Newton's three laws of motion and how they work together.

- What "state of motion," "velocity," and "acceleration" are and how they relate to each other.

- The relationship between force, mass, and acceleration.

- To use Newton's laws of motion to predict what will happen in simple interactions.

O ur world is not static; it is constantly changing. People walk, clouds drift, rain falls, cars travel, and flowers grow. What would life be if we and the world did not change and progress from one state to another? A world without change is impossible to imagine.

Change and motion are intertwined. Stop for a moment and look around. Can you see even one example of a change occurring without motion being involved? The motion may be slow and subtle, like a tree growing. Or the moving objects may be tiny particles too small to see, like electrons moving about on an electric sign. But in all cases, without exception, if something changed, it or some part of it moved. Motion is therefore fundamental to the world around us.

This leads us to ask, "What is the nature of motion? Does it take place in a haphazard way or does it follow a set of well-defined laws? If so, what are those laws?"

Simple examples are often the most instructive so let's consider one. Imagine a soccer ball resting motionless in your front yard. You kick it and it bounces down the street, going slower

and slower until it finally comes to a complete stop, a few houses away. Why did the ball move like that?

First, the ball was motionless until you kicked it. So you might naturally conclude that something at rest will move only if a force, like a kick, is applied to it. This is correct. Forces are always necessary to create or change motion. But why did the ball stop? Perhaps it quit moving because the force from your kick "faded out." Indeed, more than two thousand years ago the great Greek philosopher Aristotle (382–322 BC) wrote:

> The moving body comes to a standstill when the force which pushes it along can no longer so act as to push it.[1]

But reflecting for a minute, you conclude that Aristotle's statement cannot be entirely true. Yes, a force was necessary to get the ball moving. However, the kick lasted for just a fraction of a second and the ball stayed in motion for a much longer period of time, well after the

kick was over. There must be more to this than Aristotle's explanation.

Aristotle was wrong. While a force of some kind is necessary to create motion, force is not necessary to sustain it. The brilliant Italian scientist Galileo Galilei (1564–1642) understood this. In his book, *Discourses and Mathematical Demonstrations Concerning the Two New Sciences,* he wrote:

> . . . [A]ny velocity once imparted to a moving body will be rigidly maintained as long as the external causes of acceleration or retardation are removed[2] . . .

In other words, an object will remain in motion so long as no impeding forces, like friction, act against the motion. This basic understanding of motion—that it persists until external forces alter it—was established as a correct principle by the mid 1600s.

The great natural philosopher and mathe-

**Aristotle**

Aristotle's concept of force being necessary to sustain all motion was thought to be true for nearly 2,000 years.

**Galileo Galilei**

Galileo understood the law of inertia several decades before Isaac Newton.

---

[1] Aristotle, Mechanics, 350.

[2] Galileo reasoned that if a ball rolling downhill gained speed, and a ball rolling uphill lost speed, then a ball rolling on a perfectly flat surface would roll forever at the same speed.

matician Sir Isaac Newton (1642–1727) built upon this foundation. In 1687, at the urging of colleagues, he laid out in the book *Principia Mathematica,* arguably the greatest single work of science ever produced, what have come to be called Newton's laws of motion.

## 2-1 The First Law of Motion

The first of Newton's laws is a refined statement of Galileo's conclusion. It can be stated as follows:

> **Every object at rest, or in uniform motion, will remain in that state of motion unless compelled to do otherwise by forces acting upon it.**

This statement of the law contains terms that we will use frequently. **Uniform motion** means motion at constant speed in a straight line. This is the same as unaccelerated motion; we will speak of acceleration later. **State of motion** means its speed and direction. An object moving with uniform motion will be said to be in a state of uniform motion. **Force** refers to a push or a pull. We will say more of forces later in this chapter.

Newton's first law applies equally well to objects at rest and objects in uniform motion; both respond to force in exactly the same way. It may seem odd that there should be this similarity. What could be more different in a state of motion than moving along versus standing still?

We may understand the sameness of the two cases, motion and rest, in the following way. Suppose you are holding a rock in your hand while riding along in a car at 70 miles per hour. Here the rock is at rest—with respect to you. However, it is not at rest with respect to an observer standing on the shoulder of the freeway, watching you speed past. That person would say your handheld rock is moving uniformly at 70 miles per hour. So we can legiti-

mately assign two different speeds to the rock, zero and 70 miles per hour. Which is correct? Both are, and we conclude that an object's speed is not a unique quantity like size or shape. Speed depends on what we measure it against.

Of course it is possible to have one law describe the motion of a rock when you ride with it, and a second law describe its motion when it is in a car moving past you. But Occam's Razor tells us it is simpler for the rock to obey a single law of nature that does not depend on what *you* are measuring the motion against. This single law is Newton's first law of motion and it applies exactly the same to objects in uniform motion as to those at rest. In fact the state of rest is just the state of uniform motion with zero speed.

It is obvious that an object at rest remains at rest if it is left alone, yet the consequences can be startling. A fun example is pulling a tablecloth off a fully set dinner table while leaving the dinner service undisturbed. The plates and goblets on the table are at rest and will remain at rest unless the tablecloth "compels" them to do otherwise. If the tablecloth is sufficiently smooth, a quick jerk will break its frictional grip on the dinner service, which remains undisturbed as the cloth flies away. A less entertaining manifestation of the law is a stopped car with passengers being struck from behind. The passengers' heads momentarily remain at rest while the car and the rest of their bodies are compelled to move forward by the force of the impact, sometimes with a harmful effect (*Figure 2.1*).

Newton's first law may not be obvious because the objects we deal with in everyday life experience multiple forces. The force of gravity seeks to pull everything down to the ground. Frictional forces cause objects to slow down or speed up. Newton and Galileo realized that the motions of objects on Earth were constantly changing under the influence of friction and gravity. But they knew that if these forces could

**Uniform Motion:**

Motion at a constant speed in a straight line.

**State of Uniform Motion:**

The condition of an object when no unbalanced forces act upon it. A state of motion always refers to being at rest or in uniform motion.

**Force:**

A push or pull on an object.

**Figure 2.1**
Both driver's heads jerk in a rear-end collision but in different directions. Why?

## SIR ISAAC NEWTON

Isaac Newton (1642–1727) was born on Christmas Day in Lincolnshire, England. Born prematurely, he was a weak and frail baby, whom no one expected to live. His father, a poor farmer who could not sign his own name, died a few months before Newton's birth. His mother had remarried by the time Newton was three years old and left him to live with his grandmother. She rejoined him when he was 14 and tried to make a farmer of him, but Newton was already preoccupied with mathematics. At age 18 he enrolled at Cambridge University and began work for the Bachelor of Arts degree. But in 1665 and 1666 Cambridge was closed because of the plague and Newton retreated to his home in Lincolnshire for the duration. It was there that many of the ideas were born that would revolutionize our concept of the world—ideas that made Newton famous.

**Sir Isaac Newton**

In 1687 Isaac Newton published in the book *Principia Mathematica* the three laws of motion that bear his name.

Newton was a complex character who seemed haunted by insecurity, possibly stemming from his childhood. In his lifetime he would develop a powerful new understanding of light and color, invent a new kind of reflecting telescope that had significant advantages over earlier instruments, and explain the motions of the heavens. He would also write some 650,000 words on the subject of alchemy and some 1,300,000 words on Biblical and theological topics (Boorstin, The Discoverers, p. 407). He was a Unitarian, but a fellow of Trinity College and found it best, at last, to leave Cambridge to become Master of the Mint from which he drew a comfortable salary. He became president of the Royal Society in 1703, was knighted by Queen Anne in 1705, and for the remainder of his life dominated intellectual life in England.

Alexander Pope summarizes the tribute to Newton with this couplet:

*Nature and Nature's laws lay hid in night:*
*God said, "Let Newton be!" and all was light.*

One can juxtapose this description with Newton's modest (and, some would say, uncharacteristic) statement to Robert Hooke, "If I have seen further than others it is by standing upon the shoulders of Giants."

Newton shared with Pythagoras a fascination with mathematics as the key to understanding the world. Newton's approach was to summarize his observations of nature into general mathematical statements. To deal with motion and change he had to invent a whole new mathematics—calculus (which he called the theory of "fluxions"). Although he was a creative genius who was constantly introducing new ideas and explanations, in his own mind he "frame[d] no hypotheses," meaning that he only summarized in formulas what could be confirmed experimentally. He made no attempt to explain the physical reasons that caused the formulas to work.

Newton's great contribution was the ability to see the world in a new way. It occurred to him, after watching an apple fall, that gravitation was not strictly a terrestrial phenomenon, but rather a universal one. He looked at the Moon, seeing what everyone had seen before him. Unlike others, however, he suddenly realized that the Moon, just like the apple, was a falling object! True, it was moving sideways in its orbit as it fell, thus always missing Earth, but it was falling, pulled toward Earth by the same gravity that pulled the apple toward Earth's center. With that insight Newton removed the distinction between celestial and terrestrial phenomena.

From Newton's time forward, the bodies of the universe and their motions—be they planets, moons, or atoms—were to be accounted for by universal laws that could be observed in experiments on earth, summarized in mathematical formulas, and then applied, to both understand and predict all the phenomena of the universe. The laws would predict the future of each body in a decisive, deterministic way. In the hands of Newton's followers and the French philosophers who followed Descartes, the world began to assume the characteristics of a giant clockwork whose motions could, in principle, be predicted and which were, therefore, "predestined." This view would dominate the philosophy of science until the twentieth century, when it was discovered that atomic particles do not obey Newton's laws of motion. The modifications to Newton's laws revealed an unpredictable randomness in the world that breaks the deterministic grip that otherwise would rule.

Newton's gift to science was to establish that we can find the laws of nature and use them to understand the system and predict its future. This was, and is, a very powerful idea.

**Figure 2.2**
An ice skater could go on forever without effort if friction were not present.

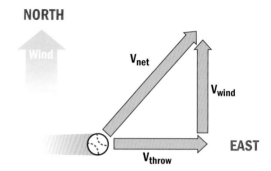

**Figure 2.4**
A baseball is thrown to the east in a wind going north. The net velocity is the addition of the two velocity arrows, to the northeast.

**Velocity:**
The speed in a particular direction of a moving body.

**Acceleration:**
Rate of change of velocity per unit time, or change of velocity divided by the time required for the change.

**Centripetal:**
Toward a center.

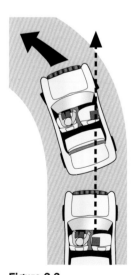

**Figure 2.3**
Why is the package "thrown" to the outside of a turn? Is the package really "thrown"?

be eliminated or canceled out by other forces, all motion would be described only by Newton's first law. One can imagine, for example, that an ice skater, once moving, could glide on forever without ever slowing down if friction between the blades of the ice skates and the ice could be eliminated completely (*Figure 2.2*).

Speaking of ice, it is a frightening experience to approach a red traffic light at an ice-covered intersection, apply the brakes, then slide on through without slowing down. After such an experience, one is easily convinced that Newton's first law of motion is valid. Turning a car on ice is also a problem because, without friction between tires and road, the car continues in a straight line no matter how the wheels are pointed. We wear seat belts so that if we are in an accident, we are held firmly to the car and slow to a stop with the car instead of continuing forward after the car's forward motion ends, striking the dashboard or windshield.

Turning a car around a corner illustrates an interesting manifestation of Newton's first law. Suppose a car makes a left turn at a modest speed. In the process a package placed next to the driver slides across the seat to the door. It may seem to a passenger sitting in the back seat that the package has moved outward under the influence of a force, but the truth is that the package, acting in strict accordance with the first law of motion, is simply moving straight ahead while the car changes its motion under the influence of an inward force! (*Figure 2.3*)

## 2-2 Velocity and Acceleration

In section 2-1 we defined the state of motion as an object's speed and direction. Speed and direction combined together are called **velocity**. We represent velocity with an arrow pointing in the direction of travel having a length proportional to the speed. Two velocities can be added by attaching the end of the second arrow to the tip of the first (*Figure 2.4*).

A *change* in an object's velocity is called **acceleration**. Like velocity, acceleration also has magnitude and direction, and can also be represented as an arrow. Acceleration can increase speed, decrease speed (which is sometimes called deceleration; *Figure 2.5*), or change the direction of an object's motion. Acceleration at a right angle to an object's velocity will change the object's direction without changing its speed (*Figure 2.6*). Such acceleration is called **centripetal** acceleration. In general, a change from uniform motion of any kind is termed an acceleration.

It is important to not confuse velocity with acceleration. Velocity is distance in a particular direction covered in a certain time, and has a measurement like "miles per hour" or "meters per second." Acceleration is the rate at which speed or direction changes, and has a measurement like "miles per hour per second" or "meters per second per second" (often just called "meters per second squared.")

As an example of how velocity and acceleration are related, consider a car heading due west at 50 miles per hour. The driver then accelerates so that the car is going 70 miles per hour 4 seconds later. During this change in velocity it accelerated at a rate of 5 miles per hour per second (50 miles per hour + 5 miles per hour per second ∞ 4 seconds = 70 miles per hour). Now suppose the car is traveling at 10 miles per hour and accelerates to 25 miles per hour in five sec-

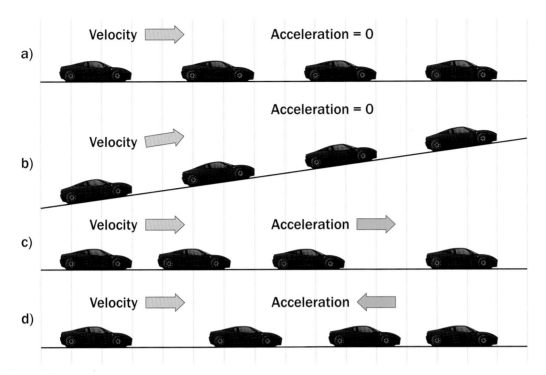

**Figure 2.5**
Successive pictures, taken at equal time intervals, of a car in four different kinds of motion. The car is accelerating in c and d but not in a and b as shown.

onds. Its acceleration in this case is 3 miles per hour per second. If it slowed from 50 to 40 miles per hour in 2 seconds the acceleration would be −5 miles per hour per second; the negative sign denoting deceleration.

The use of arrows to represent velocity and acceleration is very convenient but potentially confusing since they represent different quantities. Be careful to keep them straight! Note that the velocity and acceleration arrows of a single object can have any direction or length relative to each other.

## 2-3 Force: Introduction to the Second Law of Motion

The intuitive definition of **force**, as noted in section 2-1, is that it is a push or a pull, exerted by one object on another. Forces have direction, so when several forces act on the same object, we must consider the direction of each force as well as its strength when deciding what the total force is. The total force acting on an object is called the **net force**. Forces pushing in the same direction add together to increase net force, whereas forces acting in opposite directions add against each other, decreasing net force.

The first law of motion states that uniform

**Figure 2.6**
The puck slides in a circle on an air hockey table without friction. Its velocity (yellow arrow) is tangential to the circle, while its acceleration (blue arrow) always points to the center of the circle because the string is exerting an inward force on the puck. The acceleration therefore changes the puck's direction but not its speed.

motion—motion with no acceleration—persists unless forces compel it to change. So acceleration is caused by force. If you ever witness an acceleration, you can know with complete certainty that a net force of some kind made it happen.

But the converse is not true. If a force is present it does not have to cause an acceleration. If another force balances it out, there will be a net force of zero and no resulting change in the state of motion. Each of us experiences this every day. Gravity exerts a force on you, pulling you toward the ground. But as you sit motionless in your chair you do not accelerate toward the ground because the chair pushes upward on you with a balancing, equal force. So the net force on you is zero and you do not change your state of motion. Therefore, we say that accelera-

**Force:**
A push or pull on an object.

**Net Force:**
The sum of all the forces present on a body.

tions are caused by **unbalanced forces**, which is the net force, the amount of force not canceled out by other, competing forces.

Forces are the third, and last, quantity represented by an arrow. The arrow points in the direction of the push or pull with a length proportional to the strength. Note that the unbalanced force and acceleration arrows of a single object can have any length relative to each other but they will always point in the same direction.

Unbalanced forces are acting whenever an object moves faster, slower, changes direction, or experiences any combination of speed and direction change. The kind of acceleration caused by a particular force depends on the direction of the force. If a force pushes on an object in the same direction as its velocity, the object speeds up, like the ball thrown by the pitcher in *Figure 2.7*. It slows down if a force opposes its velocity,

**Unbalanced Forces:**

The portion of the total force that is unopposed by other forces and so will cause an acceleration. An unbalanced force means that the net force is not zero.

**Mass:**

The characteristic of a body which determines how much it accelerates when a force is applied.

**Figure 2.7**
Both pitcher and catcher exert forces that accelerate the baseball. In which direction is each force applied?

like the ball in the catcher's mitt. Forces perpendicular to the velocity cause a change in direction of motion with the object turning in the direction of the force as with a curve ball or the puck shown in Figure 2.6.

The strength of forces is measured in pounds (lb) in the English system of units and newtons (N) in the metric system. A newton is approximately one quarter of a pound.

Forces cause accelerations, but what determines the *amount* of acceleration? The strength of the force is, of course, a major factor. Stronger forces produce greater accelerations. If a particular force causes an object to accelerate from 20 to 30 miles per hour in 10 seconds, a force twice as strong would cause the same change in 5 seconds, or half the time. A force half as strong would take 20 seconds to produce the same acceleration.

## 2-4 Mass

There is also another factor. Suppose you run out of gas driving your compact car to work and coast to the side of the road near a pickup truck, which is also out of gas. You and the driver of the pickup truck decide to combine efforts and push one of the vehicles to the nearest gas station. With little thought you both choose to push the compact car, because you know that pushing the pickup would be a lot harder. In other words, you know that an equal amount of pushing force will make the smaller vehicle accelerate more than the larger vehicle. The property of an object that determines how much it will accelerate in response to an applied force is called **mass**. If mass is larger (*e.g.* the truck), acceleration will be less than if mass is smaller (the car). The greater the mass, the smaller the acceleration for a given force.

Mass is a property unique to each object and does not depend on other factors such as location. A particular force applied to a mass causes the same amount of acceleration no matter where the object is located, be it on the surface of Earth, in interstellar space, or anywhere else. If the same object experiences different accelerations at different places, it is not because the mass has changed, it is because the forces acting on it are different (*Figure 2.8*).

**Figure 2.8**
Suppose we have a fig that weighs 3.6 ounces on Earth (1 newton). The same fig will weigh only .6 ounces (.165 newtons) on the Moon and 1.4 ounces (.38 newtons) on Mars. The weight has changed in each location because Earth, the Moon, and Mars each exert a different strength of gravitational force. However, if you were to throw the fig horizontally with the same force in each location, the fig would experience the same horizontal acceleration regardless of its weight, because the mass of the fig has not changed.

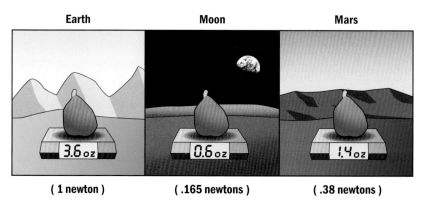

|          Earth          |          Moon           |          Mars           |
|-------------------------|-------------------------|-------------------------|
|         3.6 oz          |         0.6 oz          |         1.4 oz          |
|       ( 1 newton )      |      ( .165 newtons )   |      ( .38 newtons )    |

## STANDARDS OF MEASUREMENT

As we have already noted in this chapter, mass is the property of objects that determines how much they accelerate in response to a force. To be useful, the concept of mass must be made quantitative. To shop for dinner we need to know, for example, whether a sack of potatoes has a mass of one kilogram or two kilograms. Quantities of mass are defined by comparison to a standard. The standard measurement of one kilogram has been decreed to be the mass of a specific piece of platinum-iridium which is kept under the watchful care of the Bureau Internationals des Poids et Measures at Sevres, near Paris, France. To know if you have one kilogram of potatoes, you must directly or indirectly compare the mass of your potatoes with the mass of this piece of metal.

Obviously, neither you nor your grocer are going to take that sack of potatoes to France to make sure you're getting exactly one kilogram of spuds. To make weighing objects against standards both exact and practical, copies of the standard kilogram are supplied to government bureaus of standards around the world. Those bureaus, in turn, make exact-weight copies—some of which are split in halves, quarters, etc.—to distribute to manufacturers who make and sell commercial copies. You may have seen a box of "weights" in a chemistry laboratory that is the result of this process.

One way to find the mass of your potatoes is to balance them against known weights. Put your potatoes on one side of a scale and add standard masses to the other until both sides balance. The sum of the standard masses used equals the mass of the potatoes. You have made your comparison accurately but indirectly with the standard kilogram secured in a bell jar near Paris.

Length and time must also be given quantitative meaning by comparison to standards. For many years the standard meter was the official measurement of a long bar of metal kept with the standard kilogram in France. Improved technology now allows us to define it as how far light travels in a vacuum in 1/299,792,458 seconds.

The ancient measure of time was the Sun's position in the sky. The invention of clocks allowed greater accuracy, and was soon followed by the "invention" of the "second," defined as 1/86,400th of a day. Today we have more precise standards of time based on atomic vibrations. One second is defined as 9,192,631,770 vibrations of a Cesium 133 atom.

### Standard Kilogram

The unit of mass, the kilogram (kg), remains the only base unit in the International System of Units that is still defined in terms of a physical artifact. The standard was manufactured in 1879. It is stored in an evacuated chamber near Paris.

---

Mass should not be confused with **weight**. Weight is a measure of the force of gravity on a particular mass. Weight *does* change with location. This concept is explained more fully in Chapter 3.

A term often used in speaking of motion is "inertia." Inertia is thought of as the property that makes it hard to move an object from rest, or that keeps it moving once it has started. For this reason Newton's first law is sometimes called the "law of inertia." But there is no quantity that preserves an object's state of motion; if in motion or at rest it just stays that way. So it is better not to regard "inertia" as a quantity in and of itself, but rather as a qualitative description for mass since mass represents the difficulty of getting an object to change its state of motion.

## 2-5 The Second Law of Motion

Newton summarized the relation between force, mass, and acceleration in a simple equation, termed Newton's second law of motion:

$$\textbf{Force} = \textbf{mass} \times \textbf{acceleration}$$

or just

$$\textbf{F} = \textbf{ma}$$

Alternatively, we may write it as

$$\textbf{a} = \textbf{F/m}$$

This equation, especially the second way of writing it, shows that the acceleration of an object is directly proportional to the net force on it and inversely proportional to its mass. This means that if you double the force on an object without changing its mass, the acceleration doubles. Or if you have two objects, the first of which has twice the mass of the second, and the

**Weight:**
A measure of the force of gravity pulling on an object.

same force is applied to both of them, the first will accelerate at half the rate of the second. Can you see how this is described by the equation?

To illustrate, suppose an object has a mass of 100 kilograms. If it is pushed by a force that causes it to accelerate at a rate of 5 meters per second every second, then the second law of motion tells us that the force is $100 \times 5 = 500$ newtons. Now suppose this same force of 500 newtons was applied to a mass of 50 kilograms. The resulting acceleration would be $500/50 = 10$ meters per second every second, or twice as great.

We note that the first law of motion follows naturally from the second law when the applied force is zero. An object with no force applied to it will not accelerate and thus remain in its current state of motion. The first law may be considered as a *qualitative* statement about motion and the presence or absence of force. The second law of motion is *quantitative*. It says exactly *how much* the motion of an object of mass **m** changes when acted on by a force of magnitude **F**.

The significance of Newton's second law of motion cannot be overstated. It was the first universal principle discovered that enabled changes observed in our physical world to be described through mathematics.

## 2–6 The Third Law of Motion

The final observation of Newton that completed his laws of motion was that **forces occur only when *two* things interact with each other.** Nothing in isolation can exert a force on itself. A car can accelerate only if its wheels touch the road and push against it. If there is no interaction between the tires and the pavement, there is no force and the car does not accelerate. A boat cannot accelerate forward unless its propeller acts against the water. An airplane flies only because the angled propeller blades, or the turbine blades in jet aircraft, push the air behind them as they rotate. The forces that accelerate a rocket result from the contact between the rocket itself and the fuel that is burnt inside it and thrust out behind (*Figure 2.9*).

In every interaction two forces arise, one on each of the two interacting bodies. The magnitude of each force is the same but they are oppositely directed. This is Newton's third law of motion and can be stated as follows:

> **All forces result from interactions between pairs of objects, each object exerting a force on the other. The two resulting forces have the same strength and act in exactly opposite directions.**

If you are familiar with this law you might have expected to read, "For every action there is an opposite and equal reaction." We avoid using this common phrase because it seems to imply that one force starts the interaction and the other arises as a result. That is not what the third law says. The third law says that a single-sided interaction cannot exist. It takes two objects to interact and when they do, each object feels a distinct force. So in every interaction there will always be two forces, one on each object. These two forces have the same strength but point in opposite directions.

When the interacting objects have the same mass, the two forces cause both objects to accelerate the same amount. For example, if a person steps from a rowboat of similar mass to a dock, they are accelerated toward the dock at the same rate the boat is accelerated in the opposite direction. (Try not to fall in the water!)

However, if one object has more mass than

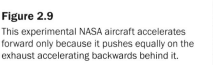

**Figure 2.9**
This experimental NASA aircraft accelerates forward only because it pushes equally on the exhaust accelerating backwards behind it.

**Figure 2.10**
Log rolling requires an understanding of the Third Law of Motion. Can you see why?

**Figure 2.11**
Using the Third Law of Motion, explain why you're no match for a banana peel.

the other, it's acceleration will be less. If its mass is considerably more than the other, its resulting accelcration can be so small the force on it *seems* negligible. When you start to walk, for example, the force that accelerates you comes from the frictional interaction between your foot and the floor. You push on the floor with your legs and the resulting interaction manifests itself as a forward force on you and a backward force on the floor. As you accelerate forward, the floor accelerates backward. But when have you ever noticed a floor accelerating backward?

The floor is firmly attached to the building, which is attached to Earth. So the floor's effective mass is that of Earth itself. By the third law of motion we can write:

**Force of you on Earth =
Force of Earth on you**

The second law of motion allows us to substitute mass times acceleration in place of force. So we have the following:

**Earth's mass × Earth's acceleration
=
Your mass × Your acceleration**

Earth's mass is $10^{23}$ times greater than your mass. So by the above equation its acceleration will be $10^{23}$ times *less* than yours. This amount is too small to be measured, let alone noticed as you sprint to class!

Earth's overwhelmingly large mass makes it seem to not accelerate at all, so let's change the situation a bit by putting a banana peel under your foot. Assume, as in cartoons, and that a slick peel will cling to your foot but not to the floor.

The equation now becomes:

**Force of you on the banana peel =
Force of the banana peel on you**

or

**Banana peel's mass × Banana peel's acceleration = Your mass × Your acceleration**

Your mass has not changed but now you are interacting with a banana peel having 1/1000 of your mass instead of Earth. The banana peel accelerates backward 1000 times more than you accelerate forward, you lose your footing and your support, gravity takes over, and you fall flat.

These examples illustrate the interconnectedness of the laws of motion. The third law of motion is a rule about forces and what they can do. The third law of motion allows us to create an equation of the forces between two interacting objects, and the second law allows us to change the equation to one of masses and accelerations. In this way, the accelerations can be solved and the resulting motion completely understood.

The laws of motion tell us how objects respond to force but they give no information about how forces arise from interactions, nor how strong a force will be in any given interaction. This information is expressed by force laws that are unique for each of the four interactions of nature. Gravity is considered in Chapter 3, electromagnetism in Chapter 4, and the two nuclear forces in Chapter 25.

# 2 STUDY GUIDE

## Chapter Framework

### A. Introduction
1. Motion and change
2. Unbalanced force creates motion

### B. The First Law of Motion
1. State of motion
2. Changing a state of motion
3. Inertia

### C. Acceleration
1. Change of velocity
2. Speed up
3. Slow down
4. Change direction

### D. Force
1. Unbalanced forces
2. Cause of acceleration

### E. Mass
1. Mass and acceleration
2. Mass and force
3. Mass and weight

### F. The Second Law of Motion
1. F = ma
2. Acceleration proportional to force
3. Acceleration inversely proportional to mass

### G. The Third Law of Motion
1. Forces come in pairs
2. Each force acts on a different object
3. Equal strength and opposite direction
4. No single-sided forces

## Comprehension

### Matching
(Choose the law that is most apparent in each scenario)
1. _____ A boat gliding through the water on a lake at constant speed in a straight line.
2. _____ An airplane circling the airport at a constant speed while waiting to land.
3. _____ A marathon runner speeding up just before crossing the finish line.
4. _____ Comparing all forces that arise when a book sits on a table.
5. _____ Describing the motion of a bench in the park.
6. _____ Comparing the forces responsible for accelerating a bullet and the recoil of a gun.
7. _____ A hot air balloon rising straight up at a constant speed.
8. _____ A submarine falling straight towards the ocean bottom at a constant speed.
9. _____ Describing the forces created as two boxers' gloves come in contact.

a. 1st Law
b. 2nd Law
c. 3rd Law

### True/False
1. _____ The laws of nature are treated differently for an object in uniform motion and an object at rest.
2. _____ If an object changes its state of motion then it must be accelerating.
3. _____ When an astronaut travels to the moon, his or her weight changes. Therefore, the astronaut's mass must also change.
4. _____ For an object to change its state of motion, an unbalanced force must act on it.
5. _____ Objects that interact always exert the same force on one another.

### Fill in the blank
1. _____ understood the law of inertia several decades before Newton.
2. If an applied force remains constant, and the object's _____ increases, a smaller acceleration will result.
3. _____ is the speed and direction of a moving object.
4. Acceleration is when the _____ of an object changes.

## Analysis

1. Which of the following explanations correctly describes rocket propulsion?
   a) The rocket shoots out gases which push on the air. The air pushing back on the rocket moves the rocket.
   b) The rocket pushes back on its own exhaust gases. These gases pushing on the rocket are responsible for the acceleration of the rocket.
   c) The motion of the exhaust gases leaves a vacuum in the air that occurs in the region in the front of the rocket. The air in this reduced pressure region pulls the rocket forward.
   d) The gases expelled from the rear of the rocket cause lower pressure regions behind the rocket. This low pressure pushes the rocket. This effect is particularly effective in a vacuum where there is zero pressure in front of the rocket.

2. When a body is acted upon by a single constant unbalanced force,
   a) it will move with a constant speed in the direction of the force.
   b) it will experience a constant acceleration in the direction of the force.
   c) it will accelerate in a direction perpendicular to the force.
   d) its resulting acceleration will increase at a constant rate.

3. If an object is moving in a straight line at a constant speed, which of the following must be true?
   a) There is a constant force acting in the direction the object is moving.
   b) There is a steadily increasing force acting in the direction the object is moving.

c) The total force on the object is zero.

d) The body is experiencing no frictional forces.

4. Restate Newton's Laws in your own words.

5. If velocity is zero, does acceleration have to be zero? If acceleration is zero, does velocity need to be zero? Give an example to illustrate your answers.

6. If there is a constant net force on an object that starts out at rest, what happens to its speed?

7. When you drive, the car engine generates a constant force as long as you give it a constant amount of gas. Why doesn't your car accelerate at a constant rate like described in the previous question?

8. Give an example of a situation where it is important to use Newton's Third Law.

9. A rubber chicken thrown into the road hits a car moving 60 mph. Justify your answers using Newton's laws.

a) Upon contact, does the car or the chicken experience the greater force?

b) Does the car or the chicken experience the greatest acceleration?

10. What two forces on Earth make Newton's First Law difficult to see? How do they prevent most objects from traveling in uniform motion?

11. How do force and mass affect acceleration?

## Synthesis

1. A semi-truck going 70 mph runs into a patch of black ice and glides across the ice. No unbalanced forces (such as friction) are present on the truck.

a) What type of motion does the truck experience after encountering the ice?

b) What law applies to the scenario?

c) If the patch of completely frictionless ice extended in front of the truck for six miles, what is the truck's speed right before reaching the end of the ice patch?

2. During a football game, a wide receiver who only weighs 160 lbs catches the football on a short curl route. From the receiver's blind side, a 270-lb linebacker running full speed hits the receiver, causing the linebacker's speed to slightly decrease and knocking the receiver into the stands.

a) What type of motion does the linebacker experience when hitting the receiver?

b) What type of motion does the receiver experience when hit by the linebacker?

c) Compare the accelerations of the two players.

Use Newton's 2nd and 3rd Laws to explain your answers.

3. A rocket in space is burning its engines, creating a constant unbalanced force on it. The force is applied to the rocket indefinitely.

a) Describe the rocket's motion. What will happen to the rocket's speed?

b) Which of Newton's laws apply to this scenario?

c) When the rocket runs out of fuel, what happens to its speed?

4. Ethan pulls on a cart that his brother, Cameron, sits on. They both head straight home with progressively increasing speed.

a) Analyze the motion of the cart by doing the following:

i) Describe the cart's motion. Is it uniform or accelerated?

ii) Identify which law(s) of motion apply.

iii) Identify all forces that are acting on the cart and which forces influence the cart's motion. A labeled diagram with arrows representing forces is often helpful here.

iv) Compare the size of relevant forces. Are the forces balanced or unbalanced?

b) Use Newton's Third Law to compare the size of the force Ethan exerts on the cart to the force the cart exerts on Ethan. Explain how the cart and Ethan can both be speeding up in the same direction, taking into account the Third Law.

c) If Cameron jumps out of the cart while Ethan keeps pulling with the same force, what will happen?

5. In a car crash between a small car and an SUV, the occupants of the small car are much more likely to be injured. Use Newton's Laws to explain why.

6. Use Newton's laws to explain how safety features in cars like seat belts, crumple- zones (places where the car's frame is designed to bend in a crash), and air bags reduce the risk of injury in a crash.

7. A boy is standing on a skateboard at rest. The boy jumps forward off the skateboard.

a) Which of Newton's Laws apply to this situation?

b) What happens to the boy and to the skateboard?

c) What would happen if the boy jumped off sideways? Why are the situations different?

# The Gravitational Interaction

*Millions saw the apple fall,*
*but Newton asked why.*
Bernard Baruch

# 3

## LEARN

- The motion of objects falling in the absence of friction.

- How the acceleration of gravity affects bodies with initial upward or sideways motion.

- How gravity explains orbiting bodies.

- The difference between mass and weight.

- The universal law of gravitation and how it was discovered.

- To predict the forces felt by bodies of different mass near the surface of Earth using the universal law of gravitation.

- The physical interpretation of gravity put forth by Einstein.

We have learned that interactions give rise to forces and forces cause things to move. In the days of Aristotle, it was generally thought that there were two fundamental interactions: gravity and levity. Gravity caused things to fall to Earth, and levity caused things to rise to the heavens. Rocks possessed gravity and descended to Earth when dropped to be with other like material. Fire, on the other hand, possessed levity, and so rose skyward, yearning to return to the similar burnings of heaven, the ancients' explanation for the stars.

It was a good beginning. The theory of levity would be recast as the buoyant force to be discussed in Chapter 6. Not a fundamental interaction itself, the buoyant force results from electromagnetic and gravitational forces spreading through a fluid. Gravity, though, is a fundamental interaction, and its modern explanation gives us insights into the nature of space and time beyond anything imagined by the Greeks.

In this chapter we will consider gravity. We will examine its strength and influence here on Earth's surface. We will study how it changes

with mass and distance and how it keeps the Moon orbiting Earth. At the end of the chapter we will discuss the nature of the gravitational interaction itself.

## 3-1 Falling Objects

You probably have hiked up a mountain and over to the brink of a cliff to throw a rock off, watching and listening as it fell, trying to hear it hit bottom. There is something fascinating about seeing a rock fall away under the pure influence of wind and gravity. Did you notice how it moved as it fell?

There is a law describing the strength of the force of gravity and how this strength changes with mass and distance. This law, discovered by Isaac Newton, is used with his laws of motion to predict how bodies move under gravity's influence. Since all objects on Earth feel a force from gravity, Newton had to understand and disentangle its effects from the motion he witnessed to derive the laws of motion.

Back to the rock. A rock dropped over a

cliff accelerates downward with increasing speed (*Figure 3.1*). If neither wind nor air friction opposed its fall, the increase is a constant value of 9.8 m/sec each second. So after one second of falling its speed would be 9.8 m/sec, after 2 seconds it would be 19.6 m/sec, after 3 seconds it would be 29.4 m/sec, and so on. This rate of acceleration is designated by the symbol **g**. In more familiar units **g** is 32 feet/sec$^2$ or about 22 miles/hour every second.

Table 3.1 lists the distances covered, velocities, and accelerations for an object falling for 10 seconds unopposed by friction. (How friction changes the values in the table is considered in Chapter 5.) Notice that **g** being constant means the value in the acceleration column does not change with time. Under this steady acceleration a speed of 220 miles per hour is reached in only 10 seconds!

**Figure 3.1**
Objects fall with increasing speed but constant acceleration if there is no friction.

**g:**
The symbol representing the acceleration caused by gravity. It is equal to 22 mi/hour per second or 32 ft/second per second or 9.8 m/second per second depending on the units.

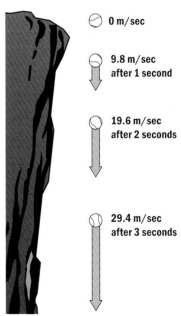

0 m/sec

9.8 m/sec
after 1 second

19.6 m/sec
after 2 seconds

29.4 m/sec
after 3 seconds

## Table 3.1 — A Falling Body in the Absence of Friction

The distance, velocity, and acceleration of a falling body in the absence of friction. Velocity is presented in units of miles per hour as well as in the more standard units of meters per second.

| Time (seconds) | Distance (meters) | Velocity (m/sec) | Velocity (miles/hr) | Acceleration (m/sec2) |
|---|---|---|---|---|
| 0 | 0 | 0 | 0 | 9.8 |
| 1 | 4.9 | 9.8 | 22 | 9.8 |
| 2 | 19.6 | 19.6 | 44 | 9.8 |
| 3 | 44.1 | 29.4 | 66 | 9.8 |
| 4 | 78.4 | 39.2 | 88 | 9.8 |
| 5 | 122.5 | 49.0 | 110 | 9.8 |
| 6 | 176.4 | 58.8 | 132 | 9.8 |
| 7 | 240.1 | 68.6 | 154 | 9.8 |
| 8 | 313.6 | 78.4 | 176 | 9.8 |
| 9 | 396.9 | 88.2 | 198 | 9.8 |
| 10 | 490.0 | 98.0 | 220 | 9.8 |

### 3-2 Uniform acceleration

As a reminder, the second law of motion says that for objects accelerating under the influence of any force, the relation

$$F = ma$$

holds true. Again the symbol **F** represents the force, **m** represents the mass, and **a** represents the acceleration. For objects accelerating under just the influence of gravity, the acceleration, **a** is the gravitational acceleration **g**.

Let's get some insights from this equation. In the previous chapter we talked about how a force on an object causes it to accelerate. In our examples the object mass **m** stayed the same so **F** and **a** were then proportional to each other: increase the force and the acceleration would also increase by the same amount. In the case of a rock falling from a cliff without friction, both the mass and acceleration of the rock are constant. So by the second law of motion, the force on the rock must also be constant. A 10 kg rock tossed off a cliff will experience an acceleration of 9.8 m/sec every second and will therefore feel a force of 98 newtons all the way to the bottom. Remarkably, tossing a rock off a cliff is all that is needed to learn that the acceleration and force of gravity are constant for any given object as it falls—at least over the height of a typical cliff. We will revisit this point in section 3-7.

Now imagine throwing a ball straight up with an initial speed of 35 m/sec (about 80 miles/hr) (*Figure 3.2*). Instead of speeding up, the ball moves slower as it rises because the force of gravity is opposing its motion. The strength of the gravitational force does not depend on whether the ball is going up or down. So the amount of acceleration is the same as before. After 1 second of upward motion, the ball's speed is 35 – 9.8 = 25.2 m/sec. At the end of another second the speed has been reduced to 25.2 – 9.8 = 15.4 m/sec; after 3 seconds, it is 15.4 – 9.8 = 5.6 m/sec; and after just 4 seconds in the air, its direction has changed and its speed is now 5.6 – 9.8 = 4.2 m/sec *downward*. From here the ball's downward speed increases each second by 9.8 m/sec.

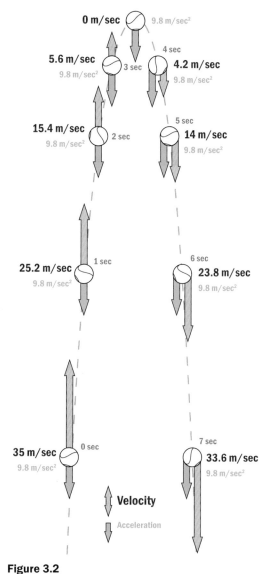

**Figure 3.2**
The acceleration caused by gravity is constant regardless of the direction of motion. The rate a ball slows while traveling upward is the same rate it speeds up when coming down.

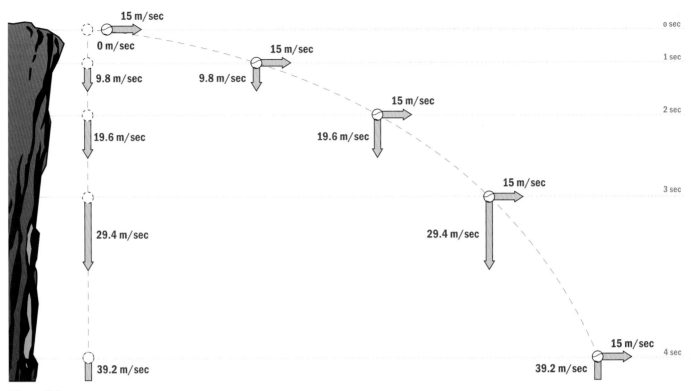

**Figure 3.3**
The ball is thrown to the right at 15 m/sec. However, it will hit the ground at the same time as if it had been simply dropped because the acceleration of all falling bodies is the same regardless of their initial velocities.

Now suppose the ball is thrown horizontally instead of vertically, with an initial speed of 15 m/sec, as indicated in *Figure 3.3*. This time it follows a curved path as it falls. Curved motion appears more complicated, so we simplify it by separating the path of the ball into horizontal and vertical parts. At the end of the first second, the ball is still moving horizontally with a speed of 15 m/sec, but it is now also falling downward with a vertical speed of 9.8 m/sec. After another second, the downward speed has increased to 19.6 m/sec while the horizontal motion remains unchanged. As things progress the horizontal part of the motion never changes, while the downward velocity continues to increase at the rate of 9.8 m/sec every second because the constant force of gravity pulls only in that direction. This change in the downward speed of the ball is the same as if the ball had no initial motion at all. It may not be obvious, but two balls positioned at the same height, with one dropped at the same instant as the second ball is thrown horizontally, will hit the ground at the same time because the downward acceleration on both is the same.

To summarize all three examples—dropping a rock, throwing a ball into the air, and throwing a ball horizontally—the initial veloc-

ities are different but the accelerations, and therefore the way the velocities change, are all the same.

## 3-3 Weight and Acceleration

Now suppose you were to drop both a basketball-sized boulder and a baseball-sized rock from the same height. You might expect the boulder to drop more rapidly than the rock because it is much heavier. But upon dropping the rock and the boulder you find that despite their difference in size and weight, their accelerations are exactly the same. Their weights do not affect how they accelerate!

We look to Newton's second law of motion for understanding. The large boulder has greater mass than the smaller rock so it is harder to accelerate. That they both accelerate at the same rate means the force of gravity on the boulder is greater than the force of gravity on the rock.

You know this, of course. **Weight** is just the force of gravity on an object and more massive things weigh more. By Newton's second law, weight (**w**) is

$$\mathbf{w} = \mathbf{mg}$$

which illustrates that the weight of an

**Weight:**
A measure of the force of gravity pulling on an object.

**Figure 3.4**
In the absence of friction all objects fall with the same acceleration regardless of their mass.

object with twice the mass is twice as great since **g** is constant. When you step on a scale to measure your weight you are really measuring the force of gravity on you. This is an accurate mass estimate only because **g** is constant.[1]

We must point out that objects all fall at the same rate of acceleration regardless of weight, only if the resistance from air can be ignored. Air friction, considered in more detail in Chapter 5, will cause lighter objects, like a leaf, to accelerate more slowly than a heavier rock. But even light objects such as feathers and leaves have exactly the same acceleration as a rock when falling without air resistance. Any two objects, lead weights or popcorn, when dropped in a vacuum simultaneously from the same height, will hit the ground at the same time, traveling at the same speed (*Figure 3.4*).

Hopefully you made certain no one was at the base of the cliff before tossing off the boulder! You know from experience that a falling boulder lands with more force than a small rock does and could cause serious injury. The above discussion just quantifies this common sense.

## 3-4 Circular Motion and the Moon's Orbit

The Italian scientist Galileo Galilei, so the story goes, proved that all objects fell at the same rate by dropping two unequal masses off the leaning Tower of Pisa. He probably did not do that actual experiment, but he did know gravity's acceleration is constant for all things and so did Newton, experimenting a century later, in a much more science-friendly society.

A popular legend claims that Newton saw an apple fall in his orchard and thus "discovered" gravity. What Newton did was look with a questioning mind at falling objects like apples and then ask if the interaction that made these earthly things fall was the same interaction that held the Moon in its orbit. Up to that time the motion of the Moon was considered to be unrelated to the gravity on Earth. The Moon was thought to be embedded in some mysterious cosmic material that kept it firmly in place,

much like a marble affixed inside a sphere of glass centered on Earth.

Newton used mathematics to show that if the following two hypotheses were true, then the interaction of gravity alone was responsible for pulling apples to Earth and holding the Moon in its orbit:

1. The force of Earth's gravity on the Moon is essentially perpendicular to the Moon's velocity.

2. The force of gravity diminishes with distance as $1/\mathbf{d}^2$ where **d** is the distance between the centers of any two gravitating bodies: Earth and an apple on the one hand, or Earth and the Moon on the other.

Our Moon circles Earth every 27.3 days. Its speed is roughly uniform, but the direction of travel is constantly curving in accordance with a centripetal acceleration pointed at Earth. In Chapter 2 we learned that when an object changes its direction of travel there must be a net or unbalanced sideways force acting on it. It doesn't matter if it is a ball twirled on the end of a string, a car turning a circular corner, or the Moon in its orbit. All of these experience a centripetal acceleration caused by a force directed toward the center of the circular path.

Newton pointed out that if a cannon on the edge of a cliff were fired horizontally, the cannon-ball would accelerate downward in an arc, like the green ball in Figure 3.3. If the projectile were fired faster with a greater initial horizontal velocity, it would travel farther horizontally before hitting the ground. In a wonderful intuitive leap, Newton pointed out that if the cannonball were fired fast enough from a tall-enough mountain, it would *never* hit the ground, because Earth's round surface would curve away at the same rate the cannonball fell. The cannonball would be forever falling but its forward velocity would never let it land; it would be in orbit! The Moon is doing just that. Its forward speed is such that it always remains the same distance from Earth (*Figure 3.5*).

Newton realized that to calculate the orbital acceleration of the moon and have it agree with the value of **g**, gravity had to diminish as the distance squared. In Newton's time, both the radius of the Earth and the distance from the Earth to the Moon were known. The ratio of these distances was 1/60. Newton used

---

[1] Actually, you are measuring the force of the scale pushing back on you, which by Newton's Third Law is equal to the force of gravity pulling down on you. Read more on this in Chapter 5.

**Figure 3.5**
Going in orbit or falling to the ground only depends on how much horizontal velocity the projectile has.

## TIDES

Because the acceleration of gravity depends on distance, water in oceans on the side nearer to the Moon experiences a greater gravitational acceleration than the Earth as a whole. This greater acceleration causes that water to bulge toward the moon, creating a high tide. Furthermore the Earth as a whole is closer to the Moon than water in the oceans on the side away from the Moon, and these oceans are not accelerated towards the Moon as much as the Earth itself. The result is that oceans on the opposite side from the Moon also appear to bulge upward, creating high tides on opposite sides of the Earth.

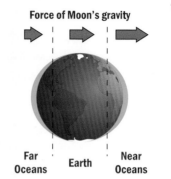

geometry to show that the Moon's centripetal acceleration was 3600 times smaller than the gravitational acceleration **g** measured near the surface of the earth. The gravitational acceleration was smaller by a factor of 3600, which is $60^2$. This was exactly the inverse squared relationship he hoped to find.

## 3-5 Gravity and the Third Law of Motion

Newton's third law of motion says two forces arise from any interaction between bodies, one force acting on each of the bodies. Throwing a rock off a cliff clearly shows the acceleration of the rock. What about Earth? Is the rock pulling up on Earth at the same time Earth is pulling down? Yes. Does Earth accelerate toward the rock in response? Yes. But as we discussed in Chapter 2, Newton's second law tells us the amount of acceleration on Earth is inversely proportional to its mass and therefore is so tiny it can hardly be measured, much less observed.

But consider the Moon. Its gravity pulls on Earth with the same force that Earth's gravity is pulling on it. With a mass of only 1.2% of Earth's mass, the Moon accelerates much more than Earth. But while the Moon's mass is considerably less than Earth's, it is still enough to make Earth accelerate noticeably. As a result, Earth wobbles in and out of its orbit around the Sun, always pulled toward whichever side the Moon is on.

Newton understood that gravity between two objects depends on the mass of both objects, not just one or the other. By looking at the symmetry inherent in the third law of motion, Newton inferred that if the force of gravity on a boulder falling to Earth was proportional to the mass of the boulder, then the force ought to be proportional to Earth's mass as well. He theorized that just as rocks with half the mass feel half the force, a planet with half the mass would create a gravitational attraction that is also half as strong. With this realization, the foundation for a universal law of gravity was finally complete.

## 3-6 The Law of Universal Gravitation

So far we have determined two important facts. First, the force of gravity is proportional to the masses of both of the objects on which it acts. Second, this force weakens as the square of the distance between their centers.

Newton unified these insights into the law of universal gravitation, or just the **law of gravity**. It can be stated as follows:

**Every object in the universe attracts every other object by a long-range gravitational interaction that obeys Newton's third law. The strength of the attractive force, F, varies with the masses, M and m, of the two**

**Law of Gravity:**

Expressed by the mathematical formula $F = GmM/d^2$ that describes the strength of the force of gravity between two objects of mass M and m separated between their centers by the distance d.

objects and the distance, d, between their centers according to the relationship

$$F = \frac{-GmM}{d^2}$$

The number G that appears in the equation is the **gravitational constant**. G relates the amount of mass to the strength of the force. In Newton's day no one knew the value of G. It can only be found through experiment and is so small, $6.67 \times 10^{-11}$ in the metric system, that the gravitational force between two 100-kilogram balls placed 30 centimeters apart is about one-millionth of a pound. Only if one of the interacting objects has a large mass, like Earth, does the force become appreciable.

The first public test of Newton's universal law of gravity (and his laws of motion as well) came when he used them to successfully calculate the time and place of the return of a comet which the English astronomer, Sir Edmund Halley, suspected was orbiting the Sun. When "Halley's" comet appeared just as Newton had predicted, the science of using mathematics based on universal laws to know future motion was born.

Using the heavens as a testing ground was successful. But one could still argue that gravity emanated only from the Sun and planets and was not present in ordinary objects, such as buildings or rocks. It was a leap of faith for Newton to hypothesize, without being able at that time to prove, that a force of gravity universally exists between any two objects that have mass. This aspect of the law was confirmed 70 years after Newton's death by Henry Cavendish (1731–1810), who developed a method of measuring the minute gravitational attraction between such ordinary objects as metal balls.

### 3–7 Acceleration Revisited

There is a final point regarding the value of the acceleration of gravity, **g**, that needs to be cleared up. At the beginning of the chapter we talked about how **g** does not change for a rock as it falls off a cliff. Every second the rock's velocity increases by the same amount. From this we concluded the force on the rock was the same at the top of the cliff as at the bottom. But the law of gravity clearly says the force of gravity

**Gravitational Constant:**

A number relating the strength of the gravitational force to the masses being attracted and their distance apart.

gets stronger as the distance between objects decreases. Therefore **g** should be *larger* at the bottom of the cliff than at the top!

As it turns out, the force of gravity *is* stronger at the base of the cliff than at the top by the amount that the law of gravity predicts, but the effect is very slight. A beach at sea level is 6,378 km from Earth's center. The top of a one-kilometer high cliff by this beach is 6,379 km from Earth's center. The difference in the force felt by a one-kilogram rock at the bottom and one at the top of the cliff is

$$\frac{G\binom{\text{mass of}}{\text{Earth}}(1\,\text{kg})}{(6378)^2} - \frac{G\binom{\text{mass of}}{\text{Earth}}(1\text{kg})}{(6379)^2} = \frac{0.0027}{\text{newtons}}$$

This difference can be easily measured with sensitive instruments but is too slight to be noticed without them. So we say the height of a cliff, even one 10 miles high, is too short to produce a *significant* difference in the force of gravity and the resultant acceleration. We will therefore treat the gravitational force and the value of **g** as being constant "near Earth's surface" and only consider the $1/d^2$ decrease for objects at distances from Earth's surface far greater than any we would encounter in normal life, such as rocket ships, satellites, and the Moon.[2]

Treating a value as being constant when it does not change significantly within the scope of interest is a common practice in science. Many fundamental values in nature such as **G**, the speed of light, the mass and charge of electrons, etc., are thought to be constant because all measurements of them find the same value within experimental error. They probably are truly constant. Other constants, like **g** or the speed of sound, vary a little depending on circumstances, but they will be considered constants in this text.

### 3–8 Gravity and Curved Space-time

Newton's Universal law of gravity was an enormous advancement in our understanding

[2] In making this assumption we are accepting an error of about 0.5%. Earth is not a perfect sphere—the north and south poles are about 21 km closer to its center than is sea level at the equator. This means the gravitational force and acceleration are about 0.5% percent stronger at the poles than at the equator and slightly smaller (about 0.03% per kilometer) at higher elevations.

## HENRY CAVENDISH AND G

In Newton's day no one knew what the mass of Earth was. So there were two unknown values, G and M, in any formula expressing the force of Earth's gravity. An experiment was needed to measure the force of gravity between two known masses so that the value of G could be determined. Once G was known, the mass of Earth could be found from simply measuring the force of gravity exerted on anything having a known mass. In the late 1700s the gifted scientist Henry Cavendish did just that.

**Henry Cavendish**

British scientist known for his work with hydrogen and his experiment that measured the gravitational force between two masses in order to calculate the density of the Earth.

Henry Cavendish was born into British nobility in 1731. Being wealthy, he used his good fortune to obtain an extensive education at the University of Cambridge and set up a well-equipped laboratory on his estate. His life was devoted to science and he made significant contributions to thermodynamics, electricity, and chemistry, including the discovery of hydrogen.

A notoriously shy man, he may have suffered from Asperger syndrome. Though active in the Royal Society (the scientific academy of the UK), he was otherwise uncomfortable in social settings and avoided people and conversation when he could. He went so far as to communicate with his female servants exclusively through written notes. Because of his asocial behavior, many of his contributions to science were not discovered until after his death when colleagues were permitted to comb through his notes.

Cavendish measured the value of G by mounting two small lead spheres on opposite ends of a lightweight metal bar suspended in the middle by a thin wire. As two large lead spheres were brought near the small spheres, the force of gravity pulled the small spheres toward them twisting the wire slightly. The force of twisting the wire was measured and using this value, G was calculated from $G = Fd^2/Mm$. A modern version of the Cavendish balance is in *Figure 3.6*.

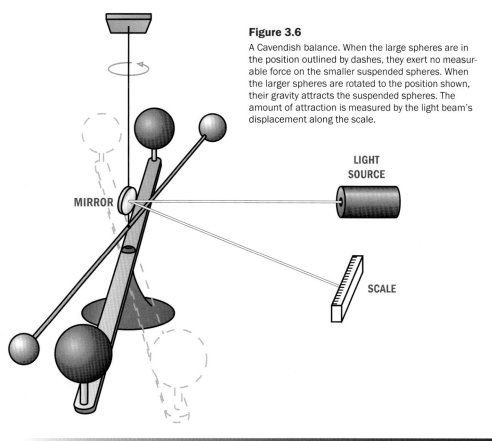

**Figure 3.6**

A Cavendish balance. When the large spheres are in the position outlined by dashes, they exert no measurable force on the smaller suspended spheres. When the larger spheres are rotated to the position shown, their gravity attracts the suspended spheres. The amount of attraction is measured by the light beam's displacement along the scale.

LIGHT SOURCE

MIRROR

SCALE

of the interactions governing the universe. The law of gravity gave rise to the science of celestial mechanics, which allowed scientists to predict positions of planets, times of eclipses, and even the tides with greater accuracy than before. The "theory" of gravity soon became "law" and its truthfulness ceased to be questioned.

Newton and others realized, though, that this law gave no insights into how gravity could act across empty space. When the Moon was thought to be embedded in a cosmic material there was no problem; forces from this material pushing on the Moon kept it in orbit. But with the law of gravitation arose the notion that such a binding material did not exist. Space could be empty and still, somehow, transmit a force between objects that do not touch. How is that possible?

In 1915 Albert Einstein (1879–1955) proposed a radical model for gravity in his **General Theory of Relativity**. It is interesting that he was looking at the behavior of motion in general and only later found that this theory also explained gravity. He started by pointing out that Newton set up two different ways of defining mass. The first was in his second law, **F** = **ma**, which allows mass to be measured by seeing how an object accelerates when pushed. The second was in the law of gravity, which allows mass to be independently measured through the force Earth exerts on it. Nothing in Newton's laws requires that those masses have the same value even though precise experiment shows those values to be the same. Einstein, guided by Occam's Razor, and the fact that all objects fall with the same acceleration, *hypothesized* that it would be simpler if those masses were the same.

**General Theory of Relativity:**

Albert Einstein's description of gravity that was published in 1915. This theory explains the relationship between the geometry of space and the flow of time in our Universe.

## GRAVITATIONAL WAVES

Newton wondered how a gravitational influence can reach across empty space between objects that do not touch. The general theory of relativity predicts that this influence can be seen in gravitational waves. If mass density were to suddenly change (as can happen when a star explodes) the changing strength of gravity transmits through space at the speed of light. Evidence for such waves has been indirectly observed in the shrinking orbits of binary pulsars (see Chapter 33) and is currently being sought directly at gravitational wave observatories at various places on Earth.

This hypothesis led to the prediction that gravity is a geometrical effect arising from a connection between space, time, and matter. Within this connection gravity can be explained through Newton's laws of the motion, particularly the first law.

Recall that the first law says objects drifting in empty space feeling no unbalanced forces go straight without accelerating. Einstein theorized that orbiting objects are doing just that, going straight through space and time (together called space-time). However a large body like Earth *affects the space-time surrounding it,* causing it to "curve." When the Moon moves, it follows the straightest possible path through *curved* space-time, which happens to be an orbit. Massive objects extend a gravitational influence by altering the space-time surrounding them!

Curving the four dimensions of space-time is impossible to visualize fully. But it can be illustrated in two dimensions by stretching a rubber sheet across a frame and placing a heavy ball in the middle, as shown by *Figure 3.7*. The ball bearing causes the sheet to sag so that a smaller bead rolling on the edge will naturally curve around in a circle. By analogy, the Moon moves in an orbit

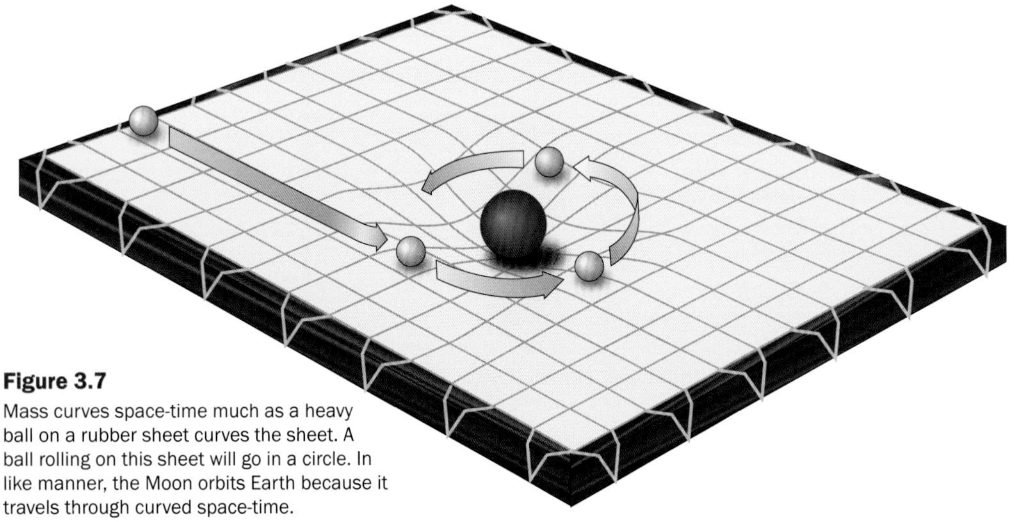

**Figure 3.7**
Mass curves space-time much as a heavy ball on a rubber sheet curves the sheet. A ball rolling on this sheet will go in a circle. In like manner, the Moon orbits Earth because it travels through curved space-time.

## GRAVITATIONAL LENSING

Perhaps the most stark and irrefutable evidence that mass curves space-time are gravitational lenses such as the one shown in *Figure 3.8*. This image is of the center of an enormously massive galaxy cluster called Abell 370. Nearly every object shown is part of this cluster. By coincidence, a few distant galaxies are also located exactly behind it. .

Light from the distant galaxy travels toward us through the heart of the cluster as shown in *Figure 3.9*. Some of this light, following curves in space-time created by the cluster, is redirected toward us creating a well-formed image at "A" and a smeared-out arc at "B". These are both illusions, there are no objects actually there. One image is well-formed and the other stretched into an arc because the mass in Abell 370 is lumpy, creating different amounts of curvature for different light paths.

The amount of mass density determines the amount of curvature. Extreme density can create curvature so steep there is no path out for anything including light. This leads us to the idea of black holes, mentioned in Chapter 33.

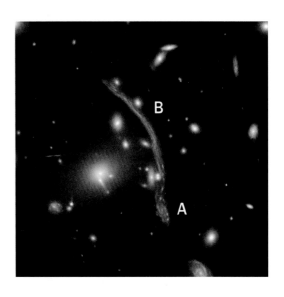

**Figure 3.8**

An image of the dense galaxy cluster Abell 370. A distant galaxy beyond Abell 370 appears both normally (A) and as a stretched arc (B) because of gravitational lensing.

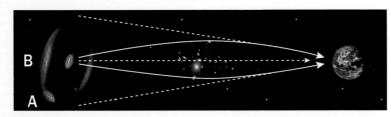

**Figure 3.9**

The galaxy behind the cluster shown in Figure 3.8 is seen as an arc (B) and an image (A) because its light passes through space-time curved by the cluster, redirecting its path.

around Earth, following the curved space-time surrounding it.

An extraordinary claim like this demands extraordinary proof. Predictions based on this theory have been tested in laboratories worldwide, passing every time. The global positioning system uses this theory (and the Special Theory of Relativity—see Chapter 7) to create accurate positions that otherwise would be off by several kilometers.

### Sources of Additional Reading

Will, Clifford. *Was Einstein Right?*

# 3 STUDY GUIDE

### A. Falling Objects
1. g = acceleration caused by gravity
2. $g = 9.8 m/sec^2 = 32 ft/sec^2 = 22 mi/hr/sec$

### B. Uniform Acceleration
1. $F = m \times g$
2. Gravity causes a constant downward acceleration
3. Gravity and horizontal motion

### C. Weight and Acceleration
1. Relationship between mass and weight
2. Acceleration from gravity is independent of mass and weight

### D. Circular Motion and the Moon's Orbit
1. Newton, an apple, and the Moon
2. Gravity acts perpendicular to the Moon's velocity
3. Gravity diminishes as $1 / distance^2$
4. Falling and orbiting

### E. Gravity and the Third Law of Motion
1. Gravity depends on the mass of both objects

### F. The Law of Universal Gravitation
1. $F = GmM/d^2$
2. The gravitational constant
3. Predicting "Halley's Comet"
4. Henry Cavendish

### G. Acceleration Revisited
1. Changes in g
2. Constants and significance difference

### H. Gravity and Curved Space- Time
1. Albert Einstein
2. How mass affects space-time

## Comprehension

### Matching
1. _____ The force of gravity on an object.
2. _____ The mathematical formula $F=GMm/d^2$ that describes the strength of the force of gravity between two objects of mass M and m separated between their centers by the distance d.
3. _____ The symbol representing the acceleration caused by gravity. It is equal to 22 mi/hour per second or 32 ft/second per second or 9.8 m/second per second depending on the units.

a. g
b. Weight
c. The Law of Gravity

### True/False
1. _____ A small ball is dropped from the edge of a cliff. One- tenth of a second later a much heavier ball is dropped from the same position. Ignoring the effects of air friction, the second ball overtakes the first.
2. _____ Although the moon is so far away, it's gravitational pull still affects Earth.
3. _____ The force of gravity increases between objects as they get farther away from each other.
4. _____ Because the Moon orbits Earth at a constant speed, it travels in uniform motion.
5. _____ A cannon ball weighs more, requiring much less force to "fall" towards Earth at the same rate as a marble.

### Fill in the Blank
1. Newton and Cavendish both contributed to proving the _____.
2. An object with great enough mass can cause a _____ in space and time.

## Analysis

1. If a feather and a brick are dropped from the same height in a vacuum, then
   a) the brick hits the ground first.
   b) they hit at the same time.
   c) the feather hits the ground first.

2. When is the force of gravity greatest on a rock?
   a) when it is at the top of a cliff.
   b) when it is just starting to fall and accelerating the most.
   c) when it is falling at uniform speed.
   d) when it is resting on the ground.

3. Jane throws a rock horizontally off a cliff. How fast is the rock traveling downward after 5 seconds (ignoring air friction)?
   a) 22 mph
   b) 88 mph
   c) 110 mph
   d) 132 mph

4. Using the Principle of Position Symmetry, the gravitational force on an object near another planet would
   a) be less on the object than if it were near Earth.
   b) be the same on the object as if it were near Earth.
   c) be greater on the object than if it were near Earth.
   d) depend on the masses of the planet and the object and the square of the distance.

5. A baseball player throws a baseball horizontally at 100 mph. You drop a penny at the exact same height immediately after the ball leaves the baseball player's hand. Air friction is negligible. Which of the following is true?
   a) The penny hits the ground first.
   b) The baseball has a greater force on it than the penny.

c) The baseball has a greater acceleration than the penny.

d) The baseball hits the ground first.

6. Why does an object weigh less on the surface of the moon than on Earth's surface?

7. The Sun has much more mass than Earth (about 330,000 times as much). Why aren't we pulled toward the Sun with 330,000 times as much force as we are toward Earth?

8. Compare the weight and mass of a baseball in four locations:

   a) On Earth's surface

   b) In orbit around Earth at an altitude of about 100 miles.

   c) On the Moon's surface

   d) Outside the solar system far from any planet.

9. Compare the definitions of weight and mass. Why does the weight of an object change from place to place while the mass does not?

10. A cannonball, originally at rest, and a marble, originally at rest, are dropped in a vacuum from the same height at the same time.

    a) What happens when they are dropped? Compare the speed and acceleration of the cannonball with that of the marble.

    b) Is the gravitational force of attraction larger on the cannonball than it is on the marble? Justify your answer using a fundamental law.

    c) Does the cannonball require a larger force to provide the same acceleration as the marble? Justify your answer using the Second Law of Motion.

    d) Explain how the cannonball with greater mass and a greater force of gravity still has the same motion as a marble with a lower mass and lower force of gravity being dropped from the same height.

11. How many forces are acting on the Moon? What force keeps the moon moving around Earth?

## Synthesis

1. A penny and a feather fall toward Earth in a vacuum tube. They begin falling at the same time.

   a) Describe what would be observed.

   b) Which of Newton's laws apply to this scenario?

   c) Use the laws of motion that you listed in (b) to explain what would occur.

2. A ride at an amusement park straps you into a seat and raises you 400 feet above the ground. Once you reach the top, you are dropped. Near the bottom, a spring slows your descent.

   a) What forces act on you during the ride? When is each force acting on you?

   b) What laws of motion would be relevant as you travel from the top to the bottom of the ride?

   c) What is the rate of your acceleration when you are in the middle of falling? What law tells you the rate of acceleration?

   d) In the middle of falling, you feel weightless. Explain why.

   e) What is the direction of the net force at the bottom?

3. Two identical encyclopedias are dropped. Encyclopedia A is dropped from five feet off the ground and Encyclopedia B is dropped from ten feet off the ground. Encyclopedia B is dropped first. When Encyclopedia B reaches exactly five feet above the ground, Encyclopedia A is dropped.

   a) Which encyclopedia has the greater force and thus the greater acceleration acting on it?

   b) Which encyclopedia hits the ground first?

   c) Which encyclopedia is traveling faster when it hits?

   d) Both Encyclopedia A's and B's covers hit the ground face down. Does Encyclopedia A or Encyclopedia B exert the greater force on the ground?

4. You take your 20-lb bowling ball on a trip with you to the distant planet Sophia. The planet Sophia has double the mass and half the diameter of Earth. Answer the following questions about the bowling ball.

   a) What is the ball's mass on Sophia?

   b) Relative to Earth, what is the bowling ball's weight?

   c) Using the Law of Universal Gravitation, explain how your answers in (a) and (b) are consistent with one another.

   d) If dropped on the planet Sophia, how does the bowling ball's acceleration compare to its acceleration on Earth?

   e) You and your bowling buddies decide to race your bowling balls by dropping them from the same height somewhere on Sophia. Your friend's ball weighs 25 lbs on Earth, a mere fraction of what your ball weighs on Sophia. Which ball hits first?

   f) Which principle of symmetry from Chapter 1 applies to this question?

5. Newton's second law says $F = ma$. But the law of gravity says $F = GMm/d^2$. Explain why you need both laws. Which aspect of a falling rock's motion is described by $F = ma$ and which aspect is described by $F = GMm/d^2$?

# The Electromagnetic Interaction

*[Because] the cathode rays are deflected by an electrostatic force as if they were negatively electrified, and are acted on by a magnetic force in just the way in which this force would act on a [moving] negatively electrified body, . . . I can see no escape from the conclusion that they are charges of negative electricity carried by particles of matter.*

*J. J. Thomson (1897)*

# 4

## LEARN

- The electrical force law and how it relates to the force between positive and negative charges.

- The electrical model of matter and its historical development.

- How positive and negative charges interact with each other on conductors and insulators.

- The connections between electricity and magnetism.

- How the force of contact and friction arises.

That some objects become "electrified" or "charged" when rubbed against other materials has intrigued and mystified people since the days of ancient Greece. One of the earliest Greek philosopher-scientists, Thales of Miletus (625–546 BC), wrote that pieces of amber, after being rubbed with wool or fur, attracted straw and bits of feathers. In 1600 William Gilbert (1544–1603), physician to Queen Elizabeth I of England, interpreted this attraction as being part of a family of phenomena he called "electrification" after *elektron,* the Greek word for amber. Gilbert hypothesized that all matter contained "electricity," which when exchanged somehow resulted in an attraction.

Electrification is easy to demonstrate. Run a plastic comb through your hair on a dry day then hold the comb close to some lint or tiny shreds of paper (*Figure 4.1*). Chances are the lint or paper bits will leap to the comb. Or slip on shoes with rubber soles, shuffle your feet across a carpet, then touch a door knob. If conditions are right you may receive a slight electrical shock and hear an unnerving "zap". For similar rea-

**Figure 4.1**
Electrification happens all the time.

sons a moving car can become electrified from air friction, giving you a shock as you touch the metal frame when you stop and get out.

You can explore electrification by rubbing one end of a hard rubber rod with a piece of fur. Hang the rod from a string without allowing anything to touch the rubbed end. Rub a second rubber rod and hold it near the first. The hanging rod will move away, repelled by the held rod. This repulsion occurs even when the rods are some distance apart. If the rods are brought closer together the repulsion is stronger.

Material other than rubber and amber can also be electrified by rubbing. Two glass rods rubbed with silk will become charged and repel each other just like the rubber rods. But bring a charged glass rod near a suspended charged rubber rod and instead of repelling they will *attract* one another (*Figure 4.2*).

Like gravity, the force from electrification—which we will just call the "electric" or "electromagnetic" force for short—is stronger at closer distances. But unlike gravity it can repel as well

**Figure 4.2**
A charged glass rod and a charged rubber rod will attract each other when close together.

**Benjamin Franklin**

Franklin was not only renowned as a statesman, but he was also an accomplished scientist.

**Electric Force Law:**

The mathematical formula $F=kqQ/d^2$ that describes the strength of the force between two objects of charge Q and q separated between their centers by the distance d.

**Electric Force Constant:**

A number relating the strength of the electric force to the charges involved and their distance apart.

**Augustin de Coulomb**

Discovered that forces between charged bodies are proportional to the charges on them, and inversely proportional to the square of their distance.

as attract. Charged rods made of the same material always repel each other. Some of these will be attracted to a charged rubber rod and some will be repelled by it. Those that are attracted to the charged rubber rod will always be repelled by a charged glass rod and vice versa.

Objects attracted to an electrified rubber rod are said to be *positively charged,* while those attracted to the glass are *negatively charged.* These terms were coined by Benjamin Franklin (1706–1790) who experimented with electricity in the years preceding the American Revolution. Following William Gilbert's lead, Franklin hypothesized electricity to be a type of invisible fluid present in all matter. He thought that rubbing different surfaces together caused the fluid to flow, leaving some objects with more than their natural share and some with less. In Franklin's hypothetical model, matter with too little fluid was "negative," or missing some of this fluid, while matter with an excess was "positive."[1]

Franklin refined his invisible fluid model through experiments in which he created "static" (unmoving) electricity by rubbing materials with cloth or fur. He stored this electricity in Leyden jars, which are specially designed glass bottles that hold charges like a battery (*Figure 4.3*). Franklin could then dispense the saved electrical charge in small amounts for careful study or, if desired, discharge the entire charge at once in a shower of sparks.

The similarity between flying sparks and lightning inspired his famous—and dangerous—experiment of flying a kite in a thunderstorm. Franklin wanted to determine if lightning was just a more magnificent manifestation of static electricity. The connection between lightning and electricity may seem apparent to us today. However, Franklin's sparks from his Leyden jars were tiny compared with lightning flashes several miles long, so to those first trying to understand, the connection was not necessarily obvious. Franklin captured electricity from a key attached to the high-flying kite's string and successfully stored it in a Leyden jar. Experiments he performed later showed that his "captured lightning" behaved in his laboratory exactly like static electricity obtained from rub-

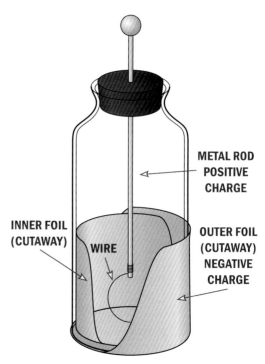

**Figure 4.3**
Static electricity was stored in Leyden Jars. Benjamin Franklin used them to show the connection between lightning and static electricity.

bing. They were different manifestations of the same phenomenon.

## 4-1 The Electric Force Law

In 1785 Charles Augustin de Coulomb (1736–1806) found through experiment a law that described the electric force. Using a torsion balance similar to that used by Henry Cavendish for gravity, de Coulomb found that the force between charged bodies is proportional to the size of the charge on them, while decreasing with the distance squared, just like the gravitational force.

This **electric force law** can be summarized this way:

> **Pairs of objects with similar charges repel each other and pairs with dissimilar charges attract each other with forces, F, that obey Newton's third law. The strength of F depends on the net charges, q and Q, of the objects and the distance, d, between their centers, according to the relationship**

$$F = kQq/d^2$$

The letter "k" represents a number called the **electric force constant.** Like the constant

---

[1] We wish that Franklin had reversed those terms because, as you will read, it was later found that the negatively charged substances gain, not lose, charged particles.

**Figure 4.4**
Every charged object is attracted or repelled by every other charged object through the electrical interaction. Objects of opposite charge attract each other. Objects of like charge repel each other.

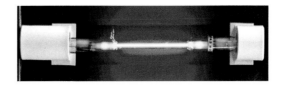
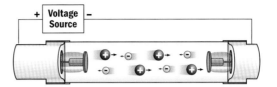

**Figure 4.5**
The glowing beam in a discharge tube is composed of negative and positive parts of atoms moving in opposite directions.

G in the law of gravity, it must be measured experimentally. But unlike G, the value of k is relatively large, with a value of about $9 \times 10^9$ in the metric system. This means a tiny amount of charge will generate the same amount of force created by a huge amount of mass. For example, if all the negatively charged material were taken from the fur and placed onto the rod and the fur and rod were put on opposite ends of a football field, the attraction between them would have a force of about $10^{13}$ tons! As it turns out, rubbing a rod with fur separates only about 1 part out of every $10^{12}$ of the charged material, easily enough to create a readily apparent force.

## 4-2 The Electrical Model of Matter

By the end of the 18th century electricity was being modeled in two ways. One was Franklin's model, which, as previously mentioned, assumed matter had a charged fluid part embedded in an oppositely charged, less mobile part. According to this model the fluid could flow in or out of objects, leaving them positively or negatively charged. A second model hypothesized the existence of two oppositely charged fluids, either one of which could flow in or out of otherwise neutral matter.

After many decades of experiments, Benjamin Franklin's single fluid hypothesis emerged as the better model. At this scientists turned their attention to understanding what the fluid was made of, how it was able to flow, and if it was composed of measurable particles. In 1897 the English physicist J. J. Thomson (1856–1940) investigated these questions by devising a Nobel-prize-winning experiment that literally tore atoms apart and examined the pieces that emerged.

First Thomson obtained a cylindrical tube with metal plates embedded in its sealed ends.

He evacuated the tube then injected a small amount of gas back into it[2]. The metal plates were then connected to battery terminals by wires running through the glass (see *Figure 4.5*). The batteries charged one plate positively and the other one negatively. Thomson increased the charge difference between the plates until a faint, glowing beam arose between them. This beam was examined to see if it obeyed Newton's laws of motion. It did, proving that electricity had to have mass. Other scientists repeating this experiment later determined that the beam was composed of two types of material, a negative, light-massed substance flowing to the positive plate and a much more massive positive substance flowing the opposite way to the negative plate.

Thomson correctly decided that the atoms of gas in the tube were being broken into charged fragments. He further learned that regardless of the type of gas used in the tube, the negative fragments always had the same charge and mass. The positive fragments, however, retained the mass properties of the original gas. From the results of his experiment Thomson created a model of the atom that will be discussed in Chapter 14.

Thomson's results clearly suggested Franklin's "electrical fluid" was a stream of particles. He called those particles "corpuscles," a term later abandoned in favor of the word **electrons**.

[2] These tubes, also called "Crookes tubes," had been invented and used earlier by many people, including William Crookes, after whom they are named. The version used by Thomson had been patented by Thomas Edison six years earlier. Although he was not the inventor, Thomson had the insight to use these tubes to examine fundamental questions about electricity. Often it is the people who come after the original invention or model who use it in its most insightful way.

**Electron:**
The basic negative charge-carrying particle in an atom.

**J. J. Thomson**

Thomson used a gas discharge tube to determine that electricity had mass.

**Robert Millikan**

Developed a way to measure the charge of individual electrons.

### Coulomb:

The unit of measure for charge; it is named after Charles Augustin de Coulomb, formulator of the Electric Force Law. The amount of electric charge possessed by a single electron or a proton is $1.6 \times 10-19$ coulombs.

### Proton:

A positively charged particle in atomic nuclei made up of three quarks.

### Neutron:

An uncharged particle in atomic nuclei made up of three quarks.

His experiment was not absolutely conclusive though. It was still possible to explain the glowing beam as a stream of pure material that could be divided into infinitely small pieces without losing its nature and properties. After all, other physical quantities, such as force and speed, can have any value, and there was no guiding principle that demanded electrical charge be different. Confirmation of the particle nature of charge came in 1910, when the American physicist Robert Millikan (1868–1953) devised an "oil-drop experiment" that isolated and measured the charge on individual particles.

In the oil-drop experiment, Millikan first sprayed light oil through an atomizer to form a mist. Friction between the emerging oil droplets and the atomizer spout caused each droplet to become negatively charged for the same reason rubbing a rod with fur negatively charges the rod. The oil drops were sprayed into a space between charged electric plates (*Figure 4.6*) and allowed to fall under the force of gravity. Selected drops were carefully examined through an eyepiece to measure their motion, size, and mass. The charge on the plates was then adjusted until the electric force pushing up on the negative droplets exactly equaled the gravitational force pulling down and the drop no longer accelerated. The gravitational force strength was then calculated from Newton's law of gravity. The charge on the plates that balanced this force was measured, and the only quantity still not known—the charge on the oil droplet—was calculated from the electric force law.

Millikan methodically repeated this experiment over several years, examining thousands of oil drops. He found that the amount of charge acquired by each oil drop was always in tiny steps of $1.6 \times 10^{-19}$ **coulombs**. Because his oil drops picked up charge only in this discrete quantity, it was clear that each step represented the acquisition of an individual particle having a charge of $1.6 \times 10^{-19}$ coulombs. This charge value is tiny meaning an enormous number is required to create even a small spark.

A saying among scientists is that yesterday's Nobel Prize is today's homework assignment. Sophisticated variants of Thomson's gas discharge tubes are the familiar fluorescent bulbs that may be providing light in your room right now. Detectors in digital cameras routinely measure the charge of individual electrons as part of the process of constructing images. Thomson and Millikan, brilliant as they were, never envisioned these modern applications when they did their experiments. Neither could today's engineers have constructed computers, cameras, and other electronic marvels without those scientists' pioneering discoveries. Discovering the particle nature of an electron may seem mundane, but it would have been impossible to advance research in electricity without it.

Later scientists would better understand the positive aspect of the electric force and the particle that carries it, the **proton**. (See Chapter 14 for more on this subject.) Protons are identical to each other in the same way each electron is identical to every other electron. A proton carries the exact same charge as an electron, only with the opposite sign. The protons and a related particle, the **neutrons**, comprise the bulk of the mass of an atom, and rarely migrate to a rubbed fur or rod. When an object becomes negatively charged it is because the electrons have moved *to* it. When it becomes charged positively it is because electrons have moved *from* it, leaving a net imbalance in favor of the protons.

The structure of matter is such that protons are held more rigidly in place in solids than are electrons. This is partly because of their mass. Electrons have little mass, about 1/1,836 that of protons. Newton's third law of motion shows that when a collection of excess electrons, like the buildup found at the bottom of a thundercloud, is attracted to a body that lacks electrons, and therefore has an excess of protons, like the

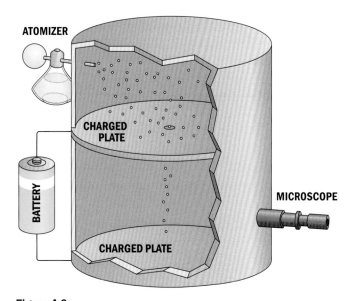

**Figure 4.6**

The electric charge of individual electrons was first measured in the Millikan oil-drop experiment.

**Figure 4.7**
In lightning, it is the less massive electrons that move.

top of the ground, the forces on each are the same but oppositely directed. According to the second law of motion the less massive electrons will accelerate more than the protons and will therefore be the ones to break free and move, causing the visible lightning (*Figure 4.7*).

This picture can be termed the *electrical model of matter*. It lacks details about how these charged particles are arranged and how they combine to create the myriad kinds of materials around us. But it does provide an adequate framework to help understand basic electricity. We can summarize the model as follows:

> All matter contains two kinds of electrically charged particles: positive protons and negative electrons. Electrons have little mass and can be quite mobile and transferable from one object to another. Protons are held rigidly in place in solid materials. Objects that have equal numbers of protons and electrons are electrically neutral. Objects with more electrons than protons are negatively charged. Those with fewer electrons than protons are positively charged. The amount of extra charge of either kind is called the "charge of an object."

## 4-3 Electric Current

Electrons are more mobile than protons, but they do not move through all materials with equal ease. **Insulators**, like rubber rods do not permit electrons to move freely on or within them. When you rub electrons off fur and onto a rubber rod, the electrons do not flow away, but remain fixed on the rod's surface. But rub a copper rod with that same swatch of fur and no negative charge will build up on this rod. Why not? The fur places as many electrons onto a copper rod as it places on a rubber rod. However, the electrons rubbed onto a copper rod quickly flow to your hand and back to the fur or to the ground because a metal rod is a **conductor**, a material that permits electrons to freely move on its surface or through its interior.

Moving electrons create an **electric current**. They move in a wire somewhat like water flows through a pipe loosely filled with gravel. The moving water represents the mobile electrons and the stationary gravel represents the fixed atoms with their protons and neutrons. Although electrons in an electric current move through the wire, no part of it is charged because there are always equal numbers of protons and electrons in the wire at any point in time.

An electrical current arises only when there is a source, like a battery, to drive the electrons. Batteries produce a **direct current** of electrons flowing in one direction, away from the negative terminal and toward the positive terminal. A current results if there is a place to which electrons can flow. Otherwise, electrons will build up on the wire and repel the electrons behind them, preventing them from entering the wire, stopping the current. Direct current is created if there is a connection back to the battery or to the ground.

Wall sockets into which household appliances are connected are like a battery with a current reversing direction 60 times per second (in

**Insulator:**
A material that does not permit electrons to flow through it.

**Conductor:**
A material that allows electrons to flow through it.

**Electric Current:**
Electric charges flowing through a conductor.

**Direct Current:**
A steady flow of electrons in one direction, typically through a wire.

the USA). This type of reversing electrical flow is called **alternating current**. Alternating current is common because it is an efficient way of transporting electrical energy. However, in this text we will not consider alternating current further.

## 4-4 Magnetism

Ancient Greeks living near the city of Magnesia, as well as some early Chinese, knew about "lodestones", possibly chunks of iron ore struck by lightning, that had the strange, unexplainable power to attract iron. Steel needles stroked with such stones would become "magnetic" as well. Around 1000 BC the Chinese created the first magnetic compasses when they found that such a needle, when freely suspended, pointed north-south.

The magnetic compass spread to Europe and in 1492 Columbus used it in crossing the Atlantic Ocean to discover the North American continent. He noted in his journal that not only did the needle deviate slightly from exact north (which was known from the position of the Polar Star), but that this deviation changed during the voyage. William Gilbert proposed a correct explanation: Earth itself was a giant magnet, with its magnetic north pole some distance away from true, geographic north.[3]

**Alternating Current:** A current of electrons that changes direction of flow.

**Ferromagnetism:** Metal alloys that are attracted to magnets or are capable of being transformed into permanent magnets are called ferromagnetic.

Magnetism is easier to demonstrate than the electric force because magnets, unlike charged rubber rods, retain their attractive powers when they are handled. You no doubt have used magnets to pick up paper clips or hold notes on a refrigerator. Metal that is **ferromagnetic**, such as iron and nickel, can be attracted to magnets, or can become a magnet itself. Non-ferromagnetic metals like silver, copper and gold cannot be attracted to magnets nor can they become magnets.

**William Gilbert**

Proposed that Earth was itself a giant magnet.

While electrified rods are always attracted or repelled by other charged rods, magnet ends are attracted and repelled by the ends of other magnets. Take a bar magnet and suspend it from a string (*Figure 4.8*). Hold another magnet and point the end stamped "S" (the "south pole") toward it. The suspended magnet will twist so that its north pole (stamped "N") moves toward the held magnet's south pole, while its own south pole moves away. Turn the held magnet around and the suspended magnet will twist as its south pole is attracted and its north pole is repelled.

[3] Earth's North Pole is actually a *magnetic* south pole and as such attracts the north poles of magnets.

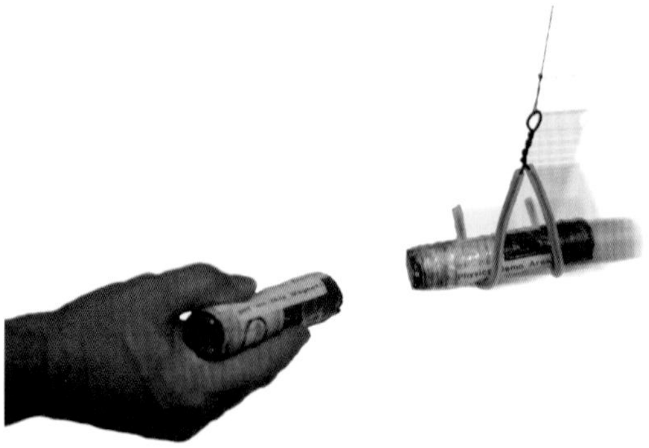

**Figure 4.8**

Opposite poles of magnets attract each other. Similar poles repel each other.

All magnets have both north and south poles. If you cut a magnet in half hoping to create two single-poled magnets, the new ends immediately become oppositely polarized magnetic poles. Cut one of the pieces in half again and again as often as you want; new poles will always appear. No magnet having only one pole has ever been discovered.

Either end of a magnet will attract unmagnetized ferromagnetic metal. It doesn't matter if you point a south pole or a north pole at a pile of paper clips, either end will attract them equally well. A refrigerator magnet might have either the north pole or the south pole in contact with the fridge. Both will fasten and hold just as tightly.

## 4-5 The Electromagnetic Interaction

William Gilbert correctly hypothesized that iron magnets and electrified amber are related but it took two centuries to prove. In 1821, Danish scientist Hans Christian Oersted (1777–1851), while demonstrating to friends the flow of electric current in a wire, noticed that the current caused a nearby compass needle to move (see *Figure 4.9*). This same phenomenon was studied in France by Andre-Marie Ampere (1775–1836), who reasoned that magnetism arises when electric charges move as currents.

Soon after it was learned that a regular iron bar can be turned into a magnet by passing a current though a wire wrapped around it. If the current is strong enough and the bar is ferromagnetic, it will remain magnetic after the current is turned off.

Magnetism, for reasons beyond the scope of this book, is a manifestation of the electric interaction for moving charges. Static electricity, unmoving on a rod, cannot create it. But this same charge moving through a wire can. Therefore the electric interaction is more properly called the electromagnetic interaction.

Michael Faraday (1791–1867), credited with many fundamental discoveries on electricity and magnetism, modeled magnetism by assuming the space around electric currents possesses a **field** in which the magnetic force is felt. This magnetic field can be mapped by using a second magnet as a probe. Imagine a magnetic compass needle freely suspended in space near a bar magnet. If we move the compass needle around, the direction it points will change as we

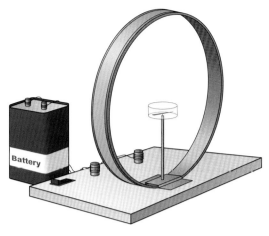

**Figure 4.9**

An experiment similar to Oersted's. When current flows through the coil, it generates a magnetic field that is strongest at the center where the compass sits. When current flows clockwise around the coil, the compass points to the right. When current flows counterclockwise, the compass needle points to the left.

**Field:**

Physical quantity existing at every point in space. Some fields arise from sources and may be thought of as the "influence" of these sources.

**Domain:**

A small section in a magnet where the magnetic force from all the atoms add together.

**Curie Temperature:**

The temperature above which a metal is no longer magnetized. The Curie temperature is unique for different types of metals.

## PERMANENT MAGNETS

If moving charges create magnetism, how can bars of metal with no charge moving through them become permanent magnets? Such metal can stay magnetized for years or even centuries. What can cause magnets to last that long?

Atoms are small magnets. In most materials the atoms are oriented randomly, canceling the overall effect so there is no net magnetism. In ferromagnetic materials, though, atoms align with neighboring atoms in small sections called **domains** (see *Figure 4.10*). Normally the domains themselves are oriented randomly so there is still no net magnetism. But when they are influenced by an external magnetic field, the domains will shift and align together, producing a net magnetic field.

Suppose the north pole of a magnet is brought close to a paper clip. The domains inside the paper clip will realign until the clip becomes a magnet with its south pole facing the magnet's north pole. The magnet's north pole attracts the paper clip's south pole and they stick together. If the magnet's south pole had been brought close to the paper clip, the domains would have realigned in the other direction. Then the clip would become a magnet with its north pole facing the magnet's south pole. Again, an attraction results.

If the domains remain aligned after the external field is gone, the piece becomes a permanent magnet. The strength of a permanent magnet depends on the type of metal and the fraction of the domains that are aligned. Permanent magnets made from special alloys, like those found in computer hard drives, can have exceptionally coherent alignment and exceptional strength.

Domain alignments eventually break down, causing permanent magnets to lose their strength with time. Heat can cause domains to lose alignment as well. When temperatures in a metal exceed a certain value, called the **Curie Temperature**, any magnetism it may have had will be lost. Permanent magnets heated above their Curie Temperature cease to be magnets. However, they can again become magnetized when the temperature is lowered.

Earth has a magnetic field but its interior is hotter than the Curie temperature and so cannot be a permanent magnet. Its magnetic field is caused by charges moving in currents like giant wires wrapped in a loop hundreds of miles around in the outer core. This is discussed further in Chapter 26.

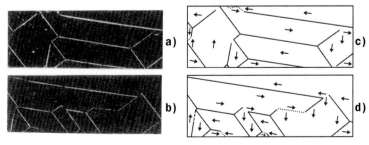

**Figure 4.10**

Magnetism arises when electric currents flow in tiny domains. Figures a) and b) are images of the domain regions in a slice of magnetic metal. Figures c) and d) are interpretations of those images showing the direction of the magnetic fields within each domain.

get closer or farther from the poles. Tracing the direction the needle points defines **field lines**. A more dense collection of field lines, like near the poles, indicates a stronger force at that location. Field lines are revealed by sprinkling iron filings on a stiff sheet of paper held over or near a magnet since iron filings act as compass needles.

The field lines of a wire, a bar magnet, and Earth itself are presented in *Figure 4.11*. For a wire the field lines are circular loops around it. For a bar magnet the field lines arch from the south pole to the north pole. Similarly, Earth's field lines start near Earth's South Pole, curve around in space and converge again near the North Pole.

### 4–6 The Forces of Contact and Friction

Atoms on the surface of all materials have electrons and protons. When two surfaces come together the atomic protons from one surface begin to repel the protons from the other surface. This repulsion strengthens rapidly until the surfaces can get no closer. This repulsion gives a surface its hardness, even though atoms themselves don't actually "touch." The force created this way is called a **contact force**.

Consider a book on a table. A downward gravitational force pulls on the book. At the same time the atoms of the book's cover and the hard tabletop repel one another, causing the book to be pushed upward. If you place your hand on the book and push down, the surfaces will get ever so slightly closer, and the electromagnetic repulsions will increase. If the increased upward electromagnetic force balances the total downward force, the book moves

no farther. If the upward electromagnetic force cannot increase enough to balance the downward force, the table breaks.

Sliding friction results from the same kind of interaction. Adjacent surfaces are microscopically quite uneven (*Figure 4.12*). These "bumps" and "hollows" scrape across each other when the surfaces slide. As they come into contact their atoms push back against each other. This push is always *against* the direction of the motion so sliding friction always causes moving things to slow down.

Contact and frictional forces are the most common manifestations of the electromagnetic interaction in our everyday lives. Every time you touch something you are feeling the electromagnetic force. If you kick a rock, the charges in the rock repel the charges in your shoe. Charges in your shoe repel charges in your toe. These forces initiate internal interactions that finally cause your brain to register pain—all from the electromagnetic interaction.

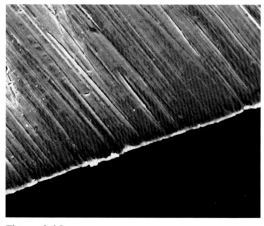

**Figure 4.12**
The "smooth" side of a steel surgical scalpel blade, as viewed at x1500 magnification under a scanning electron microscope.

**Field Lines:**

Lines coming from an object representing the strength of the force. The denser the lines, the stronger the force.

**Contact Force:**

The force arising between objects when they touch. Contact forces are a repulsion caused by the electromagnetic interaction.

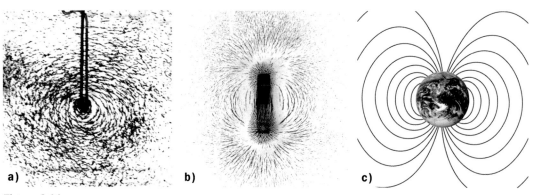

a)                                b)                                c)

**Figure 4.11**
a) The field lines of a wire. Notice how the lines form a circular pattern about it.
b) The field lines of a bar magnet. The field lines arch through space connecting the north and south poles like before.
c) The field lines of Earth. Earth's magnetic field is exactly the same shape as the field of a bar magnet.

## GENERATING ELECTRICITY

The electricity that powers society is created from other sources of power such as moving water, steam or wind. In the process kinetic energy (see Chapter 9) is converted to electrical current by generators. A generator is a set of magnets turning inside coiled wires. The other sources of power provide the energy to turn the magnets.

Generators are made possible by a further relationship between electricity and magnetism discovered around 1830 by Michael Faraday in England and Joseph Henry (1797–1878) in the United States. The relationship is known as Faraday's law and is called electromagnetic induction. The relationship says that a changing magnetic field produces an electric field. Thus when a magnet is moved near a closed wire circuit or conversely when the wire is moved past the magnet, the field strength changes, inducing an electric current in the wire (see *Figure 4.13*). Faraday's law not only allows for currents but also plays a role in the production of electromagnetic waves (Chapter 11).

**Figure 4.13**
Wind (left) and steam (right) are converted to electricity through magnets turning inside large wire coils. As the magnets turn, they come closer to then farther from the wires changing the field strength in the coils and inducing an electric current.

# 4 STUDY GUIDE

## Chapter Framework

### A. Introduction
1. Electrification
2. Positive and negative charges
3. Ben Franklin
   a. *Fluid model*
   b. *The kite experiment*

### B. The Electric Force Law
1. $F = kqQ/d^2$
2. Electrical force constant k

### C. The Electrical Model of Matter
1. J. J. Thomson
   a. *Gas tube experiment*
   b. *Discovery of electrons*
2. Robert Millikan
   a. *"Oil- drop" experiment*
   b. *Electrons as particles*
3. The Electrical Model of Matter

### D. Electric Current
1. Conductors
2. Insulators
3. Direct current
4. Alternating current

### E. Magnetism
1. Lodestones and compasses
2. William Gilbert
3. Ferromagnetic metal
4. Magnetic poles

### F. The Electromagnetic Interaction
1. Hans Christian Oersted
   a. *Magnetism and electric current*
2. Field lines

### G. Permanent magnets
1. Domains

### H. The Forces of Contact and Friction
1. Caused by the electromagnetic interaction

## Comprehension

### Matching

a. Ferromagnetic
b. Coulomb
c. Insulator
d. Electric force constant
e. Electron
f. Proton
g. Alternating current
h. Direct current
i. Contact force
j. Neutron
k. The Electric Force Law
l. Conductor

1. _____ The basic positive charge-carrying particle in an atom.
2. _____ Metal alloys that are attracted to magnets or are capable of being transformed into a permanent magnet.
3. _____ A material that does not permit electrons to flow through it.
4. _____ The mathematical formula $F=kqQ/d^2$, which describes the strength of the force between two objects of charge Q and q separated between their centers by the distance d.
5. _____ A current of electrons that changes direction of flow.
6. _____ The unit of measure for charge.
7. _____ Material that allows electrons to flow through it.

8. _____ The basic negative-charge-carrying particle in an atom.
9. _____ A steady flow of electrons in one direction through a wire.
10. _____ A repulsive force between electrons near the surface of two different objects.
11. _____ A number relating the strength of the electric force to the charges involved and their distance apart.
12. _____ A neutral particle found in the nuclei of atoms.

### True/False
1. _____ Friction comes from electromagnetic forces.
2. _____ Electric force becomes stronger if the charged objects are moved farther apart.
3. _____ Neutrons have a negative charge.
4. _____ Iron and nickel are examples of ferromagnetic metals.
5. _____ Electric currents exert forces on permanent magnets.

### Fill in the Blank
1. Millikan conducted experiments with oil drops that isolated and measured _____ on individual particles.
2. When Thomson conducted his experiments with tubes of gas, particles he called "corpuscles," but which are now known as _____, moved toward the positive end of the tube.
3. When rubber is rubbed with fur, _____ move from the fur onto the rubber, leaving the rubber with a _____ charge.
4. Moving electrons create a(n) _____.
5. _____ are regions in ferromagnetic materials where all of the atom's magnetic forces align.
6. The size and direction of electric and magnetic forces is often pictorially represented using _____.

## Analysis

1. When a glass rod is rubbed with rubber, it becomes positively charged. This is because
   a) protons are transferred from rubber to glass.
   b) protons are transferred from glass to rubber.
   c) electrons are transferred from glass to rubber.
   d) electrons are transferred from rubber to glass.
   e) electrons and protons cancel each other out.

2. Who among the following did not help contribute to discoveries in electromagnetic interactions?
   a) Henry Cavendish
   b) Benjamin Franklin

c) Thomas Edison

d) William Gilbert

3. Contact force is caused by

a) atoms randomly crashing into each other.

b) charged particles pushing against other charged particles.

c) protons of two atoms attracting each other.

d) the force of one object pushing against the force of another object.

4. Suppose you wanted to exactly double the electric force between two objects. How could you accomplish that?

a) Double the charge on both objects.

b) Double the distance between the objects.

c) Cut the distance in half.

d) Double the charge on both objects while cutting the distance in half.

e) Double the charge on one of the objects.

5. Describe an experiment that demonstrates that there are two kinds of electric charge.

6. Describe the differences between conductors and insulators.

7. Describe the important properties of a proton and an electron. What is the comparison in sizes?

8. What is electric current?

9. How do we know that there is a single electromagnetic force rather than separate electric and magnetic interactions?

10. What makes a material ferromagnetic?

# Synthesis

1. Explain how the contact and friction forces arise and play an important role in the following scenarios:

a) A book placed on a table.

b) A car tire screeching to a stop at a cross walk to avoid hitting pedestrians.

c) A space shuttle reentering Earth's atmosphere.

d) A water skier gliding across the water.

2. A rubber rod is rubbed with fur and suspended in the air. A second rubber rod that has been rubbed with fur is placed nearby.

a) What charges are on the rubber rods?

b) Do the rods attract or repel one another?

c) What law explains why this occurs?

d) As you bring the rubber rods closer together, what happens to the force between them?

e) What could you do to decrease the force between the rods, without changing the distance?

f) If you replaced one of the rubber rods with a glass rod that had been rubbed with silk, how would your answers to the above questions change?

3. Three spheres of metal are placed on stands that act as insulators. Spheres B and Y are neutrally charged. Sphere U holds a strong negative charge. Wire runs between sphere B and Y. Sphere U is brought close to sphere Y.

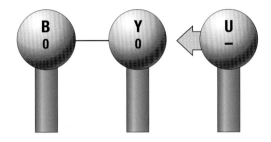

a) Because spheres B and Y hold no net charge does that mean that no charge exists on them?

b) What do we know about the amount of negative and positive charge in spheres B and Y?

c) What will sphere U do to the electrons in sphere Y as it approaches?

d) What does this do to the net charge on sphere Y?

e) What does this do to the net charge on sphere B?

f) How is it possible for charge to arise from two neutrally charged objects?

4. Describe two ways in which you could turn iron wire into a magnet. Only one of these two methods would work with copper wire. Which one and why?

5. If you scuff across wool carpet wearing rubber shoes, you will shock yourself when you reach for a metal doorknob, often before you even touch the knob.

a) What type of charge will have accumulated on your body? How do you know?

b) When you bring your finger near the doorknob, what happens to the electrons in the metal?

c) Explain why, when the metal itself is neutral, a spark will often jump from your finger to the metal before you touch it.

# Application of the Laws of Force and Motion

*It's not the long fall that kills you; it's the sudden stop at the bottom.*

**Anonymous**

## 5

## LEARN

- To identify the forces acting on an object.

- The relationship between acceleration and net force.

- The relationship between velocity and acceleration.

- How to apply the laws of motion to understand velocity in common everyday situations.

Chapters 2, 3, and 4 introduced two laws that govern force and three that govern motion. All motion encountered in our everyday lives can be understood through these laws. This chapter offers examples designed to show how the laws of motion and the interactions of gravity and electromagnetism (mainly as a contact force) work together. In each example you should first find all forces acting on each object. Combine them to find the net force. Then determine the resulting acceleration. Finally, see how the acceleration determines the subsequent motion.

As you learn how to apply these laws, you will be able to explain a wide range of phenomena. Don't let the examples intimidate or discourage you if their explanations are not obvious at first. With time and practice you will soon realize that all motion really does obey a few simple rules.

## 5-1 Finding Forces

When using the laws of motion, correctly identifying the forces on a given object often presents the most difficulty. Sometimes one or more forces go unnoticed or forces that do not influence the object may seem pertinent. Isolate in your mind the object you are analyzing and ask the questions below to help identify the interactions in which an object participates and all the forces that act on it:

1. What role does gravity play? Is it significant or insignificant? The only time gravity is insignificant, for our considerations here, is if the object being analyzed is far from Earth, the Sun, or other planets.
2. Are charged objects, current-carrying objects, or magnets involved? Are their forces attractive or repulsive?
3. What does the object touch—are there contact forces involved?
4. What is the role of friction? Does it change with time or motion?

Now inspect the forces applied to each interacting object. See which ones are balanced out. For example, the weight of a car is usually balanced by an upward contact force from the ground. Being balanced, these forces cause no vertical acceleration and can be ignored. If the car is driven off a cliff, then there is no contact force to balance gravity and it cannot now be ignored.

After you identify the forces, remember that all unbalanced forces cause acceleration in the direction of the unbalanced or net force. *If an object accelerates, then an unbalanced force caused it. If an object does not accelerate, then no unbalanced forces are acting upon the object. There are no exceptions to this rule!*

## 5-2 Standing on a Scale

We will start with a familiar situation: standing on a bathroom scale (*Figure 5.1*). As a health-conscious individual you eat right, exercise, and weigh yourself daily. Each morning you step on the scale, read your weight, and start

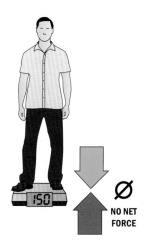

**Figure 5.1**

A scale measures the force of contact between you and the floor. If you are not accelerating, the contact force equals your weight. The green arrow represents gravity. The purple arrow represents the contact force.

53

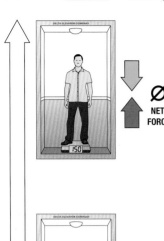

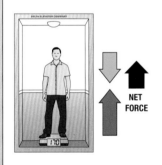

your day merrily (or sadly). If the scale isn't reading what you want, you might find some comfort in knowing that a bathroom scale does not really measure your weight. The scale measures the force of contact between you and the floor. But, alas, this contact force equals your weight when you are standing still and so the value you read *is* the correct value.

How does a common bathroom scale work? When you first step on a scale you gently accelerate downward under gravity's influence. A spring in the scale, compressed by the newly added weight, pushes back upwards with an increasingly strong force until it balances the force of gravity.[1] If the spring becomes too compressed, its upward force will exceed the force of gravity and push you back up. This is why, after you first step on the scale, you bob up and down momentarily until the forces from the scale and gravity balance and you are motionless. Now the scale reads your true weight.

You can increase the scale's reading by pushing up against a nearby towel rack and forcing yourself downward. Now the scale registers a larger value that equals the contact force from your weight plus the additional force from the push. Let go of the towel rack and you will accelerate up until the forces again balance. The spring tension will always adjust until the forces balance and you are motionless.

An accelerating scale does not display a true weight value. Standing on a scale in a moving elevator as in *Figure 5.2* demonstrates this. When the elevator rises to a higher floor, the scale's dial will first increase in value, then go back to your actual weight. When the elevator slows

[1] Contact forces in springs are proportional to the amount they are stretched or compressed.

**Figure 5.2**
The forces acting on you in a moving elevator change as the elevator's acceleration changes. The green arrow represents gravity. The purple arrow represents the contact force. Forces are balanced before starting (a), after stopping (e) and while traveling in uniform motion between floors (c). The force is unbalanced upward when you start to move (b) and unbalanced downward as you stop (d). A change in the contact force creates the imbalance in forces.

as it approaches the requested floor, your scale reading will decrease in value. After the elevator comes to a full stop at the floor level, the scale's dial once again measures your actual weight. Why does the scale behave this way?

At first, as the elevator accelerates up, the contact force pushes upward against your feet more than the force of gravity pulls you downward. The increase in the dial reading shows this increase in the contact force. After the elevator begins moving, it travels between floors in uniform motion. In this stage, no acceleration occurs and the scale indicates your true weight. When the elevator approaches the upper floor and begins to brake to a stop, the contact force weakens and becomes less than gravity. The unbalanced net downward force then brings you to a stop. As you decelerate the scale shows a smaller value because the contact force is weaker. It finally returns to the true weight value after you are completely stopped and are no longer accelerating.

Note that in all of this your weight, the gravitational force on you from Earth, never changes. While on Earth's surface, you can change your weight only by changing your mass by bulking up or dieting.

## 5-3 Jumping into the Air

A basketball player races down the floor, leaps from the foul line, glides through the air, and jams the ball through the hoop. The crowd cheers the athlete's "hang time," and the announcer exclaims how he defied gravity. The player didn't really defy gravity, but how exactly did he *look* like he did?

First consider this same basketball player just standing on the gymnasium floor. What forces act on him? Gravity pulls down and the contact force with the floor pushes up. Is he accelerating? No, so gravity is balanced by contact forces. Are there other forces to worry about? No.

The player then crouches down and pauses, getting ready to jump. As he crouches, his upper body moves to a lower level. In this process his upper body goes from being stationary, to moving, to being stationary again and so experiences two accelerations. The first acceleration down towards the floor begins the motion and the second acceleration up ends the downward motion.

**Figure 5.3**
What forces act on a jumping basketball player? (Courtesy BYU Photo, 2010)

During each acceleration the contact and gravitational forces are unbalanced. First there was a net downward force as the player relaxed his knees. His upper body accordingly accelerated down under the influence of gravity. Then there was a net upward force as he stiffened his knees and came to rest in a crouched position. At that time his upper body accelerated upward from contact forces just enough to cancel the downward motion. During this pause just before the jump, contact and gravity forces once again balance one another.

After the slight pause he jumps. This is an acceleration upward, so the forces are unbalanced. The forces became unbalanced upward when the contact force strengthened as he suddenly pushed against the floor with his legs and—by the third law of motion—the floor pushed back at the same time with equal force.[2]

Once the player is in the air, contact with the floor is broken and the contact force goes to

---

[2] This concept has been emphasized a lot but if it seems odd to think that the floor pushed back, consider what would happen if the man were pushing down with his feet just as vigorously while hanging off the floor on a chin-up bar. He can push all he wants, but if his feet are not in contact with the floor, the floor will not push back and he will not accelerate up.

zero. Now the only force is his weight, unbalanced downward. The downward acceleration that results diminishes the player's upward speed. His velocity quickly reverses direction and he accelerates back to the arena floor. His legs cushion the shock and his body comes back to rest.

Let's examine how his legs "cushion the shock." If he had come down with his legs straight and unbent, he would have experienced a sudden and painful landing. Flexed knees allowed him to break his fall more gently, by spreading his stop over a longer period of time, thus decreasing his acceleration. A smaller, gentler acceleration means a smaller, gentler force. A sudden, jarring stop means a greater acceleration and a greater force. That would be much harder on an athlete's knees and body than the longer, gentler force.

A running basketball player leaps horizontally as well as vertically when he or she jumps, gliding in an arc like the ball thrown horizontally in Section 3–2. Regardless of what it looks like, the player does not stay in the air any longer than in a standing jump with the same vertical force.

Did you notice any similarities between jumping and weighing yourself in an elevator? Both are cases where the forces of gravity and contact alternate between being balanced and unbalanced as the contact force strengthens and weakens.

## 5-4  Moving Furniture

Our next example is a student pulling a couch to get ready for the big football game party at his apartment. There are several forces involved and we must track them a little more carefully than for jumping or standing on a scale. Let us go through the checklist.

1. What role does gravity play? The weights of both student and couch are balanced by their contacts with the ground. Gravity and vertical contact forces may thus be ignored.
2. Are charged objects involved? Not beside contact forces and friction.
3. What horizontal contact forces exist? The student's feet push against the ground and the student pulls on the couch. According to the third law, the ground pushes back on

**a)**

NET FORCE = ⊘

**b)**

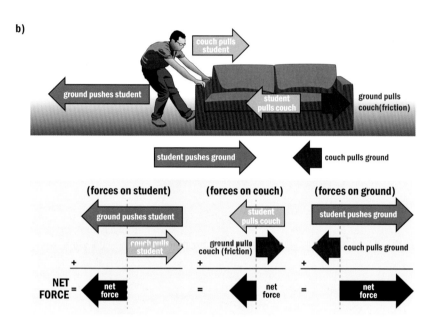

**c)**

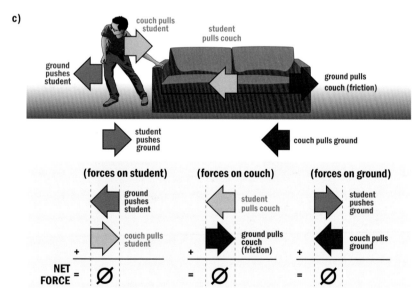

**Figure 5.4**

What forces are involved when a student pulls a couch?

a) Before moving, the student and couch have no force between them. Gravity and contact with the ground balance out and can be ignored.

b) The interactions between the three objects (student, couch, and ground) each have a pair of force arrows that are equal and opposite according to the third law. However, when we add the force arrows based on the object to which they are applied, we find that the student and couch will accelerate forward because there is a net forward force on both of them. Although they accelerate together at the same rate, the force on both is not the same because of their differing masses. The ground also experiences a net force, but Earth's mass is so large that the acceleration is negligible.

c) The student and couch now are moving forward at uniform speed. Once again there are no unbalanced forces on them. However, the student must continue to push forward to balance out the frictional force on the couch.

the student and the couch pulls back on the student.

4. What is the role of friction? There is friction between the couch and the ground pushing against the couch's motion, and between the student and the ground allowing the student to go forward.

*Figure 5.4* illustrates all the forces mentioned above. *Figure 5.4a* shows the student before he starts to pull. All forces on both the student and the couch are balanced.

Figure 5.4b shows the student accelerating forward. All force pairs arising from a single interaction are the same color in this and Figure 5.4c. Consider first the forces on the student. Again, there is no vertical acceleration so we will ignore the balanced forces of gravity pulling down and contact forces pushing up. Horizontal contact with the ground creates an opposite and equal force pair (shown in dark purple) with one force on the student and the other on the ground. Contact forces between the student and the couch create a second force pair (shown in light purple) with one force on the student and the other on the couch. The total horizontal force on the student is unbalanced to the left and the student accelerates forward.

Now look at the horizontal forces on the couch. Contact between the student and the couch creates the light-purple force pair. Friction with the ground creates the red pair, with one force on the couch and the other on the ground. The force of friction is less on the couch than is the force of the student on the couch. The couch responds to the net force and accelerates at the same rate as the student. The total force arrow on the student, though, is not the same as the total force arrow on the couch because their masses are not the same. Objects with less mass require less force to accelerate at the same rate as objects with greater mass.

In Figure 5.4c the student and couch move forward at a constant speed. There are horizontal forces on both of them that were not there before they started moving. In particular there is a backward force from friction within the couch that is balanced by the forward force from the student's legs. But because they are balanced the speed is uniform. When the student stops pulling, the friction force acting backward becomes unbalanced, causing the couch, and the student with it, to decelerate to a stop.

Notice in Figure 5.4b that when the student accelerates forward there is a net force on Earth. This force is required by the third law. Hopefully from the discussions in Chapters 2 and 3 you realize that this means that Earth must accelerate backwards at the same time the student and couch accelerate forward. But Earth with its huge mass accelerates an unmeasurably small amount.

## 5-5 Air Friction

A housefly buzzes along a train track, flying directly at an oncoming train. Both are moving in a straight line at five mph (*Figure 5.5*). As long as they are not touching there is no interaction and therefore no force between them. Then the unobservant fly slams into the oncoming train. At that moment the fly and the train both experience forces which are opposite and equal. The fly's motion reverses direction while the train continues on, seemingly unaffected.

As you hopefully can see by now, the train's change in motion must differ from that of the fly's because their masses are different. Let's consider the difference.

Suppose the train weighs 100 tons while the fly weighs one-thousandth of an ounce, which is roughly $10^{-8}$ tons. According to the third law of motion

$$\frac{\text{force of train}}{\text{on the fly}} = \frac{\text{force of fly}}{\text{on the train}}$$

The second law allows us to substitute mass times acceleration in place of force. So we have

$$\frac{\text{fly's}}{\text{mass}} \times \frac{\text{fly's}}{\text{acceleration}} = \frac{\text{train's}}{\text{mass}} \times \frac{\text{train's}}{\text{acceleration}}$$

Rearranging the terms we have the following:

$$\frac{\text{fly's acceleration}}{\text{train's acceleration}} = \frac{\text{train's mass}}{\text{fly's mass}}$$

$$= \frac{100 \text{ tons}}{10^{-8} \text{ tons}}$$

$$= 10^{10}$$

(Note that we have said mass is not weight but we used weight in the formula. We can do this because the ratio of train-to-fly weight is the same as the ratio of train-to-fly mass.)

In plain language, that formula says the fly accelerates ten billion times ($10^{10}$) more than

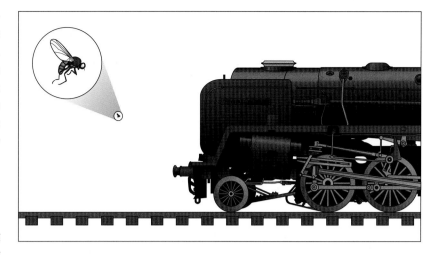

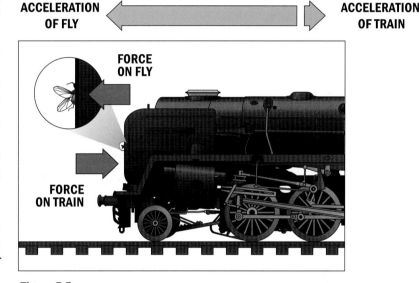

**Figure 5.5**
At the moment of impact, both the fly and the train experience the same force. But the fly accelerates 1010 times more than the train does.

## EARTH'S ROTATION

Many forces push randomly on Earth's surface. Most of them create negligible accelerations. Earth continues to revolve, basically unaffected. However, there is one acceleration on Earth's surface that is big enough to have a noticeable effect on Earth's rotation rate. As mentioned in Chapter 3, the Moon's gravity pulls on Earth's oceans and they move in response, creating daily tides. As the ocean tides move in response to the Moon's gravity, the net effect is to cause Earth's rotational speed to slow down from friction with the water. To compensate for this slowing, the atomic clocks that are the standard time keepers for the world are adjusted yearly by adding one or two seconds as needed at midnight on January 1. Tides have been slowing Earth's spin ever since its formation. Fossil records indicate that 400 million years ago an Earth day was only 22 hours long.

the train does. The fly changes speed from five mph to the right to five mph to the left for a total change in speed of 10 mph. The train accelerates one ten-billionth of this amount so its speed slows down by only one billionth of a mile per hour. No wonder the train seems unaffected.

This example was chosen to illustrate accelerations and force. It is also a good introduction to air friction. As a train goes down the track, it comes into contact with a huge number of air molecules, each like a tiny microscopic fly. Each molecule accelerates out of the way when the train collides with it. Each collision causes the train to accelerate backward. The change in speed caused by the collision with one air molecule is very, very small, much less than the change in speed caused by the fly since an air molecule has a much smaller mass than a fly. However, there are so many air molecules that the tiny force exerted by each one adds up quickly and ultimately creates a significant effect on motion.

Air friction exerts a force on automobiles, airplanes, falling objects, etc., that increases rapidly with increasing speed. A car going 60 mph experiences four times the frictional force than it does when going 30 mph. At 120 mph the force is 16 times greater. To balance the increased frictional forces at faster speeds, a car engine must push with greater force at faster speeds than at slower speeds.

If air friction and friction internal to the car did not exist, a driver could get on a level freeway, accelerate up to speed, turn off the engine, and coast to his or her destination using no more fuel. While that is not possible in the real world, modern cars are often designed for better gas mileage by using tilted windshields and sleek, rounded fronts that minimize air friction by striking the air as indirectly as possible.

## 5-6 Sky Diving

A pilot flying an airplane wants to drop an object on a target on the ground far below (*Figure 5.6*). To do this the pilot must release the object well before the airplane is actually over the target. While trying to figure out exactly when to release the package, the pilot remembers that, in accordance with the first law of motion, the object will drift horizontally at the same speed as the airplane as long as there are no unbalanced horizontal forces, such as air friction, acting on it. Without friction the pilot would just see the package descend directly below the plane, neither getting ahead of nor falling behind as shown in *Figure 5.6a*. So to hit the target, the package should be released at the right time so as to hit the ground just as the plane flies over the target.

In reality, air friction creates an unbalanced horizontal force backwards on the dropped package. As a result its forward motion slows down, and it drifts behind the airplane as shown in *Figure 5.6b*. Air friction against the bottom of the package also pushes against its downward vertical motion, causing it to hit the ground at a later time as well.

The amount of air friction affecting the downward movement of the package depends on the size and shape of the package. *Table 5.1* gives the vertical acceleration that would result if the object were an average-sized sky diver free-falling from an airplane. It is the same as Table 3.1 except that air friction is now taken into account.

The forces, acceleration, and velocity of a

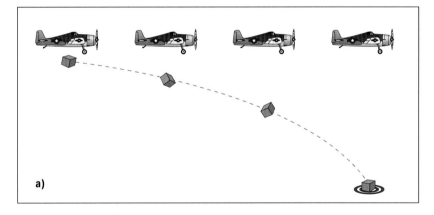

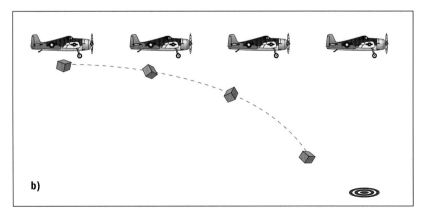

**Figure 5.6**
a) In the absence of air friction a package dropped from an airplane will stay directly under the airplane as it falls.
b) With air friction, the package slows in both its forward and its downward motion as it falls.

## Table 5.1 — A Falling Body with Air Friction

The distance, velocity, and vertical acceleration of a free-falling skydiver, taking friction into account. Velocity is presented here in familiar units of miles per hour as well as the more standard units of meters per second. Compare with Table 1 in Chapter 3. A terminal velocity of approximately 130 mph is reached after about 25 seconds.

| Time (seconds) | Distance (meters) | Velocity (m/sec) | Velocity (miles/hr) | Acceleration (m/sec2) |
|---|---|---|---|---|
| 0 | 0 | 0 | 0 | 9.80 |
| 1 | 4.9 | 9.8 | 22.0 | 9.52 |
| 2 | 19.4 | 19.3 | 43.3 | 8.70 |
| 3 | 43.1 | 28.0 | 62.9 | 7.50 |
| 4 | 74.9 | 35.5 | 79.7 | 6.09 |
| 5 | 113.4 | 41.6 | 93.4 | 4.72 |
| 6 | 157.4 | 46.3 | 103.9 | 3.49 |
| 7 | 205.5 | 49.8 | 111.8 | 2.51 |
| 8 | 256.5 | 52.3 | 117.4 | 1.75 |
| 9 | 309.7 | 54.1 | 121.4 | 1.19 |
| 10 | 364.4 | 55.3 | 124.1 | 0.83 |
| 20 | 935.9 | 57.6 | 129.5 | 0.01 |
| 30 | 1513.2 | 57.7 | 129.6 | 0.00 |

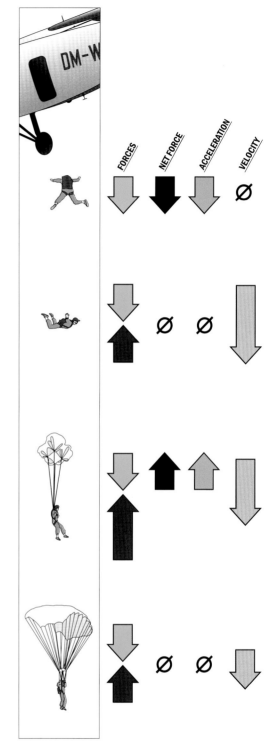

**Figure 5.7**

Force, acceleration, and velocity experienced by a sky diver during free fall. Notice how the forces, acceleration, and velocity all inter-relate to provide a safe landing. (The green arrow represents gravity, and the red arrow represents air friction.)

sky diver are shown in *Figure 5.7*. At zero seconds, the instant when the sky diver jumps from the airplane, the acceleration is 9.8 m/sec², the full acceleration of gravity. At this moment the sky diver has no vertical speed, experiences no vertical air friction, and gravity pulls on the sky-diver's body unopposed by any vertical contact forces.

As the skydiver falls faster and faster, the upward frictional force on her steadily increases. This force pushes against the downward force of gravity, decreasing the net, unbalanced force downward. After 30 seconds the speed and resulting friction have increased to where friction balances gravity and the net force and acceleration go to zero. At that point the velocity remains constant. This is called the terminal velocity. For an average-sized person the terminal velocity is about 130 mph.

The force exerted by air friction depends on surface area as well as speed. Suppose our sky diver jumps from an airplane and reaches a speed of 130 mph. She then pulls her ripcord, the parachute expands open, and the total surface area suddenly increases by a factor of 20.

The force of air friction now suddenly increases by a factor of 20 as well. The total force on the sky diver is now unbalanced upward. This unbalanced upward force gives her an upward acceleration causing her downward speed to decrease.

As she slows down, the upward frictional force now decreases. Her speed will continue to decline until friction again balances with gravity at a speed of about 15 mph, slow enough to land safely.

## 5-7 The Broken Elevator

Suppose you enter an elevator at the top of a 10-story building. Just after you get in, the elevator cable breaks and you start to plunge to the ground far below. Is there anything you can do to save your life? Quickly you decide to try and cancel out the speed of the elevator's fall by jumping up as hard as you can just before the elevator hits the bottom.

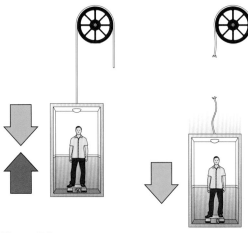

**Figure 5.8**
When the elevator cable breaks, the elevator no longer exerts a force on you. Your weight is unbalanced, and you and the elevator accelerate downward together at the same rate.

Understandably anxious, you immediately crouch down and prepare to jump. But instead of moving down to the elevator floor, your head goes down, your feet go up, and you seem to be suspended motionless in the middle of the elevator car! "What is going on here?" you ask as you continue to plummet downward.

Let's analyze the forces.

1. What role does gravity play? Gravity pulls both you and the elevator car down
2. Are charged objects involved? No.
3. What is the role of contact forces? Before the cable broke, contact between the cable and the elevator car held the car up. Contact between your feet and the elevator car floor pushed you up. When the cable broke both contact forces went away.
4. Is friction present? Yes, there will be air resistance in the elevator shaft pushing against the car as it falls. We will ignore it for this example.

Recall from Chapter 3 that all objects accelerate at the same rate regardless of their mass. In the absence of air friction the elevator car will accelerate at the same rate that you accelerate. Both you and the car will fall with increasing speed until you both hit the bottom of the shaft in 2.5 seconds at a speed of over 50 mph.

Although you, inside the elevator, are speeding up as you fall, the elevator accelerating downward at the same rate makes you unaware of your increasing velocity. You seem to be "weightless," floating in the air, ignorant of your impending doom. NASA uses this same effect, but in a controlled, non-life-threatening way, to train astronauts for outer space weightlessness. A specially outfitted NASA airplane takes trainees high in the air then dives down at the same acceleration rate as gravity. The astronauts float freely in the bay of the plane for a few minutes until the pilot pulls the aircraft out of the dive and flies back up to repeat the experience.

Going 50 mph in a falling elevator car is a significant speed. To save yourself you must try to cancel it out before you and the faulty elevator reach solid ground. Suppose you do manage to jump up with a mighty force just before hitting the ground. In a split second you accelerate from 50 mph to zero. Does this save you? Unfortunately, the answer is no.

It turns out that the amount of force behind such a huge acceleration would be just as hard on your body as hitting the ground. Only stopping gently with a smaller acceleration, and therefore a smaller force, will save you. (You might be relieved to know that all modern elevators have emergency brakes that stop them gently and safely if a cable breaks. No one has ever been killed in a falling elevator car).

## 5-8 Going into Orbit

NASA's space shuttle sits poised at Cape Canaveral, ready to launch on an important scientific mission into space. As the count hits zero, rockets ignite, vapors pour from the exhaust nozzles, and the ship shudders and slowly lifts off. Gaining speed, it quickly rises up and beyond spectators' views as it enters the clouds.

The third law explains how a shuttle launch occurs. When the engines fire up, they begin to burn fuel inside their internal chambers. This creates an expanding exhaust that pushes against the entire surface of the chamber walls. The structurally strong, rigid chamber walls in turn push back. Burning, expanding gas escapes only

**Figure 5.9**

The shuttle Endeavor accelerating at about 29m/s2. The shuttle lifts off because the upward force created when exhaust gases are ejected through the exhaust nozzles exceeds the downward force of gravity. The crew experience a force up to three times greater than gravity during liftoff.

through nozzles at the bottom of the chambers because here nothing opposes the gas's tremendous pressure.

The exhaust nozzles allow an unbalanced force downward on the gases, as shown in *Figure 5.9*. As the burning and expanding gases push out of the nozzles, a force equal and opposite pushes up on the shuttle in accordance with the third law. If the gases had not escaped downward, the shuttle could not have launched upward.

Just after launch, the shuttle tilts from vertical flight to a more horizontal trajectory pointed toward the east. As with the projectile from Newton's cannon in Chapter 3, to go into orbit the space shuttle needs to increase its *horizontal* speed as it lifts above Earth. By the time the engines are turned off, it will be above the atmosphere going fast enough horizontally to ensure that even though gravity is accelerating it downward, it will never hit Earth.

While in orbit, the shuttle is in a state of **freefall** similar to the plummeting elevator in the previous example. Freefall describes anything that falls under the pure influence of gravity and no other forces. Unlike the broken elevator, where air friction was ignored for our convenience, a shuttle is in true freefall because it orbits high enough above the atmosphere to avoid significant frictional forces. Thus, the

**Figure 5.10**

When in orbit, the shuttle no longer needs to fire its rockets. It drifts along in free fall under the sole influence of gravity.

shuttle drifts along without additional help from the rockets.

Astronauts are pinned to their seats as they accelerate into space. As soon as the shuttle engines stop, they are no longer pressed against their seats and begin to freefall as well. This state is incorrectly called "weightlessness." The astronauts have weight because gravity is still pulling them towards Earth.[3] But just as a person in a broken elevator accelerates downward at the same rate as the elevator car, the astronauts are accelerating around in an orbit at the same rate as the shuttle. Being in freefall with the same acceleration as the shuttle makes the astronauts appear to be weightless. We could more correctly say they are "contact forceless."

For the shuttle to reenter Earth's atmosphere, it is first maneuvered around to point the exhaust nozzles forward. The rockets are fired to decelerate and slow the shuttle's forward motion. Its velocity no longer carries it forward enough to miss Earth and it descends down and glides to a landing in Florida.

## 5–9 Centripetal Acceleration Revisited

Now consider any object traveling in a circle at constant speed. The object might be the space shuttle orbiting Earth, a planet moving around our Sun, a ball twirled on the end of a string, a child on a merry-go-round, or a car turning a street corner. We know from the discussion in

**Freefall:**

The act of always falling under the pure influence of gravity.

---

[3] Of course, being now 600 kilometers farther from Earth's center than they were before launch, their space weight is about 20 percent less than their Earth weight.

Chapter 2 that a net sideways force must exist on each of the objects. This force pulls toward the center of the circle that they move on, causing them to constantly turn towards the center.

If the direction of the force is difficult to visualize, imagine the objects' movements if there were no sideways force in action. All would travel in a straight line. Only a sideways force pushing or pulling an object toward the center of the circle can change its motion from a straight line to a circular path.

Sideways forces are called **centripetal** or "center-seeking" forces. The word *centripetal* does not describe the interaction from which the force arises. Instead, it describes the direction in which the force acts (sideways to the motion) and the kind of acceleration it causes (turning or changing direction). The strength of the net force required to cause an object to move with circular motion depends on the radius of the circular path and the object's speed and mass. It can be derived from the second law of motion and has the following mathematical form:

$$\text{Force} = (\text{mass} \times \text{speed}^2)/\text{radius}$$

An object moving in a circle experiences an inward force with exactly this strength. If the force is weaker, the object turns less tightly and forms a larger circle. If the force is stron-

**Centripetal Force:**

A force sideways to the motion of an object. Centripetal forces cause objects to turn toward the center of a circle.

**Figure 5.11**
Sideways forces cause objects to turn toward the direction of the force. The stronger the force, the tighter the turn.

ger, the object turns more tightly and forms a smaller circle.

## 5–10  A Final Perspective

Let's stop and consider again what we are doing when we apply Newton's laws of motion and the force laws.

Science assumes every phenomenon in the Universe has a cause. It further assumes that the relationship between all causes and their effects is governed by a small number of laws. If this were not true we would be forced to memorize thousands of details about how different objects

## IF THE FORCE IS IN, WHY DO I FEEL PUSHED OUT?

You know from experience that you will be pressed against the right side of a car traveling around a left-hand curve at high speeds. We considered this in Chapter 2 but let's revisit it again in more detail. The car pushes inward on you with a real contact force; that is the centripetal force causing you to change direction. You, in turn, push out on the car, in accordance with Newton's third law. That is also a real force.

A similar situation is sitting on a wheel at a fun house while it rotates. As the wheel rotates faster, you eventually slide off. The centripetal force holding you on the wheel is friction. If the wheel rotates fast enough, friction is unable to hold you on and you slide off in a straight line, according to Newton's first law.

Because in both cases you move, or try to move, away from the center of the circular motion, you may think there is a force outward on you. But you are really only tending to move in a straight line, in accordance with the first law of motion. Occasionally it is stated that a "centrifugal force" (fleeing the center) pushes you outward or presses you against the car door. But there is no outward force on you; the only horizontal force on you is a centripetal force inward. Slightly restated, only one force is needed to cause a person to move in a circle—the centripetal force. In like manner, there is no force that supposedly "throws" a passenger's head forward when a car stops, or "throws" him or her from the car in an accident. The passenger is simply obeying Newton's first law.

**Figure 5.12**
Only the force of the bar pulling the girl towards the center of the merry go round keeps her rotating. The moment she lets go, she will travel in a straight line.

react under different circumstances to make sense of our world. Or, worse still, the Universe would behave in an unpredictable, whimsical way and we would have no understanding of it at all.

Newton's laws of motion and the force laws for gravity and electromagnetism have been tested for hundreds of years and found to be valid in an immense number of experiments and applications. As we have seen so far in this book and will see in future chapters as well, they correctly describe the motion of objects from the size of molecules to the size of galaxies. They are accurate for speeds from zero to tens of thousands of kilometers per second. Their discovery changed history. Through them, mankind stopped seeing nature as being capricious and mythical. We began to understand that all of nature was obedient to certain definable, testable, and repeatable rules.

Viewed from our vantage point now, it all seems simple. The actual discovery of these laws, however, took mankind many hundreds of years. If it is so simple, why did it take so long?

When we face the experiences and tests of life without guidance, they can be extremely bewildering. Selecting those experiences that lead to general principles is difficult when they seem at first to be no different from less enlightening actions. The contribution of a genius such as Newton is to separate the important from the unimportant and then combine the whole into broad laws that can explain almost everything. Only then can the rest of us stand back and exclaim, "How obvious!"

## MAGNETIC LEVITATION

Newton's laws of motion are illustrated most naturally using the gravitational interaction. But there is one example of motion created by the electromagnetic interaction worth considering. Recent advancements in engineering are making it increasingly possible that some day magnetically levitated, or *maglev*, trains will be built to connect major cities. The physical principles they are based on are a good illustration of how the electromagnetic force can be harnessed.

Electric currents passing through wires create a magnetic field. Two coils beside each other with currents going in opposite directions will create magnetic fields that repel. These fields can be quite strong if the current is large enough. The repulsion can be strong enough to cause a maglev train car to lift an inch or more above a magnetized track.

Maglev trains would not have their own engines. Instead, their cars would be fitted with large guidance magnets attached to their undercarriages. The trains would run in a guideway like that shown in *Figure 5.13*. Electric coils would line the guideway. Some of the coils would repel the large magnets on the train's undercarriage, levitating the train just above the guideway bottom. Once levitated, power would be supplied to coils within the guideway walls to create a system of changing magnetic fields that both push and pull the entire train forward. The electric current supplied to the coils in the guideway walls would alternate to change their magnetic polarity. This change in polarity would cause the magnetic field in front of the train to pull the vehicle forward, while the magnetic field behind the train would repel or push it in the same direction.

Maglev trains now in the experimental stage in Japan, Europe, and the U.S. are of several designs, but all float on a cushion of air, eliminating friction. The lack of friction and the trains' aerodynamic designs allow them to reach speeds of more than 300 mph, about half the speed of a commercial airliner. Developers predict that maglev trains will someday link cities that are up to 1,000 miles apart. At 300 mph, you could travel from Salt Lake City to Los Angeles in just over two hours.

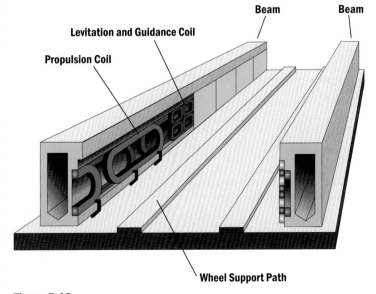

**Figure 5.13**
A diagram of the track of a maglev train rail.

## Comprehension

This chapter deals with applications of laws presented in Chapters 2–4. For comprehension questions, please review the questions at the end of those chapters.

## Synthesis

### First Law

1. Provide an example of an object at rest that is experiencing no forces.

2. Provide an example of an object in uniform motion that is experiencing no forces.

3. Provide an example of an object at rest that is experiencing two or more forces. What forces act on the object? How do their sizes compare?

4. Provide an example of an object in uniform motion that is experiencing two or more forces. What forces act on the object? How do their sizes compare?

5. Why doesn't the First Law apply to an object experiencing a single force.

6. Do the First and Second Laws of Motion ever apply to the same object at the same time? Explain.

### Second Law

1. Provide two examples of an object experiencing an unbalanced force in the direction it is moving. What do these objects have in common?

2. Provide two examples of an object experiencing an unbalanced force opposite the direction it is moving. What do these objects have in common?

3. Provide two examples of an object experiencing an unbalanced force perpendicular to the direction it is moving. What do these objects have in common?

4. Give two examples of an object with zero velocity that is accelerating.

5. Give two examples of an object accelerating while moving at constant speed.

6. How many forces are acting on the moon? What is causing these forces? Why does the moon move around its orbit? Why doesn't it hit Earth?

7. If you have 2 balls, a 1kg ball and a 2kg ball, and you push on them with the exact same force, how do the accelerations compare? Why?

8. Because all objects near the surface of Earth experience the same gravitational acceleration when dropped, does this mean that they are experiencing the same gravitational force? Why or why not?

9. On Earth, people often exercise by playing catch with a medicine ball (an extremely heavy ball). Would the same exercise work on a space station? Why or why not?

10. In science the word "weight" means the gravitational force acting on an object. Using this definition, are objects in orbit around Earth weightless? Explain your answer.

### Third Law

1. When a book is at rest on a table, its weight and the contact force from the table are equal and opposite. Are these forces an action–reaction pair? Explain your answer.

2. 10-year-old Brianna challenges her 4-year-old sister Lindsey to an arm wrestling match. Brianna wins without trouble. How is this possible if Lindsay pushes on Brianna as hard as Brianna pushes on Lindsey?

3. The BYU Society of Physics Students (SPS) challenges the BYU football team to a tug of war, with the one condition: that the SPS get to pick the playing field. The football team accepts, and the SPS announce that the match will take place at the Seven Peaks Ice Arena with the football team on the ice and the physics students standing on the concrete in the entrance to the rink. The SPS will try to pull the football players off the ice onto the concrete, and the football players try to pull the SPS off the concrete onto the ice. The first team to have a player touch the boundary between ice and concrete wins. Use Newton's Second and Third Laws to explain the strategy of the SPS.

## Common Misconceptions About Newton's Laws

Anyone who has been around young children for long has watched as they repeatedly drop things, seemingly fascinated just to watch them fall. One of the advantages students have when studying Newton's laws is that they have been experimenting with these laws from the time they first started tossing peas off their high chair. So they already have a reasonably good understanding of how things behave. The disadvantage is that some of their pre-conceived notions are incorrect. What follows is a list of common student misconceptions about Newton's laws.

The following ideas are ***incorrect.*** If they sound reasonable to you, please go back and review the appropriate material. Hopefully looking at common mistakes now will help prevent them on exams.

### 1. Misconceptions about motion

a.  An object must always accelerate in the direction it is moving. If you are moving upwards, you are accelerating upwards. If you are moving backwards, you are accelerating backwards. For example, if you throw a ball straight up, it accelerates up for the first part of its trajectory, then accelerates downward as it returns to the ground.

b.  An object has no acceleration if its speed is zero. For example, a ball is not accelerating at all at the highest point of its trajectory.

If either of these sentences sounds plausible to you, you should review section 2–2 on acceleration and the examples of the elevator found in section 5–1 and jumping into the air found in section 5–2. Acceleration depends on how speed or direction is changing. It does not depend on any current value of velocity.

### 2. Misconceptions about Newton's First Law

a.  An object experiencing a net force of zero has no forces acting on it. For example, an object is only at rest if there are no forces acting on it.

b.  Forces can only be balanced when an object is at rest.

c.  If an object is moving, there must be a net force in the direction it is moving. Once you remove this force, the object will come to rest. (This misconception is very common and very difficult to get rid of. For example, until recently there was a state high school core curriculum which required teachers to teach that there were two forces on the moon, an inward force to make it move in a circle and, incorrectly, a force pushing it in the direction it moves.)

If any of these statements seems correct please review sections 2–1 and 5–6 which describe objects that move at a constant speed with no net force. If you believe c, also review section 5–8. Be aware that many people hang on to misconception c on the grounds that "something must have pushed on the moon in the past to get it moving." If a force acted on an object at some point in the past, that does not mean it is acting on the object now. As discussed in 5–8, the rocket engines don't push on the ship once they are turned off.

### 3. Misconceptions about Newton's Second Law

a.  Acceleration depends only on the size of the force, not on mass. For example, because gravitational acceleration is the same for all objects, Earth's gravity must pull on everything with the same amount of force.

b.  In outer space, in the absence of gravity, all objects accelerate the same in response to the same force. Without gravity, it is as easy to push a one-ton piece of equipment as it is to push a piece of paper.

c.  If there is a net force acting on an object its speed must change. For example, because the speed of the moon is constant, the forces on it are balanced: gravity balances the centripetal force.

If either options a or b seems correct, see sections 2–4 and 2–5. Mass always matters. If you believed statement c, review section 5–9. The force on the Moon is most certainly not balanced, and the Moon accelerates. A change in direction is also an acceleration.

### 4. Misconceptions about Newton's Third Law

a.  The "action" force and "reaction" force can both act on the same object. For example, when a book is sitting on a table, the book's weight and the contact force from the table form an action-reaction pair.

b.  An object's motion is determined by Newton's third law, especially when it is at rest. In the example above, the reason that all the forces on the book are balanced is because of the 3rd law of motion.

c.  The third law doesn't apply to objects in accelerated motion. A rocket accelerates forward because it pushes harder on its exhaust than the exhaust pushes back.

d.  The third law doesn't apply to objects in motion. If you are pushing a chair across the floor at constant speed, the force you exert on the chair must be larger than the force the chair exerts backwards on you.

e.  When two things collide, the larger object exerts a larger force. For example, when a fly hits the windshield of a train, the train exerts more force on the fly.

Sections 2–6, 5–4 and 5–5 all apply Newton's Third Law. If any of the above statements appear to be true, you should review these sections looking specifically for reasons why it is incorrect. If a careful review still leaves you wondering why the statement is wrong, please ask your teacher or a teaching assistant.

# Forces in Fluids

*All the water in the world cannot sink the smallest boat—until some gets inside.*

*Anonymous*

# 6

Newton's laws of motion and gravity pertain to everything that has mass, large or small. We have used large familiar objects to illustrate these laws. An exception in Chapter 5 was when we discussed how a force of friction arises from microscopic molecules pushing against objects moving through air. Let's explore the idea of forces in air a little further.

Air, like all gases and liquids, is classified as a **fluid** because it flows. All fluids push with friction against the motion of objects moving through them. The friction becomes stronger when objects move faster because the acceleration of the molecules it strikes is greater, and that requires greater force. The amount of friction also depends on the number of molecules that contact the object. Denser fluids with molecules closer together, like water, generate greater friction than thinner, less dense fluids like air.

Friction is only one aspect of force within fluids. There are forces from gravity and pressure as well. Mathematical formulas have been developed to describe how these forces behave. Like the formulas for friction, they are built upon

Newton's laws, the law of gravity, and models of how molecules respond to the electromagnetic interaction.

Rules of fluid behavior are used everywhere in our lives. They are the basis of well-designed heating and air-conditioning systems. They allow engineers to plan and build massive dams and water and sewage systems. Sportsmen fly hot-air balloons and go scuba diving in accordance with them. On a grander scale, these rules are used to explain the flow of rivers, the movement of mountains, the drift of continents, and even the behavior of the Universe itself when it was just a few minutes old. In this chapter we will consider some aspects of forces in fluids.

## 6–1 Pressure

Forces exerted by fluids are best described by **pressure**. Pressure is defined mathematically as

$$\text{Pressure} = \text{Force}/\text{Area}$$

To illustrate what this formula means,

assume you weigh 160 pounds and are standing motionless on a sidewalk. You are supported by 160 pounds of contact force and therefore, according to Newton's third law, are exerting 160 pounds of contact force down against the cement. This force is exerted by your feet, which have a surface area in contact with the cement of, let us say, 80 square inches. If the 160 pounds of contact force is dispersed evenly on your feet, then there is a force of $160/80 = 2$ pounds on every square inch of the area of contact. In other words, two pounds per square inch is the pressure you are placing on the sidewalk.

Suppose you stand on one foot. Now the 160 pounds is distributed over half the previous area and the pressure increases to 4 lbs/in². If you stand on tip-toe and the area of contact is now reduced to about 4 square inches, the pressure increases to 40 lbs/in². Quite a difference! Your toes will soon begin to hurt as they experience all that contact force (see *Figure 6.1*).

Pressure is a more crucial issue in many situations than force alone. For example, a pound is a relatively small force, but if distributed over

**Fluid:**

Anything that flows. This refers to gases such as air and liquids such as water.

**Pressure:**

The total force on an object divided by the area over which the force is applied.

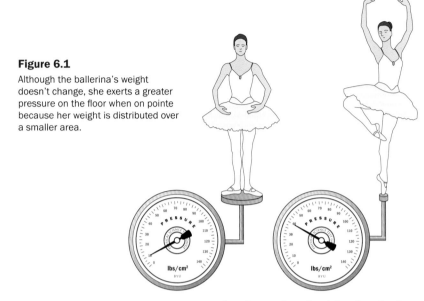

**Figure 6.1**
Although the ballerina's weight doesn't change, she exerts a greater pressure on the floor when on pointe because her weight is distributed over a smaller area.

a square that is one hundredth of an inch on a side, the pressure would be 10,000 lbs/in². Materials unable to bear this type of pressure will break even though this same force would not cause any damage when spread over a much larger area. A 98-pound woman rocking back on spike high heels puts more pressure on the point

of contact with the ground than a four-ton elephant's broad feet. Spike heels are designed to be fashionably attractive, but because they exert so much force on such a small area, they may make dents in the floor and must be exceptionally strong to not break when worn.

## 6-2 Pressure in Unbounded Fluids

Fluids can be wholly or partially contained. If they are wholly contained they are called "bounded". Space does not permit a full treatment of bounded fluids here. However a basic explanation is in the sidebar "Pressure in Bounded Fluids" for those who are interested.

Fluids that lack boundaries on one or more sides, like the oceans or the atmosphere, we call "unbounded." Unbounded fluids are pulled toward the earth and held in place by gravity. If allowed to continue flowing, they will move downward until there is no lower place to go and the flow stops. We consider here only fluids that are no longer flowing and are at rest, and we do not consider friction. Four basic rules apply.

## PRESSURE IN BOUNDED FLUIDS

Fluids that are completely confined inside a container are called "bounded" fluids. Examples would be a balloon or bottle of water with the cap screwed on tightly. The Frenchman Blaise Pascal (1623–1662) discovered that if a pressure is brought to bear on one side of a bounded fluid, this pressure will spread throughout the fluid, causing this same amount of pressure to be exerted on all other sides as well.

Ordinary striped toothpaste is a great example of the distribution of pressure through a bounded fluid. White toothpaste can be injected into a tube with different colored paste injected at the same time on the sides along the entire tube length, as shown in Figure 6.2. When a person squeezes the tube, in the middle or at either end[1], the tube pressurizes uniformly so that the white and colored paste experience the same pressure and come out together.

Hydraulic systems use Pascal's Law to harness and amplify force to lift and move heavy objects. Consider the bounded fluid in the curved cylinder in Figure 6.3. The piston on the right side has a total area of 100 in², while the piston on the narrow left side has an area of just 25 in². A force of 1 lb/in², or 25 pounds in all, bears down on the left side. This pressure distributes throughout the fluid and emerges on the right side with the same strength of 1 lb/in². However, the area of the right-side piston is four times greater than the left. So the total force on the right side piston is also four times greater, or 100 pounds.

[1] Whether or not a person should squeeze the tube at the end or in the middle is a question science is powerless to solve. Sorry.

**Figure 6.2**
Uniform distribution of pressure makes the different stripes of toothpaste emerge from the tube in the same proportions as they were inside.

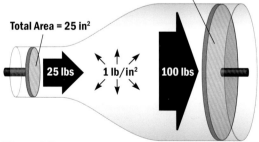

**Total Area = 100 in²**

**Total Area = 25 in²**

25 lbs    1 lb/in²    100 lbs

**Figure 6.3**
The pressure on the left side is the same as the pressure on the right side and everywhere in the container. But since the area of the right piston is four times greater that the area of the left piston, the total force on the right piston is four times greater than the force on the left piston.

### 1. Pressure depends on depth only and is greater at greater depth.

You can determine the pressure at any level within a fluid (air or water) by picturing a column of the fluid that rests above a particular area. The contact force on that area at the bottom of the column will equal the weight of the column. At greater depths, the weight of the column is greater and so the pressure is greater. The pressure of air at sea level is 14.7 lbs/in$^2$. Therefore the weight of the air in the atmosphere above a square inch is 14.7 pounds. The top of Mount Everest is above 70% of the air, so air pressure there is only 4.5 lbs/in$^2$. In contrast, the water pressure in the deepest trench of the ocean floor is over 16,000 lbs/in$^2$.

Pressure does not depend on the surface area or volume of a fluid, but only upon depth (Figure 6.4a). As amazing as it seems, a 100-foot tall dam holding back a reservoir the size of Texas feels less pressure than a 300-foot tall dam holding back a one square-mile lake. Engineered dams such as these, or simple dams of sandbags holding back a high river, are thinner at the top than at the bottom because the pressure is smaller at the top.

### 2. Pressure is the same for all points at the same depth.

If pressure changed from place to place at the same depth, the fluid would flow from high pressure zones to low pressure zones reducing the differences to zero and stopping the flow. Consequently for any specific depth pressure has the same value everywhere (*Figure 6.4b*). When we speak of air pressure at sea level, which is a fixed depth in the fluid of the atmosphere[1], we make no exceptions for local terrain such as mountains or valleys. Pressure at sea level near a mountain in France is the same as at sea level in a valley in Brazil or anywhere else in the world.

### 3. Pressure at a given depth is independent of direction.

At any given point, the pressure coming from any direction is the same. A tiny pressure sensor held at a fixed location will read the same value regardless of whether it points up, down,

or sideways. This is illustrated in *Figure 6.4a* by the pressure arrows at each point having the same length regardless of direction.

The atmosphere exerts a pressure of 14.7 lbs/in$^2$ over the entire surface of your body, in all directions. This may seem incredible because the total force on your body is thousands of pounds, enough to crush even a hard-bodied weight lifter to a pulp. We are not crushed because the pressure inside our bodies balances the outside air pressure. We usually do not even notice air pressure.

### 4. Pressure is always perpendicular to the surface of a submerged object.

When a boat floats on water, the water in contact with its bottom exerts pressure perpendicular to its surface. With a totally submerged object like a submarine, pressure similarly pushes inward everywhere against the hull. If the pressure should ever push in a sideways direction, the fluid would flow until all sideways forces balance, leaving only the pressure in the perpendicular direction, the direction the fluid cannot flow. (See *Figure 6.4c.*)

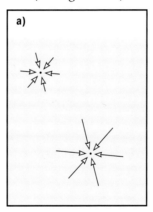
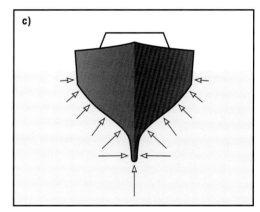
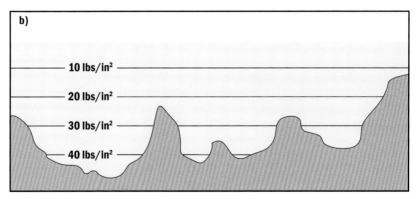

**Figure 6.4**

a) The pressure in a fluid is always greater the deeper you go. At any given point, the strength of the pressure, given by the length of the arrows, is the same from all directions.

b) Pressure at the same depth in a fluid is the same regardless of local terrain.

c) Pressure in a fluid is always perpendicular to the submerged surface. The arrows on the hull indicate the direction of the pressure.

---

[1] The distance of sea level from the center of Earth varies slightly from the poles to the equator because Earth is not quite spherical. But the water and air have reached a state of rest, so their pressure is the same everywhere.

### 6-3 The Buoyant Force and Archimedes' Principle

Have you noticed that an object immersed in water seems to weigh less than when it is out of the water? Neither its mass nor the force of gravity on it changed when it was submerged. However, an object is undeniably easier to lift when under water. Why?

Consider the submerged ball in *Figure 6.5*. We know from the fourth law of pressure that a fluid pushes inward everywhere on a submerged object. From the first law we know that pressure in the fluid increases with depth. Looking at the pressure arrows in *Figure 6.5*, we see that the forces pushing horizontally on the ball balance out. However, the pressure on the bottom pushing up is greater than the pressure on the top pushing down. As a result there is a net upward contact force, called a **buoyant force**. This force balances out some of the object's weight, making it seem to weigh less.

There is a remarkably simple way to determine the buoyant force. First imagine that the space occupied by the submerged ball in *Figure 6.5* is instead filled with water (see *Figure 6.6*). Water at rest has balanced forces throughout. The only forces on this ball of water are gravity and the buoyant force. Because they are balanced, the buoyant force must equal the force of gravity, which is, of course, the weight of the ball of water.

Now look again at the immersed ball in *Figure 6.5* and consider that it exactly fills the space previously occupied by the water. The surrounding water, not concerned that the ball of water has been replaced by a physical ball, exerts the same net upward force on the physical ball that it previously exerted on the ball of water that used to be there. This force is therefore equal to the weight of the water displaced by the ball. This is the buoyant force. This rule, known as *Archimedes' Principle,* can be stated as follows:

> **An object immersed in a fluid experiences an upward buoyant force caused by contact interactions with the surrounding fluid. The strength of this force equals the weight of the displaced fluid.**

Archimedes (287–212 BC) was a brilliant man who lived in the Greek city of Syracuse in Sicily. Archimedes' Principle is so named because he used it to establish the actual gold content of a royal crown. (See side box "Archimedes and the Crown of Gold")

### 6-4 Floating and Sinking

An object in a fluid experiences two forces: gravity pulling downward and the buoyant force pushing upward. The object accelerates in the direction of the net force, which is the direction of the stronger of these two forces. An object sinks if the force of gravity exceeds the buoyant force and rises if the buoyant force is stronger.

Consider the solid lead ball and air-filled beach ball in *Figure 6.7*. Both are the same size and have the same volume. When they are submerged they displace the same amount of water and experience the same buoyant force (shown

**Buoyant Force:**

A force pushing upward on objects immersed in a fluid.

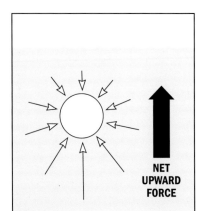

**Figure 6.5**
Because forces in unbounded fluids increase with depth, all objects in a fluid feel a net upward force called a buoyant force.

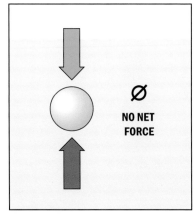

**Figure 6.6**
The buoyant force (purple arrow) on a ball of water exactly equals its weight (green arrow). If they were not equal, the water would flow until a balance was achieved.

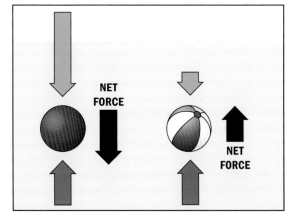

**Figure 6.7**
A lead ball and a beach ball, both of equal volume, are shown. Because they displace the same amount of water, the buoyant force on each is the same. But the heavier lead ball sinks while the lighter beach ball floats because their weights are so different.

as purple arrows). But the force of gravity (shown as green arrows) is much greater on the lead ball than it is on the beach ball. Therefore the net force on each is different. The buoyant force on the beach ball exceeds the force of gravity and the beach ball rises to the surface. Gravity exceeds the buoyant force on the lead ball and it sinks to the bottom.

Now imagine two objects that have the same weight but different volumes (*Figure 6.8*). Suppose they are both made of iron but the larger ball is hollow and the smaller ball is solid. Since the hollow ball is larger, the buoyant force acting on it is larger. If the larger ball's buoyant force exceeds its weight, the net upward force will cause the ball to rise to the surface. The buoyant force on the smaller solid ball is

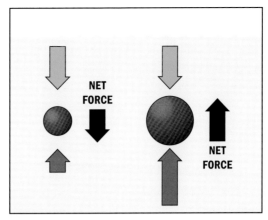

**Figure 6.8**
A solid iron and a hollow iron ball, both of equal weight, are shown. Because they displace different amounts of water, the buoyant force on each is different. The larger hollow ball floats while the smaller solid ball sinks because their buoyant forces are so different.

## ARCHIMEDES AND THE CROWN

Archimedes was a brilliant mathematician and inventor who lived in Syracuse on the east coast of Sicily during the second Punic War. He was the first to understand the significance and utility of simple machines: the lever, the pulley, and the inclined plane. As an advisor to the King of Syracuse, he spent much of his time and talent devising ingenious ways to fend off invading Roman forces.

Deciphering which stories of antiquity are true and which are not is often difficult. This is particularly true of the tales of Archimedes because his city and its records were destroyed when Syracuse fell to Rome in 211 BC. The story of Archimedes weighing the crown of gold dates to 100 BC and likely has some truth to it, although the exact way he accomplished it is still uncertain. Whatever the truth may be, Archimedes' Principle derives its name from the following story.

The King of Syracuse asked Archimedes to determine if a crown he owned was pure gold or gold alloyed with cheaper silver. Chemical tests for purity were possible but required a piece of the crown be destroyed and the King would not allow the crown to be defaced.

Archimedes knew that 1) silver is less dense than gold and 2) the buoyant force is equal to the amount of displaced water. He suspended the crown from one end of a scale and balanced it with an equal mass of pure gold suspended from the other end. He then immersed the crown and gold lump together in a bowl of water (Figure 6.8).

If the crown were pure gold, it would have the same density and volume as the counterbalancing gold lump. When submerged, both would displace the same amount of water, experience the same buoyant force, and the scale would remain in perfect balance. However, if the crown were partly silver it would have a greater volume than the pure gold lump, displace more water, and experience a greater buoyant force. As a result when both the crown and the lump were submerged, the total force down on the crown would be less than the downward force on the gold lump and the scale would tilt upward on the crown side as shown in Figure 6.9.

As the story goes, the crown was seen to be higher in the water than the gold lump, thus failing the purity test to the demise of an unfortunate artisan. It is also said that Archimedes discovered this technique while sitting in a public bath. He became so enthused at his discovery that he went running naked into the streets shouting "Eureka! Eureka!" (I have found it! I have found it!)

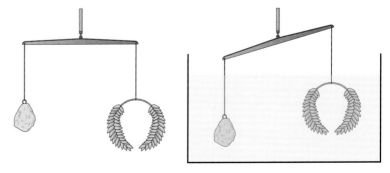

**Figure 6.9**
Archimedes was able to determine the purity of a crown of gold by using the buoyant force to check the crown's density.

less than that on the hollow ball. If the volume of water it displaces weighs less than that ball's weight, the solid ball will sink even though its weight and the weight of the hollow ball are the same.

For solid objects, the rules regarding floating and sinking relate to **density**. The definition of density is

$$density = mass / volume$$

Use of Archimedes' Principle shows that if a solid object has a greater density (or more mass per cm³) than the fluid in which it is placed, it will sink. If its density is less than the fluid's density, it will float. This is true regardless of the size of the object.

A solid object that is less dense than the fluid will float at a level where the buoyant force equals the weight of the entire object. The greater the difference between the density of the object and the density of the fluid, the higher the object will float.

Icebergs illustrate this point. The density of ice is 90% of the density of fresh water. Therefore 90% of an iceberg's total volume will displace enough fresh water to equal the iceberg's total weight. An iceberg in a freshwater lake floats with 90% of its volume below the water and 10% above (*Figure 6.10*).

Freshwater ice is only 70% the density of the ocean's salt water. When a freshwater glacier "calves" an iceberg and currents carry it out into the open ocean, that iceberg will float higher, with 30% of its volume above the water line and only 70% of its volume beneath the surface.

Objects that are not solid all the way through may or may not float depending on their shape. Consider an aluminum sailboat. Aluminum, like iron, is denser than water, but like the hollow iron ball in Figure 6.8, aluminum boats still float because they too obey Archimedes' Principle.

Boats have broad bottoms and mostly empty interiors. The broad bottoms cause them to displace a large volume of water after sinking a relatively small distance. The mostly empty interior decreases the weight of the boat to where the buoyant force balances the weight before the boat sinks down very far into the water (*Figure 6.11*).

Every boat and ship, regardless of its size, its shape, or what it is made of, is designed to displace a mass of water equal to its own weight and the weight of its passengers and cargo well before it is submerged. If a boat springs a leak and takes on water then the weight of the incoming water adds to the overall weight of the boat, causing it to sink lower. If the boat's sides sink below the surface and water comes pouring in, the boat—now completely incapable of displacing more than its weight in water—will sink to the bottom.

**Density:**

An object's mass divided by its volume.

a)

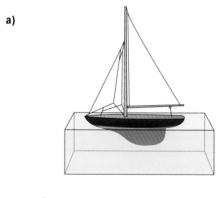

b)

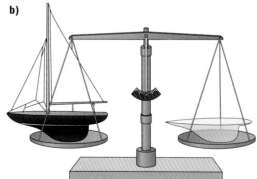

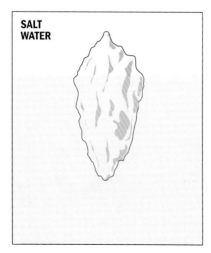

**Figure 6.10**

Solid objects like icebergs float if they are less dense than water. Freshwater ice is 90% the density of freshwater and floats 90% submerged. Freshwater ice is just 70% the density of heavier saltwater and floats 70% submerged.

**Figure 6.11**

a) A sailboat sinks in water until its entire weight equals the weight of the water it displaces.

b) The shape of the displaced water is the shape of just the submerged portion of the boat.

## 6–5 Buoyancy in the Atmosphere and Earth's Crust

Balloons filled with helium float in accordance with Archimedes' Principle. Helium is a gas that is much lighter than air. When the weight of the balloon together with the weight of the helium inside the balloon is less than the weight of the air it displaces, the balloon rises. A balloon of the same size filled with average temperature air could never rise because the balloon itself has weight and the density of the air inside the balloon is the same density as the air outside it.

Hot air balloons are able to overcome the pull of gravity and rise because the air inside them is made less dense than the air outside. When a hot air balloon envelope (the large colorful part) is first partially filled with air, it lies on the ground, unable to lift. The balloon operators then ignite propane burners which heat and expand the inside air, reducing its density. When the combined weight of the cage, passengers, envelope and hot air becomes less than the weight of the air displaced by the expanding envelope, the balloon floats upward.

Air and water are both fluids, but there is a major difference between them. Water, like most liquids, has essentially the same density wherever it is, regardless of its depth in an ocean or lake[2]. A ball light enough to rise through water will always come to the surface because the buoyant force does not change with depth (*Figure 6.12a*).

However air, unlike water, decreases in density with height. As a hot air balloon rises, the buoyant force on it decreases as the density— and therefore the weight—of the surrounding air decreases (*Figure 6.12b*). The rising hot air balloon will eventually reach a point where the forces on it are balanced and it will hover, neither ascending nor descending. To descend, the operator reduces the buoyant force by either letting air out of the envelope or by allowing it to cool and contract.

An interesting example of buoyancy occurs between Earth's crust and mantle. As we discuss in Chapter 26, the outer layer of the mantle is

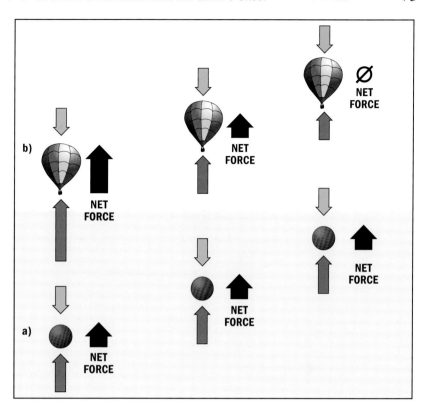

**Figure 6.12**

a) Solid objects in water will float or sink but not hover because water (very nearly) keeps the same density with depth.

b) A balloon in air will hover because the buoyant force decreases with height as air density decreases.

hot enough to have some characteristics of a fluid. The continents and ocean basins float in the upper mantle just like ships or icebergs float in water. The crust beneath Earth's oceans is quite dense, but is less dense than the mantle. The oceanic crust sinks just far enough into the mantle that the resulting buoyant force supports the crust's weight and the weight of the water above. (See *Figure 6.13*.)

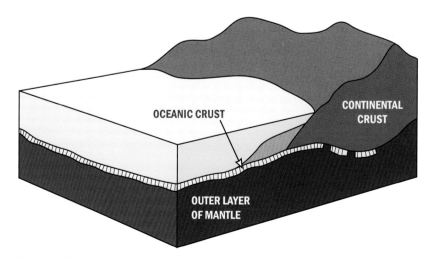

**Figure 6.13**

Earth's crust floats on the outer layer of the mantle. Although the continental material is lighter than the oceanic material, it is thicker and has a greater total weight. As a result, continents float deeper in the mantle than ocean basins.

---

[2] In reality, water density does change slightly with depth as temperature, pressure, and salinity vary. In this book we will ignore these effects and assume that densities of liquids are the same throughout.

Each continent, and indeed each individual mountain, has "roots" extending far enough into the mantle to provide the buoyant force necessary to support it. The taller a mountain or the more massive a continent, the deeper the roots. Just as larger icebergs have more volume below the surface than smaller ones have, a large mountain has more volume below the surface of the land than a smaller mountain has. If material mass increases on a mountain or continent—by the formation of a glacier or the eruption of a massive lava flow—the underlying crust sinks, over time, deeper into the mantle. If material is removed—by erosion or the melting of a glacier—the underlying crust will rise.

## 6-6 Convection

A manifestation of the buoyant force we will encounter several times in this book is convective currents, like those that create winds. If a fluid has different sections within it that are at different temperatures, those sections will also have different densities. The hotter, less dense sections will tend to rise while the denser, cooler sections will tend to sink, creating circulation.

Lava lamps illustrate this. Lava lamps are containers filled with fluid and lumps of a waxy substance. When the lumps are cool they are denser than the surrounding fluid and sink to the bottom where the light is. The light heats the lumps, which expand, become less dense than the fluid, and rise. At the top, away from the heat source, the wax cools and shrinks to the former density, then descends to be reheated and rise again in a never-ending cycle. The cycle

**Convection:**

The process by which energy is moved from one place to another by being stored in matter as internal energy, then moving the matter from one place to another.

of heating, rising, cooling, and falling forms the basis of all convective currents.

A similar example can be found at the beach. Water temperature changes slower than land temperature. During the day as the Sun beats down equally on both water and land, the temperature of land increases more than the temperature of the ocean bordering that land as in *Figure 6.14a*. The air over the warmer land becomes less dense than the air over the cooler ocean water and rises relative to it. As the warm air rises, the cooler ocean air flows in to take its place. The warmer air then circulates out to the ocean, cools, and sinks down to replace the cooler air that moved toward the land. This motion creates a circular flow bringing cool surface breezes in from the ocean to the land during the daytime.

At night the land loses heat faster and the process reverses. The air over the land becomes denser than the air over the ocean. This air sinks relative to the ocean air, and the air circulates in the opposite direction. The surface winds now blow away from the land (*Figure 6.14b*).

Circulation in a fluid caused by differences in temperature and density is called **convection**. In Chapter 9 we learn that convection is an important way energy is transported from place to place. Convection ovens use circulating air inside the oven chamber to spread heat uniformly and quickly. In Chapter 30 we discuss how convection creates the many broad circulation patterns in Earth's atmosphere and oceans. And in Chapter 27 we see how convection in Earth's mantle is part of the process driving crustal plates from place to place on Earth's surface.

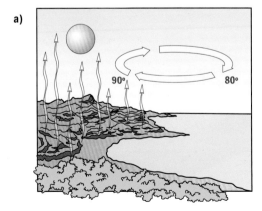

**Figure 6.14**

a) Daytime convection pattern near a seashore. Because the land is warmer, surface air currents blow into land as the air over it rises.

b) Nighttime convection pattern near a seashore. Because the water is now warmer, surface air currents blow away from the land as the air over the ocean rises.

*Science is a way of thinking much more than it is a body of facts.*

Carl Sagan

# 6 STUDY GUIDE

## Chapter Framework

### A. Introduction
1. Friction in fluids
2. Forces in fluids

### B. Pressure
1. Pressure = Force/Area

### C. Pressure in Unbounded Fluids
1. Four basic rules of pressure
   a. *Pressure depends on depth*
   b. *Pressure is the same for all points at the same depth*
   c. *Pressure at a given depth is independent of direction*
   d. *Pressure is always perpendicular to the surface of a submerged object*

### D. The Buoyant Force and Archimedes' Principle

### E. Floating and Sinking
1. A balance between gravity and buoyancy
2. Density

### F. Buoyancy in the Atmosphere and Earth's Crust
1. Atmospheric density changes with height
2. Water density is assumed to be constant

### G. Convection
1. Temperature changes density
2. Density differences cause convection

## Comprehension

### Matching
1. _____ The force on an object divided by the area over which the force is applied.
2. _____ Circulation in a fluid caused by temperature and density differences.
3. _____ Fluids pulled toward Earth and held in place by the force of gravity.
4. _____ Equals the weight of the displaced fluid.
5. _____ Anything that flows.
6. _____ Type of fluids where pressure acts with equal force on all areas of the confining walls.

a. Fluid
b. Buoyant Force
c. Convection
d. Unbounded fluids
e. Bounded fluids
f. Pressure

### True/False
1. _____ Air is considered a fluid.
2. _____ If an object is floating, the buoyant force on it is larger than its weight.
3. _____ Frictional forces increase when an object moves faster through a fluid.
4. _____ A man standing in a swimming pool weighs less because water partially shields him from the full force of gravity.
5. _____ Objects that float in air, such as helium balloons, are weightless.
6. _____ If you apply a specific force over a larger area, the pressure decreases.

### Fill in the Blank
1. Pressure in an unbounded fluid increases with _____.
2. Lava lamps provide an example of _____ currents.
3. If an object is completely submerged, the buoyant force is equal to the weight of _____. If it is floating, the buoyant force is equal to _____.
4. The total force on an object at any depth equals the _____ of the column of fluid directly above it.

## Analysis

1. If a block of wood floats with half its volume submerged,
   a) the buoyant force is equal to half the weight of the block.
   b) the weight of the block is the same as that of the displaced water.
   c) the volume of the block is the same as that of the displaced water.
   d) the buoyant force is equal to twice the weight of the displaced water.
   e) the buoyant force is equal to twice the weight of the block.

2. The buoyant force on an object submerged in a fluid can be changed by
   a) changing the volume of the object without changing its weight.
   b) changing the weight of the object without changing its volume.
   c) changing the density of the fluid.
   d) Both (a) and (c) are correct.

3. In convection currents, warmer air rises and cooler air descends. Which of the following is correct?
   a) There is a buoyant force on the warmer air, but there is not a buoyant force on the cooler air.
   b) The gravitational force pulls harder on each kilogram of cooler air than it does on a kilogram of warmer air.
   c) The buoyant force on the warmer air is upward, while the buoyant force on the cooler air is downward.
   d) The warmer air has a lower density than the cooler air which it displaces.
   e) The warmer air has a higher density than the cooler air which it displaces.

4. The base of a dam is reinforced in case the pressure increases in the future. Which of the following would cause such an increase?
   a) An increase in the volume of water going through the dam's spillway.
   b) A change of climactic patterns that would

increase the lake's depth over the next several years.

c) An excavation of a side canyon to increase the lake's area.

d) A large number of boats creating larger wakes that will hit the dam with greater force.

5. Which exerts the largest amount of force on the ground? (Note: in b, c, and d, water has been removed to keep the level the same as in a.)

a) A swimming pool full of water

b) An identical swimming pool full to the exact same level with a 200-lb log floating on top

c) An identical swimming pool full to the exact same level with two 170-lb people floating in it

d) An identical swimming pool full to the exact same level with a 50-lb block sitting on the bottom

6. Explain why pressure is a useful way of talking about forces exerted by fluids.

7. How do convection currents form?

8. State and explain the four rules that describe how pressure distributes through a fluid at rest.

9. Identify the following as an unbounded or bounded fluid.

a) Can of shaving cream

b) Bowl of water

c) Fluid in a hydraulic system

d) Mountain lake

e) Venus' atmosphere

10. Scuba divers can get the bends if they change pressure too rapidly. Would it be more dangerous to surface rapidly from a depth of 40 ft. in the ocean, or a depth of 40 ft. in a narrow pool formed in an old quarry?

11. How do contact forces and pressure give rise to the buoyant force?

12. In grade school you are told that density determines whether an object will float or sink. In this course you are told to compare buoyant and gravitational forces. Explain how the two are equivalent.

13. In Chapter 5 it was essential to understand that acceleration comes when the forces on an object are unbalanced. Explain why understanding the motion of a body on or inside a fluid almost always involves balancing two or more forces.

## Synthesis

1. If you drop a rock into water, the buoyant force remains virtually unchanged as it sinks, but if you release a helium balloon, the buoyant force changes as it rises. Explain why.

2. A few days after you purchase a helium balloon, it will float in mid-air with the string barely touching the floor. As long as you don't touch it, the balloon does not move. (Hint: Helium molecules are so small they pass through the skin of a balloon over time.)

a) What can you conclude about the net force on the balloon?

b) After a few days most helium balloons no longer float in the air. Why do you suppose this is?

c) Explain how your answers in (b) and (c) relate to one another.

3. Two large rubber balloons are filled with helium at ground level and released. One balloon rises rapidly and pops. The other balloon drifts for hours at about the same level.

a) What forces act on the balloons after they are released?

b) What is the direction of the net force when the balloons first begin to move?

c) What will happen to the air pressure around the balloons as they rise?

d) What will happen to the volume of the balloons as they rise?

e) What can you conclude about the balloon that popped when compared with the one that did not?

4. If you have two identical cups, filled as shown, can you make the cup with the most water float in the cup that contains the least water? Explain.

5. Three spheres of the exact same volume are submerged in a tub of water. After the spheres are lined up, they are released. The spheres are made of plastic with the same density as water, ice, and iron.

6. Compare the weights of the three spheres.

7. Compare the buoyant forces on the three spheres.

8. What direction does the net force push on each of the spheres?

9. What happens to each sphere after it is released?

10. The ice sphere will rise to the top of the water then bob up and down and eventually come to a stop with part of the sphere protruding above the water's surface. Why does it stop with a certain portion of the sphere protruding out of the water?

# Motion at High Speed

*The most beautiful thing we can experience is the mysterious. It is the source of all true art and all science. He to whom this emotion is a stranger, who can no longer pause to wonder and stand rapt in awe, is as good as dead: his eyes are closed.*

*Albert Einstein*

**7**

## LEARN

- Why motion must be described relative to a reference frame.

- The two postulates that are the foundation of the special theory of relativity.

- What the special theory of relativity says about space and time.

- How to describe the attributes of length, time, and simultaneity for objects moving near the speed of light.

- Both experimentally established and thought-based demonstrations of the special theory of relativity.

Scientific knowledge has grown exponentially since the closing years of the 17th century, when Sir Isaac Newton formulated his laws of motion and gravity. By linking the logic and precision of mathematics to the physical world, Newton and others gave the physical sciences a language through which exact inquiry and communication could flourish.

The industrial revolution began in England a few decades after Newton's death. This was not a coincidence, his laws helped create it. Technology emerging from burgeoning industry created experimental tools to control and measure force, mass and speed to increasing precision, allowing us to better test and refine our understanding of nature's laws.

How do we best test a law of nature? One way is to examine it under extreme conditions. An extreme condition for the laws of motion is high speed. So what do we mean by "high speed"?

In Newton's era, the fastest a person could move was about 20 m/sec (50 mph), the speed

of a fast quarter horse. Then came the automobile and speeds quadrupled: Normal freeway speeds are 30 m/sec (75 mph) while race cars routinely approach speeds of 100 m/sec (225 mph).

Air and space travel increased travel speeds again. Commercial jets routinely fly faster than 240 m/sec (550 mph). A space shuttle in orbit travels at 8,000 m/sec (18,000 mph). One of the fastest man-made objects ever, the Voyager I space probe, currently moves at 17,400 m/sec (39,000 mph). (see *Figure 7.1.*)

At each of these speeds Newton's laws are perfect, but we do not consider even the fastest of them to be "high speed". in this chapter. We reserve that term exclusively for objects moving

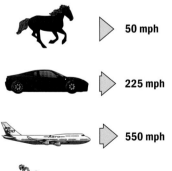

50 mph

225 mph

550 mph

**Figure 7.1**

A comparison of velocities. The arrows for the first three objects are not accurate in their length because the velocities are so small. However, the arrows for the satellite and the beam of light are proportionally accurate. The satellite's arrow is exactly six inches in length. When compared with the length of the arrow of the beam of light, it is evident that even the fastest objects in our lives travel but a fraction of the speed of light.

39,000 mph

670,000,000 mph

**The arrow for the beam of light extends 1.6 miles off the edge of the page.**

near the absolute limit of speed—the velocity of light traveling through empty space. This speed, denoted by the letter "c," is approximately $3 \times 10^8$ m/sec or 300,000 km/sec ($6.70 \times 10^8$ mph).[1]

Speeds close to that of light are never reached in everyday travel. Even the fastest rocket ships ever built, or that might ever realistically be built, travel at speeds less than one-ten-thousandth the speed of light. However, high speed atomic-sized particles called "cosmic rays" do strike Earth from outer space at speeds close to that of light. And scientists have built and operate machines that accelerate sub-atomic particles to high speeds for laboratory study. Through these we have learned experimentally how real objects behave at high speeds.

So the question we ask is: "Do Newton's laws work the same for speeds close to the speed of light as they do for cars traveling 75 mph down the freeway?" To our amazement, we have learned that *they don't!* At 30 percent of the speed of light, $\mathbf{F} = \mathbf{ma}$ incorrectly predicts the acceleration of an object by 15 percent. At 80 percent of the speed of light, the prediction errs by more than 460 percent!

At high speeds, Newton's laws of motion must be modified by rules that are part of a theory called the "Special Theory of Relativity." This theory—really a well-established law—gives us marvelous and unexpected insights into the very nature of time and space.

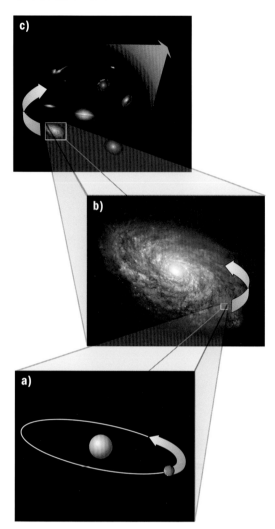

**Figure 7.2**

a) Earth moves about the Sun.

b) The Sun rotates in the Milky Way Galaxy.

c) The Milky Way has its own motion with respect to other galaxies.

## 7-1 Motion and Relativity

Determining motion may seem trivial: A person standing still anywhere on the surface of Earth is motionless, and an airplane, a horse, or a snail moving past that person has motion. We have made this assumption tacitly in our discussions of motion thus far. But it isn't that simple. A person standing on the surface of Earth really *isn't* motionless. For starters, Earth spins around in a circle every 24 hours, creating day and night. Earth also moves around our Sun, which orbits the center of our galaxy, which moves in other ways as well (*Figure 7.2*; Refer to

---

[1] The exact speed of light is 299,792.458 km/sec, but assuming it is 300,000 km/sec is adequate for our purposes. Light has this speed only in the vacuum of space. Through the atmosphere it interacts with air molecules, which slow it down. This effect is touched upon in Chapter 11.

the sidebar "Your Everyday Motion.") With all these motions taking place at the same time, our "real motion" is difficult to define.

Newton was aware of this and postulated that a place existed, perhaps where God dwells, that could be considered the ultimate place of rest. He considered that God, the "Prime Mover," started the heavens in motion by pushing them from this place of rest. Mortal man's "true motion," then, could be measured relative to this location. But, as Newton admitted, this idea could not be tested and was therefore unusable for science.

A better approach is to first note that motion is always defined with respect to something else. When we say we are standing motionless, we almost always mean with respect to the surface of Earth. When we say Earth moves in its orbit at 30 km/sec, we mean with respect to

## YOUR EVERYDAY MOTION

Newton's First Law tells us that every state of motion feels just like any other state of motion as long as there is no acceleration. Life, therefore, feels the same whether a person is flying steadily through the air on an airplane, traveling at constant speed and direction in a car, or standing still in a classroom. This is fortunate because we undergo many different motions each day. It would be distracting to say the least if we felt them all.

We spin around with Earth, making one full revolution on a radius of 6,370 km every 24 hours. This spinning moves a person on the equator at 0.5 km/sec. Spinning in a circle is an accelerated motion that we would normally be able to feel. We don't notice it because the magnitude of the acceleration, only 0.034 m/sec$^2$, is so small that the acceleration of gravity, 9.8 m/sec$^2$, easily masks it.

Earth orbits the Sun at a velocity of 30 km/sec (*Figure 7.2*). The Sun spins around the center of the Milky Way Galaxy at 220 km/sec. The Milky Way orbits about the center of a mass of nearby galaxies (called the "Local Group") at about 120 km/sec. The entire Local Group falls toward the center of a cluster of galaxies in the constellation of Virgo at a speed of about 250 km/sec. The Virgo cluster, in turn, falls toward a point called the "Great Attractor" in the constellation of Centaurus at a speed of about 570 km/sec.

The ultimate measure of our motion is with respect to a low-energy photon field, called the "cosmic microwave background", that is left over from the "big bang." (See Chapter 34.) The light in this field is oriented randomly, creating a background that is uniform in all directions. Scientists have measured the Doppler shift (see Chapter 10) of this field caused by the total motion of Earth. This measurement indicates that our Sun moves at a speed of about 600 km/sec toward the constellation of Hydra. This is a large velocity, but we do not feel it because our acceleration is very, very small.

All the velocities quoted above are measured with respect to another frame of reference. When we run out of references to compare against, we simply stop measuring!

---

the Sun. Motion is always and only measured with respect to "reference frames," like the surface of Earth or the Sun, which have their own state of motion as well. Because we can measure motion with respect to many different reference frames, no value can be declared as the most correct measure of how we are moving. In other words, "absolute motion"—motion defined with respect to some place that is absolutely at rest—does not exist.

The idea that motion is only determined with respect to other objects and therefore has no absolute value is called **relativity**. To illustrate what this means, suppose you are driving an automobile down the freeway at 75 mph. If you take the car as your reference frame, you can say you are motionless, because you are motionless within the car. You can also accurately say you are moving forward at 75 mph if you use the roadside as your reference frame. If you ignore the looks of pity from the people you are talking to, you can say that the roadside is moving backwards at 75 mph with respect to the car. All these viewpoints are equally legitimate as far as the laws of nature are concerned.

## 7-2 Motion Symmetry

We have learned that objects accelerate only when they experience an unbalanced force. Now if we measure our motion relative to an object that is accelerating forward, we may incorrectly think we are accelerating backward, even though we don't feel a force. To prevent this mistake, we divide motion into two general classes: accelerated and non-accelerated. If we measure our motion from a perspective that is not accelerating, i.e., one that is in uniform motion, we say we are measuring from an **inertial frame of reference**. If we measure motion from a perspective that is accelerating, we say we are measuring from a **non-inertial frame of reference** (*Figure 7.3*).

**Figure 7.3**
The riders on the Octopus are in a non-inertial frame of reference, while those watching are in an inertial frame of reference.

**Relativity:**
The idea that motion is only defined relative to other objects, which may have their own motion. There is no such thing as an "absolute" motion measured against objects that are absolutely at rest.

**Inertial Frame of Reference:**
A state of motion that is experiencing no acceleration.

**Non-inertial Frame of Reference:**
A state of motion that is undergoing an acceleration.

True inertial frames of reference do not exist on Earth's surface because Earth is spinning and its surface is constantly accelerating around in a circle. However, the acceleration from this rotation is gentle enough to ignore for most situations (see "Your Everyday Motion"). With this caveat, we will consider places on or near Earth's surface, such as a scientific laboratory or a car or airplane or anything traveling in otherwise uniform motion, to be inertial frames of reference.

All experiments conducted in an inertial frame of reference will unfold in accordance with Newton's laws. The results of those experiments therefore will be the same regardless of the frame's location or velocity. This idea, called motion symmetry, is defined as follows:

**The laws of nature remain the same for all observers in inertial frames of reference.**

Motion symmetry is as fundamental as the related principles of position and time symmetry introduced in Chapter 1.

Motion symmetry does *not* apply to non-inertial frames of reference because the acceleration of the reference frame is reflected in all measurements made relative to it. To illustrate this, imagine that you wake up one morning and find yourself in a windowless room. Scattered around the room are many kinds of experimental equipment. A note on the table next to your bed says you are either in a windowless airplane cruising at 30,000 feet on your way to London or that you are in the basement of a warehouse going nowhere. The note further explains that if

you can prove which of these choices is correct by conducting an experiment, the person who played this trick on you will pay you one million dollars.

You excitedly accept the challenge but quickly realize you are probably going to fail. A steady cruising airplane and the basement of a warehouse are both inertial frames of reference. Motion symmetry tells you that no experiment or measurement can differentiate between them. So you sit back on the bed, dangling a plumb-bob in front of your face as you think. The plumb-bob reminds you that it hangs down in the same way for all inertial frames of reference because gravity, in obedience to a law of nature, is the same in all inertial frames. Suddenly, to your amazement, you feel a slight force to one side and watch the plumb-bob drift in that direction. Excitedly, you realize this cannot happen in the basement of a warehouse but it *can* happen when an airplane accelerates by turning. A turning airplane becomes a non-inertial frame of reference, the experiment of hanging a plumb bob gives a different result than you would get in the basement of a warehouse, and you get the million dollars (right about the time you really wake up!).

The science that studies non-inertial frames of reference is called the *General Theory of Relativity*. That theory, already discussed in Chapter 3, establishes close connections between gravity, acceleration, and curved space-time. In this chapter only inertial frames of reference will be discussed.

## 7-3 Galilean Relativity and the Speed of Light

As mentioned in Section 7–1, **velocity** can have different values depending on how we choose to measure it. Consider a woman riding a train going north at 10 m/sec (*Figure 7.4*). She gets up and strolls to the rear of the car at 0.5 m/sec. A man seated in the same car measures her motion at 0.5 m/sec, moving south. However, a rail worker standing beside the train tracks measures her motion past him to be 9.5 m/sec, moving north. His measured value of 9.5 m/sec is the train's speed of 10 m/sec minus her walking speed of 0.5 m/sec. Then a pilot flying due west high over the train at 30 m/sec measures the woman's motion. The woman's walking motion,

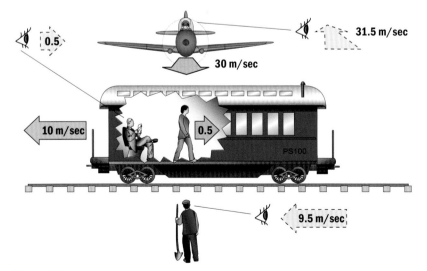

**Figure 7.4**
A lady walks on a train while a plane flies overhead. How many different speeds can be assigned to her? Are any speed values truer than the others?

the train's motion, and the airplane's motion add together as vectors such that the pilot sees the woman moving at 31.5 m/sec, mostly toward the east.

No paradox exists. Different speeds are measured because the train moves with respect to the rail worker and the pilot moves with respect to both him and the train. Properly add or subtract these motions and all three observers will agree that the woman moves north at a speed of 9.5 m/sec relative to the surface of Earth.

This common-sense connection between velocities referenced to different frames is called **Galilean relativity**. One would reasonably expect all moving things, including light, to obey it.

In 1887, the great experimental physicist Albert Michelson (1852–1931) and his colleague, Edward Morley (1838–1923), attempted to show that light obeyed Galilean relativity by measuring the gains and lags to its speed caused by the orbit of Earth. In a laboratory at Case Western Reserve University in Cleveland, Ohio, they constructed a delicate apparatus called an interferometer that could measure a change in the speed of light as small as 5 km/sec. They expected to find light beams traveling in the direction Earth orbits moving 30 km/sec slower because Earth is traveling with the beam at 30 km/sec. And they expected light beams traveling in the opposite direction to be moving 30 km/sec faster because Earth was now going against the beam (*Figure 7.5*).

After years of trying, Michelson and Morley found that in either orientation the measured value of a light beam's speed remained unchanged! Disappointed, they proclaimed their experiment a failure. But they did not fail. Modern experiments have shown at a much higher level of precision that light indeed travels the same speed regardless of the velocity of the people emitting or measuring the light. In other words, *light does not obey Galilean Relativity.*

Return to the example of the woman on the train (*Figure 7.6*). Suppose that instead of walking through the rail car toward the rear of the train, she shines a light toward the back of the rail car. As the light shines, she sees it travel at 300,000 km/sec. The rail worker sees the light beam and also measures its speed to be 300,000 km/sec. Somehow the train's speed is irrelevant! The pilot flying overhead measures the light's

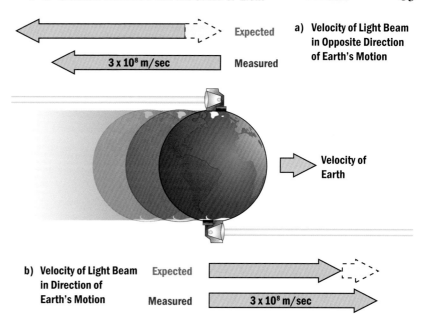

**Figure 7.5**

Results of the Michelson/Morley experiment. Whether a light beam travels against Earth's orbital motion (a) or with it (b), the measured value of its speed is the same. The dotted arrows show the expected effect of Earth's motion.

speed and gets the same answer, 300,000 km/sec. The speed of light receives neither a boost nor a slowing from the motion of the receiver or sender.

This result challenges our ability to understand! Only two explanations are possible. It could be that nature has special rules just for adding the velocity of light to other velocities. Or it could be that adding the velocity of light follows the same rules as all velocity additions, we are just not using the proper rules!

**Galilean Relativity:**

The notion that a final speed vector can be computed by directly adding all individual velocity vectors together according to the rules of Euclidean geometry.

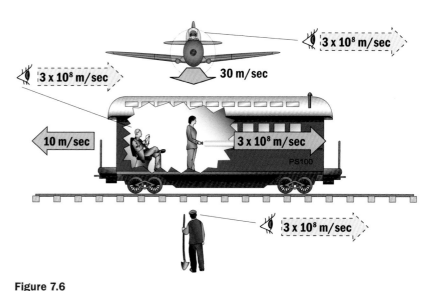

**Figure 7.6**

While different speeds can be assigned to the woman's motion, only one value is found for the speed of light. Light does not obey Galilean Relativity.

## 7-4 The Special Theory of Relativity

Guided both by Occam's razor and motion symmetry, Albert Einstein reasoned that it is simpler if all velocities, including that of light, added together by the same rules. Einstein and others, particularly the Dutch physicist Hendrik Lorentz (1853–1928), discovered a set that kept the speed of light the same for all inertial frames while reducing to Galilean relativity at slow speeds. These rules, together with their predictions about time, mass, and space, are the **special theory of relativity**.

The special theory of relativity rests upon two assumptions:

1. The laws of nature are the same for all observers in inertial frames of reference (i.e., the principle of motion symmetry).

2. The speed of light in a vacuum has a constant value of approximately 300,000 km/sec, regardless of the speed of the device emitting the light or the speed of the observer receiving the light.

Einstein actually formulated this theory before he learned of the Michelson-Morley experiment. In 1905 it was known that the equations governing electromagnetism violated motion symmetry. Lorentz found a mathematical transformation relating space and time that repaired the violation but could not explain why the transformation should be applied. Einstein showed that if the speed of light were the same for all observers, Lorentz' transformations could be derived in a simple, straightforward manner. Furthermore, his derivation indicated that Lorentz' transformations should be applied to *all* moving things regardless of their speed, not just light.

Einstein's straight-forward derivation took the bold and unprecedented position that space and time are not absolute quantities. Lengths of objects shrink and their clocks tick at slower rates when they move past at high speeds. Events that are simultaneous for us are not simultaneous when they are viewed by someone else moving past us. In other words, not only does absolute motion not exist, but neither do absolute space and absolute time! A true revolution in our understanding had begun!

**Special Theory of Relativity:**

The theory of how objects in inertial frames of reference behave at high speeds.

**Gedanken Experiment:**

A situation of logic contrived to illustrate a particular effect.

## 7-5 Simultaneity

Einstein explained his theories using hypothetical stories he referred to as **gedanken** or "thought" experiments. Gedanken experiments are contrived situations designed to highlight certain effects. Einstein used the following gedanken experiment to explain how the simultaneity of events is altered at high speeds.

A train moves along the tracks at 75% of the speed of light.[2] A woman we'll call Jane stands in the middle of one of its flatbed trailers. (See *Figure 7.7a.*) A man, Tom, stands on the side of the tracks, as shown in *Figure 7.7b.* As Jane passes by Tom, lightning bolts strike both the front and rear of Jane's flatbed car. Of course neither Tom nor Jane will know—or can know—that her car has been struck by lightning until the light from those strikes reaches them.

In the following, we will first consider the events from Tom's point of view—his frame of reference—(*Figure 7.7*). Then we will consider them from Jane's (*Figure 7.8*).

In *Figure 7.7b* the two lightning bolts strike. According to Tom, Jane moves forward into the light beam coming from the forward strike as shown in *Figure 7.7c.* Next light from both forward and rear strikes reaches Tom at the same time and he concludes that the bolts hit simultaneously as in *Figure 7.7d.* Finally, as shown In *Figure 7.7e,* light from the rear strike catches up to Jane, who has been moving away from it.

You don't easily dismiss being hit by lightning! Tom and Jane get together later and discuss what happened. Tom exclaims, "Wow, wasn't that amazing! When you passed me on the train, two lightning bolts hit simultaneously at the front and back of your car!" Jane agrees that the lightning strikes were amazing but disagrees that they hit simultaneously. "No", she says, "I was first hit in the front then I was hit in the back."

*Figures 7.8a-f* present the experience according to Jane. In *Figure 7.8b* the front of Jane's car is hit by lightning. In *Figure 7.8c* it is hit again but on the back. Standing in the center of the car, she sees the forward strike first

---

[2] Which is absurd for a train, of course. Einstein used trains because trains were the fastest means of transportation when he published his theory. Had Einstein developed this gedanken experiment today he might have talked about rockets or space ships instead, even though traveling at 75% the speed of light is absurd for them as well.

**Tom's Perspective**                    **Jane's Perspective**

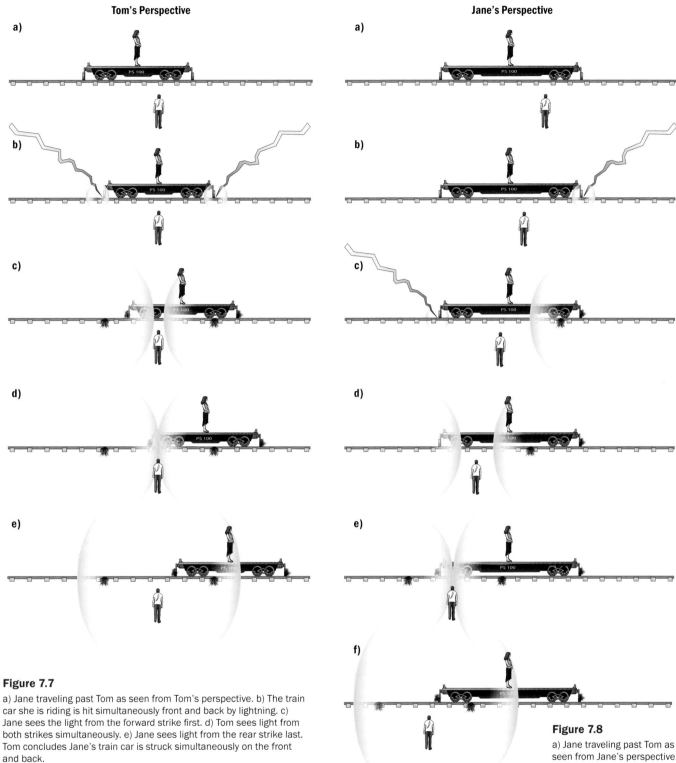

**Figure 7.7**

a) Jane traveling past Tom as seen from Tom's perspective. b) The train car she is riding is hit simultaneously front and back by lightning. c) Jane sees the light from the forward strike first. d) Tom sees light from both strikes simultaneously. e) Jane sees light from the rear strike last. Tom concludes Jane's train car is struck simultaneously on the front and back.

**Figure 7.8**

a) Jane traveling past Tom as seen from Jane's perspective. b) The train car she is riding is hit first on the front by lightning. c) Light from the front strike travels to Jane. d) Jane sees the light from the forward strike. At about this same time lightning strikes the rear of the train car. e) Tom sees light from both strikes simultaneously. f) Jane sees light from the rear strike last. Jane concludes her train car is struck first on the front and then on the back.

(*Figure 7.8d*) and then the rearward strike later (*Figure 7.8f*). But Jane can understand why Tom thinks the strikes are simultaneous (*Figure 7.8e*) because Tom, moving backwards relative to her, is moving away from the earlier strike and toward the later one.

Tom and Jane agree on two fundamental facts: 1) the light from the bolts reaches Jane at different times, and 2) the light from the bolts reaches Tom at the same time. But they disagree on who is moving toward or away from the light beams. This, in turn, means they disagree on what the other person should measure for the speed of those light beams. Tom thinks

Jane should measure a faster speed than "c" for the forward bolt because she is moving into it and a slower speed than "c" for the rearward one because she is moving away from it. Jane, in turn thinks Tom should measure a faster speed for the rearward bolt because he is moving toward it and a slower speed for the forward one because he is moving away from it.

Of course, both Tom and Jane are wrong about the other person's view of the speed of light. According to the second relativity postulate and the Michelson-Morley experiment, light from the forward and rearward bolts has the same constant speed for both Jane and Tom; their motion is irrelevant. Since Jane sees the light arriving at different times, she has no choice but to conclude that the lightning strikes were *not* simultaneous. The forward strike had to occur before the rearward one! And since Tom sees the light arriving at the same time, he can only conclude that the lightning strikes *were* simultaneous. The forward and rearward strikes had to occur at the same time!

A confused Tom and Jane seek advice from Albert Einstein's ghost. "Which of our perspectives is correct?" they ask.

"Both are correct," he replies. "By the first postulate of special relativity Tom's point of view is not superior to Jane's point of view, and Jane's is not superior to Tom's. Both views are equally valid."

Thus, *simultaneity is relative. Observers moving relative to each other will experience the same events at different times.* We stress that this is not magic, nor is it a psychological effect. There is an actual difference in when events occur in time.

## 7-6 Time Dilation

Einstein formulated a second gedanken experiment to explain how the flow of time slows for objects moving past us. In this story Jane, the lover of open-air railroad rides, is once again on a rail car moving at 75% the speed of light past Tom who is again beside the railroad tracks. This time Tom and Jane each hold identical "light clocks."

A light clock is two mirrors facing each other with a light beam bouncing back and forth between the two mirrors. Each bounce of the light pulse is one "tick" of the clock. Tom's light clock is shown in *Figure 7.9*. The distance between mirrors, labeled "D," is four meters. The time it takes light to travel that distance is $4 \div (3 \times 10^8) = 1.3 \times 10^{-8}$ seconds. So Tom and Jane both measure $1.3 \times 10^{-8}$ seconds between the ticks of their clocks.

Now Tom observes Jane's clock passing him at a speed of $0.75c$, as shown in *Figure 7.10*. From Tom's perspective, the light beam in Jane's clock travels in a diagonal path instead of up and down. So the light must go three meters horizontally as well as four meters vertically for a total distance of five meters between the mirrors, the hypotenuse of the triangle formed by the speeds of the light beam and the train car.

Now if the speed of light had been boosted by the train's speed, Tom would see the light beam in Jane's clock still take $1.3 \times 10^{-8}$ seconds to travel the distance between mirrors. But, of course, it doesn't. The speed of light Tom sees in Jane's clock is the same speed "c" as the light in Tom's clock. Therefore, Tom will see a longer

**Figure 7.9**

A stationary light clock. A pulse of light bounces back and forth between two mirrors spaced 4 meters apart. Each reflection of the light beam between the mirrors is a "tick" of the clock.

**STATIONARY**

D = 4 meters

**Figure 7.10**

For a light clock traveling at 0.75c, the beam travels 3 meters horizontally as well as 4 meters vertically, for a total "hypotenuse" distance of 5 meters. Because light always has the same speed, the time between ticks is greater. Therefore, moving light clocks are measured as running slow.

**IN MOTION**

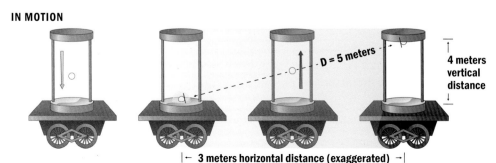

D = 5 meters

4 meters vertical distance

|← 3 meters horizontal distance (exaggerated) →|

time interval between ticks in Jane's clock than in his clock because the beam in Jane's clock travels an extra meter between ticks. The prediction from this gedanken experiment is that *we measure moving clocks running slow.* This effect is known as **time dilation**. We again stress that this is not an illusion, The difference is real— and testable.

An experiment was performed in 1931 in which "muons" were used to prove the reality of time dilation. Muons are sub-atomic particles that can be created in laboratories. Being unstable, they exist for only $2 \times 10^{-6}$ seconds, on average, before they change or "decay" into different particles. This average lifetime functions as a clock.

Cosmic rays, which are high speed particles from outer space, constantly bombard Earth's upper atmosphere creating fast-moving muons in the process. Some of these muons race down through the atmosphere toward Earth, moving at 99% of the speed of light.

Scientists transported muon-detection equipment to the top of a mountain to measure the number of muons created there by cosmic rays (*Figure 7.11*). Once they understood this number, they moved their equipment to the base of the mountain. The mountain was tall enough that only the fastest, longest-lived muons, five percent of those created at the top, should have made it to the bottom. Instead, more than half the muons arrived at the bottom intact. This large number of muons traveled the greater distance because their speed caused their time to slow down relative to our time. The average lifetime of $2 \times 10^{-6}$ seconds measured when they were at rest was lengthened to be many times longer than this and in that longer time interval they traveled to the mountain bottom before decaying.

## 7-7 Length Contraction

Consider again the gedanken experiment with the two lightning bolts, Tom and Jane might have tried to resolve the issue of simultaneity by measuring the distance between the scorch marks left on the tracks by the bolts. If the strikes were indeed simultaneous then the distance between the scorch marks would be exactly the length of the car. But if lightning struck the front first then the back, the distance

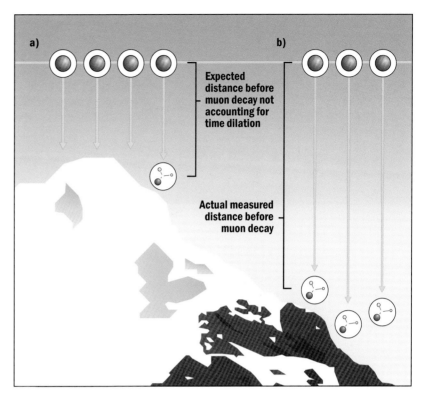

**Figure 7.11**

a) Muons created at the top of the atmosphere by cosmic rays travel down toward Earth at speeds near the speed of light.

b) Because of time dilation, they live longer when traveling than when at rest. More make it to the bottom of a tall mountain than would otherwise make it if there were no time dilation.

between marks would be less because the car moved between strikes.

When the distance is measured, it is found to be shorter than the car, but not as short as Jane expected. To make a long story short, The only way the simultaneous (for Tom) and front-then-back (for Jane) sequence of lightning strikes can be reconciled with the measured distance between scorch marks is if the rail car length is shorter when moving than it is when at rest! Jane, and anybody else riding with the car, does not perceive a shortening.

The conclusion then is that *when we measure the lengths of objects moving past us, we find their lengths to be shorter in the direction of their motion than if we measured their lengths while traveling with them.* This effect is called **length contraction.**

The evidence for length contraction is not just from gedanken experiments. A machine at Stanford University called a linear accelerator is capable of accelerating particles up to $0.99999999995c$ (*Figure 7.12*). At these speeds, the tube that the particles travel through contracts from 2 miles to just over one inch in length, from the particle's perspective! The

**Time Dilation:**

The slowing of a clock as its speed approaches the speed of light as measured by an observer not moving with the clock.

**Length Contraction:**

The shortening of an object along its direction of motion as its speed approaches the speed of light, as measured by an observer not moving with the object.

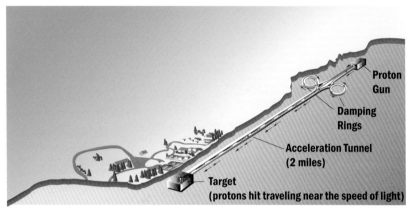

Proton
Gun

Damping
Rings

Acceleration Tunnel
(2 miles)

Target
(protons hit traveling near the speed of light)

**Figure 7.12**

At the Stanford Linear accelerator the special theory of relativity is used in accelerating particles up to 0.99999999995c.

design and engineering of the accelerator took this length contraction into account when the machine was constructed. Otherwise the linear accelerator would not work.

## 7-8 The Twin Paradox

Critics of the special theory of relativity concocted a gedanken experiment of their own, called the "twin paradox," to show what many thought was a weakness in the theory. Leaving Tom and Jane and their railroad car, the critics offered the story of two identical twin babies, Jane and Sally, who are sent to visit their grandparents, who live on the planet Alderaan, 10 light years from Jane and Sally's home here on Earth (*Figure 7.13*). However, the rocket ship only has room for one twin, so Sally makes the trip first while Jane waits her turn.

Jane watches Sally's rocket ship lift off and fly at 0.99*c* toward Alderaan. Jane, truly a precocious baby, knows that at these speeds Sally's clock runs very slow. So Jane expects that Sally will age slower than Jane. However, her equally intelligent twin Sally on board the rocket ship knows that it is valid to say Jane, and Earth, are

**Figure 7.13**

a) Baby Sally takes a trip to Alderaan 10 light years away at near the speed of light while Jane stays home.

b) As they travel Sally accelerates.

c) When Sally returns, they find that time for Sally, the twin who experienced acceleration, ran slow. Jane has aged 20 years while Sally is still a few months old.

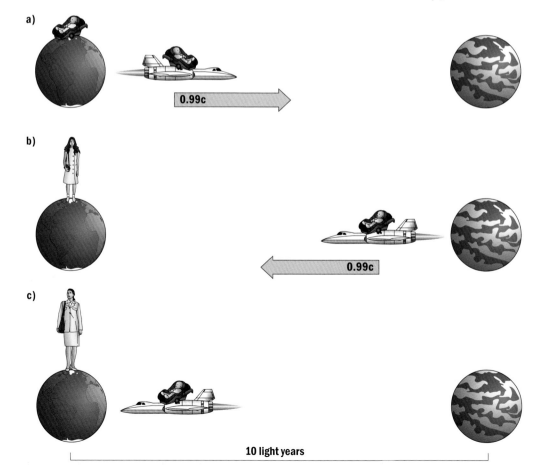

a)

0.99c

b)

0.99c

c)

10 light years

## ALBERT EINSTEIN

Albert Einstein is arguably the greatest scientist who ever lived. He was born in Ulm, Germany, but received his early schooling in Munich. He did not show much proficiency at school work and rebelled against the regimentation of German education. One of his teachers suggested he drop out of class because he was so disruptive. One of his uncles tried to help him by giving him private instruction in the rudiments of algebra, which seemed to arouse his interest in mathematics.

Albert Einstein, 1879–1955.

Einstein's family was Jewish, but did not practice their religion. The young Einstein went through a period of intense interest in Judaism, but became disillusioned with organized religion. He later wrote:

> Suspicion against every kind of authority grew out of this experience . . . an attitude which has never again left me, even though later on, because of a better insight into the causal connections, it lost some of its original poignancy. (Albert Einstein, Philosopher-Scientist, New York: Harper, 1945, p. 5)

But Einstein was not necessarily atheistic. Many of his later statements would be sprinkled with references to God: "God does not play dice!" "God is subtle, but He is not malicious!" In fact, a colleague, Niels Bohr, once asked Einstein to "Stop telling God what to do!" Einstein's God is best described as a pantheistic awe for the harmony and order he found in nature.

At the age of sixteen, Einstein decided to study electrical engineering at the Swiss Federal Polytechnic University in Zurich, but he failed the entrance examination. To prepare for a second try, he enrolled at the high school at Aarau. When the university finally admitted him, his interest had shifted to theoretical physics. He skipped class to study on his own the

Einstein took violin lessons as a boy at the insistence of his mother. As a youth he disliked the lessons and not long after quit taking them. He returned to playing the violin as an adult and came to enjoy Mozart's violin sonatas.

writings of Ludwig Boltzman, James Clerk Maxwell, Herman Helmholtz, and others. He relied on the meticulous notes of his friend and fellow student, Marcel Grossmann, to prepare for examinations.

He received his Ph.D. in 1905 from the University of Zurich and intended to teach, but could not find an academic position. He then took a job with the patent office in Berne where he made preliminary evaluations of patent applications.

The work was not taxing, so Einstein had time to think and to write about subjects far removed from his bureaucratic job responsibilities. In 1905, which may be the most remarkable year in the history of science, the recently graduated, completely unknown patent clerk published four papers. Each contained a great discovery Einstein had made in the field of physics: the creation of the special theory of relativity, the establishment of the equivalence between mass and energy, the explanation of Brownian motion, and the photon theory of light.

Einstein was a major force in the development of theories of the atom and how captured electrons behaved. Although he never was in complete agreement with the scientists of his day on all aspects of atomic theory, his questions developed and refined atomic theory as it is now generally accepted. His greatest intellectual triumph probably came with his publication of the general theory of relativity, which first appeared in print in 1916. As a theory of gravity, it boldly and accurately predicted that gravity was the manifestation of a curvature of space and time.

A young Albert Einstein

From 1932 until his death in 1955, Einstein lived in the United States; he hoped to discover a "unified field theory" that would unify the laws of physics under a single model.

moving at $0.99c$ away from Alderaan, and therefore Sally should see Jane's clock running very slow too. In other words, Sally thinks that Jane will age slower than Sally. A paradox! Both see the other's clock running slow. How can that be?

The story has two frames of reference: Earth and the rocket ship. Earth is an inertial frame during the entire trip. The rocket ship is an inertial frame when gliding between planets. However, the rocket ship is a non-inertial frame when it accelerates to take off and decelerates to land both on Alderaan and on Earth and non-inertial frames are the realm of the general theory of relativity, not the special theory. So Jane, on Earth, and Sally, in the rocket ship, do not have equivalent experiences and we have to invoke the general theory of relativity to understand whose time really runs slow.

Twenty years pass by. Sally's rocket ship makes the trip to the planet, turns around, and returns to Earth. Jane, now twenty years old, anxiously awaits the reunion with her twin sister. The rocket lands and out crawls baby Sally, only a few months older than when she left! Although both saw the other's clock run slow, Sally, the twin who experienced the acceleration, is the younger one on their reunion.

The effect of acceleration on time was confirmed by J. C. Hafele and R. E. Keating in October, 1971. Hafele and Keating flew four highly accurate atomic beam clocks on regularly scheduled commercial jet flights eastward around the world. It was expected that the flying clocks, compared with reference clocks at the U. S. Naval Observatory, should have lost 40 billionths of a second. The lost time was observed just as predicted.

Surveying and navigation have been revolutionized by the global positioning system (GPS). GPS receivers calculate positions from timing signals sent from high-orbiting, fast-moving satellites. These receivers use relativity theory to compensate for the time dilation of the satellites. Without this correction they could not generate the highly accurate positions that they do.

**Spacetime:**

Space and time connected together into one continuum by the special theory of relativity.

## 7-9 Space and Time

Time dilation and length contraction seem like science fiction. Are space and time really that flexible and dependent on speed? Yes, but

there is more to the story. An insightful perspective on length contraction and time dilation was given by Hermann Minkowski (1864–1909), a German mathematician and instructor to Albert Einstein. Minkowski found that the theory of special relativity could best be understood if space and time were bound together in a four-dimensional space called **space-time**.

As stated in Chapter 3, space and time are intertwined. Think about the Pythagorean theorem, which you studied in high school geometry. Following the symbols used in *Figure 7.14a*, the Pythagorean theorem says:

$$\mathbf{a}^2 + \mathbf{b}^2 = \mathbf{s}^2$$

where **s** is the length of a line segment and **a** and **b** are its projection onto the **x** and **y** axes.

Now rotate the same line segment **s** on the page as shown in *Figure 7.14b*. The projection of line segment **s** onto the **x** and **y** axes now has new values which we will label **a'** and **b'**. The values for **a'** and **b'** are different than they are for **a** and **b**, but it is still true that

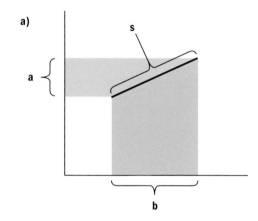

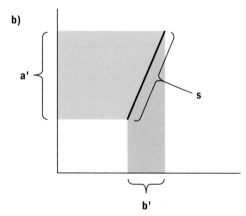

**Figure 7.14**

The line segments in a) and b) have the same length, s. In b) the line segment is rotated so that more of its length is measured in the vertical axis and less in the horizontal axis than in a). By analogy, when an object moves at high speed, more of its aspect is measured in time and less of its aspect is measured in space.

$$\mathbf{a'}^2 + \mathbf{b'}^2 = \mathbf{s}^2$$

In other words, the length of **s** does not change just because we rotated it.

A similar relation holds true for measurements in space-time. If we measure the spatial separation, **l**, and the time separation, **t** between two **events**, we can form a "hypotenuse" of sorts in space-time by writing

$$\mathbf{l}^2 - (c\mathbf{t})^2 = \mathbf{s}^2$$

When we measure an object moving past us, we will get different values for its length and time than when it is at rest with respect to us. But this formula tells us that its length and time will change together such as to keep the value of **s** the same. In this sense, time and space are interrelated and faster speeds can be thought of as causing a rotation of sorts in space-time.

The interconnection of space and time was a bold, imaginative leap. Without it there was no hope of reconciling the two postulates of special relativity. Building upon it, this interconnection soon led to the idea of black holes and big bang cosmology which we will encounter in Chapters 33 and 34.

# 7 STUDY GUIDE

## Chapter Framework

### A. Introduction
1. Newton's Laws of Motion break down at high speeds

### B. Motion and Relativity
1. Motion is only defined with respect to a reference frame
2. There is no such thing as absolute motion

### C. Motion Symmetry
1. Inertial frames of reference
2. Non-inertial frames of reference

### D. Galilean Relativity and the Speed of Light
1. Michelson/Morley experiment
2. Light does not obey Galilean Relativity

### E. The Special Theory of Relativity
1. Two assumptions
   *a. Motion symmetry*
   *b. Speed of light constant*
2. Motion, space, and time are related

### F. Predictions of Relativity
1. Simultaneity is relative to motion
2. Moving clocks run slow
   *a. Muon experiment*
3. Moving objects' lengths contract

### G. The Twin Paradox
1. Time really slows down for the twin who accelerated
   *a. Atomic clocks on airplanes*

### H. Space and Time
1. Intertwined into space-time

## Comprehension

### Matching

a. Relativity

b. Non-inertial frame of reference

c. Inertial frame of reference

d. Gedanken experiment

e. Motion symmetry

f. General Theory of Relativity

g. Special Theory of Relativity

h. Galilean Relativity

1. _____ An object or location that is experiencing no acceleration.
2. _____ An object or location that is undergoing an acceleration.
3. _____ The observation that the laws of nature are the same for all inertial frames of reference.
4. _____ The theory that considers non-inertial frames of reference.
5. _____ The notion that separate speed vectors can be added together in a "straight-forward" way to form a total velocity vector.
6. _____ The idea that motion is only defined relative to other objects, which may have their own motion.
7. _____ The theory that describes how nature behaves when encountering high speeds.
8. _____ A situation of logic contrived to illustrate a particular effect.

### True/False
1. _____ The laws of nature remain the same for any inertial frame of reference.
2. _____ We call any object moving without acceleration an inertial frame of reference.
3. _____ A laboratory on Earth's surface is a true inertial frame of reference.
4. _____ Motion symmetry only works for inertial frames of reference.
5. _____ "Absolute motion" only exists in outer space.
6. _____ According to Einstein, absolute space and time don't exist.
7. _____ Light does not obey Galilean Relativity.
8. _____ The speed of light in a vacuum has a constant value.
9. _____ The faster a clock moves, the faster its time runs.
10. _____ An astronaut in a spaceship moving near the speed of light will observe all of the objects within the spaceship to be shorter than they were before the spaceship took off.

### Fill in the Blank
1. When traveling near the speed of light, length _____ and time _____.
2. Time and space are intertwined into what is called the _____.
3. Newton's laws are insufficient for objects traveling at _____ speeds.
4. The two types of motion are _____ and _____.
5. True inertial frames of reference do not exist on Earth's surface because Earth is _____.
6. As objects move past us at high speeds, we see more of their _____ aspect and less of their _____ aspect.

## Analysis

1. Non-inertial frames of reference
   a) have no unbalanced forces acting on them.
   b) feel an unbalanced force.
   c) accelerate.
   d) both (b) and (c).

2. Which of the following is in accelerated motion?
   a) A spaceship that isn't experiencing a net force.
   b) A merry-go-round that is spinning at a constant rate.
   c) A hippopotamus sliding straight across a frictionless surface.
   d) None of the above.

3. You are traveling in a straight line down the freeway with your cruise control set at 55 mph. Assuming you can choose any reference point you please, which of the following viewpoint(s) would be scientifically legitimate?
   a) You are at rest.
   b) You are moving forward at 55 mph.
   c) The freeway is moving backward at 55 mph.

d) You are speeding up from 0 to 55.

e) All of the above.

f) Only (a), (b), and (c).

4. How does the chapter define "high speed"?

   a) Faster than the speed of sound.

   b) Faster than a speeding bullet.

   c) Faster than the speed of light.

   d) Slightly slower than the speed of light.

5. In what direction do moving objects contract?

   a) In all directions.

   b) In the direction perpendicular to the direction of motion.

   c) In the direction of motion.

   d) Moving objects expand, not contract.

6. From the scientists' reference frame, the muon experiment demonstrated

   a) time dilation.      c) mass increase.

   b) length contraction.      d) simultaneity.

7. What are the two assumptions of the Special Theory of Relativity?

8. What are some of the predictions of the Special Theory of Relativity?

9. What is the difference between the Special and the General Theories of Relativity?

10. What is a "light clock"?

## Synthesis

1. You are enjoying an enthralling Physical Science lecture in a windowless room when your professor insists that the entire classroom is moving straight toward the Pacific coast at 350 mph.

   a) Is there any experiment you could perform to prove your professor wrong? Why?

   b) Now the professor says the classroom is spinning at 60 rpm. Can you prove your professor wrong? Why?

   c) Name and state the scientific principle on which you based your answers.

2. A railcar travels at 3/4 the speed of light, and your friend happens to be on it. As you stand on the ground watching your friend pass by, lightning bolts strike both the front and the back of your friend's railcar.

   a) If he saw the lightning bolts strike the front and the back of the railcar simultaneously, you will disagree. What do you say happened? Why? Note: this is different from the situation in the book.

   b) To find out who is right, you and your friend meet on the ground and decide to measure the distance between the scorch marks and compare it to your measurement of the length of the car. Are your measurements what you expected it to be? Are your friend's measurements what he expected it to be?

   c) What does the distance between the scorch marks illustrate about the lengths of moving objects?

   d) Who was right about the timing of the lightning strikes? What can you conclude about events that are simultaneous in one reference frame?

3. Your friend is on the railcar again traveling past you at 3/4 the speed of light. You are both holding identical light clocks.

   a) From your perspective, how does the distance between the mirrors of your friend's light clock compare to the distance between the mirrors of your own?

   b) How fast is light traveling between your mirrors? How fast is light traveling between your friend's mirrors?

   c) Based on the distance between the mirrors and the speed at which the light is traveling, what can you conclude about your friend's light clock?

   d) From your friend's perspective, does the distance between her mirrors appear to be any different than normal? Does time seem to be passing at a different pace than it normally does?

4. A disgruntled co-worker impatiently orders you to "get moving." You kindly respond that you are already moving. Support your argument by explaining the relativity of motion.

5. If the idea of motion symmetry is true, why do some people experience motion sickness? Why is it more common to get sea sick than car sick?

6. Suppose you're in a bus traveling at 60 mph. You throw an orange toward the front of the bus at 20 mph. Then you send a light beam toward the front of the bus at the speed of light.

   a) From the perspective of a pedestrian observing the bus from the sidewalk, how fast was the orange traveling?

   b) From the perspective of the same pedestrian, how fast is the light beam moving?

   c) What can you conclude about the applicability of Galilean relativity?

7. Even though Newton's laws of motion hold perfectly in everyday life, they become increasingly inaccurate as speeds approach the speed of light. Does this mean that Newton's laws are not "true laws of nature"? What arguments can you make that say they are true laws? Which arguments can you make that say they are not true laws?*

*(Note that at everyday speeds the laws of motion as stated in the Special Theory of Relativity simplify to Newton's laws of motion.)

# Conservation Laws

## 8

## LEARN

- The Laws of Conservation regarding:

  - mass

  - atomic mass number

  - charge

  - linear momentum

  - angular momentum

  - energy

- Which of the above quantities are conserved in a given situation.

- How to apply the appropriate laws to predict the outcomes of simple situations.

To make cookies, you must know what type of ingredients you'll need. And just knowing that cookies are made of flour, butter, sugar, and eggs, etc., isn't enough. As a cook, you also need to know how much of each ingredient to mix together to have them come out right and in the right amount. If you use a recipe you know how many cookies you'll get each time because your recipe allows you to predict exact quantities.

Similarly, one of the ultimate goals of science is to predict outcomes quantitatively. To do this, the scientist needs to write quantitative equations much like cookie recipes. This means it is necessary to identify measurable properties of matter, such as mass, charge, etc., that stay the same regardless of circumstance. Doing so allows you to write an equation stating that these properties are equal before and after a physical process. Any quantity that remains constant through a process is called a **conserved quantity**.

Some conserved quantities are more interesting than others. The equation "2 = 2," while

true and easy to demonstrate, isn't very useful, but equations like "1 can of juice concentrate + 3 cans water = 1 quart juice" are very informative. This type of equation relates conserved quantities as they are transformed or transferred in physical processes. Conserved quantities allow us to write equations where the two sides are not trivially identical, yet are still equal.

In this chapter we define several important conserved quantities, explain ways in which they can change without varying the total, and discuss why they are important in science.

## 8-1 Conservation of Mass

One basic conservation law has already been hinted at in the paragraphs above. Every time a cook combines 2 cups of flour, 1 cup of butter, 1 cup of sugar, and 1 large egg,[1] the same amount of cookie dough will be produced, and the same number of cookies (3 dozen) can be

made. If the cook accurately weighs the ingredients and then weighs the dough, it will be found that the dough weighs exactly the same amount as the combined weight of the ingredients before they were mixed together. Weigh the finished cookies, however, and their combined weight will be found to be slightly less than the total weight of the dough, even when every visible smear of mix has been scraped from the bowl and added to the dough.

Careful observation of cookies fresh from the oven will show some steam rising from them (*Figure 8.1*). If the cook could carefully gather

**Conserved Quantity:**

Unchanging in time. A quantity is "conserved" if the amount of that quantity does not change in time, even though processes may be changing its form.

**Figure 8.1**
The steam rising from the cookies consists of water molecules that were originally part of the cookie dough.

[1] For better sugar cookies, we suggest adding 1 tsp vanilla and 1/2 tsp almond extract. If you're using unsalted butter, add 1/4 tsp of salt.

95

all of the steam together and add its weight to the weight of the cookies, the total weight would once again be the same as the weight of the original ingredients. Conduct the same experiment with a recipe for peanut-butter cookies or macaroons or peach upside-down cake and you get the same result. The cook has discovered an important law of conservation of mass of cookie and cake ingredients: The total mass of the ingredients in each recipe will be equal to the total mass of the resulting cookies or cake, plus a small amount of steam. (As before, we are inferring mass by measuring weight. They are not the same of course, but are interchangeable here because they are proportional.)

This basic principle extends far beyond the admittedly fascinating study and practical use of cookies. It turns out that in most physical processes[2], regardless of the materials or the heat or time involved, if a careful accounting is made for all the mass the process started with, the total mass in the end product will be the same. Mass can change form, or transfer from one object or place to another, but the total amount does not change. This concept is called the law of *conservation of mass.*

The physical process can be simple, like the flow of water. Suppose a gardener streams water from a hose at a rate of 1/4-liter per second. Then he decides to spray the water over his plants by putting his thumb over the end of the hose. He partially blocks the hose end, the water speeds up, and it sprays farther as expected. In this process his thumb didn't create or destroy water; the same 1/4-liter worth of mass comes out the smaller opening each second. When the opening was restricted, pressure built up making the water speed increase until the flow rate was the same as before. The law of conservation of mass tells us exactly how much faster the water had to move to keep the flow rate the same.

Conservation of mass is used regularly to understand chemical processes. The *Carbon Cycle* is a prime example (*Figure 8.2*). Animals release carbon dioxide into the air when they exhale and fossil fuels release carbon dioxide into the atmosphere when they burn. Plants extract atmospheric carbon dioxide as part of their metabolism. A growing tree takes in car-

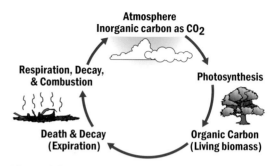

**Figure 8.2**

The Carbon Cycle is an example of conservation of mass. Trees do not create wood out of nothing, but convert CO2 and water into new wood.

bon dioxide through its leaves and water and minerals from the ground through its root system and recombines them to make new wood. In this process the mass of the carbon dioxide is neither created or destroyed, just transformed. If the amount of carbon dioxide released into the air is equal to the amount being stored by plants, the level of carbon dioxide in the atmosphere will remain constant. If burning fossil fuels releases more carbon dioxide than plants can absorb, the amount of carbon dioxide in the atmosphere increases.

This brings us to another interesting point. It isn't just the total mass that is conserved in the carbon cycle. The total amount of carbon also stays the same. Whether the carbon is contained in carbon dioxide molecules, wood molecules, or transformed into nearly pure carbon as charcoal, the total amount of carbon doesn't change. This suggests another conservation rule dealing with the building blocks of matter.

## 8-2  Conservation of Fundamental Particles

In Chapter 1 some fundamental building blocks of matter were introduced and briefly discussed. A primary aim of science is and has always been to discover the smallest pieces of matter from which all other matter derives.

The standard procedure in this quest is to smash matter into tiny pieces with increasingly high-tech hammers such as particle accelerators. (*Figure 8.3.*) The assumption is that as the hammers get bigger, at some point the pieces flying off won't get any smaller. When that happens we pick through the debris, find the smallest, unbreakable particles, and identify them as the fundamental building blocks. Once these

---

[2] Note that we said most, not all. This means that there are some situations where mass changes. We will discuss these more in the next chapter.

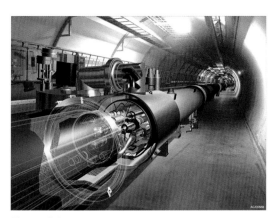

**Figure 8.3**
The current matter-smashing hammer of choice is known as a particle accelerator. Electric forces are used to accelerate groups of atoms up to speeds very close to the speed of light. Two or more groups are then sent slamming into each other head on. This is a diagram of the Large Hadron Collider at CERN. (Courtesy CERN)(See also Figure 7.12.)

smallest constituent parts are known, their total number should be a conserved quantity, always staying the same through any process.

Carbon is made of one type of atom and the total mass of carbon does not change in chemical processes. Since the mass of carbon is carried by its atoms, this means the number of carbon atoms does not change in chemical processes. The same is true of any of the 92 naturally occurring atoms. When the "hammer" used to break matter up is a chemical process, the total number of atoms of any given type remains the same. It is a cornerstone rule of chemistry that there must always be the same number of atoms of each element at the beginning and end of a chemical reaction. For this reason atoms were historically considered to be fundamental particles.

However, there is no law of conservation of atoms, because when the forces are large enough, in atomic bombs for example, atoms can be broken down into protons, neutrons, and electrons. For a while, scientists thought that the protons, neutrons, and electrons might be the fundamental particles. With electrons, at least, this still appears to be true. No matter how hard our highest-tech scientific hammer hits an electron, it resolutely remains an electron. However, extreme force will transform protons and neutrons.

Experiments in smashing matter have led to the discovery of many likely fundamental particles. These fall naturally into two types or classes. The first type, the **leptons**, includes the electron and a few other electron-like particles.

## ATOMIC HISTORY

The word "atom" comes from the Greek *atomos* which means "indivisible." Ancient Greek philosophers came up with the idea of a smallest particle and coined the term, although they had very little idea what this smallest particle was. Over several thousand years alchemists made a diligent effort to transform lead into gold, assuming that because the two metals had similar properties they had to be made up of the same stuff. With the Renaissance and its accompanying systematic approach to observation, scientists of that era found that certain materials could not be changed. Those materials that couldn't be broken down any further were called "elements." It was assumed that each element had to be made of a different fundamental particle, and the word "atom" was taken to describe these particles.

One of these is the muon introduced in the previous chapter as being produced by high energy cosmic rays striking Earth's upper atmosphere. Another is the tauon. Both muons and tauons are just like electrons only much more massive.

The lepton class includes three types of a particle called a neutrino. Neutrinos have no charge, very little mass, and are very hard to detect because they pass unchanged through almost all materials.

Each of these six particles has an anti-particle cousin (see the box on anti-matter) making a total of 12 leptons in all. The anti-particle of the electron has its own name, the "positron".

Any lepton can be changed into a different lepton so the number of individual leptons is not always conserved. But the total number of leptons is conserved. In other words, there is a law known as the conservation of lepton number which says that any lepton can turn into any other, but the total number of leptons will always stay the same.

The second class of fundamental particles is the **quark**. Quarks cling so tightly to

**Lepton:**
Electrons and other electron-like particles such as muons.

**Quark:**
The elementary particles of which protons and neutrons consist. A proton and a neutron each consist of three quarks.

## ANTI-MATTER

Since the 1930s it has been recognized that for each kind of atomic particle, there is another kind of particle—an "anti-particle"—corresponding to it. The anti-particle has charge and other features with names like "spin" and "parity" that are opposite from the particle. These must be taken into account (e.g., as negative numbers) in conservation laws. However, all masses are positive, except for the photon (Section 11–5) which has zero mass. A particle and a corresponding anti-particle may be created together from energy if there is enough equivalent mass in the energy for both of them.

other quarks that it has never been possible to separate a quark completely from a proton or neutron. Even so there is strong evidence that every proton is composed of three quarks, and each neutron is also composed of three quarks. Under the right conditions, a quark can change into another type of quark turning a neutron into a proton and vice-versa. However, as with the leptons, the total number of quarks does not change. Because physical processes cannot pull or pry quarks out of their protons and neutrons, this has the added effect that the number of protons added to the number of neutrons, known as the **atomic mass number**, does not change. This conservation law is known as *conservation of atomic mass number*.[3]

**Atomic Mass Number:**

The total number of protons + neutrons in the nucleus of an atom.

**Figure 8.4**
Rubbing a balloon on your head does not create charge; it simply redistributes existing charge.

### 8–3 Conservation of Charge

Just as mass is the property of matter that reacts to one fundamental force (gravity), charge is the property of matter that reacts with electromagnetic forces. And, just like mass, total charge is conserved. If you add up the total amount of positive charge and subtract the total amount of negative charge, that number will remain the same before and after any physical process.

This should not come as a big surprise after reading Chapter 4. When you scuff across the carpet in your tennis shoes, you are not really creating charge but just moving existing charge around, sometimes with mildly shocking results. All matter, including the tennis shoes and carpet, is made of protons, neutrons, and electrons. The neutrons have no charge, but both protons and electrons are charged particles.

Electrons are found around the outside of atoms and are transferred fairly easily from one object to another. So scuffing tennis shoes across carpet does not create electrical charge, the rubber on the bottom of the shoes is stealing electrons from the wool or nylon in the carpet. The shoes and the person wearing them inherit a negative charge from the extra electrons taken up during the scuffing, while the carpet is left with a positive charge. The total number of electrons doesn't change from conservation of elec-

tron-like particles, the total number of protons + neutrons doesn't change from conservation of atomic mass number, and the total charge is still the same.

### 8–4 Conservation of Linear Momentum

Newton's First Law states that when there are no unbalanced forces on an object, its velocity will not change. If it is at rest, it stays that way. If it is moving, it keeps moving in a straight line at a constant speed. So velocity in the absence of forces is conserved. But this is a fairly boring situation.

We can make life more interesting by having our chosen object explode! In an explosion, the forces all come from within the object, specifically, the different pieces pushing against each other. Newton's Third Law says the pieces push against each other with equal and opposite forces, so the total directional force on all the pieces together is still zero. Newton's First Law still applies for the object as a whole, and the total "motion" of all of the pieces added together cannot change (*Figure 8.5*).

While it doesn't seem necessary to define what we mean by the "motion" of a single object, it is more important to define what we mean when we talk about the motion of a group of

---

[3] For those who find it interesting enough to pursue , please see http://www.fnal.gov/pub/inquiring/matter/madeof/ for a fine discussion of the standard model of matter written by scientists at Fermi National Lab and geared toward the general public.

**Figure 8.5**

When a firecracker explodes in midair, the path of the center of the explosion is exactly the same as the path the firecracker would have followed if it had never exploded. Since there are no horizontal forces, the central point of the remnant pieces keeps moving at a constant horizontal speed.

fragments of different masses moving in different directions at different speeds. In this situation the quantity that stays the same is the mass times velocity. If the mass of each fragment is multiplied by the fragment's velocity and then added together, taking into account the direction, that sum will be exactly equal to the mass of the original object times its velocity.

This quantity is called an object's **linear momentum**. As long as there are no net external forces applied, the total momentum of an object or set of objects that interact with each other is conserved.

Conservation of momentum is often used to determine the speed and direction two objects were traveling before a collision or to predict the speed and direction of objects after a collision. In the instance of a car crash, the vehicles skid to a stop after the collision. By measuring the skid marks, police can determine the speed and direction the cars were going immediately after they hit. Conservation of momentum may then allow them to reconstruct how

fast and in what direction the cars were moving before the crash.

Pool sharks use the same principles in reverse. They have direct control of the speed and direction of their cue ball before a collision, and because of conservation of momentum, this means that with practice they are able to predict the motion of the ball or balls that they hit after the collision (*Figure 8.6*). However, few pool sharks learned about conservation of momentum in school.

## 8-5 Conservation of Linear Momentum at High Speeds

It has already been pointed out that Newton's Second Law, **F=ma**, doesn't work at high speeds. Therefore, it makes sense to take a good look at what happens to conservation of momentum when objects are moving at speeds close to the speed of light.

Suppose two bored astronauts decide to pass the time by blowing things up. One of their

**Linear Momentum:**

An object's mass times its velocity. Measures the amount of motion in a straight line.

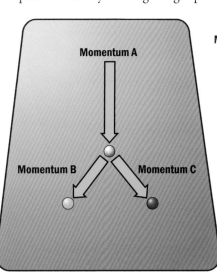

Momentum A = Momentum B + Momentum C

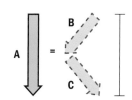

**Figure 8.6**

The momentum of the cue ball before it collides with the other balls is exactly the same as the total momentum of the balls after the collision.

explosions succeeds in sending two equal fragments off in exactly opposite directions at ¾ the speed of light, one heading towards the front and the other towards the back of their ship. (*Figure 8.7a.*) Since the total momentum to start with was zero, and the ending momentums cancel out because one velocity is to the right and one is to the left, momentum is conserved, according to the astronauts.

Now, to see how motion near the speed of light affects things, we need to look at what happens from the point of view of the space shuttle's ground control crew on Earth. Let's say that the astronauts' ship is traveling away from Earth at ¾ the speed of light. Therefore the object was moving ¾ the speed of light before the explosion. After the explosion, ½ of it isn't moving at all in Earth's frame of reference (¾ the speed of light forwards + ¾ backwards is zero). That means if there were no changes to the law, in order to conserve momentum, the remaining piece needs to be moving forwards at 1½ times the speed of light.

There is a problem with this answer: nothing can travel faster than the speed of light. As you well know the beam of a flashlight shined by the astronauts has the same speed to the astronauts as to the ground crew. The second half of the hurtling object is moving slower than light speed according to the astronauts, so it must be moving slower than light speed according to ground control, too. As it turns out, if ground control measured the speed of the exploded object before it crashed into some vital part of the astronauts' equipment, they would find it to be going 96% of the speed of light.

Because the speed of the second half of the object is too small for momentum conservation, it appears that linear momentum is not conserved at high speeds. After all, **F = ma** is not conserved. However, in this case a basic assumption of science we have already studied demands that it still be conserved even at relativistic speeds.

A mathematician and contemporary of Einstein named Emmy Noether (1882–1935) showed that conservation of momentum is a direct result of position symmetry which, as taught in Chapter 1, is one of the underlying assumptions of all science. If momentum isn't conserved, then position symmetry would not hold true, and scientific law staying the same from place to place would be challenged. This made physicists very willing to accept the idea that conservation of momentum holds at high speeds and look for a solution.

So how might the description of the motion of the pieces of the exploded object change to preserve conservation of momentum? The problem can be solved if the mass of the second half has increased because of its speed. In other words, an object's mass depends upon speed, instead of being a constant. In fact, if we assume that momentum is conserved we can, from that assumption, work out exactly how the mass depends upon speed. It turns out that mass increases with speed by the same factor that we found in calculating length contraction or time dilation.

You may properly object that our earlier law of conservation of mass is now violated. Not to worry; all will be set right in Chapter 9.

Experiments in devices called cyclotrons, which can accelerate charged particles up to speeds very close to the speed of light, verified this. The faster the particles move, the more

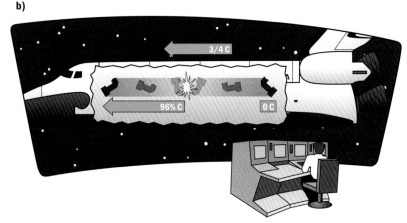

**Figure 8.7**

a) From the point of view of the astronauts there is no momentum before the explosion, and equal and opposite momentum after.

b) From the point of view of Ground Control, the explosion stops 1/2 of the object but the other half is not moving twice as fast.

**EMMY NOETHER**

Emmy Noether was born in Germany in 1882, the daughter of a math professor. She wanted to follow in her father's footsteps, but none of the universities of her day would allow a woman to enroll as a student.

After auditing courses for two years, she took and passed the entrance exams for the doctoral program. A year later, the university where her father taught agreed to accept her as a student in good standing. She received her doctorate in mathematics in 1907.

Emmy taught classes for free under her father's and other professor's names for several years, until being granted official status as a professor in 1919. In 1933, when the Nazis came to power, she fled Germany and came to the United States where she taught at Bryn Mawr and Princeton until her premature death from illness two years later.

force is required to accelerate them. Because mass is the ratio of force to acceleration, this means that the mass has to be increasing. The relativistic increase in mass not only solves conservation of momentum at high speeds, it also explains the apparent breakdown of Newton's second law. We will discuss how the mass increases in the next chapter.

## 8-6 Conservation of Angular Momentum

Most small children have discovered that linear motion is not the only type of conserved motion. When riding a bicycle, they quickly learn that it is easier to keep upright when the tires turn faster. Or that tops will stay balanced on a point only if they are spinning. There is a quantity associated with spinning or "angular motion" that also is conserved.

This quantity is called **angular momentum**. For a single object orbiting about a point, like the Moon orbiting around Earth, the angular momentum depends on the mass of the object, how fast it is moving, and how far it is from the center of its orbit. The equation is

**Angular momentum = mass × speed × radius**

The same relationship works for spinning tires where most of the mass is at the same distance from the hub. With more complicated objects, like tops, where different parts of the objects are at different distances from the cen-

ter of rotation, it is necessary to add the angular momentum values at different positions to figure out its total value.

If there are no external forces speeding up or slowing down the rotation, a spinning object will keep the same angular momentum. So anything that is spinning will tend to keep spinning in the same direction. This is why a moving bicycle is so much easier to keep upright. For the bicycle to fall over, the direction its tires spin has to change from a vertical plane to a horizontal plane. Just as it is hard for a car with large linear momentum to turn a corner, it is hard for a bicycle wheel with large angular momentum to tilt downward. Balancing on a moving bike, therefore, is not that hard but balancing on a stationary bicycle is quite a trick.

Another consequence of conservation of angular momentum comes from the way both speed and distance play into the equation. Imagine a ball on a string spinning in a circle (a tether ball is close enough.) What happens if the string is pulled in to make it shorter? In terms of conservation of angular momentum, mass × speed × radius of the circle must stay constant. If the radius of the circle gets smaller, the speed must increase to compensate and the ball will speed up. Also, the distance the ball must travel to make a complete revolution is now smaller. So as the string gets shorter, the ball spins around faster.

This effect is particularly useful for ice skaters, gymnasts, divers, and participants in any other sport in which there is a lot of spinning

**Angular Momentum:**

Angular momentum is a quantity that measures the amount of rotational motion an object has.

or flipping (*Figure 8.8*). If a diver needs to speed up her rotation to enter the water properly, she pulls her arms and legs into a tuck position to bring them closer to the center of rotation. To slow rotation down, she pushes her arms and legs out into a layout position. The change in speed can be even more dramatic in figure skating. Skaters often enter a spin with their arms and legs extended out away from their body. They then pull their legs close together and their arms in tight against their torsos and naturally spin at a much faster speed just from conservation of angular momentum.

## 8-7  Conservation of Energy

We have talked about how momentum is conserved when a physical process plays out naturally with no external forces involved. The last conservation law we present in this chapter applies even when external forces are present.

Everyone knows that when a rubber ball is thrown hard enough at a wall, the ball will bounce back in the opposite direction. The ball's forward momentum is not conserved in this case because an external force—from the wall—acts on the ball reversing its direction. However, the ball bounces off at very nearly the same speed it traveled before hitting, so something stayed the same, or very nearly so. Similarly, if a rubber ball is dropped on a hard surface, it will bounce back to almost the same height from which it was dropped. Its speed and direction both changed during this bounce, but again something stayed almost the same for it to return to almost the same point from which it fell. This "something" quantity that is conserved in both of these examples, and in all experiments we've yet been able to devise, is called the "energy."

Conservation of energy—that energy can be neither created nor destroyed—is an

**Figure 8.8**

Because angular momentum is conserved, divers can control their rotational velocity by tucking their limbs. The frames are taken at equal intervals. Note that in the first four frames the diver is in a "pike" position and completes 1/2 of a revolution between frames. When he stretches out, he only makes 1/3 of a revolution in the same amount of time.

extremely powerful law. Energy in it various forms must be carefully defined and tracked; but once this is done, we find no exceptions to the law whatsoever. This law—sometimes called the First Law of Thermodynamics—is, to our knowledge, absolutely universal, more so than Newton's second law, which, as we have seen, has had to be modified. Because of its universal applicability, conservation of energy is used extensively in all of the science disciplines and throughout the rest of this book. Rules defining energy and how it is transferred are so important we have devoted the entire next chapter to them.

*Science has found that nothing can disappear without a trace. Nature does not know extinction. All it knows is transformation.*

Wernher von Braun

# 8 STUDY GUIDE

## Chapter Framework

**A. Introduction**
1. Conserved quantity

**B. Conservation of Mass**
1. Cookies and the Carbon Cycle

**C. Conservation of Fundamental Particles**
1. Leptons
2. Quarks
3. Atomic mass number

**D. Conservation of Charge**

**E. Conservation of Linear Momentum**

**F. Conservation of Linear Momentum at Very High Speeds**
1. Momentum or mass
2. Emmy Noether

**G. Conservation of Angular Momentum**
1. Angular momentum = mass × speed × radius

**H. Conservation of Energy**

## Comprehension

### Matching

a. Atomic mass number

b. Angular momentum

c. Conserved quantity

d. Carbon cycle

e. Fundamental particles

f. Linear momentum

1. _____ Any quantity that remains constant.
2. _____ The process by which carbon is transferred through the atmosphere to living organisms and back to the atmosphere.
3. _____ Obtained by adding the number of protons to the number of neutrons.
4. _____ An object's mass times its velocity.
5. _____ An object's mass times its speed times its distance from the center of its orbit.
6. _____ Small, unbreakable constituents of matter.

### True/False

1. _____ All physical objects must obey a general law of conservation of mass.
2. _____ There is no law of conservation of atoms.
3. _____ Protons and neutrons are fundamental particles.
4. _____ Electron- like particles are considered to be fundamental particles.
5. _____ Atomic mass number is always conserved.
6. _____ Neutrons, protons, and electrons are all charged particles.
7. _____ Electrons can easily be transferred from one object to another.
8. _____ Scuffing across the carpet with your tennis shoes creates a charge that didn't previously exist.
9. _____ The motion of a single object subject to no net forces is conserved.
10. _____ 10. ____ Particles moving at high speeds require less force to accelerate than slower particles.
11. _____ 11. ____ Linear momentum is the speed at which an object moves.

## Fill in the Blank

1. Any quantity that is equal before and after a physical process is called a _____ quantity.
2. _____ is the property of matter associated with electromagnetic forces.
3. A spinning ice skater is applying conservation of _____.
4. There is evidence that every proton and neutron is composed of three _____.
5. At high speeds, conservation of _____ holds, not conservation of mass.
6. Linear momentum depends on _____ and _____.
7. Anything that is spinning will tend to keep spinning in the same _____.
8. The forces in an explosion come from _____ the object.
9. According to Newton's Third Law, in an explosion, the different pieces push against each other with _____ and _____ forces.

## Analysis

1. At low speeds, mass can
   a) change in form.
   b) transfer from one object to another.
   c) change its total amount.
   d) both (a) and (b).

2. Which of the following quantities remain(s) constant in the Carbon Cycle?
   a) Total amount of carbon dioxide.
   b) Total amount of carbon.
   c) Total mass.
   d) All of the above.
   e) (b) and (c) only.

3. 3. Angular momentum depends on which of the following?
   a) The mass of the object.
   b) How fast it's moving.
   c) How far it is from the center of its orbit.
   d) All of the above.

4. What does it mean for a quantity to be conserved?

5. Name the six conservation principles discussed in this chapter.

6. What are the two classes of fundamental particles?

7. If you weigh all of the ingredients before mak-

ing a cake, and then you weigh the finished cake, what will you find? What accounts for the missing weight?

## Synthesis

1. You are spinning in a swivel chair with your arms and legs straight out. What happens if you pull your limbs in toward you? What conservation principle explains this?

2. You scuff across wool carpet while wearing tennis shoes. You become negatively charged.

   a) Where does the charge come from? What happens to the electrons in the carpet?

   b) Does the carpet become positively or negatively charged?

   c) What has happened to the total charge of the system? What has happened to the total number of electrons? What has happened to the sum of the protons and the neutrons of the system?

   d) What two conservation principles account for this?

3. Your friend is trying to learn to ride a unicycle without much success. Your friend first wants to learn to balance while the cycle is stationary before attempting to pedal. Using conservation of angular momentum, explain why your friend may be having difficulties.

4. In terms of the Carbon Cycle, explain why a growing plant doesn't violate conservation of mass. What conservation principle accounts for this?

5. Explain how it is possible for police to determine the speed and direction of two vehicles before a crash by measuring the skid marks. What conservation principle allows them to do this?

6. Explain how pool sharks take advantage of conservation of momentum to improve their game.

7. Explain how the speed of light being a constant for everyone leads to the conclusion that mass increases with speed.

# Energy

*Work is of two kinds: first, altering the position of matter at or near the earth's surface relatively to other such matter; second, telling other people to do so. The first kind is unpleasant and ill paid; the second is pleasant and highly paid.*

Bertrand Russell

**9**

## LEARN

- How energy is defined.

- The different forms of mechanical energy.

- The different forms of internal energy.

- Energy transfer processes: work, conduction, convection, and radiation.

- How mass and energy are equivalent.

Learning usually requires us to define and understand new terms. Whether a term represents an object or a scientific principle, the more accurately we understand its meaning, the more appropriately we will use it. In science, we can have trouble defining the exact meaning of a term because observation and experiment first teach us what something does rather than what that something is. Consider that "mass" is defined as "a factor in Newton's second law," or "a factor in determining gravitational pull," but these words tell us how mass affects other things rather than saying exactly what mass is. We accept this because science is the analysis of how things behave to find out what they are. In that spirit, we start our study of energy by defining what it does.

### 9–1 What Is Energy?

One general definition of energy is that it is "a measurement of an object's capacity to change things around it." A more traditional definition is that "energy is the ability to exert a force on an

object while it moves through some distance in the direction of the applied force." By either definition, energy is a property associated with force and an object's position or motion. This property is often transformed but always conserved.

There are two general types of energy: that which is dependent on position and that which is dependent on motion. Energy that depends on the position of an object or the positions of an object's constituent parts is known as **potential energy**. Energy that depends on an object's motion is known as **kinetic energy**.

Types of energy are further broken down into **mechanical** or macroscopic and **internal** *or* microscopic energies, based on whether the energy depends on the position or motion of the whole object or on the atoms and molecules that make up the object.

Energy units are perhaps not as familiar as those of distance or volume. The metric unit of energy is either the "joule", named after James Joule (1818–1889), a pioneer in the study of heat, or the "kilowatt hour" (kWh), the unit used by power companies.

## JAMES JOULE

James Prescott Joule was born in England in 1818. A brewer by trade, he pursued scientific inquiry as a hobby. His experiments to determine if the recently invented electric motor was more efficient than the steam engines used in his brewery led to his discovery of the relationship between heat and mechanical work.

## 9–2 Types of Mechanical Energy

### Kinetic Energy

We have defined energy as the capacity to change things. A car is most definitely changed in a collision, so if we had a formula for kinetic

**Potential Energy:**

Energy that depends on the position of an object or on the positions of an object's constituent parts.

**Kinetic Energy:**

The form of energy associated with motion. The kinetic energy of an object in motion is given by $KE = \frac{1}{2}\text{mass} \times \text{speed}^2$

**Mechanical Energy:**

A name given to the kinetic or potential energy of large, macroscopic objects.

**Internal Energy:**

A name given to energy hidden within matter but manifest by the temperature of the matter, the shape of the matter, the physical state of the matter (solid, liquid, gas), the chemical composition of the matter (i.e., the kind of energy that might be released by burning or explosion of a substance), etc.

**Figure 9.1**
The faster a car moves, the more kinetic energy it has.

**Gravitational Potential Energy:**

The energy stored in an object that has the potential to fall. Near the surface of Earth, the increase of gravitational potential energy of an object that is lifted is given by GPE = weight × height.

energy, we could calculate how much damage a moving vehicle could cause in a crash. Obviously, the faster a car moves the more damage it can cause, so kinetic energy must depend on speed (*Figure 9.1*). And the more massive a vehicle is, the more destruction it can cause, (hence the army's tendency to use extremely heavy vehicles), so kinetic energy must also depend on mass (*see Figure 9.2*).

**Figure 9.2**
The more massive a vehicle is, the more kinetic energy it has. This tank has no kinetic energy, however, because it is parked.

The formula for kinetic energy at low speeds is

$$\text{Kinetic energy} \ = \ \tfrac{1}{2} \, \textbf{mass} \times \textbf{speed}^{\,2}$$

Why is speed squared in this basic formula? Ask yourself if you would rather try to catch a 20-gram bullet coming at you at 300 mph or a 300-gram baseball traveling at 20 mph. Speed is squared because it plays a more important role than mass in determining how much change an object can cause. For instance, a car hitting a wall while traveling 50 mph is at least twice as likely to kill the driver as a car hitting that same wall while traveling at 35 mph. By the formula,

the kinetic energy of a car going 50 mph is twice that of one going 35 mph and therefore twice as deadly.

Recall from Chapter 7 that speed is measured relative to other objects. Since kinetic energy depends on speed, it must also be a quantity that is measured relative to other objects. In other words, just as there is no absolute value for speed, there is no absolute value for kinetic energy.

### Gravitational Potential Energy

A student who has dropped a 15-pound bowling ball on his foot learns quickly that a falling object changes things, and not necessarily for the better! (*Figure 9.3*). This change is possible only because gravity pulls the bowling ball toward Earth. Energy derived from gravity's pull is called **gravitational potential energy**. The amount of energy depends on the attracted object's height and weight. The higher the bowling ball, or any object, is from Earth's center (or the student's foot), and the heavier the object is, the more memorable this brief experience with gravitational potential energy becomes.

The formula for gravitational potential energy is

$$\textbf{Potential energy} = \textbf{weight} \times \textbf{height}$$

Height, like motion, is also measured relative to something else, so gravitational potential energy, like kinetic energy, is a relative measure as well. When comparing potential energies,

**Figure 9.3**
The bowling ball's gravitational potential energy depends on its weight and the height from which it was dropped.

we pick a convenient reference point on or near Earth and measure heights from that fixed point. For most situations, the floor of a room or a nearby lawn or sidewalk makes a convenient reference point. However, to measure the change in energy of an airplane flying from mountainous Denver to flat Los Angeles, sea level would probably be a more convenient reference point for the airplane's height.

The formula of energy = weight × height works well on Earth's surface but is actually a special case of a more general formula. The general formula tracks how weight decreases with distance and can be used to find the gravitational potential energy of meteoroids or other astronomical objects drifting far from Earth's surface. In this formula the gravitational potential energy still depends on "height", now defined as the distance between the centers of objects and "weight," still defined as the size of the gravitational force they exert on each other.

Recall that as two objects are moved farther apart, the gravitational force between them decreases. Even so, their gravitational potential energy increases with greater separation. So a can of tuna high above Earth on the space station has more gravitational potential energy than one on the kitchen counter even though it weighs 10% less than it would on Earth's surface. This is because the farther apart objects are, the faster they will move when they come back together and the more kinetic energy they will gain.

To illustrate, a chunk of solid rock the size of a garbage truck falling 100 feet onto a concrete parking lot will probably destroy several cars and break up the concrete where it landed. But a chunk of solid rock the size of a mere garbage can, falling from 100 miles up has much greater destructive capability and will probably vaporize on impact, create an enormous crater where the parking lot used to be, and kill any nearby dinosaurs. Asteroids and comets impacting on Earth are dangerously energetic because of their great mass but more from the high speeds they gain by falling through long distances.

### Electrical Potential Energy

Children are taught at an early age not to stick their fingers or any objects into electrical outlets for obvious reasons. There is clearly some

capacity for change, and therefore energy, associated with electricity.

The electromagnetic force naturally tries to pull positive and negative forces back together. So electric-power generating plants must use force to separate positive and negative charges from each other, as is done through chemical forces to create the positive and negative ends of a 9-volt battery.

A really inquisitive student might test the ability of positive and negative forces to reunite by sticking a 9-volt battery in his or her mouth (despite childhood lessons to the contrary). Touching both positive and negative contact points with a conductor provides a path for electrical charge of opposite sign to come back together. This can cause destructive change like the pain in your tongue[1] or constructive change like powering a toy car or an mp3 player.

This example of **electrical potential energy** is similar to our description of gravitational potential energy: For gravity, greater mass and greater separation create more gravitational potential energy. For electricity, greater charge creates more electrical potential energy. But there is a twist on separation.

Just as with gravity, the electric potential energy for objects that have *opposite* charges *increases* as the distance between them *increases* (*Figure 9.4a*). The farther apart oppositely charged objects are, the faster they will move as they come back together by the natural law of electrical attraction, and the more change they can cause along the way. Therefore, potential energy for unlike charges is the *greatest* when the charges are *far apart*.

Opposite charges (positive and negative) attract, but like charges (positive and positive, or negative and negative) repel. If two same-type charges are placed close to each other, they will want to move apart, not together. The closer the charges are, the stronger the repelling force, and the farther they want to go to get away from each other. Thus, in contrast to the situation for unlike charges, electrical potential energy for objects with the *same* charges *decreases* as the distance *increases* between the charges. Potential energy for like charges is *greatest* when the two charges are *closest* (*Figure 9.4b*).

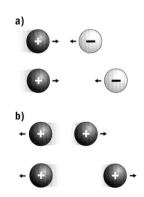

**Figure 9.4**
When is the energy the largest for each set of charges?

---
[1] and may also generate more respect in the student for accepting, without question, authority as a legitimate source of knowledge.

Whether we are considering like or unlike charges, the amount of potential energy depends on the size of the force between them. For any given distance of separation, the potential energy will be *larger* if either charge is larger.

## 9-3 Transforming and Transferring Mechanical Energy: Work

Energy has been transformed in all the examples of energy we've studied so far. In fact, to make energy work for us, it must be transformed from one form to another. In the process, the total energy is conserved; none is either destroyed or created.

How does the form of energy change when, say, a rubber ball is dropped towards the floor? It has gravitational potential energy from being held at shoulder level above the ground. When the ball is released it starts to move in the direction of the gravitational force. As it moves, its distance from Earth decreases, so it starts to lose gravitational potential energy. However, as it drops its speed increases. This means it is gaining kinetic energy. (*Figure 9.5.*)

The falling ball loses potential energy and gains kinetic energy. Just before it reaches the ground, its potential energy is zero and its kinetic energy is the same as the potential energy was before the ball was dropped. The total energy—potential plus kinetic—never changed. The energy has changed from potential to kinetic, but the sum of the two is exactly the same at all points. Therefore, total energy

**Work:**

The technical name given to the process by which energy is transferred to or from an object by an agent that exerts force on the object and the object moves along the direction of the force.

is conserved. Again, the gravitational potential energy isn't lost as the force of gravity pulls the ball down. It is turned into kinetic energy.

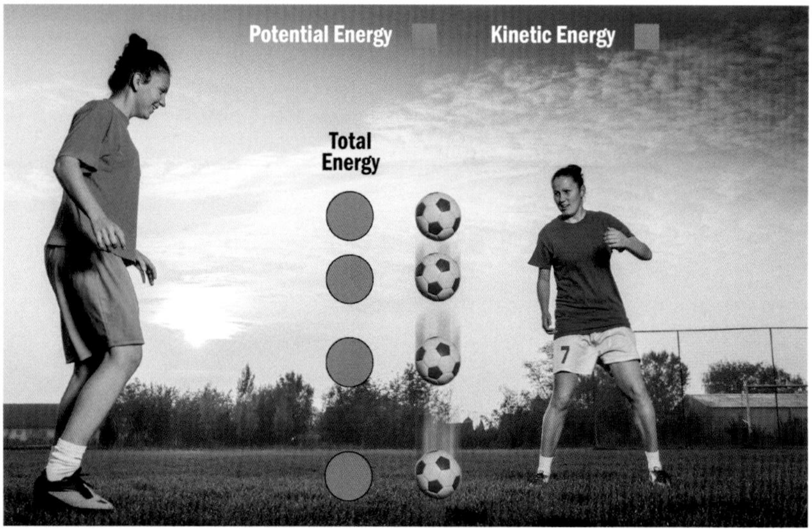

At the moment the ball hits the floor, all of its energy is now in the form of kinetic energy. After bouncing, the ball's kinetic energy gradually transforms back into gravitational potential energy as it rises against the force of gravity. Once the ball has returned to its original position, it again has the same amount of gravitational potential energy it had at the beginning of our experiment.

Mechanical energy is transformed or transferred when a force moves an object along in the direction of that force. The word that has been commandeered by scientists to describe such energy transformations is **work**. Be warned, the term *work* in a physical science class means something quite different from the standard English definition. *Work*, as a science term, refers to energy transferred as an object is moved in the direction of an applied force. The formula for work is

**Work = force × distance parallel to the direction of the force**

A person sitting at a desk typing on a computer is doing very little actual work, as defined above. Pushing down on the keys moves them a small distance in the direction in which they were pushed, but the size of the force and distance is almost insignificant. A student carrying a 70-lb backpack and moving along at a fairly constant speed across level ground likewise does no work on the backpack. The student is exerting a force on the backpack (70 lbs. upward), and is moving it through a distance along the ground. However, the force is up and the distance is sideways. The backpack wasn't moved in the direction of the applied force, so the student is doing no work at all on the backpack. The backpack has the same gravitational potential energy and the same kinetic energy. No energy transformations have taken place. (*Figure 9.6a.*)[2]

Doing work on an object—moving the object in the direction of an applied force—is necessary to change the mechanical energy of

**Figure 9.5**
The total energy of the ball stays the same while the way it is divided between kinetic energy (purple) and gravitational potential energy (orange) changes.

---

[2] You may wonder why your back aches if you're not doing any work. The muscles in your back are contracting through a distance every time a muscle fiber "fires," so you are doing work on your back muscles. You are just not doing any work on the backpack.

**Figure 9.6**

a) No matter how heavy the backpack is, the student is doing no work on it by simply lugging it around campus at a constant speed. Its gravitational potential energy and kinetic energy remain the same.

b) Work is done on the backpack only by changing its height (gravitational potential energy) or its velocity (kinetic energy).

that object. To change the backpack's energy, the student can do one of two things: change its speed or change its height. The student can apply a forward force to the backpack to speed it up. A forward force is a force in the direction the student is moving, so the student is doing work on the backpack and increasing its kinetic energy. To change height, the student could veer off the level and beaten track to climb some stairs. Now a displacement is created along the direction of the upward force the student exerted on the backpack. Thus, the student would again be doing work on the backpack and increasing its gravitational potential energy (*Figure 9.6b*).

Work is not a form of energy; it is a process of transferring or transforming energy. Doing work can change the amount or form of mechanical energy, but the total energy is still the same. It is important in science and industry to be able to identify such transfers of energy.

## 9-4 Types of Internal Energy

It is fairly easy to account for the energy in mechanical situations like the bouncing ball experiment. You can see the ball dropping and speeding up as it heads toward the floor, changing potential energy to kinetic. In other situations, like the student with the backpack hiking up stairs, one can see that the gravitational potential energy is increasing, but it is more difficult to identify the form from which it transferred. There are many types of energy

that depend on the positions and motions of the atoms and molecules that make up objects rather than the position or motion of the entire object. As mentioned in Section 9-1, these energies are collectively labeled as internal energies.

Internal energy, because it deals with positions and motions of objects on an atomic scale, can be difficult to track. Whenever mechanical energy seems to appear or vanish, a more careful look will show that it was actually transformed from or into some type of internal energy. Internal energy is a large and important part of the physical sciences and so will be discussed in more detail in later chapters. We introduce a few important categories here.

### Thermal Energy

One of the more blatant examples of seemingly disappearing energy happens every time a driver brakes her car to stop at a red light. The car initially had a great deal of kinetic energy. When the driver pushed on the brakes, the kinetic energy decreased until it was gone. Where did that kinetic energy go?

When the car's brakes are first depressed by the driver's foot, the brake pads exert a force on the wheels as they rotate through a distance. Energy is transferred because of work done by the brake pads, so the first place to look for the lost energy is in the brake pads. They are hot, and that heat is the car's transformed kinetic energy. This **thermal energy** is molecular kinetic energy, and will be explained further in Chapter 13.

When energy seems to vanish, it tends to end up as heat. The bouncing ball discussed at the beginning of this chapter doesn't quite go back to the same height it started from, but the ball (if it could be examined in midair with a very sensitive thermometer) would be found to be slightly warmer than it was before it was dropped. Friction with the air and within the ball at the bounce transformed some of the energy into thermal energy. The same is true of most processes. As will be discussed in Chapter 18, a little energy gets transformed into thermal energy even when the frictional forces are very small, as in a pendulum swinging. (See *Figure 9.7*.)

The law of conservation of energy is the reason why there are no **perpetual motion machines**. Hopeful inventors through the years

**Thermal Energy:**

Total kinetic energy of random motion of molecules in a material.

**Perpetual Motion Machine:**

A perpetual motion machine is something that keeps moving forever without any energy being added.

**Figure 9.7**
If he doesn't keep pumping, the swing will eventually stop. What happens to the mechanical energy?

**Conduction:**

The transmission of an electric charge or heat through a conducting medium without perceptible motion of the medium itself.

**Convection:**

The process by which energy is moved from one place to another by being stored in matter as internal energy, then moving the matter from one place to another.

have tried every possible—and some impossible—designs to circumvent that law. As a perpetual motion machine goes through its cycle, a tiny bit of energy is lost to thermal energy. That loss eventually removes all mechanical energy from the machine and it stops.

Even though losing energy to thermal energy is ubiquitous, the transformation between mechanical energy and thermal energy was one of the last pieces to fit into the law of conservation of energy. It wasn't until the mid-1800s that scientists measured the size of frictional forces and the distance through which they were applied carefully enough to show that the work done by friction was directly proportional to the thermal energy increase.

### Heat Transfer Processes

One reason it took so long to identify thermal energy as a type of energy is because of the way it transfers from one object to another. It behaves in a way that is analogous to the way

fluids behave, and so for many years thermal energy—often called "heat"—was thought to be some sort of flowing physical fluid.[3] That flow is called "heat transfer".

Moving a fluid from one place to another, like water from a well to a fire for instance, can be done one of three ways: a) Line up a bucket brigade where people who are not moving pass buckets of water from one person to the next, b) give each person a bucket to fill up at the well and then carry to the fire, or c) use a pump to lift the well water to a hose that can be used to spray water directly from the well onto the fire (*Figure 9.8*). The manner in which heat is transferred can be classified as one of three analogous types: conduction, convection, or radiation.

**Conduction**—Conduction takes place when objects having different temperatures are placed in direct contact with each other. The energy moves from the hotter object to the cooler one. Just like the stationary people in the bucket brigade, matter acts as a stationary conduit through which the heat moves. Matter is not exchanged, just energy.

Examples of conduction include burning one's hand when a roommate says that the pan left on the stove has cooled down, cooking eggs by submerging them in boiling water, or cooling down a can of soda by surrounding the can with ice. No material is being exchanged between the two objects, but energy is moving through direct contact.

**Convection**—Convection takes place when hot material moves and transfers its heat to colder material. Heat carried by hot material is

---
[3] The idea that heat was a fluid was taken pretty much for granted through the 18th and most of the 19th centuries. This fluid was called "caloric." The word "calorie" is a vestige of this idea.

**Figure 9.8**

a) Passing buckets of water from one stationary person to the next is analogous to the way heat is transferred through conduction.

b) People running back and forth with buckets of water is analogous to the way moving material transports heat in convection.

c) Spraying water directly from a well is analogous to transferring heat directly through radiation.

just like people running with buckets of water. Convection can either occur naturally or be forced.

Baseboard heaters raise the temperature of the air around them. The less dense warm air rises and is replaced by cooler, denser air near the floor. As the warm air mixes with the cool air, the temperature in the room as a whole goes up. This is natural convection. Convection by atmospheric currents described in Chapter 6 is of this type.

A standard furnace uses fans to help the process along. Air is heated inside the furnace and then blown through ducts to all the rooms in the house. The air mixes and the temperature inside the house increases. This is forced convection.

**Radiation**—This process is a direct transfer of energy from one place to another without any need for intervening matter. The nearly 100,000,000 miles (160,000,000 km) between the Sun and Earth is mostly empty space, yet the Sun is able to heat Earth by energy transferred in the form of sunlight. In an example closer to home, the heat from a campfire on a cold night can be felt by a person sitting near the fire even though the surrounding air is cold. The reason the camper's side facing the fire feels so much warmer than the side facing away is because of the radiative heat transfer from the fire.

### Chemical Potential Energy

As that campfire radiates its energy towards its grateful campers, one might logically ask where that burning-log energy came from in the first place. The logs are not falling, slowing down, losing charge, or doing anything else that decreases their mechanical energy. They are, however, turning from wood into chunks of carbon, carbon dioxide gas, and water vapor.

One type of internal energy has to do with the way atoms are organized to make molecules. Atoms have differing amounts of energy, depending on how they are bonded together. Air and dynamite both contain hydrogen, nitrogen, carbon, and oxygen. However, dynamite has quite a bit more destructive capacity than air because the atoms are bonded together in molecules with energetically different structures and properties. Energy associated with, or within, chemical bonds is known as **chemical potential energy**.

### Elastic Potential Energy

Another type of internal energy dependent on the position of atoms and molecules is **elastic potential energy**. When a material is in equilibrium, all the forces on any point in the material balance out. In many substances, if molecules in the material are displaced from this equilibrium position, the resulting unbalanced forces will push them back toward the equilibrium point.

Springs and rubber bands provide the most familiar examples of this type of energy. A rubber band has a relaxed position. If you stretch a rubber band, you have to exert a force through the distance you stretch it. You are storing energy as you move the molecules farther apart than they were in their equilibrium position. If you let go of the rubber band, the force pulling the molecules back to their equilibrium position converts this stored energy into kinetic energy. (See *Figure 9.9*.) Springs behave likewise and return to the equilibrium position whether stretched or compressed.

**Figure 9.9**
When you jump on a trampoline, the kinetic energy you have when you first hit the trampoline is converted into elastic potential energy when you stretch the springs and fabric. As the springs and fabric return to their equilibrium position, the trampoline exerts an upward force on you through the distance the trampoline is stretched. The work done on you transforms this elastic energy back into kinetic energy, which in turn becomes gravitational potential energy.

Elastic potential energy is also present in the compressed carbon dioxide used to propel everything from clothesline model rockets to whipped cream from a can. The process of compressing the carbon dioxide forces its molecules unnaturally close together inside a strong can or cartridge. The pressure of the compressed gas inside the cartridge is higher than the pressure outside, so when the cartridge is punctured or the nozzle is opened there is an unbalanced force pushing the carbon dioxide out of the can and an equal and opposite force on the container. This stored elastic energy is converted into kinetic energy of the gas and possibly the can.

In some situations, the stored elastic energy is not converted into mechanical energy but is just transferred to neighboring molecules. Molecules that are pushed together move back to a new equilibrium position, and in so doing push their neighbors, forcing them to also find a new equilibrium position. (See *Figure 9.10.*) The energy doesn't change form but moves through the material from one group of molecules to the next. Methods of transferring elastic energy this way will be discussed in greater detail in Chapter 10.

**Nuclear Potential Energy:**

The energy stored in the nucleus of an atom.

**Figure 9.10**
When someone standing in a group of people invades the personal space of another, that person instinctively moves to reach their "equilibrium" position, resulting in a chain reaction as the person who moved invades the space of another person, who then moves in to a new equilibrium position. This situation is analogous to how molecules behave in ways that return them to their equilibrium position.

## Nuclear Potential Energy

The nucleus of an atom has two competing forces acting inside it. A strong nuclear force in each atom holds its protons and neutrons together and an electromagnetic force pushes its protons apart.

Inside the nucleus, the strong force overwhelms the electric repulsion. The protons are held closely together giving the nucleus a high electrical potential energy. Details on how the total nuclear energy changes as protons and neutrons are combined and separated are discussed in Chapter 25. However, it is appropriate to mention some basic information about nuclear energy at this point in our overview of the various types of energies.

Ever since the first nuclear bombs ended World War II in a spectacular and devastating show of energy, everything we know about nuclear energy has been closely associated with Albert Einstein, relativity, and probably the most famous equation of our day, $E=mc^2$. Most American high school students have heard and probably memorized the $E=mc^2$ equation in the context of nuclear energy studies, without having any idea of what the equation means. Now, of course, you know that Einstein's theory of relativity is about what happens when objects travel close to the speed of light. **Nuclear potential energy** is about the positions of protons and neutrons in a nucleus. The connection between a relativity-related equation and the energy released by nuclear explosions isn't exactly obvious. But we are about to look at what happens to energy at high—really high—speeds.

## 9-5 Relativistic Energy and Mass–Energy Equivalence

We have learned that kinetic energy depends on mass and speed. The maximum speed of anything is the speed of light. Light speed is the same for all observers, and despite the hopes of entire generations of science fiction authors and readers, nothing can travel faster than the speed of light.[4] Additionally, in

---

[4] This can be demonstrated with a gedanken experiment. Suppose I am in a spaceship moving 50% faster than the speed of light, 450 million meters each second, as measured by you. For some reason I decide to turn on a flashlight and point it forward. In my reference frame light travels 300 million meters each second, so the light would be 300 million meters in front of the spaceship after one second. In

the previous chapter the law of conservation of momentum showed that a moving object has more mass than an otherwise identical stationary object. This means that when we discuss energies of objects moving at high speeds, we must take into account their increased mass.

Readers studying the previous chapter may have wondered exactly where the additional mass came from and where it would go when the object slowed down. Einstein, in a remarkable leap of intuition, showed that *mass is related to energy*. He used conservation of momentum and equations for the momentum of light to show how the energy of an object and its mass are related. He determined that an object emitting light would lose mass proportional to the energy it radiated away. The equation he derived

_____

your frame the light also travels 300 million meters each second, while the space ship has traveled 450 million miles in the same second. So you conclude that the light is 150 million miles behind the spaceship. While it is possible to explain differences in distance, a single beam of light can't be both in front of and behind the space ship at the same time. The principle of non-contradiction doesn't bend that far. This means it is impossible to travel faster than light.

was the now classic, deceptively simple $E = mc^2$, where "E" stands for energy, "m" stands for mass and "c" stands for the speed of light— 300,000,000 m/s.

This equation solves the mystery left from Chapter 8 of how mass changes with speed. If something is moving fast, it has more energy, so it has more mass. If you slow something down by exerting a force on it, you are doing work and transferring energy away from the object. Less energy means less mass. But as long as the energy is still there, so is the mass, regardless of what form the energy takes.

Particle accelerators, like CERN in Switzerland, routinely turn kinetic energy and electrical potential energy into mass (and vice-versa). During a nuclear process like fission or radioactive decay, when the starting and ending the masses are measured, the mass change corresponds exactly to the changes in nuclear energy. The recent discoveries of gravity waves from merging black holes confirmed that mass changes with changes in gravitational potential energy.

## ENERGY TO MATTER, MATTER TO ENERGY

Einstein's discovery of $E=mc^2$ predicted that, in some situations, mass can be created out of energy and energy out of mass. In "pair production," done in laboratories, scientists use controlled high-energy light beams to produce electrons and positrons. When the energy of the light is greater than the combined mass of these two particles multiplied by the speed of light squared, this matter–anti-matter pair can emerge from the energy. Typically, the anti-matter positron exists only a short time before it collides with a matter electron. The collision annihilates both electron and positron, and their combined mass is turned back into energy.

Another important prediction is that any time an object releases energy, there will be a corresponding drop in the object's mass. In a nuclear reaction (Chapter 25), we can accurately predict how much energy will be released simply by measuring the change in the mass caused by the reaction. Nuclear power plants are possible because large amounts of useful energy, sufficient to power cities, are available from small changes of mass in nuclear reac-

tions. Because in $E = mc^2$ the speed of light squared is a very large number, small mass changes produce large energy changes.

But now write Einstein's equation as $m = E/c^2$. We now see, going the other way, that typical energy changes produce only small mass changes. The energy released by burning 1 kg of gasoline (1/4 gallon) changes the mass of the gas by only 0.0000000005 kg. We cannot measure changes in mass that small. Even in nuclear reactions, which have the largest changes of energy known in nature, the mass changes by less that 0.1% of the total mass.

Changes in mass due to energy transfers are so small that unless we are dealing with a nuclear reaction or an object with the extraordinarily large kinetic energies of something moving at close to the speed of light, they will be insignificant. For this reason, effects of mass-energy equivalence are not perceived in normal situations, and mass and energy are conserved independently. Only in extreme cases do we need to consider the combined conservation of mass-energy.

This conclusion is true in general. The energy of any object—whether it is kinetic energy, potential energy, or any kind of internal energy—will be manifest as mass. That is, if you do an experiment to determine the ratio of force to acceleration (Newton's second law), energy present will appear as part of the mass. If you do a gravitation experiment to determine what factors to put in Newton's law of gravitation, that energy will show up as mass. We can say either that energy *has* mass, or that energy *is* mass.

The conservation laws for mass and energy now become unified in one conservation law, sometimes called conservation of mass-energy.

The rest mass of an object must be augmented by any energy present in accordance with the relation $E = mc^2$. However, in everyday situations this augmentation is so small it can be ignored.

## 9-6 Conclusion

The different types of energy discussed in the chapter are summarized in *Table 9.1*. Conservation of energy and energy transformations are widely used physics concepts, and will prove very important in subsequent chapters.

### Table 9.1 — Types of Energy

**Mechanical**

**Internal**

**Potential**

Gravitational

Chemical

Electrical

Elastic

Nuclear

**Kinetic**

Kinetic

Thermal

*All the life of the universe may be regarded as manifestations of energy masquerading in various forms, and all the changes in the universe as energy running about from one of these forms to the other, but always without altering the total amount..*

*Sir James Jeans*

# 9 STUDY GUIDE

## Chapter Framework

**A. What Is Energy?**
1. Exerting force

**B. Types of Mechanical Energy**
1. Kinetic energy
2. Gravitational potential energy
3. Electrical potential energy

**C. Transforming and Transferring Mechanical Energy: Work**
1. Total energy
2. Work = force × distance parallel to direction of force

**D. Types of Internal Energy**
1. Thermal energy
   a. *Perpetual motion machines*
   b. *Heat transfer processes—Conduction, convection, radiation*
2. Chemical potential energy
3. Elastic potential energy
4. Nuclear potential energy

**E. Relativistic Energy and Mass-Energy Equivalence**

## Comprehension

### Matching

a. Potential energy
b. Mechanical energy
c. Internal energy
d. Gravitational potential energy
e. Perpetual motion machine
f. Kinetic energy
g. Work
h. Conduction
i. Nuclear potential energy
j. Convection
k. Chemical potential energy
l. Elastic potential energy
m. Radiation

1. ____ Depends on an object's position.
2. ____ Depends on the position and motion of the object on the atomic scale.
3. ____ Weight times height.
4. ____ Depends on the position and motion of the whole object.
5. ____ Moving an object in the direction of an applied force.
6. ____ Something that keeps moving forever without any energy being added
7. ____ Depends on an object's motion.
8. ____ Energy moves through direct contact.
9. ____ Heat is transferred when the hot material moves around.
10. ____ Direct transfer of heat from one place to another without any need for intervening matter.
11. ____ Energy associated with chemical bonds.
12. ____ Depends on the position of atoms and molecules.
13. ____ Depends on the positions of protons and neutrons in a nucleus.

### True/False

1. ____ Speed plays a more significant role than mass in determining an object's kinetic energy.
2. ____ Gravitational potential energy decreases as the distance between two objects increases.
3. ____ If an object remains stationary, then no work is being done on it.
4. ____ In the process of conduction, both matter and energy are exchanged.
5. ____ The closer the protons and neutrons are to each other, the lower the nuclear potential energy will be.
6. ____ Mass and energy are really two ways of measuring the same thing.
7. ____ The heat you feel on your face from a campfire when the surrounding air is cold is an example of radiation.

### Fill in the Blank

1. Kinetic energy depends on _____ and _____.
2. When traveling near the speed of light, mass _____.
3. When a cold object and a hot object are placed in direct contact with each other, energy moves from the _____ object to the _____ object.
4. The transfer of heat from the Sun to Earth is an example of _____.
5. Besides stupidity, sitting on a hot stove is an example of _____.
6. Baseboard heaters and standard furnaces heat the house by _____.
7. In the equation E = mc2, E stands for _____, m stands for _____ and c stands for _____.

## Analysis

1. Energy can be defined as
   a) a measure of destructive capacity.
   b) the ability to exert a force on an object while it moves through some distance in the direction of the applied force.
   c) both (a) and (b).

2. If you move two positively charged objects closer together, then electrical potential energy
   a) increases.
   b) decreases.
   c) stays the same.

3. Two objects with opposite charges are brought closer together. Electrical potential energy
   a) increases.
   b) decreases.
   c) stays the same.

4. As you dribble a basketball, which of the following quantities is/are conserved?
   a) Gravitational potential energy.
   b) Kinetic energy.
   c) Internal energy.
   d) Total energy.

5. If an object has kinetic energy, then it must
   a) be electrically charged.

b) be moving.

c) be in an elevated position.

d) be at rest.

6. Work is always done on an object when

a) more than one force is applied to the object.

b) the object moves at a constant speed in a straight line.

c) a force moves the object through a distance in the direction of the force.

d) all of the above.

7. If you're skiing downhill, which of the following must be true?

a) Your internal energy decreases.

b) Your kinetic energy increases.

c) Your gravitational potential energy decreases.

d) You fall.

8. A mass on a spring is bouncing up and down. Which of the following are conserved?

a) the elastic energy

b) the gravitational potential energy

c) the kinetic energy

d) the total energy

e) the total momentum

9. Name two examples of objects with elastic potential energy.

10. What is the speed limit of the Universe?

11. What is meant by the conservation of mass-energy?

12. What are two consequences of mass-energy equivalence?

13. Describe the important energy transfer and transformation mechanisms (work, conduction, radiation, and convection).

14. Air and dynamite contain many of the same elements. What makes dynamite so much more destructive than air?

15. Why are perpetual motion machines unrealistic? What happens to the energy that makes them impossible?

## Synthesis

1. Describe the energy changes that occur when an athlete pole-vaults, beginning with the athlete eating breakfast and ending after the athlete hits the mat.

2. You walk into a computer lab and see many students doing homework. However, based on what you learned in Physical Science, you conclude that no one is really doing much "work" at all. What leads you to this conclusion?

3. You accidentally drop your cell phone off a balcony. You know that the only thing that could possibly console you would be to examine the tragedy using your understanding of Physical Science.

a) What kind(s) of energy does the phone have before it falls?

b) What kind(s) of energy does it lose as it falls?

c) What kind(s) of energy does it gain as it falls?

d) What kind(s) of energy does it have just after it hits the ground and stops?

e) How does the total amount of energy in (d) compare with that in (a)? How do you know?

4. A frictionless pendulum is set in motion.

a) What kind of energy does it have at the highest point of its swing?

b) What kind of energy does it gain as it swings downward?

c) As it swings upward again, what kind of energy does it lose? What kind does it gain?

d) How does the conservation of energy apply to this situation?

5. Now consider a real pendulum (with friction).

a) What kind of energy does it have at the highest point of its swing?

b) What kind of energy does it gain as it swings downward?

c) As time passes, what happens to the maximum height of each swing? If you attached a sensitive thermometer to the pendulum, what would happen to its temperature as it continued to swing?

d) What will be the fate of the pendulum? What kind of energy will it have at that time?

e) How does the conservation of energy apply to this situation?

6. A constant force propels a rocket ship through space.

a) Describe the resulting speed and acceleration of the rocket ship.

b) Is there a limit to how fast the rocket ship can go? If so, what is it?

c) What is the relationship between mass and energy? What happens to the energy transferred to the rocket ship at high speeds?

d) What effect does this have on the rocket ship's acceleration?

7. Explain how pressing on the nozzle of a Ready Whip container releases the whipped cream. What type of energy does the compressed carbon dioxide have?

# Waves

*Neither can the wave that has passed by be recalled, nor the hour which has passed return again.*

**Ovid, poet of ancient Rome**

# 10

## LEARN

- What waves are.

- The similarities and differences between transverse and longitudinal waves.

- The four properties every wave possesses.

- The four different types of wave behavior and give examples of each.

- What standing waves are and how they are created.

- About the Doppler effect and how it changes wavelength and frequency.

It is relaxing to lie on an ocean beach for hours and watch as waves wash up on the shore, sometimes gently, sometimes with greater force. In a steady rhythm, neither rushing nor pausing, they arrive in a sequence as seemingly eternal as the energy they bring. Small wonder poets, writers, and lovers often seek the wave-caressed beach to better collect their thoughts and lives. But waves aren't just physical poetry. Waves are a means of conveying energy throughout the world and Universe.

In Chapter 9, we learned that energy is transported by conduction, convection, and radiation. Conduction transports internal energy through stationary matter while convection transports internal energy from place to place through matter that moves. Radiation transmits energy through the emptiness of space without any assistance from matter at all. In addition to these three mechanisms, energy is also transferred by **mechanical waves**, a term referring to waves that move through matter.

A mechanical wave is a "disturbance" with a repeating shape. The energy of the disturbance

travels through the matter via particles vibrating or bobbing in place. This is illustrated by the waving rope in *Figure 10.1*. Here a rope, stretched between two people, is rapidly moved up and down on one end, creating ripples. The ripples travel the length of rope to the other person, bringing kinetic energy with them. As the wave travels down the rope, individual parts of the rope move up and down and then return to their starting points after the wave has passed by.

**Figure 10.1**
It is the disturbance that is propagated from one place to another, not parts of the medium itself.

Water waves behave in the same manner. Throw a rock into a pond and the energy of the splash spreads away from the impact point as a circular wave. Sticks and leaves floating on the surface of the pond bob as the wave passes by. Like the parts of the rope, the sticks and leaves and the water they float on return to their original position after the wave has gone by (*Figure 10.2*).

Yet another example of how a wave works is "doing the wave" in a football stadium. The wave starts when cheerleaders coax a section of fans into standing up and sitting down. Then their neighbors to one side do the same. If everyone feels the spirit of the moment, the act of standing up and sitting down circles the stadium. This "disturbance" goes around the arena while the people themselves, "the particles of matter" if you will, stay at their seats standing up and sitting down in sequence with their neighbors.

Water waves, waves along a rope, and waves in a football stadium have several features in common. Each travels through something tangible, call it a "material" or "medium", which supports the wave's motion. Each medium has

**Mechanical Wave:**
A traveling disturbance in material that transports energy.

**Longitudinal Wave:**

A wave in which the molecules of the medium vibrate in the same direction as the wave propagates.

**Compression Wave:**

A longitudinal wave driven by the force of pressure.

**Transverse Wave:**

A wave in which the molecules of the medium vibrate at right angles to the direction the wave propagates.

**Shear Wave:**

A transverse wave driven by shearing forces between molecules.

**Surface Wave:**

A wave that travels along the surface of a medium.

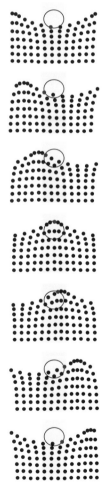

**Figure 10.2**

Water moves in a circular pattern as a surface wave passes through it. Notice that the red water particle on the surface will return to its original position after the wave passes.

an equilibrium shape. For water the shape is a level surface, for the rope it is a straight line, and for the football stadium it is people sitting in their seats. Each of these waves causes a deviation from this equilibrium shape.

Materials that propagate waves always have a force within them that restores the material to its equilibrium shape. Internal forces within the rope cause it to return to a straight line. Gravity causes the surface of water to return to being flat. Forces attempting to restore the medium to its equilibrium position cause waves to be propagated. Without restoring forces, there would be no waves.

## 10-1 Wave Types

Mechanical waves are of two different types, defined by the direction the medium's molecules vibrate when the wave passes by. If the molecules vibrate in the *same* direction the wave moves, the disturbance is a **longitudinal** wave. Longitudinal waves driven by pressure are also called pressure or **compression** waves (see *Figure 10.3*). If the molecules instead vibrate at *right angles* to the wave direction, it is a **transverse** wave. Transverse waves driven by shearing stress are called **shear** waves (see *Figure 10.4*).

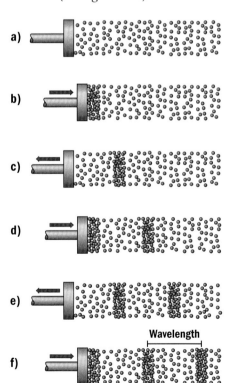

**Figure 10.3**

In a longitudinal or compression wave the material vibrates back and forth in the same direction the wave propagates.

Both compression and shear waves travel through the *interior* of a medium. **Surface waves**, such as water waves, travel along the surface of a medium. They usually contain both longitudinal and transverse motions which together give a net circular or elliptical path to the surface molecules. Beneath the surface a short distance, the material is undisturbed (refer back to Figure 10.2).

In this chapter we only consider compression and shear waves with one exception—light. Light is a transverse wave, but is not restored by material shearing forces, so it is not a shear wave. Light is a special entity which is described separately in Chapter 11. But because it is familiar, we use light occasionally in this chapter to illustrate general wave properties.

### *Compression Waves*

As previously noted, a compression wave passing a point causes the molecules at that point to vibrate back and forth in the direction the wave is moving (*Figure 10.5*). These waves travel through all states of matter—solids, liquids, gases, and plasmas (See Chapter 12 for a more detailed discussion on states of matter.) In solids molecules are bound in place and the force of binding provides the restoring force

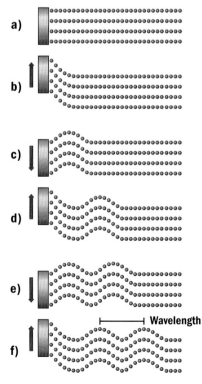

**Figure 10.4**

In a transverse or shear wave the material vibrates up and down at right angles to the direction the wave propagates.

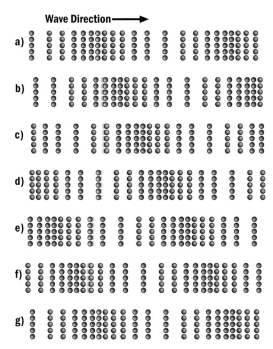

**Figure 10.5**

The motion particles undergo when a compression wave passes. Notice their position oscillates *parallel* to the wave direction.

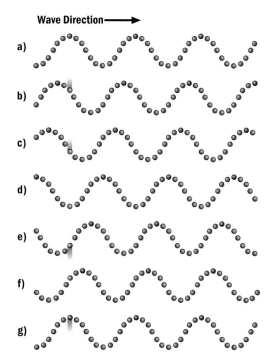

**Figure 10.6**

The motion particles undergo when a shear wave passes. Notice their position oscillates *perpendicular* to the wave direction.

necessary to propagate the wave. In liquids, gases, and plasmas, the molecules are not rigidly bound to each other as they are in solids, yet they still resist being compressed enough to provide a restoring force.

As an example of a compression wave, imagine a person standing in a line of people who are holding hands and singing. For some reason, the person starts swaying side-to-side with the music, parallel to the line. This makes those on either side also start swaying side-to-side. This movement propagates along the line as a wave of swaying people.

Sound is a compression wave. A vibrating object in contact with the air, like a speaker diaphragm, causes a series of compressions and decompressions in the surrounding air. These travel outward in all directions causing a series of back-and-forth forces on objects they strike, such as a human eardrum. The energy from the wave is transmitted to the eardrum and the hearer understands it as sound.

### Shear Waves

Forces in a shear wave stretch the bonds between molecules up and down in a direction that is sideways or perpendicular to the direction the wave propagates (*Figure 10.6*). These sideways forces are called "shear" forces, giving this wave its name. Shear forces can be exerted on all states of matter. However, the molecules in liquids, gases, and plasmas are not rigidly bound to one another and drift away in the direction the force pushes them. Only in solids do binding forces pull the molecules back to their equilibrium positions. As a result shear waves propagate only through solids.[1]

A person slamming his fist on a table creates a shear wave. The sudden force of fist hitting table causes a wave of vibrational energy to travel in all directions through the table, making, say, a book on anger management on the far end of the table jump. "The wave" of football fans is a shear wave because the people stand up and down while the wave travels at right angles to their motion.

Whether a wave is compression or shear, its energy decreases as the wave spreads through the medium. Eventually the correlated wave movement dissipates into chaotic molecular motion. At this point the wave disappears with its energy becoming part of the overall thermal energy of the medium.

---

[1] Surface waves on a pond or lake do have a shearing motion in them. This is because at the surface of a liquid, gravity acts as a restoring force pulling the molecules back down to their original positions. Inside fluids this effect doesn't work, so shear waves do not travel inside fluids.

## 10–2 Wave Properties

**Crest:**

The part of a wave where the particles are displaced a maximum amount above or in front of their equilibrium position.

**Trough:**

The part of a wave where the particles are displaced a maximum amount below or behind their equilibrium position.

**Amplitude:**

The maximum amount that a particle will displace from its normal, undisturbed position when a wave passes through it.

**Wavelength:**

The distance between successive similar parts in a repeating wave.

**Frequency:**

The number of wave amplitude crests that pass a particular point in space every second.

**Wave Speed:**

The rate at which a specific wave disturbance travels from point to point.

*Figure 10.7* is an illustration of both a compression and a shear wave "frozen" in space to show how particle displacement changes with location. The places of maximum forward or upward displacement are called **crests**. The points of maximum downward or backward displacement are called **troughs**. Half-way in between crests and troughs the particles are at their equilibrium positions. How particles vibrate back and forth between crest and trough when a wave passes by can be completely described by four properties: *amplitude, wavelength, frequency, and speed.*

**Amplitude**, labeled in Figures 10.7a and 10.7b, is the maximum distance a particle moves from its natural resting place. In other words, amplitude is the distance a particle travels when going from its equilibrium position to a crest or trough. The greater the amplitude, the more energetic the wave. For sound waves, amplitude is loudness. A loud sound, as from a police siren or a really unhappy baby, has large amplitude. A weak sound, such as a whisper ("Wake up, dear. It's your turn to feed the baby."), has small amplitude.

**Wavelength**, as shown in Figure 10.7a and Figure 10.7b, is the distance between successive repeating parts of a wave such as the crests or troughs. Audible sound waves have wavelengths ranging from a few centimeters to several meters long. Visible light wavelengths are on the order of a few millionths of a meter in length. Wavelength in visible light relates to color; red is longer wavelength and violet is shorter wavelength. Wavelength in audible sound waves relates to pitch. Longer wavelengths produce lower tones while shorter wavelengths produce higher tones.

**Frequency** measures the number of wave crests passing a particular point every second. If the waves of Figure 10.7 were "unfrozen" and allowed to fly through space in their natural manner, a succession of crests and troughs would be seen going by. Frequency is a count of the number of crests that pass by a fixed point in one second. The unit of measure is "oscillations per second," or *hertz* in honor of Heinrich Hertz (1857–1894), a German physicist who studied the production and reception of radio waves in the late 19th century. Frequency in visible light relates to color; red is lower frequency and violet is higher frequency. Frequency in audible sound waves relates to pitch. Higher frequencies produce higher tones while lower frequencies produce lower tones.

Our ears are sensitive to sound frequencies from 20 to 20,000 hertz. "A" above middle C has a frequency of 440 hertz. Octaves represent a doubling or halving of frequency. Waves from earthquakes have frequencies as low as 10 or 20 hertz, explaining why the items they vibrate often create a low rumbling sound. Frequencies of radio waves (the values listed numerically on the dials of AM and FM receivers) range from a few thousand hertz to several million hertz.

**Wave speed** is the rate that the disturbance travels through the medium. Wave speed depends on the medium's elastic properties, its density, and the type of wave going through it. In a given medium, compression waves travel faster than shear waves. For either type of wave the speed is independent of the amplitude, wavelength, or frequency; a loud shrill scream travels with the same speed as a low whisper.

Speeds vary greatly between different materials. Sound waves in air travel at about 340 m/sec (760 mph). Compression waves from earthquakes travel through stiff rock layers at 5,500 m/sec (12,000 mph) or more.

Frequency, wavelength, and speed are related by the formula:

$$\text{wave speed} = \text{frequency} \times \text{wavelength}$$

This important relation says that in one second, a single wave crest travels a distance equal

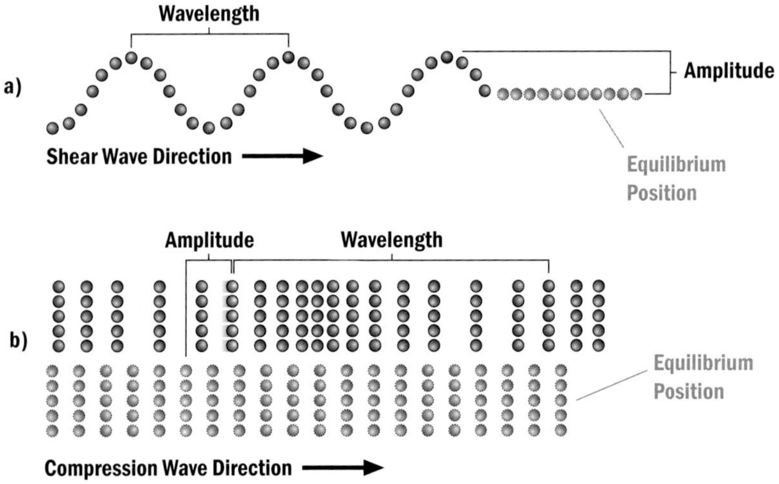

**Figure 10.7**

An illustration of amplitude and wavelength for the shear wave (a) and the compression wave (b) from Figures 10.5 and 10.6. Wavelength is always measured parallel to the wave direction. Amplitude is measured from the equilibrium position, or the natural position of the particles before the wave, in the direction the particles move.

## TSUNAMI

In 2011 a tsunami hit northern Japan killing tens of thousands of people and doing untold billions of dollars in damage (Figure 10.7). In 2004 a devastating tsunami raked Indonesia, Sri Lanka, India and Thailand, killing over 230,000 people. It was the deadliest natural disaster in recorded history.

What are tsunamis and why are they so destructive?

Compression and shear waves propagate through materials while surface waves propagate along surfaces. A tsunami is a wave that looks like a surface wave but, unlike one, the material displaces through the entire depth of the ocean, not just the surface. This may be several miles making the gravitational potential energy from this displacement enormous. Only the Earth's crust, shifting on the ocean bed, can create such a displacement.

When earthquakes occur they can push land up or down or sideways (See Chapters 26 and 27). If a strong quake occurs on the ocean floor it may move the land and all the water above it up or down. As the water settles back in place, the energy of displacement moves outward in a wave that can travel 500 mph. The amplitude at this point is just the distance the floor shifted vertically, typically a few feet. Therefore a tsunami at this point in the open ocean is not dangerous. The amplitude is only a meter or two and its wavelength can be over one hundred miles long making the rise to the crest very gentle. They are not only benign over deep water but are actually difficult to detect. Ships rarely notice their passage.

When the wave approaches land the situation changes. Gravitational and kinetic energy from the deep displacement gets concentrated in shallower depths. Friction causes the wave speed to slow and water to pile up. Wave-length shortens and trough and crest amplitudes increase causing the ocean to first recede then surge onto land like a fast-moving tide (Figure 10.8). The latter surge makes the water seem to come up from the local area itself leading to the name of "tsunami" which means "harbor wave."

**Figure 10. 8**

Waves of tsunami hit residences after a powerful earthquake in Natori, Miyagi prefecture, Japan, Friday, March 11, 2011. (AP Photo/Kyodo News)

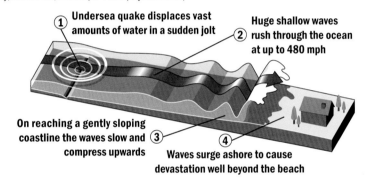

1 Undersea quake displaces vast amounts of water in a sudden jolt

2 Huge shallow waves rush through the ocean at up to 480 mph

3 On reaching a gently sloping coastline the waves slow and compress upwards

4 Waves surge ashore to cause devastation well beyond the beach

**Figure 10.9**

A schematic showing how tsunami energy concentrates on the shore.

to the length of a wavelength multiplied by the number of wavelengths going past in that second, which is the frequency.

Because wave speed is the product of wavelength and frequency, these two properties have an inverse relation. It is always true that *high frequency corresponds to short wavelengths and low frequency corresponds to long wavelengths. (Figure 10.10.)*

Consider a sound wave in air with a frequency of 34 hertz or roughly three octaves below middle C. Its speed is 340 m/sec. Therefore its wavelength will be 340/34 = 10 meters.

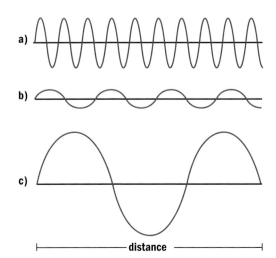

**Figure 10.10**

Three waves all travel the same distance in one second (meaning they have the same speed). Wave (a) with its shorter wavelength will necessarily have more oscillations than waves (b) or (c) over the same distance. Wave (c) has the longest wavelength and therefore the lowest frequency (number of oscillations). Notice that although the three waves all have different amplitudes, that does not have any impact on speed, wavelength, or frequency.

| Table 10.1 — Wavelength and Frequency | | |
|---|---|---|
| Wavelength (meters) | Frequency (hertz) | Speed (m/sec) |
| 3.4 | 100 | 340 |
| 10 | 34 | 340 |
| 20 | 1.7 | 340 |
| 1000 | .34 | 340 |

If the frequency is twice as great at 68 hertz, or two octaves below middle C, then the wavelength is 5 meters. *Table 10.1* shows this relationship for several different sound frequencies.

## 10-3 Wave Phenomena

All waves, regardless of their type, exhibit four characteristic behaviors: *reflection, refraction, diffraction, and interference.* Conversely, any phenomenon that displays all four of these characteristics has to be a wave. We can test an unknown energy transfer process for all four properties to see if it is a wave or not.

### Reflection

Waves "bounce," or **reflect** when they encounter abrupt changes in the nature or density of the medium they travel through. Water waves in a bathtub reflect when they encounter the denser, solid tub walls. Sound waves in air reflect as echoes when they strike the solid wall of a canyon. Reflection determines the acoustical properties of rooms and auditoriums (*Figure 10.11*).

We are all familiar with the reflection of light from mirrors, but we may not realize that light reflects to some degree off nearly all other

**Reflection:**
The act of bouncing off a surface.

**Refraction:**
The act of changing direction when passing from one medium to another.

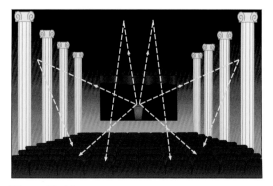

**Figure 10.11**
Much of the sound you hear in a room is from reflections off the walls and ceiling.

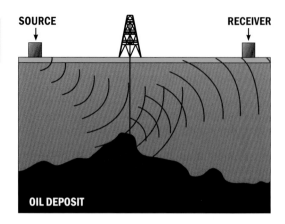

**Figure 10.12**
Reflecting waves are used to probe the interior of Earth to find layers of different material and structure.

surfaces as well. Light illuminating a room reflects and bounces rapidly around until virtually every surface is sending some light off in every direction. The reflections are so pervasive that wherever we stand, reflected light reaches our eyes, allowing us to see. Without reflection, we would be able to see almost nothing.

Geologists use earthquake waves to "see" inside Earth in much the same way we use light to see objects around us (*Figure 10.12*). Earth's interior is not uniform but is composed of a variety of structures, as explained in greater detail in Chapter 26. Waves created by explosions or other means travel into Earth's crust and reflect back upward from the boundaries between these structures. The reflected waves reach the surface where sensitive instruments detect and measure them. Analyzing these signals provides information about rock and mineral layers, oil deposits, ore deposits, and even the structure below Earth's crust.

### Refraction

Waves may penetrate boundaries as well as reflect from them. When traveling from one medium to another, the wave speed often changes. When speed changes, the wave's direction changes as well (*Figure 10.13*). This phenomenon is called **refraction**.

Light travels more slowly through glass and other transparent materials than it does through air. When light enters glass at an angle and slows down, the wave crests "bunch up." The slowing and bunching occurs first on the side of the wave that first strikes the glass surface, causing the wave to bend in that direction. This effect is similar to what happens to an automobile when

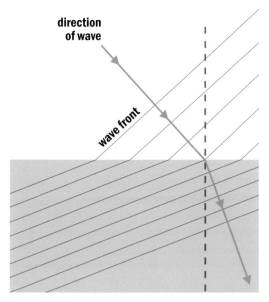

direction
of wave

wave front

**Figure 10.13**
When a wave penetrates into material of greater density, the slower speed causes the wave direction to change.

its left-side and right-side brakes work unevenly. If one side of a car slows down first when applying the brakes, the car will veer in that direction.

Because of refraction, objects inside denser material appear to be at different positions than they really are. A fish will appear to be higher in the water than it is. A stick in water will appear to be bent (*Figure 10.14*).

When the light wave exits the glass it reverts to the speed it had before entering. This speed-up causes it to refract back to the direction it had at first. So for example, light exiting a plane glass window bends back to its original direction, making objects seen through the window appear normal.

The light path through glass can be manipulated by curving the glass surface. The lenses of eyeglasses, telescopes, microscopes and other

**Figure 10.14**
A partly submerged stick appears to be bent. Why?

optical instruments use refraction by curved glass to focus light.

Sound travels faster in warm air than in denser cool air, causing sound waves to refract when moving through air layers of differing temperatures. Refraction can also be observed in ocean waves washing up on gently sloping beaches. An ocean's wave speed depends on the depth of the water. Waves moving from deep to shallow water become slower as they approach the beach. This slowing causes refraction that always steers the wave more directly into the beach.

### Diffraction

**Diffraction** is the spreading of a wave around corners or obstacles or through an opening (*Figure 10.15*). Diffraction allows sound to be heard around a corner, even when the hearer is not in a direct line with the source. Water waves spread after they pass through a narrow opening in a breakwater, disturbing an area behind the opening that is much broader than the opening itself. The spreading becomes more pronounced as the opening becomes smaller (Figures 10.15b and 10.15c).

The amount of diffraction depends on the size of the wavelength relative to the size of the opening. If the hole is large compared to the wavelength, little diffraction occurs. Diffraction increases as the opening's size decreases in comparison with the wavelength's size.

Although light is a wave, we typically do not notice it diffract because its wavelength is microscopically short and we rarely view anything through holes that small. However, if we cause light to pass through a small opening, perhaps by closing our eyelids until only a tiny slit is left through which light may pass, diffraction blurs the images we see.

An example of the dependence of diffraction on wavelength is the ordinary microwave oven. Visible light has very short wavelengths, much shorter than the size of the holes in the protective screen of the oven door. So it travels out through the holes with very little diffraction, and we see the food inside with no trouble. But the microwaves have wavelengths much bigger than the hole size, so they diffract considerably through the holes, canceling each other out on the outside through destructive interference (see below), and we are protected from them.

**Diffraction:**
The changing of direction of waves to bend around corners and spread as they encounter obstacles.

a)
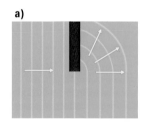

b)
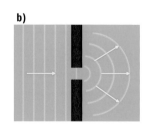

c)
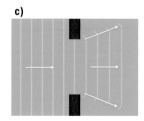

**Figure 10.15**
Diffraction takes place when waves go through holes in barriers, around obstacles, or around corners. The larger the opening in a barrier, the smaller the diffraction (as shown in c).

## Interference

**Interference** occurs when two or more waves travel through the same medium at the same time. At some locations these waves will add together to create a greater disturbance. In other locations the waves subtract, creating little or no disturbance.

Imagine two rocks dropped near each other in an otherwise smooth pond (*Figure 10.16*). Each rock creates a set of circular surface waves. Both sets of waves pass through points on the surface at the same time. At points where the waves are in synchronization, the crests and troughs from both waves arrive together, causing the amplitude to be greater than it would be for either wave alone. Here the two waves enhance each other in **constructive interference**.

Between regions of constructive interference, the waves are out of synchronization. Crests from one wave will try to cause the water to rise while troughs from the other wave will try to make the same water fall. Here the two waves cancel each other in **destructive interference**.

Interesting acoustical effects occur when sound waves interfere. Sound coming from a single musical instrument being played in a room reflects from the walls and diffracts around obstacles. As reflected waves overlap, areas of constructive and destructive interference can occur, making the instrument sound louder or softer depending on where you sit. Auditoriums often have panels or curtains to absorb sound and minimize interference from reflected waves.

Interference can take place between sounds from two different instruments, or between an instrument and a frequency "standard" like a tuning fork. Musicians use interference to tune their instruments by listening for "beats." A beat is a slowly changing amplitude caused by alternating constructive and destructive interference. Unlike the spatial interference described above, beats are heard by all listeners, regardless of where they are, when the instrument frequency is close to, but not identical with the standard. The beat frequency becomes slower as the instrument becomes more in tune.

Other forms of energy transportation besides waves, such as convection, will reflect and refract. However, diffraction and interference are unique to waves. In the example where two rocks were tossed into a pond, the waves from a single rock would, by themselves, cause a disturbance at all points on the water surface. But add *more* disturbance energy to the pond by tossing in a second rock and some points experience *less* disturbance than before. Waves are the only transmission we know of that exhibits this kind of cancellation.

## Standing Waves

Reflection and interference can come together under the right circumstances to create a phenomenon called a **standing wave**. Imagine a rope with one end attached to a wall while the other end is grasped and shaken up and down. The wave from the shaking travels down the rope, reflects from the wall and travels back to the end where it started. If the frequency and wavelength are adjusted so that the reflected wave is synchronized with the original wave,[2]

---

[2] As a reminder, "synchronized" means that the reflected

---

### Sidebar definitions

**Interference:**

The canceling and enhancing effect that occurs when two waves move through the same space at the same time.

**Constructive Interference:**

When two or more waves passing through the same space at the same time both disturb the medium in the same way so that the resultant amplitude is larger than the amplitude of each individual wave separately.

**Destructive Interference:**

When two or more waves passing through the same space at the same time both disturb the medium in opposite ways so that the resultant amplitude is smaller than the amplitude of each individual wave separately.

**Standing Wave:**

A wave characterized by lack of vibration at certain points, between which areas of maximum vibration occur.

---

 - - - **constructive interference**     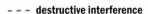 - - - **destructive interference**

a)

b)

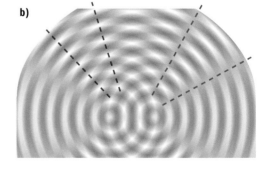

**Figure 10.16**

a) Dropping a rock in a pond will create circular waves. In this illustration color indicates depth; the darker blue represents wave troughs, and the white represents wave crests.

b) Dropping two rocks close to each other will create waves that cause constructive and destructive interference. Notice that constructive interference causes lines of higher contrast or amplitude between troughs and crests (blue and white) while destructive interference creates muddy purple lines with low amplitude.

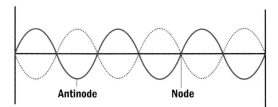

**Figure 10.17**
Standing waves created when waves of the same wavelength move through a string from opposite ends. The solid and dashed curves show the string at two different times.

the reflected wave will have its troughs and crests in perfect alignment with the wave being generated. In this case a pattern such as shown in *Figure 10.17* will be formed, in which the waves seem to "stand" in place.

Standing waves on a rope have places of constructive and destructive interference along the entire length. *Figure 10.18* shows one, two, and three standing waves. The points of no motion are places of destructive interference called **nodes**. The points of maximum motion are places of constructive interference called **antinodes**.

Only waves with wavelengths that are divisible into the rope length with no remainder will create standing waves, as illustrated in *Figure 10.18*. If the wavelengths are not exactly divisible into the rope length, the reflected wave will not synchronize with the original one. Places of constructive and destructive interference will drift on the rope and neither nodes nor antinodes will be established as in the bottom example of *Figure 10.19*.

wave has its troughs and crests in perfect alignment with the wave being generated.

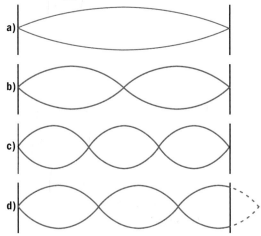

**Figure 10.19**
To get standing waves between two stationary points at the ends of a string, the wavelengths must just fit the space between the points. Wave patterns (a), (b), and (c) are allowed; a standing wave will not occur in pattern (d).

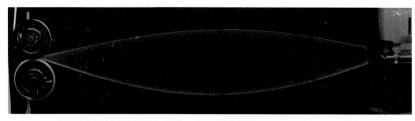

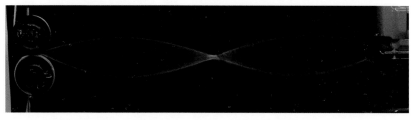

**Figure 10.18**
Images of one, two, and three standing waves in a vibrating string. The places of no vibration (nodes) and maximum vibration (antinodes) are clearly visible. The number of antinodes equals the number of standing waves.

Standing waves can also occur in two-dimensional media, such as a drumhead. In these cases, the nodes are lines rather than points, but the idea is the same. Two dimensional surfaces can sustain standing waves in two directions at once, giving them a greater variety of standing wave patterns than is possible for a one-dimensional rope. A few standing wave patterns in a square metal plate are shown in *Figure 10.20*.

As you might imagine, standing waves may also exist in three-dimensional objects. We will find in Chapter 16 that three-dimensional standing waves are the key to creating the structure of atoms.

All musical instruments generate standing waves within them—on the strings of a guitar or violin, in the air columns of a clarinet, trumpet, or organ, or on the surface of a drum as noted above. The standing waves vibrate the air, filling it with sound waves of the same frequency. Large instruments like kettle drums produce long wavelength, low-pitched notes. Small instruments like piccolos produce short wavelength, high-pitched notes. The varying shapes, sizes, and reflective properties of each musical instrument create the particular set of standing waves that gives each its own unique sound. The performance of a magnificent symphonic

**Node:**
A location of no vibration in a standing wave.

**Antinode:**
A location of maximum vibration in a standing wave.

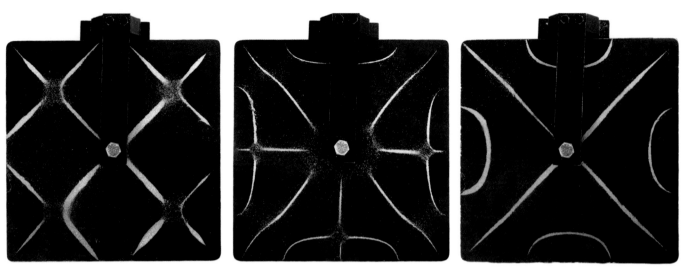

**Figure 10.20**
Standing wave patterns on a square metal plate. The rich variety in patterns comes from interference between waves of different wavelength set up in each of the two dimensions.

orchestra, where waves of all different lengths and frequencies blend harmoniously together, is perhaps the most satisfying manifestation of interference created by mankind.

### Doppler Effect

**Doppler Effect:**
A change in the observed frequency of a wave occurring when the source and observer are in motion relative to each other.

Finally we consider how the motion of whatever is generating or receiving waves alters wavelength and frequency. This alteration is called the **Doppler effect** or **Doppler shift** after Christian Doppler (1803–1853) an Austrian mathematician who first described it. It plays an important role in sensing and measuring motion.

Consider the waves generated by the boat in *Figure 10.21*. The boat's forward motion shortens the distance between crests in that direction. At the same time, it lengthens the distance between crests behind it. This makes the wavelength in front of the boat smaller and the wavelength behind the boat larger. Because frequency and wavelength are inversely related to each other, the wave's frequency in front of the boat is higher and the wave's frequency behind the boat is lower. So a wave's frequency is higher if the source moves toward the receiver and lower if the source moves away from the receiver.

The same effect occurs if the receiver moves

## HARVEY FLETCHER'S CONTRIBUTION

Native Utahn Harvey Fletcher (born 1884 in Provo, UT) was a leading authority in the fields of psychoacoustics and acoustical engineering. He graduated in 1907 with a B.S. degree from Brigham Young Academy. After teaching at his alma mater for a year, Harvey went to the University of Chicago for his Ph.D. His dissertation, under the direction of Robert Millikan, involved building the oil-drop apparatus to measure the electrical charge of an electron (see page 44). He was awarded the first *summa cum laude* degree in physics at the University of Chicago in 1911.

In 1916 he was offered a position with the engineering staff of the Research Department at Bell Telephone Laboratories. He became head of the Acoustics Department at Bell Labs and was appointed Director of all of the Physical Research there in 1933. He held 19 patents and published 51 papers and 2 books. He is credited with the development of the hearing aid and the audiometer, and was the first to demonstrate stereophonic sound reproduction. He was also instrumental in the development of sound encoding on film. This allowed sound and picture to be synchronized for cinema, and along with stereo sound, set the foundation for our modern movie sound experience.

Dr. Fletcher died July 23, 1981 in Orem, Utah. In addition to his scientific achievements, Harvey Fletcher was a loving husband (he married Lorena Chipman in 1908), a faithful father of his 7 children, a dedicated gardener, and a fishing enthusiast.

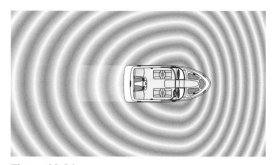

**Figure 10.21**
Wave crests are closer in front of the boat than behind it because of the motion of the boat.

**Figure 10.22**
Sound waves from a moving car are closer together in front of the car in the same way that water waves are closer in front of a moving boat. Waves behind the car are father apart than those in front. Where would the pitch be higher?

toward or away from the source of the waves. Consider a boat that cruises through a lake and runs into the on-coming wake of another boat. The moving boat encounters the wake's wave crests more rapidly than it would if sitting stationary. So the frequency the boat measures is higher. If the boat were moving away from the wake, it would encounter the crests less rapidly and measure a lower frequency.

The same amount of Doppler shifting takes place regardless of whether the sender or receiver moves. Therefore the Doppler shift measures only the relative speed between the sender and receiver and not any sort of absolute motion of either one. This is as expected by the principle of motion symmetry (Chapter 7).

The Doppler effect is sometimes heard in everyday sounds. You have probably heard a police car, its siren blaring, drive toward you on its way to some emergency. The siren moving toward you has a higher frequency, and therefore a higher pitch, than if the police car were parked (*Figure 10.22*). When the police car passes, the sound immediately drops to a lower frequency and pitch. The amount of this frequency change depends solely on the speed of the car, not its distance, loudness, or any other factor.

Doppler radar is used by weather stations to predict storm movements. A Doppler radar bounces a radio signal off a distant storm cloud and receives it back again. The amount of Doppler shifting in the received signal tells the weatherman the speed of the cloud towards or away from the station, allowing them to predict when the storm will arrive.

# 10 STUDY GUIDE

## Chapter Framework

**A. Waves**
1. Transport energy
2. Travel through a medium needs restoring force

**B. Wave Types**
1. Longitudinal
2. Transverse
3. Surface

**C. Wave Properties**
1. Amplitude
2. Wavelength
3. Frequency
4. Wave Speed
5. Characteristics
   a. Crests and troughs

**D. Wave Phenomena**
1. Reflection
2. Refraction
3. Diffraction
4. Interference
   a. Constructive and destructive
5. Standing Waves
   a. Nodes and antinodes
6. Doppler Effect

## Comprehension

**Matching**

a. Reflection
b. Shear wave
c. Wavelength
d. Standing wave
e. Antinode
f. Equilibrium position
g. Frequency
h. Refraction
i. Interference
j. Wave speed
k. Compression wave
l. Amplitude
m. Node
n. Diffraction

1. ____ A wave where the medium is displaced parallel to the direction the wave travels.
2. ____ The maximum distance that a particle moves from its resting position when a traveling wave passes through it.
3. ____ The rate that a single wave peak travels in a medium.
4. ____ A wave's ability to bend around corners and spread behind holes.
5. ____ A place in a medium where a molecule naturally resides.
6. ____ The change in speed and direction as a wave moves from one medium into another.
7. ____ The result of confined waves interfering in such a way that destructive and constructive interference always occur in a fixed location.
8. ____ Occurs when two or more waves travel through the same medium at the same time.
9. ____ The distance between successive similar parts in repeating waves.
10. ____ The act of bouncing off the boundary between two different mediums.
11. ____ A fixed position of destructive interference in a standing wave.
12. ____ Wave where the forces stretch the bonds between molecules in a direction that is perpendicular to the direction the wave travels.
13. ____ The number of wave crests passing a particular point every second.
14. ____ A fixed position of constructive interference in a standing wave.

**True/ False**
1. ____ Compression waves travel through all different states of matter.
2. ____ Musical instruments use standing waves to produce sound.
3. ____ Waves cause the medium they travel through to change from its equilibrium shape.
4. ____ Doppler shift measures the absolute speed of the sender.
5. ____ The major determinants in wave speed are the wave's frequency and amplitude.
6. ____ Standing waves occur any time two waves interfere with each other.

**Fill in the Blank**
1. Mechanical waves travel through a _____ that supports the waves' motion.
2. Shear waves only travel through _____.
3. Geologists use _____ waves to "see" inside Earth.
4. The amount of diffraction depends on the size of the _____ relative to the size of the opening the wave passes through.
5. _____ equals frequency x wavelength.
6. Another name for a compression wave is a _____ wave.

## Analysis

1. Which of the following is an example of refraction?
   a) An echo that bounces off a nearby wall
   b) Two waves in a lake coming together to form a larger wave.
   c) Sound from a TV in a nearby room that passes through an open door
   d) Eyeglasses correcting a person's vision

2. Which of the following is a shear wave?
   a) A rope pulled tight and plucked
   b) Human speech
   c) The sound from a car horn
   d) A wave traveling towards the shore of a lake
   e) a and d

3. What necessarily decreases if you increase wavelength of a sound wave?
   a) Amplitude
   b) Frequency
   c) Speed

d) Volume

4. What happens to the sound emitted from a radio as it moves away from you?

   a) Its wavelength would decrease.

   b) Everything would remain the same.

   c) Its wavelength would increase.

   d) Its amplitude would increase.

   e) Its frequency would increase.

5. Locations in an auditorium where sound becomes soft or muffled could be places of

   a) constructive interference.

   b) antinodes.

   c) diffraction.

   d) refraction.

   e) destructive interference.

6. If you double the frequency of a soundwave

   a) the speed of the wave stays the same

   b) the speed of the wave increases to twice its original value

   c) the speed of the wave decreases to one half its original value

7. The amplitude of a sound wave is a physical quantity that determines the

   a) pitch.

   b) loudness.

   c) quality.

   d) wavelength.

   e) velocity.

8. When light from an object like a star is collected and spread out the resulting "rainbow" of colors is called a spectrum. Light, like other waves, can be Doppler shifted. If the spectrum of a star is studied, and the frequencies are shifted towards the higher, blue end of the spectrum, what can you conclude about that star?

   a) It is far away.

   b) It is moving away from Earth.

   c) It is close to Earth.

   d) It is moving towards Earth.

9. What is a mechanical wave?

10. How do glass lenses prevent refraction from reversing itself when leaving the glass?

11. Why don't shear waves travel through liquids?

12. Explain how reflection of waves in a standing wave might create constructive and destructive interference.

13. Why doesn't changing frequency and wavelength affect wave speed?

14. What conditions need to be met in order to produce a standing wave?

15. If someone is standing around a corner why can you hear them talking? Why can't you see them?

## Synthesis

1. What is the difference between diffraction and refraction? Give and explain an example of each.

2. How do panels and curtains in an auditorium minimize wave interference?

3. Why do waves travel through dense material faster than materials that are not as dense?

4. Tools like ultrasound, sonar, and seismology give us information about things we cannot see or touch. What properties of waves allow this?

5. Instructions on stereo speakers tell you to install them certain distances away from walls or other hard surfaces. Why would this be important?

6. Mechanical waves move energy from one place to another. So do the heat transfer processes of radiation, convection, and conduction. Compare and contrast how these three phenomena move energy through a medium. Can you think of any other ways that energy can be moved through materials?

7. A magnifying lens uses refraction to make objects appear larger. Light also refracts when going through a plate glass window as well, yet images seen through windows do not normally appear larger. Why?

8. Should sound have the same speed through gases made of lighter particles than in gases made of heavier particles? Justify your answer using Newton's Second Law of Motion.

9. You can make your voice sound higher by breathing helium. Why do you suppose this is the case? (Hint: The wavelength of sound is fixed by the size of your throat and vocal chords. But the speed of sound through helium is faster than it is through air.)

# The Properties of Light

*Give light, and the darkness will disappear of itself.*

**Desiderius Erasmus**

## 11

## LEARN

- How the speed of light has been measured.

- The different types of electromagnetic radiation.

- Why we believe light to be a wave.

- Why we believe light to also be a stream of particles.

- The evidence for and ideas behind the theory of wave-particle duality.

Light, like matter and energy, is a fundamental part of the Universe. The warmth and energy light brings from our Sun makes life possible. Light illuminates our surroundings, allowing us to see, move, learn, and function as a society. Light is so much a part of living itself that we often take it for granted.

We are quite familiar with how light behaves but do not yet completely understand what it is. Some evidence tells us light is a wave transporting energy like the waves discussed in Chapter 10. Other evidence supports light being a stream of particles, transporting energy like convection does. Beside these two choices, our everyday experience provides no other clues for what light could be. Light is a usual everyday phenomenon that seems to be quite unusual.

In this chapter we discuss the nature of light and how it travels and interacts with matter. We dwell considerably on the historical development of our understanding of light for its insights into light itself and also scientific inquiry. We will find that to explain experimental results we must consider light to be a wave in

some circumstances and to be a stream of particles in others. Comprehending this dual nature remains one of the most interesting challenges in science.

## 11-1 The Speed of Light

In Chapters 7 and 9 we discussed how light travels faster than any other known entity. It moves so rapidly that the renowned 17th century mathematician and philosopher René Descartes (1596–1650) believed it traveled instantaneously with infinite speed. Galileo Galilei knew that light moved very fast but thought its speed was finite. To test this hypothesis he and a colleague each took covered lanterns and stood on adjacent hill tops. Galileo uncovered his lantern and the colleague in turn uncovered his own lantern as soon as he saw light from Galileo's lantern. By measuring the time between when he uncovered his lantern and when he saw light from his colleagues' lamp, Galileo inferred a speed for light of at least 500 km/sec.

This value is fast but, as you might imagine from knowing how slowly one's reflexes work, it was nowhere near the actual speed.

In 1676, Danish astronomer Olaus Roemer (1644–1710) measured the speed of light by observing Jupiter's moons. Every week these moons are eclipsed several dozen times as they orbit behind Jupiter. When Jupiter was farthest from Earth, these eclipses came 22 minutes later than they did when Jupiter was nearest. Roemer correctly concluded that the later eclipse times were an illusion arising from light taking 22 minutes longer to travel from Jupiter to Earth when Jupiter was most distant (*Figure 11.1*). The speed of light was then calcu-

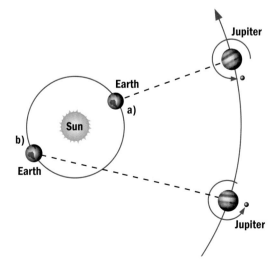

**Figure 11.1**
Roemer found that light from Jupiter took 15 minutes longer to reach Earth in position b) than in position a). From this he was able to estimate the speed of light.

lated by dividing the difference in the distance to Jupiter by 22 minutes.

Armand Fizeau (1819–1896) devised a rotating toothed wheel like the one shown in *Figure 11.2* to measure the speed of light more precisely. In the earliest versions of his experiment, a beam of light passed through a gap in the wheel's teeth, traveled over eight kilometers to a mirror, then was reflected back towards the device where it was blocked by a tooth which had rotated into its path. Knowing the wheel's rotation speed, the gap sizes between the teeth, and the distance to the mirror, Fizeau was able to accurately calculate the speed of light.

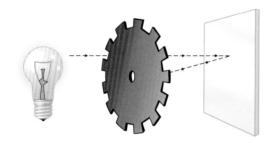

**Figure 11.2**
A method by which the speed of light can be measured. The wheel advances one tooth while a light pulse travels to the mirror and back.

Today we use high-speed electronic sensors to easily measure time intervals shorter than one-billionth of a second, the time that it takes light to travel one foot. Using these sensors to time light racing to a mirror and back we have found its speed to be 299,792.458 km/sec. This is over 900,000 times the speed of sound, 30,000 times the speed of our fastest rockets, and 10,000 times the speed of Earth in its orbit. Light can travel around Earth in 0.13 seconds, from Earth to the Moon and back again in 2.6 seconds, from the Sun to Earth in 8.3 minutes, and from the Sun to Neptune on the edge of the solar system in just over 4 hours.

The time it takes light to travel between objects is a convenient way of expressing large distances in space. The average Earth-to-Sun distance of 93 million miles is often expressed in its light-travel time of 8.3 light-minutes. The distance from Earth to the nearest star, Alpha Centauri, is 4.3 light-years, and the distance to the farthest galaxies we know of is more than 10 billion light years.

## 11-2 The Wave Nature of Light

So what exactly is light? Let us first consider the evidence of it being a wave. If light is a wave it will reflect, refract, diffract, and interfere. In Chapter 10 we noted how light reflects as shown by an image in a mirror, and how it refracts as demonstrated by a stick half-submerged in water looking bent (see Figure 10.13).

Testing for diffraction and interference requires more careful experimentation. Recall that wave diffraction is noticeable only when the wavelength is comparable to the size of the opening the wave goes through. Visible light has wavelengths between 4 and $8 \times 10^{-6}$ meters, so diffraction is noticeable only when it is projected through holes of this size.

Sir Isaac Newton didn't know the wavelength of light was that small. So when he observed objects in a strong beam of light casting very sharp shadows, he incorrectly reasoned that no diffraction was taking place at all. If it were, he thought, the shadow edges would be blurred, causing the shadow to look fuzzy. The sharpness of the shadows was taken to be evidence that light was a stream of particles.

Newton knew that a particle model of light was as consistent with reflection and refraction as a wave model was. Particles striking a mirror reflect like balls bouncing off a wall. In the interface between two media (like air and water) these particles would be like tennis balls striking and passing through a piece of tissue paper. The tissue paper would rupture, but the speed of the balls would be slowed as they passed through in just such a way to account for the refraction. With no evidence for diffraction, Newton's particle hypothesis was accepted as being correct until about 1800.

But light *does* diffract! This can be easily demonstrated using modern lasers and tiny holes in thin sheets of metal. *Figure 11.3* illustrates diffraction of a light beam sent through such a series of very small holes. Hole "a" is the largest and hole "c" is the smallest. If light were a stream of particles, the light spot behind the smallest hole would be the smallest one. Instead, it is the largest as is expected for a diffracting wave.

Interference was the most difficult of the four wave qualities to discover. The first definitive demonstration of interference was in 1801

a)

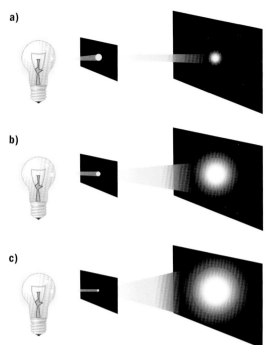

b)

c)

**Figure 11.3**
The diffraction of light. The light spot emerging from the smallest hole diffracts the most, proving that light is a wave.

a)

b)

**Figure 11.4**
a) Light passing through a single slit diffracts to either side of it.

b) Light passing through two slits diffracts and interferes as well, creating a series of bright lines (constructive interference) and dark lines (destructive interference).

by Thomas Young (1773–1829), a London physician and distinguished scholar in many subjects. Young announced his success to the world with this preamble:

> Much as I venerate the name of Newton, I am not therefore obliged to believe that he was infallible. I see . . . with regret that he was liable to err, and that this authority has, perhaps, sometimes even retarded the progress of science.

Young showed both interference and diffraction by inventing a simple yet profound test called the "double-slit experiment." To understand how it works, consider a thin sheet of metal with a small narrow slit in it. Light of a single wavelength passing through the slit diffracts out in a fan-like pattern as shown in *Figure 11.4a.*

Now suppose we create a second slit of equal size next to the first slit. When light passes through this second slit it also diffracts. Diffraction from both slits causes the emerging light to overlap, giving rise to places of constructive and destructive interference. As a result, the pattern of light striking the screen behind the slits alternates between bright and dark lines. At the location of the bright lines, the two waves combine constructively, creating a stronger wave than before. Between the bright lines, the two waves combine destructively, so that no light energy arrives at the screen. *Figure 11.4b* sketches the resulting pattern of bright and dark lines. *Figure 11.5* is an image of an actual pattern created by a laser beam passing through a double slit.

Young's double-slit interference pattern proved undeniably that light travels through space as a wave. The demonstration is most dramatic at any one of the dark lines. When only one slit is open, light illuminates and brightens the entire area behind the slit. However, when *additional* light passes through the other slit, areas behind the first slit now become *dark*. Such is the nature of interference as pointed out in Chapter 10. Waves are the only phenomenon we know that will do this. Particles, like bullets, would never cancel out or bend through a slit!

When Thomas Young proved light's wave nature with the double-slit experiment, he also discovered that the spacing between bright lines for red light exceeded the spacing between bright lines for blue light. This was proof that different colors have different wavelengths. Blue light has a smaller wavelength than red light and does not diffract as much. As a result, the pattern of bright and dark lines in blue light is more compressed than it is in red light.

Diffraction and interference can be seen by viewing a distant light source, such as a street

**Thomas Young**

An exceptional scholar. In addition to discovering light interference, he made breakthrough discoveries in anatomy, linguistics, and astronomy.

**Figure 11.5**
A photograph of the interference pattern found when red laser light passes through a double slit.

lamp or car light, through a handkerchief, or other thin fabric. The weaving in the fabric creates a checkerboard of tiny slits the size of light's wavelength. Viewing the source of the light through the cloth replicates the double-slit experiment, but with the slits being both horizontal and vertical. Viewed through the material, the light appears interlaced in a checkered pattern top to bottom and side to side with alternating light and dark spots from constructive and destructive interference. Separate colors may even be noticed in the interference pattern because, as mentioned above, the locations of constructive interference depend on wavelength.

Diffraction gratings use the dependence of interference on wavelength to create colorful rainbows as shown in *Figure 11.6*. A diffraction grating is a piece of glass or plastic upon which a large number of long parallel grooves are scratched close together. The undisturbed glass between the scratches acts as a set of narrowly-spaced slits. When a ray of white light passes through a grating, constructive interference breaks it into a series of rays separated by broad, dark regions. The direction of the rays depends on wavelength, with the redder light bent further out than the blue light. As a result, a bright image viewed through a diffraction grating has a rainbow image of it visible on either side.

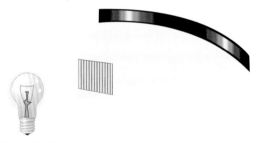

**Figure 11.6**
A diffraction grating separates light into its component colors by means of interference.

## 11-3 Does Light Need a Medium to Travel?

Light comes to Earth from stars and the Sun through the emptiness of space. Yet we learned in the previous chapter that waves need a medium through which to travel. If light is a wave, what is the medium that carries it?

After light was understood to be a wave, it was postulated in the 1800s that space was filled with a light-carrying substance called the "luminiferous ether," or just "ether." The ether had to be very stiff, like a solid, because light is a transverse wave (see section 10–1). But at the same time it also had to be unresistive enough that planets could orbit through it without losing forward motion to friction. Could such a thing really exist?

The Michelson-Morley experiment discussed in Chapter 7 was designed to probe the nature of the ether as well as to measure the expected boost to the speed of light from Earth's orbital motion. When no boost was found, the existence of ether was questioned and eventually this hypothesis was abandoned. Inspired by electromagnetic theory, we instead saw how light could travel in "fields" that exist in otherwise empty space. But what does that mean?

First recall that in Chapter 4, the electromagnetic field was introduced as being the conveyor of the electromagnetic interaction. We learned in that chapter that iron filings can trace the magnetic aspect of this field around a magnet, revealing its strength and direction. In that same chapter we also learned of the electric force law and how the electric force diminishes with distance from a charged object. In Chapter 8 we learned of the conservation of charge. These three ideas were developed independently of each other.

Then in the mid-1800s, James Clerk Maxwell (1831–1879) combined the electric force law with the laws of magnetism and the law of conservation of charge to form a set of equations that seamlessly describe the electric and magnetic interactions. This set of laws, known as **Maxwell's equations**, firmly established that electricity and magnetism were different manifestations of the same interaction. They describe the strength and direction of electromagnetic fields at any location in space and how the forces within these fields change when the charges creating them move.

Some remarkable discoveries came from Maxwell's equations. In particular, they show that a charge vibrating up and down will create an electromagnetic field that propagates outward as a transverse wave. Unlike the mechanical waves explained in Chapter 10, these waves travel through empty space and are not vibrations of matter; rather, they are varying electric and magnetic fields radiating outward from the source. They are transverse waves because the

---

**Maxwell's Equations:**

A set of four fundamental laws, expressed in mathematical form, that govern electricity and magnetism and their interrelationship. The Electrical Force Law is included in Maxwell's Equations.

**James Clerk Maxwell**

The Scottish physicist James Clerk Maxwell (1831–1879) did revolutionary work in electromagnetism and the kinetic theory of gases. After graduating (1854) with a degree in mathematics from Trinity College, Cambridge, he held professorships at Marischal College in Aberdeen (1856) and King's College in London (1860) and became the first Cavendish Professor of Physics at Cambridge in 1871.

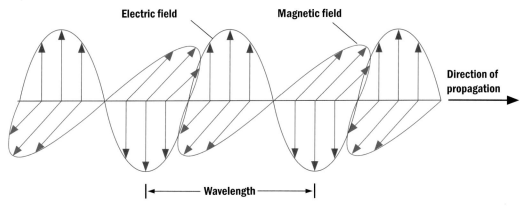

**Figure 11.7**
The force vectors from an electromagnetic wave are perpendicular to the direction the wave travels. The electric and magnetic force vectors are also perpendicular to each other.

directions of the electric and magnetic field vectors of the wave are perpendicular to the direction the wave travels (*Figure 11.7*).

One can find the speed of the predicted waves from Maxwell's equations. When Maxwell calculated this speed, he found that it was exactly the speed of light as measured by Fizeau! This remarkable agreement could not be a coincidence and on December 8, 1864, he told the scientists of the British Royal Society:

> The agreement of the results seems to show that light . . . is an electromagnetic disturbance propagated through the field according to electromagnetic laws.

The correspondence between the theoretically predicted speed and the actual measured speed of light strikingly confirmed the connection between electricity, magnetism, and light. Furthermore, Maxwell's equations predicted that other waves existed in addition to light. These waves were hypothesized to have the same speed as light but different frequencies and different wavelengths ranging from zero to infinity. Eventually they were created in laboratories and harnessed to create radio, television, radar, and other devices of modern communication. With his equations, Maxwell unified electricity, magnetism, and optics—and changed the world.

## 11-4 The Electromagnetic Family

The family of waves predicted by Maxwell's equations is collectively called **electromagnetic radiation** and is the energy-transferring radiation described in Chapter 9. Grouped in order from low frequency to high frequency, they are: radio waves (AM, FM, VHF, UHF), micro-

waves, infrared radiation, visible light (red to blue), ultraviolet radiation, x-rays, and gamma rays (*Figure 11.8*). Visible light is just the relatively small range of frequencies that our eyes see.

The colors of the rainbow influence some names: ultraviolet (UV) light is "bluer than blue" and infrared (IR) light is "redder than red." Our eyes are not sensitive to these wavelengths but instruments are. The night vision

**Electromagnetic Radiation:**

Radiation originating in a varying electromagnetic field, such as visible light, radio waves, x-rays, and gamma rays.

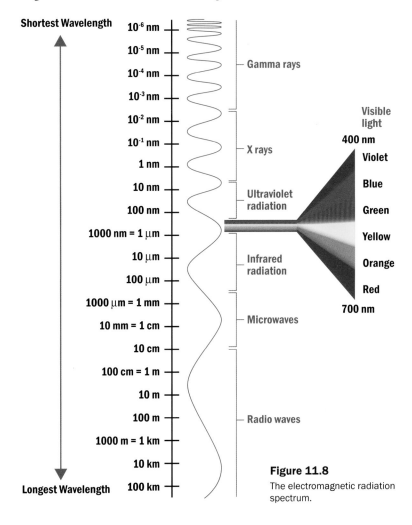

**Figure 11.8**
The electromagnetic radiation spectrum.

goggles used by the military detect the infrared radiation emitted by warm-blooded creatures. T-shirts designed to "glow" in the presence of black lights do so by absorbing UV light and emitting visible light.

Electromagnetic waves radiate out whenever an electric charge *accelerates*. Radio, television, and cell phone signals come from electrons accelerating in antennas. Electrons accelerating in the hot outer layers of our Sun create visible light. X-rays form when fast electrons suddenly decelerate to a stop in an x-ray tube.

Radio and television signals travel through space from broadcast antennas or satellites to radios and television sets. When they arrive they exert forces on the electrons in a receiving antenna, which cause the electrons to move in the same pattern that created the wave. This motion can be detected by sensitive electronics in the radio and television set and converted into sound or pictures. Visible light interacts with electrons in the retina of the eye or in a digital camera, causing reactions that relay visual information to the brain or preserve it in a memory chip.

## 11–5  The Particle Nature of Light

Thomas Young's double-slit experiment settled the debate over the nature of light for nearly a century. But the debate was not over. In 1887, Heinrich Hertz (1857–1894) discovered a curious property of light that triggered a revolution of thought, culminating 18 years later in a new model of light.

Hertz discovered that shining light on some types of metal caused them to eject electrons. The ejected electrons possessed more energy if the light had a shorter wavelength, like ultraviolet light, than if its wavelength were longer. This attribute, called the **photoelectric effect**, was unexpected and puzzling.

In the wave model of light, a wave striking the surface of a metal imparts energy to all electrons encountered. If this energy is great enough, electrons will be ejected. As we learned in Chapter 10, the energy in the wave is given by the amplitude. Since greater brightness equals greater amplitude, brighter light should cause metals to eject electrons with greater energy. However experiments showed that a dim ultraviolet light ejects electrons from metals with

high energy, and a very bright red light ejects no electrons at all. Brightness does not associate with amplitude or energy in the way the wave model predicts!

Such photoelectric experiments led to the clear conclusion that light energy is associated with *frequency*. Wave-based theories formulated to explain why higher light frequencies had higher energy all failed. Soon it became obvious that the wave model of light was unable to explain this.

In 1905 Albert Einstein introduced a new model of light that explained the photoelectric effect simply and perfectly. This bold return to Newton's ideas of light assumed that light was composed of particles called **photons** that had energy but neither mass nor charge. The energy of a photon is given by Planck's equation, which is

$$\textbf{Energy} = \textbf{h} \times \textbf{frequency}$$

where h is a previously known value called **Planck's constant**, a small number equal to 6.63 $\times 10^{-34}$ in the metric system of units. Because the formula says that each photon of light carries an amount of energy proportional to its frequency, doubling the frequency doubles the energy. Ultraviolet light with its higher frequency possesses greater energy per photon than lower frequency red light. In this model a beam of light is brighter when it has *more photons,* not because each photon has more energy.

Max Planck (1858–1947) was the first to have written this equation, but in a different context and he did not realize how fundamental the formula was. Einstein generalized it to all electromagnetic waves in all situations.

To explain the photoelectric effect, think of photons as being like bullets. Fire bullets at marbles and a marble will go flying if a bullet of sufficient energy hits it. In the same way, an electron flies off metal when a photon of sufficient energy hits it. Ultraviolet photons hold enough energy to eject electrons in cases where red photons do not. Making the red light beam brighter increases the number of photons, but since each red photon still cannot eject an electron, an increase in brightness will not cause electrons to be emitted.

Another example of how photons interact with matter is digital photography. Digital cameras capture photons using a rectangular array

---

**Photoelectric Effect:**

The ejection of electrons from metals when light is shined on the metal's surface.

**Photon:**

A particle of light. It possesses energy, frequency, and wavelength but neither mass nor charge.

**Planck's Constant:**

A value when multiplied by the frequency of light, gives the energy of the photon of light at that frequency.

**Max Planck**

The German physicist Max Planck (1858–1947) developed the equation proposing that the energy of a photon had to be a multiple of a specific value (Planck's constant). This idea of "quantized" energy emissions is the foundation of quantum mechanics.

# PHYSICS OF BROADCASTING

Broadcast technology is everywhere. We watch TV, listen to radio, retrieve information over the Internet, talk on cell phones, and stream videos on tablets and smart phones. All of these systems use electromagnetic waves to transport their information. How do they do it? How can an electromagnetic wave carry a voice or music or picture? Each system has its own technology, but a few basic ideas are common to them all.

First, a transmitter generates a simple wave called a "carrier wave." The carrier-wave frequency is the value a radio or TV is tuned to when different stations or channels are selected. Cell phones automatically choose a unique carrier-wave frequency for the area or "cell" they are in each time a phone call is placed. The purpose of the carrier wave is to transport an encoded signal.

Sound or picture information is encoded onto a carrier wave through

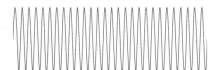

**Figure 11.9**
The carrier signal.

**Figure 11.10**
The modulating signal.

**Figure 11.11**
The carrier signal with amplitude modulation.

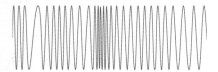

**Figure 11.12**
The carrier signal with frequency modulation.

a process called "modulation." Carrier waves are modulated by changing either their amplitude or frequency or both. AM radios use amplitude modulation (AM) while FM radio, television, and cell phones use frequency modulation (FM).

A simple early means of AM communication was Morse Code. In Morse Code, the code key turned the transmitter on and off, causing the amplitude of the carrier wave to go from nothing to full power whenever the key was pressed. The information sent was a series of long and short signals encoded to represent the alphabet. A person on the receiving end translated the resultant "dots and dashes" first into letters and then into words.

An AM radio transmitter modulates the carrier signal amplitude smoothly in direct proportion to the energy of the sound as shown in Figures 11.9–11.11. The carrier wave transports this modulated signal through space where a radio antenna picks it up. The radio generates its own signal at the frequency of the carrier wave and subtracts it off the received signal, leaving only the modulated signal. The speakers amplify that signal and reproduce it as a voice or music.

AM radio has a few technical weaknesses. Most natural and man-made radio noise is AM in nature. AM receivers have no means of rejecting that noise, causing the reception clarity to degrade rapidly with distance from the source. Also, quiet sounds generate a weaker signal than loud sounds because the amplitude is modulated down. This requires all AM receivers to have circuits to compensate for the signal level differences.

These problems are overcome when the frequency is modulated instead of the amplitude (Figure 11.12). In FM signals, a positive peak in the modulating signal pushes the carrier frequency slightly higher while a negative peak pushes it lower. At the receiving end, a discriminator circuit subtracts the car-

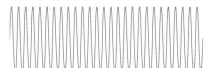

**Figure 11.13**
The carrier signal.

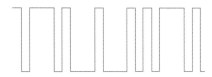

**Figure 11.14**
A digital modulation.

**Figure 11.15**
The carrier signal with digital modulation.

rier wave off and converts the remaining frequency variations to the original signal. Because the recovered audio is dependent only on the frequency and not amplitude, no compensation for different signal levels is required and the noise picked up during transmission is much less than with AM signals.

There are other types of modulation, but all are variations of AM or FM. Digital radio or cell phones modulate the frequency in a stream of "ones" and "zeros," creating a signal that is analogous to a rapid FM Morse code (Figures 11.13–11.15). The digital signal is constructed by computer chips that are programmed to turn sound or picture information into a stream of ones and zeros. Receiving cell phones take the encoded stream and reconstruct it as the original signal, according to the code scheme. Because coding schemes can be as varied as our imaginations allow, digital signals are virtually limitless in the type of information they can convey. And since they only communicate an "on" and "off" state like a Morse Code transmitter, they are not as susceptible to noise as either standard "analog" FM or AM encoding.

of tiny electronic light detectors called pixels. Neighboring pixels count the number of red, green, and blue photons that strike them. This information is read by a computer chip to generate a color picture.

Thousands of experiments have verified the existence of photons of light. Our own eyes, in fact, work by detecting individual photons. We do not notice individual photon strikes with our eyes because even the dimmest light beam contains so many photons that images always appear continuous and smooth.

## 11-6  Wave–Particle Duality

Let us back up and review for a minute. Young's double slit experiment proved light diffracts and interferes like a wave. But the photoelectric effect proves it interacts with metals like a particle. What happens when these two experiments are combined?

The pattern of bright and dark bands produced by a *bright* laser was shown in Figure 11.5. Now try the experiment again using a laser so *dim* that the photons arrive infrequently. When a high-speed camera records the interference pattern of faint laser light shining through two narrow, closely-spaced slits, a random pattern of dots appears, as shown in *Figure 11.16a*. In this image the exposure time is so short that only a few photons appear. Increasing the exposure time produces a collection of bright dots that looks less random, as in Figure 11.16b. Although the pattern is spotty, it begins to look like interference. For longer exposures, the

number of dots increases until the entire range of light and dark is filled in, as shown in Figure 11.16c. Now the interference pattern is clearly visible.

And so we come to a dilemma. If light were not a wave there would be no interference pattern. But if light were not a stream of photons, the pattern would not build up one spot at a time. How do we reconcile this?

We have found that every time we devise an experiment to measure light's wave properties, such as wavelength or interference, it works. And every time we devise an experiment to measure light's particle properties, such as photon position and energy, it also works. Is light a wave? Is light a particle? Yes.

In our everyday experience particles and waves have complementary natures. Particles are localized lumps. Waves are spread-out disturbances. The Principle of Non-contradiction says that when two contrary propositions are offered, both cannot be true. So are these propositions, that light is wave or particle, totally contradictory?

As noted in Section 10–3, little diffraction or wave spreading occurs for small wavelengths. Electromagnetic waves of high frequency have such small wavelengths that diffraction is not observable, or hardly so. We can think, therefore, of electromagnetic waves in this range as traveling in straight lines with little spreading. They act mostly like moving particles and we typically call them "rays," like X-rays and gamma rays. Longer wavelength electromagnetic waves exhibit more diffraction, more bending, more

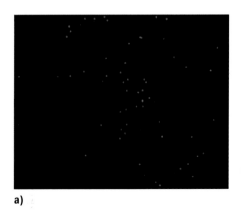 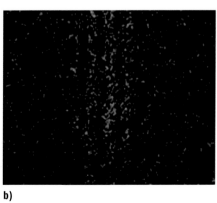 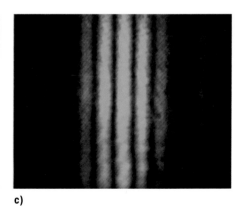

a)    b)    c)

**Figure 11.16**

A digital camera is used to measure very dim laser light after it passes through two narrow, closely-spaced slits. a) The camera image with a very short exposure time. The measured laser light appears as a random collection of dots. b) A longer exposure time. The collection of dots is less random. They cluster in some areas and not in others. c) A very long exposure time. The interference pattern is built up by the collection of dots. It looks like the interference pattern in Figure 11.5.

Photos courtesy of the *American Journal of Physics*. T. L. Dimitrova and A. Weis, "The wave-particle duality of light: A demonstration experiment," *Am. J. Phys.* 76, February 2008.

wave-like behavior, and we typically call these "waves," like radio waves or microwaves. This provides some insight. If diffraction is negligible, electromagnetic waves behave much like particles. If it is prominent, they behave like waves. So in this sense electromagnetic waves have characteristics of both waves and particles at once. We say they possess wave-particle duality.

There is a second clue to reconciling these two natures. Consider again the double slit experiment illustrated in Figure 11.16. To review, an interference pattern can occur only if light is a wave because particles don't interfere. However, the interference image on the detector is being constructed one dot at a time. This can occur only if light is a stream of photons arriving one after another.

The photons do not strike the paper at random places. They have a greater probability of striking the locations where the image is brightest and a lower probability of arriving at the darker locations. In other words, the image of an interference pattern in Figure 11.16 builds up because regions where constructive wave interference occurs have a high probability of being struck by a photon and regions where destructive interference occurs have a low probability of being struck by a photon.

We can successfully describe this aspect of wave-particle duality by treating light as a stream of particles arriving at locations predicted in a probabilistic fashion from the wave model. In other words, the particle part of wave-particle duality tells us how the light is *detected* and the wave part tells us how the photons *travel* and *where* they will be detected. This will be discussed further in Chapter 15, where we will learn that particles of matter also possess wave-particle duality.

### References

1. Mason, Stephen F., *A History of the Sciences,* MacMillan, 1962. p. 468.

# 1.1 STUDY GUIDE

## Chapter Framework

**A. The Speed of Light**
1. Galileo, Olaus Roemer, Armand Fizeau

**B. The Wave Nature of Light**
1. Shows All Four Wave Properties
2. Thomas Young
3. Double Slit Experiment

**C. The Medium of Light Waves**
1. Field
2. James Clerk Maxwell
3. Maxwell's Equations

**D. The Electromagnetic Family**
1. Electromagnetic Radiation
   a. *Radio to gamma rays*
   b. *Acceleration of charged particles*
2. Broadcasting
   a. *Amplitude modulation*
   b. *Frequency modulation*

**E. The Particle Nature of Light**
1. Photoelectric Effect
2. Light Energy Associates with Frequency
3. Photons

**F. Wave-Particle Duality**

## Comprehension

### Matching I
Match the experiment with what it proved about light.

a. Particle
b. Wave

1. \_\_\_\_ Handkerchief held up to light.
2. \_\_\_\_ Interference pattern created by the double-slit experiment.
3. \_\_\_\_ Photoelectric effect.
4. \_\_\_\_ Picture formed by low intensity light.
5. \_\_\_\_ The way digital cameras operate.
6. \_\_\_\_ Single spot of light after passing through a double-slit experiment.

### Matching II
Match the word to its corresponding definition.

a. Interference pattern
b. Photon
c. Electromagnetic radiation
d. Photoelectric effect
e. Wave-particle duality
f. AM
g. FM

1. \_\_\_\_ Carrier wave modulated by changing the frequency.
2. \_\_\_\_ The ejection of electrons from metals when high frequency or UV light is shined on the metal's surface.
3. \_\_\_\_ Possessing both wave and particle properties.
4. \_\_\_\_ A particle of light. It possesses energy, frequency, and wavelength but neither mass nor charge.
5. \_\_\_\_ A series of bright lines separated by dark areas.
6. \_\_\_\_ Carrier wave modulated by changing the amplitude.
7. \_\_\_\_ Radiation originating in a varying electromagnetic field, such as visible light, radio waves, x-rays, and gamma rays.

## True/ False

1. \_\_\_\_ Sharp shadows ultimately prove that light doesn't diffract and is therefore a particle.
2. \_\_\_\_ Light is an electromagnetic disturbance spread throughout space according to electromagnetic laws.
3. \_\_\_\_ Galileo accurately predicted the speed of light using two lanterns.
4. \_\_\_\_ The photoelectric effect shows that frequency of light determines whether or not an electron will be discharged.

## Fill in the Blank

1. The _____ experiment first proved that light created interference patterns.
2. Roemer measured the _____ by using Jupiter's moons.
3. Maxwell's equations predict the strength and direction of the _____.
4. The particle nature of light becomes evident when light is _____.
5. The wave nature tells us how light _____.
6. Electromagnetic radiation is given off when charged particles _____.

## Analysis

1. Traveling at the speed of light, Diana and Anna go on a trip that takes them 10 light seconds. How far did they travel?
   a) 350,000 km
   b) 2,997,925 km
   c) 6,230,543 km
   d) 1,876,232 km

2. The difference between blue light and red light is that
   a) red light has more energy per photon.
   b) red light has a higher speed.
   c) blue light has a higher speed.
   d) red light has a longer wavelength.
   e) blue light has a longer wavelength.

3. One night Sam looks at a street light through the screen of a window or door. He carefully observes the apparent image. The image reveals light streaks extend outward from a central bright spot. The outward streaks are also seen to consist of a series of light and dark spaces. When the same light is viewed without looking through a screen no streaks are seen. The presence and pattern of the streaks are due to
   a) diffraction and interference.
   b) refraction and interference.
   c) diffraction and refraction.
   d) reflection and refraction.
   e) reflection and diffraction.

4. Of the following, the one with the least energy per photon is
   a) infrared light.
   b) x-rays.
   c) blue light.
   d) red light.
   e) ultraviolet light.

5. The wavelength of red light (700 nanometers) is longer than the wavelength of violet light (400 nanometers). Which of the following statements is true?
   a) The photon energy of red light is highest because the wavelength is longest.
   b) The photon energy of both colors is the same because light travels with a constant velocity.
   c) The photon energy of violet light is highest because the frequency is highest.
   d) The photon energy of the light waves depends on the wave amplitudes which are not given.
   e) The photon energies of both colors are small, which make it difficult for the eye to see.

6. How does the double-slit experiment show that light has interference properties?

7. List the different types of electromagnetic radiation in order from the lowest frequency to the highest frequency.

8. What four characteristics does light exhibit that shows its wave nature?

9. Using the principle of non-contradiction, explain and justify what the chapter concludes about the nature of light.

10. How do scientists think that light travels through space?

11. Why do scientists use light years as a unit of measurement when speaking of large distances in space?

12. Light is described as a transverse wave. However, it travels through empty space where there are no molecules to move perpendicularly to the wave. So how can we call it a transverse wave?

## Synthesis

1. If a door between a brightly lit room and a dark one is left slightly ajar, there will be a band of light on the floor. If the door is slowly closed, what happens to this band of light? Why?

2. When very dim light is used to make a photograph, what happens to the image? If very dim light was used in a double slit experiment, what would happen to the image? How does a double slit experiment done with dim light show the dual nature of photons?

3. How did luminiferous ether filling space allow scientists to continue considering light as a wave?

4. Why does a diffraction grating cause colors in light to separate? In what order should colors appear?

5. Upon seeing the sharp image of shadow, Newton concluded that light was not a wave. He did not know the wavelength of light. Why might this knowledge have changed his conclusion?

6. In a photoelectric effect experiment using visible light, what happens when you change the brightness of the light source? What happens when you change the frequency of the light source? How does the photoelectric effect prove that light behaves as a particle? What would have happened if light were just a wave?

7. Light transports energy like the mechanical waves described in Chapter 10 but with a profound difference. Contrast the understanding of energy in mechanical waves with the understanding of energy in light.

8. Scientists speak of light traveling through a field that inhabits empty space. Would you call this an hypothesis, theory, law, or model? Why?

# Physical Properties of Matter

*Although nature commences with reason and ends in experience it is
necessary for us to do the opposite, that is to commence with
experience and from this to proceed to investigate the reason.*

*Leonardo da Vinci*

# 12

## LEARN

- How the four states of matter are defined and how density changes from state to state.

- How the states of matter of several common materials depend on temperature.

- To distinguish between compression, tension, and shear forces, and how these forces differ with the states of matter.

- The different types of spectra and why objects have different colors.

- The difference between conductors, ionic conductors, and non-conductors.

- The continuous model of matter and list what it fails to explain.

Having considered interactions, forces and motion, we now contemplate the entity that *does* the moving and interacting; matter itself. Back in Chapter 1 we introduced its most basic building blocks: quarks, protons, neutrons, electrons, atoms and molecules. We considered the charged electrons and protons further in Chapter 4. Here we begin an examination of matter to learn how these basic particles interact together to form the variety of material that makes up the universe. We will learn many facts but more importantly we will contemplate the workings of the scientific method and how this has brought about our current understanding of those facts.

Our inquiry into matter begins with comparing and contrasting physical properties. This "method of Aristotle," practiced by the great Greek philosopher centuries ago, gives us our first question to explain: why are some properties the same and why are others different?

Imagine you are given a box of unrecognizable items that you wish to comprehend. Knowing nothing about them, you test them all in a

variety of ways to determine their properties. These properties include:

- Their physical state at room temperature
- The temperatures at which they change physical state
- Their density in various physical states
- Their respond to different types of force
- Their color
- Whether they conduct electricity

Other physical properties could be identified but this set is very useful for exploring and diagnosing some of the most fundamental properties and is a good place to start.

## 12-1 States of Matter

Matter can exist in four states: solid, liquid, gas, or plasma. A **solid** is rigid with a fixed volume and shape. Large forces are often required to change that shape. You are familiar with solids, which include ice, wood, steel, cloth, paper, etc. **Liquids** are not rigid and change shape

when poured from one container to another. But like a solid, the volume of a liquid does not change, even when the shape of its container changes. **Gases** are not rigid, nor are their volumes fixed. A gas moved from one container to another adopts the shape of the new container and expands or contracts to fill its volume as well.

By changing conditions like temperature and pressure, matter will change from solid to gas, from gas to liquid, from liquid to solid, and so on. Consider water (*Figure 12.1*). Water becomes solid ice at or below 32° F (0° C). The volume of an ice cube is fixed and determined by the size of the partitions in the ice cube tray. If you want crushed ice, you must exert a consider-

**Solid:**

A physical state of matter that is characterized by rigidity and resistance to changes in size and shape.

**Liquid:**

A physical state of matter that readily changes shape to match its container but that resists changes in volume.

**Gas:**

A physical state of matter that readily changes both shape and volume to match its container.

**Figure 12.1**

States of Matter: a) solid,  b) liquid, and c) gas.

147

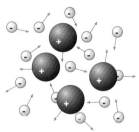

**Plasma:**

A physical state of matter characterized by fluid properties in which positive and negative charges move independently.

able force on the cubes to break them down into smaller bits. Between 32° F (0° C) and 212° F (100° C) water is a liquid and flows freely from the tap. You can measure a liter of liquid water using a measuring cup. If you pour that liquid into an irregularly shaped vase you still have a liter of liquid. Large forces do not have to be applied to get the liquid to assume the inside shape of the vase. Heat the water in a tea kettle above 212° F (100° C) and it boils into its gaseous form, steam, where it will escape from the kettle and expand through the volume of the kitchen.

In addition to these three familiar states, matter can exist in a fourth state called **plasma**.

A plasma is a gas of positively and negatively charged particles. The positively charged particles are atoms that have lost their electrons. The negatively charged particles are the electrons that were lost.

Although not as familiar as the other states, plasma is the most common form of matter in the Universe. Two naturally occurring examples of plasmas are the northern lights, which have mesmerized sky watchers since the dawn of civilization, and solar winds blowing off the surface of the Sun. Plasma TVs build a picture from tiny gas cells that glow as plasmas when charged. Photos of these and other plasmas are shown in *Figure 12.2*.

Our most frequent experience with a plasma is turning a fluorescent light on or off. Inside every fluorescent light tube is a gas of argon and mercury. When turned on, the gas becomes a glowing plasma of ionized argon and mercury atoms and freely moving electrons.

The establishment of four distinct states of matter is not perfect because there are materials that do not fall cleanly into any of those categories. Silly Putty® or Jello® at room temperature are both in states that fall somewhere between a solid and a liquid. A ball of Silly Putty has a fixed volume but is not rigid. Unlike a liquid, however, it doesn't immediately change its shape when it is moved to a new container. But over time relatively small forces like gravity can cause its shape to change (*Figure 12.3*). Materials like Silly Putty behave more like one or another state of matter depending on the temperature or pressure. If a lump of Silly Putty is put in the freezer, it becomes brittle and hard, like a solid. If the lump is heated it may become fully liquid-like.

What do these observations tell us about the nature of matter? They give us our first clues about the forces that hold its basic building

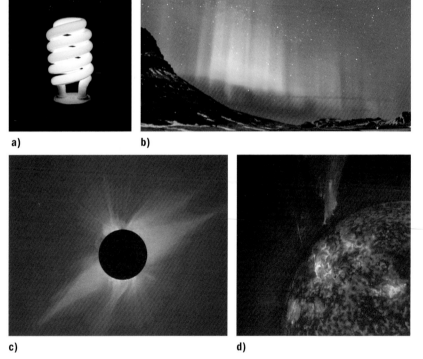

a)

b)

c)

d)

**Figure 12.2**

Four examples of plasmas.

a) A fluorescent lamp contains a plasma (a mixture of positively charged argon and mercury ions plus electrons). Energy from the plasma causes a coating inside the lamp to give off white light. In this picture, part of the coating is removed so that you can see the actual blue glow of light given off by the plasma.

b) A plasma display screen with a picture of the "Aurora Borealis" or Northern Lights. During times of high solar activity, the atmospheric gases can be ionized to form plasmas and give rise to the beautiful Northern Lights.

c) A solar eclipse showing the corona, a plasma that makes up the Sun's atmosphere.

d) Another photo of the Sun's corona. Ionized gases stream from the surface forming the solar wind.

**Figure 12.3**

Time-elapsed pictures show that Silly Putty® changes its shape slowly over time under the influence of gravity.

blocks together, forces that enable these building blocks to form larger structures—from elephants to mountain ranges to the universe itself. Behavior in different states tells us the forces holding solids together are somehow different from those that keep liquids together, and even more different from those associated with gases and plasmas.

## 12-2 Temperature and Changes in State

*Table 12.1* shows the melting and boiling temperatures of some common materials. The exact values of the numbers are not as important for our purposes as are the correlations and trends. What substances have the lowest melting temperatures? Which ones have the highest melting temperatures? Does the substance with the lowest melting temperature also have the lowest boiling temperature? How do the melting and boiling points of water compare to the lowest and the highest temperatures found in Table 12.1?

The materials in Table 12.1 are arranged from lowest to highest melting temperature. Water changes from solid to liquid and liquid to gas in the middle of the temperature range. Organisms on Earth's surface require this temperature range to live. Another material in the

## TEMPERATURE SCALES

There are three different scales that are commonly used when measuring temperature, each named for one of the scientists who originally developed or proposed it.

Fahrenheit (°F) originated in 1724 in Germany and today is primarily used only in the United States and a few small territories.

Celsius (°C) was actually developed concurrently by several scientists working independently, but is named for a Swedish scientist who proposed a version in 1742. It is the common scale used everywhere else in the world as part of the International System of Units.

Kelvin (K) was proposed in 1848 by Lord Kelvin and has as it's 0 point the lowest possible temperature. It is measured in kelvins, not degrees, although the amount of a kelvin is about equivalent to a degree Celsius. It is often used by scientists.

Table 12.2 compares the measurement of some key temperatures on the three different scales.

### Table 12.2 — Temperature Scales

| K | °C | °F | |
|---|---|---|---|
| 0 | -273 | -459 | Absolute zero |
| 273 | 0 | 32 | Water freezes |
| 310 | 37 | 98.6 | Normal human body temperature |
| 373 | 100 | 212 | Water boils at sea level |
| 755 | 482 | 900 | Oven on "clean" setting |
| 5,773 | 5,500 | 9,900 | Our Sun's temperature |
| 10,273 | 10,000 | 18,000 | Temperature of a blue star |

### Table 12.1 — Properties of Materials

Melting and boiling temperatures of representative materials. Densities are given at temperatures near the state changes. Densities are hard to measure at high temperatures, so information for liquid salt and the metals is not available.

| | Melting Temperature °C | Boiling Temperature °C (under 1 atm pressure) | Density g cm$^{-3}$ | | |
|---|---|---|---|---|---|
| | | | solid | liquid | gas |
| Helium | doesn't form solid except under high pressure! | -269 | doesn't form a solid | 0.122 | .00018 |
| Hydrogen | -259 | -253 | 0.078 | 0.071 | .0001 |
| Neon | -249 | -246 | 1.44 | 1.21 | .00082 |
| Nitrogen | -210 | -196 | 1.09 | 0.81 | .0013 |
| Ethanol | -117 | 78.5 | 1.3 | 0.80 | .0020 |
| Water | 0 | 100 | 0.90 (0°C) | 1.00 | .0006 |
| Table salt | 801 | 1413 | 2.2 | not available | not available |
| Copper | 1083 | 2567 | 8.9 | not available | not available |
| Gold | 1065 | 2807 | 19.3 | not available | not available |
| Magnesium Oxide | 2830 | 3600 | 3.6 | not available | not available |

table, ethanol, also changes state at mid-range temperatures like water.

Notice there is no melting point for helium. Helium, the gas that makes both party balloons and the Goodyear® blimp rise above the crowds, is a truly remarkable material. It is the only known substance that does not form a solid just by cooling. Helium only solidifies when it is both very cold *and* subjected to strong pressure. Helium even boils at a very cold temperature.

Of all the substances shown in the table, only those that are elements (see Chapter 17) form plasmas. The other substances first break down into elements, which can become plasmas.

Looking at Table 12.1, we can make a few hypotheses about matter. We will test these in upcoming chapters.

> *Hypothesis 1:* The temperature at which a change in state takes place tells us something about the strength of the force that holds bits of matter together in that particular state.

> *Hypothesis 2:* A type of matter whose particles are held together strongly in its solid state will melt at a higher temperature than will one in which the forces between particles are weaker.[1]

You might form similar hypotheses about the change in state of a liquid to a gas.

What predictions can we make based on these hypotheses? Here are a few: Table salt and metals like gold and copper are held together by stronger forces than water or ethanol. Water and ethanol boil at higher temperatures than are required to boil helium and neon, so forces holding bits of liquid helium or neon in place are weaker than forces holding together bits of water or ethanol. Are these predictions accurate? We will see.

---

[1] In the next few chapters that deal with atoms and molecules, we shall occasionally use the terms "strong force" and "weak force" to characterize the magnitudes of electrical forces between atoms or molecules, just as we needed to do in Hypothesis 2. Sometimes in science, as in life, words can have very different meanings. Chemists who rarely deal with processes taking place inside atomic nuclei don't have to worry about those two fundamental forces—the Strong force and the Weak force—that occur within the nucleus. Nuclear physicists don't worry about the interactions between atoms that lead to molecules or that influence melting and boiling points. Because the two sets of scientists rarely talk to one another, confusion doesn't reign. We will hope that you can recognize our different uses for the same terms from the context of the chapter.

## 12-3 Density

We learned about density when Archimedes' Principle was presented in Chapter 6. To review, remember that density is defined as the "mass per unit volume of a substance," or

$$\text{density} = \text{mass/volume}$$

Table 12.1 shows the density of some materials presented in units of grams per cubic centimeter ($g/cm^3$). The density of liquid water is $1.00 \ g/cm^3$. Therefore 20 cubic centimeters of liquid water has a mass of 20.0 g. Twenty cubic centimeters of solid gold would have a mass of 38.6 grams.

Notice in Table 12.1 how the density of a substance changes as it goes from one state to another. Which states tend to be the densest? Which are the least dense? Are there any exceptions to the general trends?

Large changes in density occur when a material undergoes a change of state. As a general rule, matter is denser as a solid than as a liquid, and *much* denser as a liquid than as a gas. Notice that the metals show the highest densities. They also have high melting points, while the materials having the lowest densities also have very low melting points.

The density of a material can be used to distinguish it from other materials. Diamonds and cubic zirconia look very much alike to the unaided eye. Diamond, by far the more desirable gem of the two, is extremely hard but is not as dense as cubic zirconia. Using Archimedes principle, the two materials can be distinguished by whether they float or sink in a liquid approximately four times the density of water (*Figure 12.4*).

Water is a rare exception to the general trend in density changes stated above. Near its melting temperature ice is actually less dense than liquid water, and so ice cubes and icebergs float. There would be serious consequences for life on planet Earth if water behaved like most liquids. Ice that formed in the winter would sink to the bottom of the ocean, lake or pond. Ice at the bottom of thick bodies of water would not experience enough of the warming rays of the Sun to melt in the spring and summer. Each winter more ice would freeze and sink, never to melt. Eventually there would be little liquid water on the planet and life as we know it would cease to exist.

**Figure 12.4**
In a liquid whose density is about 4 g/cm³, diamonds float while cubic zirconia sinks. Therefore, we can conclude that diamonds have density less than 4 g/cm³ while cubic zirconia have a density greater than that. (See Chapter 6.)

What do these observations tell us about the nature of matter? One important fact is that materials in any state retain their nature as "helium" or "water" or "copper". Therefore their basic building blocks are not changing. Secondly, because the density changes with state, the building blocks must be arranged differently while in the different states. With the exception of water, when matter changes from a liquid to a solid, its building blocks are packed closer together. When it changes from liquid to gas, its building blocks become much farther apart.

## 12-4 Responses of Matter to Forces

We did not worry much about how objects responded to force when studying Newton's Laws of Motion. Now, as part of observing the behavior of matter, let's characterize the different states of matter according to the effect forces have on them.

A simple activity, pictured in *Figure 12.5*, illustrates ways forces can act on solids. First, hold this textbook between the palms of your hands and push the front and back covers together. This is a **compression**-type force. Now, grab the top and bottom edges of the book and pull them apart. This is a **tension**-type force. Place the book flat on a table. Push against the right edge of the top of the book while simultaneously pushing in the opposite direction against the bottom of the book's left edge. This is a **shear**-type force.

Compression forces are "pushing" type forces. They tend to reduce the volume of an object, hence the name compression. Tension forces are "pulling" forces. Tension forces tend to stretch an object, increasing its length in the direction of the applied force. Shear forces are twisting forces. They distort the shape of an object.

In Chapter 10 we learned of compression and shear waves. As you might imagine, compression waves are caused by compression forces and shear waves are caused by shear forces. Tension forces play a role in waves too when they pull material back to its equilibrium point after the force has displaced it.

The book is a solid and resisted your efforts to apply force in all three cases (i.e., the book didn't squeeze down to a thin sliver when compressed.) We can generalize this result for all solids: Solids can sustain or "support" all three types of forces. "Support" here means that it resists the force applied.

Would you get the same results if you made the same pushing, pulling, and twisting exercises with a liquid or gas? Imagine pushing down the plunger of a syringe filled with water. You can feel the resistance to the compression force you exert. Similarly, if you try to stretch a column of

**Compression Force:**

A force that is applied in such a way as to compress a material.

**Tension Force:**

A force that is applied in such a way as to stretch a material.

**Shear Force:**

A force that is applied in such a way as to twist or deform a material.

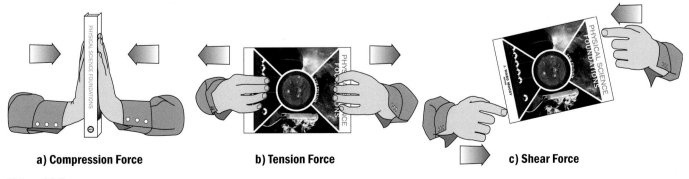

a) Compression Force        b) Tension Force        c) Shear Force

**Figure 12.5**
Types of forces.

liquid, such as sucking water up a straw, it would resist your efforts. The liquid will move up the straw but not stretch in the process. Liquids resist compressing and stretching just as solids do. Therefore, liquids also support compression and tension forces.

Now, what about shear forces? Imagine putting your hands into a large bucket of water. Try to exert a shear force on the water between your hands as you did for the book. Do you feel the same resistance? Does the volume of water start to rotate or change shape? No. Liquids do not support shear forces.

Lastly consider what happens when similar forces are applied to helium or some other gas. Matter in a gaseous state will support neither tension nor shear forces. You can't draw out a column of gas, nor twist or reshape it like you can a liquid or solid. However, gases do sustain compression forces. They will shrink to a smaller volume when squeezed but will push back. Therefore they sustain compression forces but without the same strength as a liquid or solid.

Plasmas will not be considered here because they contain ionized particles. The electromagnetic force dominates their behavior and the resulting behavior is very complex and beyond the scope of this textbook.

What does a material's response to forces while as a solid, liquid, or gas reveal about the forces holding the building blocks together in each state? We have hypothesized that they are different. The observations just made strengthen that hypothesis.

## 12-5 Color

Isaac Newton, already well-known for his laws of motion, also discovered that white sunlight could be separated into all the colors of the rainbow (*Figure 12.6*). The colors, when combined together create what we perceive as white light.

Recall that light has wave properties and that color is determined by wave frequency. The complete range of colors or frequencies of all electromagnetic radiation is referred to as the **electromagnetic spectrum** (refer back to Figure 11.8). The human eye only sees colors between red and violet. Some living creatures, bumblebees, for example, can sense higher-frequency

**Electromagnetic Spectrum:**

The entire range of radiation including, in order of decreasing frequency, cosmic-ray photons, gamma rays, x-rays, ultraviolet radiation, visible light, infrared radiation, microwaves, and radio waves.

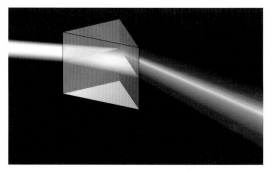

**Figure 12.6**
White light goes through the prism and is separated into its component colors.

ultraviolet light while snakes are sensitive to lower-frequency infrared light.

The overall color of an object depends on the portions of the spectrum that an object absorbs or reflects. We see red tulips because the pigments in the petals of the flower reflect the red colors of the spectrum in greater proportions than the other colors. The flower's green leaves reflect more green (*Figure 12.7*).

The color of a material is related to the internal structure of that object. The warm yellow color of pure gold is different from the cool white color of pure silver, telling us there is something different about the two materials.

All materials give off light when they are heated to high temperatures. The electric burner

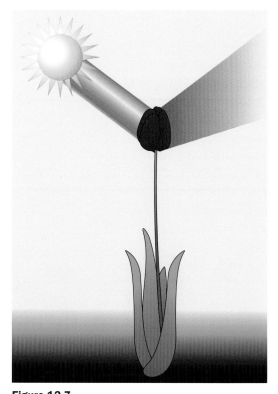

**Figure 12.7**
The tulip petals appear red because more red light is reflected from the petals than other colors.

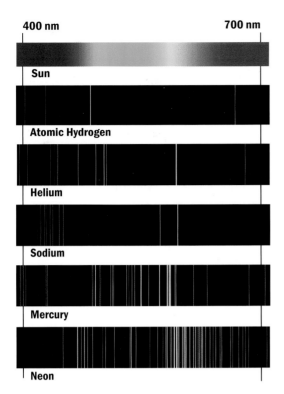

400 nm                    700 nm

Sun

Atomic Hydrogen

Helium

Sodium

Mercury

Neon

**Figure 12.8**
This figure contrasts the continuous spectrum of the Sun (top) with the discrete spectra of gaseous materials. The numbers 400 nm and 700 nm refer to the wavelengths of light at each end of the spectrum. Longer wavelengths correspond to lower frequencies. Black represents the absence of color. (1 nm = $10^{-9}$ m.)

on a stove begins to glow with red light when it reaches a temperature of about 700° C. Our Sun, whose surface temperature is near 5,500° C, gives off all colors of light. That is why bright sunlight appears white. The Sun and anything that gives off all colors has a **continuous spectrum**.

Gases of pure materials like hydrogen, helium, and neon, however, give off only a few colors of light when they are heated to a plasma by an electrical discharge. We call these **discrete spectra**. *Figure 12.8* shows the continuous spectrum of the Sun contrasted with discrete spectra from different materials. The spectrum of each material is distinctive and can be used to identify it. In fact, the element helium was first identified from its light in the spectrum of the Sun, long before it was discovered on Earth.

## 12-6 Electrical Conductivity

Finally we ask "Which materials conduct electricity?" We can test by using the electrical circuit shown in *Figure 12.9*. Material with unknown properties is connected in a circuit

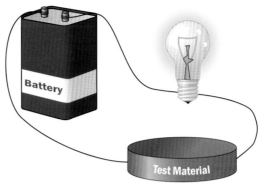

**Figure 12.9**
The circuit used to test the electrical conductivity of a material. If the test material conducts electricity, the electricity will flow through the entire circuit, lighting the bulb.

with a battery, to provide electrical potential energy, and a light bulb that glows when current is flowing. The bulb glows only if the unknown material is a **conductor**. *Table 12.3* gives the conductivity results for several materials tested this way.

We find that metals in a solid or liquid state always conduct electricity. Some materials conduct electricity when in either a liquid state, or dissolved in water, but not as a solid. These materials are called **ionic conductors**. Sodium chloride, common table salt, is an ionic conductor, a property that is important in the functioning of our bodies. In general, salts, which are compounds of metals and nonmetals (see Chapter 22) are ionic conductors.

A material that does not conduct electricity

**Conductors:**
Materials that conduct electricity in the solid and liquid state.

**Ionic Conductors:**
Materials that do not conduct electricity in the solid state, but do when molten or dissolved in water.

**Continuous Spectrum:**
A spectrum in which the colors blend gradually together without noticeably abrupt changes or missing colors.

**Discrete Spectrum:**
A spectrum of separate and distinct colors in which not all colors are present.

## Table 12.3 — Electrical Conductivity of Materials

| Conductors | Ionic Conductors | Non-Conductors |
|---|---|---|
| Solid Copper | Sodium Chloride Crystals | Pure Liquid Water |
| Solid Gold | Sodium Chloride Dissolved in Water | Pure Solid Water |
| Solid Aluminum | Magnesium Oxide Crystals | Liquid Ethanol |
| Solid Iron | Liquid Magnesium Oxide | Sugar Crystals |
| Solid Titanium | | Sugar Dissolved in Water |

in any of its physical states or when dissolved in water is referred to as a **non-conductor** or insulator. Sugar and ethanol are common non-conductors.

Pure, distilled water is a non-conductor in either its solid or liquid state. But impurities like the salts and minerals found in common tap water make it slightly conductive. For this reason electrical appliances should never be used near a bathtub or swimming pool.

Gases do not normally conduct electricity. However, lightning bolts and the sparks associated with static electricity *are* brief discharges of electrical energy through air which of course is a gas. This happens when electrical energy ionizes the air, making it a plasma, and plasmas do conduct electricity.

## 12-7 Continuous Model of Matter

With matter catalogued by properties, we next ask how these properties, coupled with the laws of force, conservation of energy, knowledge of light, etc, enable us to begin to answer the "why?" questions about matter.

We need a "model"—a mental picture of the realms we cannot see—to begin explaining the properties. There are many we might formulate, but, guided by Occam's Razor, we will start with the simplest possible model and adapt it as evidence shows its limitations.

What is the simplest model of matter we could form? A very simple one is the "continuous" model that says matter has no internal structure. It supposes we could subdivide solids, liquids and gases into smaller and smaller pieces and their properties would stay the same no matter how small the piece.

The properties of matter discussed in this chapter immediately reveal this model's deficiencies. The continuous model offers no insights into why the densities of the states are so different. Nor can it say anything about why different substances have such radically different melting and boiling temperatures. It offers us nothing to explain the phenomenon of electrical conductivity, either. To improve this model and explain these diverse observations, we go next to one of the great discoveries of mankind: the molecular model of matter.

**Non-conductors:**

Material which do not conduct electricity in any of their physical states.

*Give me matter, and I will construct a world out of it!*
Immanuel Kant

# 12 STUDY GUIDE

## Chapter Framework

### A. States of Matter
1. Solid
2. Liquid
3. Gas
4. Plasma

### B. Melting and Boiling Temperatures

### C. Densities and States of Matter

### D. Response to Forces
1. Compression
2. Tension
3. Shear

### E. Color
1. Electromagnetic spectrum
   a. *Continuous spectrum*
   b. *Discrete spectrum*

### F. Electrical Conductivity
1. Conductors
2. Ionic Conductors
3. Non-Conductors

## Comprehension

### Matching

1. _____ Forces that are not in a line which push opposite corners of an object in opposite directions.
2. _____ A spectrum of separate or distinct colors.
3. _____ A force that when applied compresses the material.
4. _____ A physical state of matter that is characterized by rigidity and resistance to changes in size and shape.
5. _____ A physical state of matter characterized by fluid properties but in which positive and negative charges move independently.
6. _____ A material that is a non-conductor of electricity as a solid but that conducts electricity when dissolved in water or melted.
7. _____ The whole range of colors (frequencies) of light.
8. _____ A physical state of matter that readily changes both shape and volume to match its container.
9. _____ A substance that readily allows an electric current to flow through it.
10. _____ A force that stretches material.
11. _____ A characteristic of matter associated with the light reflected off the matter to an observer.
12. _____ A physical state of matter that readily changes shape to match its container but that resists changes in volume.
13. _____ A spectrum in which the colors blend gradually together without noticeable abrupt changes or missing colors.
14. _____ Mass per unit of volume of a substance.
15. _____ A substance that does not readily allow

a. Gas

b. Electromagnetic spectrum

c. Continuous spectrum

d. Liquid

e. Non-conductor

f. Ionic conductor

g. Plasma

h. Compression force

i. Shear force

j. Solid

k. Color

l. Tension force

m. Density

n. Discrete spectrum

o. Conductor

electric current to flow through it in any of its physical states.

### True/False

1. _____ For the majority of materials at a given pressure, solids are the densest state of matter and gases are the least dense.
2. _____ The continuous spectrum consists of separate, distinct colors.
3. _____ All materials become plasmas if heated to a high enough temperature.
4. _____ Gold's physical state is always a solid.
5. _____ Liquids assume the shape of their container.
6. _____ All materials fall cleanly into the categories of solid, liquid, gas, or plasma.
7. _____ All matter melts at 0° C (32° F) and boils at 100° C (212° F).

### Fill in the Blank

1. An object appears blue if it _____ blue light.
2. Scientists formulate _____ to provide a mental picture of material, such as matter.
3. _____ forces are pushing forces, and _____ forces are typically stretching forces.
4. Glass is an example of a(n) _____ .

## Analysis

1. Which of the following processes does not produce a change in states?

   a) Melting gold        d) Boiling ethanol
   b) Condensing steam     e) Falling objects
   c) Freezing water

2. Neither sugar nor salt conduct electricity when they are in the solid state. Salt, however, does conduct electricity as a liquid while sugar does not. In classifying these materials we say that

   a) sugar is an ionic material and salt is nonionic.
   b) sugar is a nonionic material and salt is ionic.
   c) both are nonionic.
   d) both are ionic.
   e) both are equally good conductors in solution.

3. Which of the following can sustain shear forces?

   a) Liquid helium       d) Rocks
   b) Steam               e) Two of the above
   c) Chocolate milk

4. Which of the following materials forms the most dense liquid (see Table 12.1)?

   a) Ethanol             d) Nitrogen
   b) Hydrogen            e) Water
   c) Neon

5. You have five solid metal cubes of the same volume (1 cm3). The mass of each cube is given in the following table:

| Gold | Iron | Nickel | Platinum | Zinc |
|------|------|--------|----------|------|
| 19.3 | 7.86 | 8.9 | 21.5 | 7.14 |

Which sequence gives the correct elements in order of increasing density.

a) Zinc, Iron, Nickel, Gold, Platinum

b) Gold, Iron, Nickel, Platinum, Zinc

c) Iron, Zinc, Nickel, Platinum, Gold

d) Platinum, Gold, Nickel, Iron, Zinc

6. Which has greater density, an ice cube or an iceberg?

7. Describe what is meant by "plasma" and give an example of plasma that occurs in nature.

8. Show, in a sketch, how compression, tension, and shear forces can be applied to a material.

9. Why is tap water a conductor while pure water is not?

## Synthesis

1. Refer to the table and figure to answer the following questions:

   a) Suppose you carefully poured each of the liquids into a container so that no mixing took place. With reference to the figure below, what substance would be liquid 2?

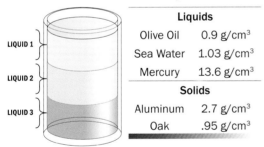

| Liquids | |
|---------|---------|
| Olive Oil | 0.9 g/cm³ |
| Sea Water | 1.03 g/cm³ |
| Mercury | 13.6 g/cm³ |
| **Solids** | |
| Aluminum | 2.7 g/cm³ |
| Oak | .95 g/cm³ |

   b) If you dropped a small solid wooden ball made of oak and an aluminum ball of the same size into the container, again doing it carefully to minimize mixing of the liquid layers, where would you find each ball?

2. Choose five materials and list them in order of increasing density.

3. List and briefly describe the different characteristics used to classify matter. With each category of characteristics give examples of matter that demonstrate those characteristics.

4. You exert forces on many objects while doing many activities. In the following activities, which kind(s) of force is(are) being applied?

   a) Tearing a piece of paper in half

   b) Pushing a thumbtack into a bulletin board

c) Pulling taffy

d) Using an electric beater to mix cake batter

5. Dad is baking bread and kneading it with his hands.

   a) If he presses straight down on the dough as shown by the arrows in the figure, what kind of force is present?

   b) If he kneads the bread by pushing down and then pushing outward, what forces are present? In the outward push, the dough is both rotated and stretched.

6. Many of the street lamps you see along a highway use the light from gaseous sodium. Based on Figure 12.8, would you expect the light from these lamps to be pure white? If not, what color of light might you expect to come from them? (Remember that pure white light comes from a balance of all the colors of the rainbow.)

7. Why would an object look different when illuminated by a mercury vapor lamp than when seen under sunlight? (See Figure 12.8 for the colors of light given off by such a lamp.)

8. The liquid-solid change of state for water occurs with an important difference from most other matter. What is this difference and why is it important for life on Earth?

9. Summarize what observations you have made from Table 12.1 by answering the following questions:

   a) For most types of matter, what sequence of states corresponds to increasing density?

   b) For a given type of matter, which has the higher temperature: melting or boiling?

   c) If a material has a low melting temperature, what can you predict about its boiling temperature?

   d) Do metals (copper and gold) and salts (table salt and magnesium oxide) have high or low melting temperatures?

10. Samples recovered from a space mission to the moon included a specimen that had a melting temperature higher than 1000° C. The specimen conducts electricity only when in the liquid state. Which group of materials would you expect this specimen to be most like?

    a) salts such as table salt sodium chloride

    b) metals such as copper and iron

    c) ethanol and water

   Explain your answer.

11. The continuous model is very simple and qualitative. It simply says that matter has no internal structure; we can subdivide solids, liquids, and gases into smaller and smaller masses of each, but the properties say the same. What are some deficiencies of this model?

# The Molecular Model of Matter

*If we assume that the last breath of, say, Julius Caesar has by now become thoroughly scattered through the atmosphere, then the chances are that each of us inhales one molecule of it with every breath we take.*

*James Hopwood Jeans*

# 13

## LEARN

- The four essential assumptions of the Molecular Model of Matter.

- How this model explains Brownian motion.

- How this model accounts for the different states of matter and changes between them.

- How this model explains temperature, heat, and internal energy.

- How this model explains heat conduction and gas pressure.

- The limitations of this model.

A scientific model is a tool we use to explain why nature behaves as it does. We formulate them from what we have observed in the past and test them by what they predict will be observed in the future. They are how we build insight from direct measurements into realms where our instruments cannot easily penetrate. In studying matter, models are essential since its fundamental parts are so small and mobile that direct measurements are difficult or impossible.

The natural sciences are not the only disciplines that rely heavily on models. Economists use models to predict the future financial health of, say, the U.S. Social Security program. Meteorologists rely heavily on models to predict the weather. The models of specific programs or weather patterns change rapidly as new information becomes available. Often several different models will be developed, each assuming slightly different conditions and emphasizing different factors. New information leads to different model details and different predictions.

The proof of models is how well they pre-

dict future events, be they in the economy, in the weather, or in a tube of gas. It is triumphant when the predictions are realized for it tells us our models must be largely correct. But, almost ironically, the greatest advancements come when predictions are not realized, for that means we have the opportunity to significantly improve the limits of our understanding.

## 13-1 The Molecular Model of Matter

In the previous chapter, we collected a database of physical properties for different kinds of matter. We saw that the simple, continuous model of matter could not even begin to explain the properties observed and that a better model was needed.

Our next, greatly improved model is called the **molecular model**. This model rests upon the following four key assumptions:

**1. Matter consists of tiny, indivisible particles called molecules.**

Unlike the continuous model, the molecu-lar model assumes that matter cannot be subdivided into infinitely small pieces. It assumes that as we consider smaller and smaller scales, we eventually reach a fundamental building block, the **molecule**, that cannot be divided further.

Molecules are very tiny. They are so small that one teaspoonful of water contains more molecules than there are teaspoonfuls of water in all the oceans put together. We can't see molecules with even the highest magnifying light-based microscopes. But since about 1990 instruments have been developed that allow us to image these small particles more directly.

Please keep in mind that this model takes the *molecule* to be the fundamental, indivisible building block. No doubt your previous schooling has taught you that molecules are built from atoms. In this book we have already discussed liberally the protons and electrons from which atoms are made to explain the electric force, internal energy, light, and plasmas. We ask that you suspend for this discussion any consideration of the structure of molecules. That structure will be considered in detail as our pro-

**Molecular Model:**

Also known as the kinetic theory of matter, characteristics of the molecular model are:

1) Matter consists of tiny particles called molecules. 2) Each different kind of matter consists of a different kind of molecule. 3) The molecules in matter are in constant motion. 4) Molecules move and interact in accord with laws of motion, the laws of force and the laws of conservation.

**Molecules:**

The tiniest particles of a substance that retain all the physical properties of that substance.

gression along the models continues. For now we consider properties that are explained by the existence of molecules, knowing that this will not be the last word in matter models.

**2. Different kinds of matter are made up of different molecules.**

The helium gas that is in the balloons you buy for a birthday party contains molecules that are small, light, and fast-moving. The forces between them are very weak as evidenced by helium's extremely low boiling temperature. The molecules in the air tend to be light and fast moving. Water molecules are light enough to rise as water vapor but are attracted to each other enough to join together and fall as rain drops. Organic molecules, like those that make up our skin and hair, are much more massive still.

Each of these substances are distinct because they have different molecules. The differences between their molecules primarily create the different physical properties that each substance exhibits.

**3. Molecules are in constant motion.**

Molecules are continuously moving. They may move so fast that they fly upward into the air. They may move so slow that their motion is reduced to a vibration in place. But they never completely stop moving.

**4. Molecular motion is governed by Newton's laws and all the laws of nature.**

A gas molecule will move in a straight line until it collides with another molecule or the wall of its container, all in accordance with Newton's first law of motion. When molecular collisions occur, Newton's third law describes the interaction. During collisions, molecules will exchange energy and change speed and direction in accordance with Newton's second law and the laws of conservation of energy and momentum. Molecular speeds can be fast but rarely if ever approach the speeds where the theory of relativity needs to be invoked.

## 13-2 Molecular Motion and States of Matter

### Brownian Motion

In 1827, Robert Brown (1773–1858) observed the motion of pollen grains suspended in water under a microscope. He found that the pollen grains would occasionally twitch

## ATOMIC MICROSCOPY

Scientists use sophisticated instruments called scanning tunneling microscopes (STM) to see molecules more directly. Figure 13.1 shows a photograph taken through an STM of a solid crystal of nickel. This image was magnified at least 1 billion times, as compared to the 1,500 times maximum magnification power of many standard light microscopes. Each blue cone represents a nickel molecule which in this case is a single nickel atom. The diameter of each cone is set by the diameter of the nickel atom plus a little additional space needed to accommodate the jiggling motion of bound molecules described in this chapter. Another STM image (Figure 13.2) shows iron atoms placed on a layer of copper atoms. The copper atoms appear only as the soft hills in the blue layer because they are not well resolved in the image.

**Figure 13.1**
An image of a layer of nickel atoms taken by a scanning tunneling microscope. The magnification is about 1 billion times.

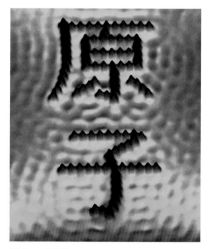

**Figure 13.2**
An image of iron atoms deposited on a layer of copper atoms spelling the word "atom" in Japanese. The copper atoms are only visible as the ripples in the blue background.

and jump for no apparent reason. This motion became known as **Brownian motion.** An early explanation of Brownian motion was that the pollen was animated by some sort of life force. Later it was shown that dust particles in air exhibited this same jerking, twitching motion. Since dust particles, unlike pollen particles, are not from living plants, this interpretation was abandoned.

The notion that matter was built from fundamental particles was commonly held by most people in the early 1900's. But a formal, direct proof was still lacking until 1905 when Albert Einstein successfully modeled Brownian motion as being caused by molecular bombardment. Einstein's model assumed only that molecules were in constant motion and obeyed Newton's laws of motion and conservation of energy. From this he predicted quantitatively how the larger pollen or dust grains should move when bombarded by the very tiny water molecules. His predictions were perfectly correct.

### States of Matter

Chapter 12 detailed the physical characteristics of the four states of matter: solid, liquid, gas, and plasma. *Figure 13.3* depicts these first three states using the molecular model.

The molecules in a solid are arranged in an orderly fashion, with the molecules packed so close to one another that they almost touch. In a liquid, molecules are not packed tightly together, but are still relatively close. Molecules in a gaseous state are in contact with each other only when they collide.

Molecules in gases move freely throughout the entire volume of their container. Molecules in a liquid state move throughout the liquid's

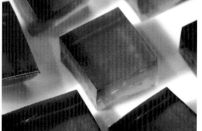
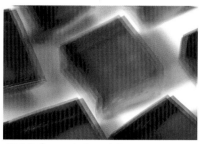

a) Jello® on a stationary plate    b) Jello® on a shaken plate

**Figure 13.4**
The quivering, jiggling motion of Jello pieces on a gently shaken plate resembles the nature of molecular motion in the solid state.

volume, but they are not completely free from the attraction of their neighboring molecules. In the solid state, molecules vibrate in place.

To visualize the motion of molecules in a solid, imagine some lumps of Jello® arranged on a flat plate as shown in *Figure 13.4*. If you gently shake the plate back and forth, the Jello® pieces jiggle around, but do not move from one end of the plate to another. Molecules in a solid vibrate about a fixed position like the lumps of Jello®.

Collisions among molecules and between molecules and container walls take place in both the liquid and gas states. This constant molecular motion allows gases and liquids to assume the shape of their containers. The jiggling of a solid object's molecules is not enough to make the solid flow like a liquid or expand like a gas.

### States of Matter and Density

Do the pictures in Figure 13.3, make more clear the trends in density that you noted in Table 12.1? Each cube in this figure has the same volume, so the cube with the most molecules will have the greatest density. So the close packing of molecules in the solid compared to the liquid and gas means that the solid has the

**Brownian Motion:**

The constant, irregular motion of very fine particles (such as fine dust or smoke) suspended in a fluid and observed with a microscope. Brownian motion is taken as evidence for molecules, which collide with the observed particles and cause the jittery motion.

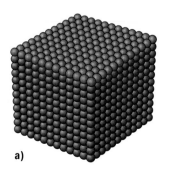
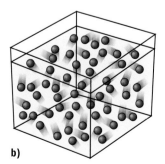
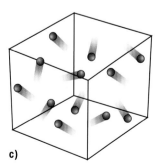

a)    b)    c)

**Figure 13.3**
The states of matter as pictured in the molecular model of matter. In all three states the molecules are in motion.
a) In solids, each molecule only jiggles about a central point.
b) In liquids, they move less freely, but stay within a certain volume.
c) In gases, the molecules can move throughout their container.

greatest density. In the gas, there is much empty space between molecules, which are far apart on the average. The low density of a gas is due to the small number of gas molecules, and therefore lower mass, in a given volume. A liquid usually has a density that is between the density of a gas and a solid because it contains more molecules than gases, but fewer molecules than solids having the same volume.

### States of Matter and Internal Energy

In Chapter 9 we learned of internal energy. With the exception of nuclear potential energy, internal energy has two basic forms related to the nature of molecules: thermal or heat energy and chemical and elastic potential energy. The molecular model nicely explains these two forms of internal energy.

Molecules are in a state of constant motion and so possess kinetic energy. The faster they move, the more kinetic energy they have. Molecules also feel forces from other molecules which get stronger as the molecules get closer. Therefore, they also possess a potential energy that depends upon the average distance between molecules. Because molecules are close together in solid matter and much farther apart in gases, the molecular model predicts that the different states of matter have different amounts of both molecular kinetic energy and molecular potential energy. Let's consider the kinetic energy further.

## 13-3 Internal Kinetic Energy and Temperature

Remember Scottish physicist James Clerk Maxwell from Chapter 11? In addition to developing equations for electromagnetic fields, Maxwell used the molecular model assumptions and several mathematical and statistical principles to discover the speeds of molecules in a gas. Maxwell's derivation is viewed by many scientists as a true thing of beauty, a grand example of scientific logic and mathematical rigor.

Maxwell found that molecules have an average speed with some always going faster and some always slower. To illustrate, consider how people drive. On a moderately busy six-lane freeway some cars (perhaps driven by senior citizens or folks talking on cell phones) travel

significantly below the speed limit. Others (perhaps those driven by teenage boys or anyone in a cherry-red convertible) can be found going much, much faster than the posted speed. Most cars will be going near the speed limit.

Then, think of driving on a suburban street in a school zone. In a school zone, just about all of the cars would be to be moving at 20 mph with a small number moving a bit slower or faster. It would be unusual (and unlawful) to find cars going 65 mph in this zone.

A state trooper sitting with a radar gun on the side of the freeway or a police officer by the school could count the number of cars going at each speed and create graphs to represent their results. Because there are many more cars passing by on the freeway than by the school, it makes sense to report the results as the fraction of cars going a particular speed. That way, the results from both observations would cover the same range: 0 to 1, and they could be plotted on the same graph.

Now back to Maxwell. Maxwell found a formula that lets us calculate the fraction of molecules going a particular speed if we know the mass of the molecules and the temperature of the gas. Consider three balloons filled respectively with helium, nitrogen, and argon, all at room temperature. Molecules of helium have little mass, nitrogen has more and argon has the most. *Figure 13.5* displays the speeds of the molecules inside the balloons. The y-axis of each plot gives the fraction of molecules going at the speed given by the x-axis.

Notice that each line in the plot has a maximum or peak value showing the speed with which the largest number of molecules moves. The peak for argon—the heaviest gas—occurs at

**James Clerk Maxwell**

In addition to his equations on electromagnetic fields, Maxwell did revolutionary work on the kinetic theory of gases.

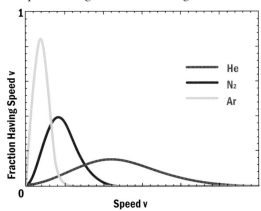

**Figure 13.5**

This graph shows the distribution of speeds for collections of different molecules at room temperature (25° C).

the lowest speed and with a large fraction, so it is a very popular speed indeed. Argon is like the school zone with a large majority of molecules moving near the same speed. Just as it would be unlikely to see a car moving at 65 mph near a school, it is unlikely that heavy argon atoms will move significantly faster than the average.

In contrast, the peak for the lighter helium atoms occurs at a higher speed but the fraction value is fairly low. Helium atoms behave like the cars on the freeway. The range of freeway speeds is very large; some cars are going very fast, others slowly. Likewise, the helium atoms have a broad distribution. Since the helium atoms have more speeds at which they can move, the most popular speed is found for a smaller fraction of atoms.

Maxwell's formula also predicts what happens if we change the temperature for a given type of molecule. *Figure 13.6* shows the distribution for nitrogen atoms at three different temperatures. Notice that at the lower temperature the distribution is slower and narrower, with most of the molecules moving close to the same speed (think of the cars near the school). As the temperature increases, molecules move faster on average and with a wider range of speeds (think of the cars on the freeway).

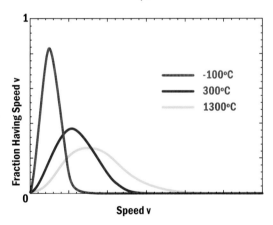

**Figure 13.6**
The distribution of speeds for a collection of nitrogen molecules at three different temperatures.

The mathematics of the molecular model tells us that the average kinetic energy (**KE**) of a collection of gas molecules is related to its temperature in this way:

$$\text{Average KE} = \frac{3}{2}kT$$

where **k** is a constant and **T** is the temperature on the Kelvin Scale (**T** = **t** + 273.15, where **t** is the temperature in Celsius). Increasing the

temperature of a gas increases its average kinetic energy.

This equation says the average kinetic energy of all gases will be the same at the same temperature. All three gases in Figure 13.5 are at the same temperature, so the three collections of gases all have the same average kinetic energy. Mathematically, we can write that as

$$\frac{1}{2}m_{He}v^2_{He} = \frac{1}{2}m_Nv^2_N = \frac{1}{2}m_{Ar}v^2_{Ar}$$

where **v** is an average speed of each type of molecule. This relationship shows that light molecules must have higher average speeds than heavy ones at the same temperature. So molecules such as helium that are not as massive as the others must move at greater average speeds than the others to have the same average kinetic energy. This is why the peak speed for argon in Figure 13.5 is lower in value than the peak for helium.

This general conclusion about average kinetic energy and temperature of molecules in a gas also applies to the other states of matter. In liquids the average speed molecular speed is higher for larger temperatures. In solids the vibrational amplitude is higher for larger temperatures. This is summarized in the following way:

**For matter in any state, temperature is a measure of the average kinetic energy of the molecules.**

Therefore, when different items are at the same temperature, their molecules have the same average kinetic energy. If the temperature of an item changes, its internal kinetic energy also changes.

We note that the total amount of internal energy in an item also depends on how much matter it has. If each molecule has the same kinetic energy then increasing the number of molecules increases the total amount of that energy. We do not get seriously burned by a spark from a bonfire, whereas we would be burned by a large, massive ember at the same temperature.

Next, let's see about the relation between internal energy and changes in state.

## 13-4 Internal Energy in States of Matter

If the internal energy in matter is set by temperature, then the states of matter—which occur at different temperatures—likely possess different amounts of internal energy. To know for sure we must know the amount of potential energy each state possesses as well as the amount of kinetic energy. We can learn this from a simple experiment

Imagine a closed pan containing water with a thermometer immersed in the liquid like that shown in *Figure 13.7* and put it into a freezer.

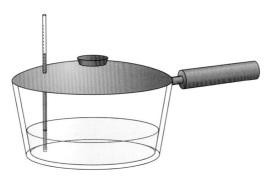

**Figure 13.7**
A closed vessel with a small amount of water and a thermometer to measure temperature.

Leave it there until all the liquid water is frozen and the temperature is below 0° C. Then take the pan out, put it on a stove and turn on the heat. Watch the temperature carefully as the ice first melts to water and then the water boils off as steam.

As you watch the thermometer, you will see the temperature of the water change as shown in *Figure 13.8*. Initially, when all the water is

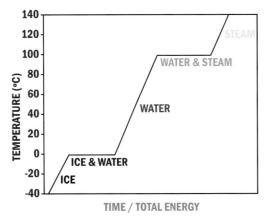

**Figure 13.8**
A graph of the changes in temperature of the closed vessel in Figure 13.7, as heat energy is put in at a constant rate. Temperature increases when there is only one state present, but is constant when one state is converting to another.

solid ice, the temperature rises until it comes to 0° C. Then, as the ice begins to melt, the temperature stays fixed at this value. It stays at 0° C as long as both liquid water and solid ice are present. When all the ice is gone and the water is all liquid, the temperature begins to rise again. It keeps increasing until the liquid starts to boil at 100° C. Again the temperature stays constant until all of the liquid has boiled off, after which it rises again.

In this experiment energy is constantly being put into the pan of water. The temperature increases *only* when the pan holds a single state of matter—just solid, just liquid, or just gas. When two states of matter are present, the temperature stays the same: 0° C for ice/water and 100° C for water/steam even though energy is still going in.

Solid ice at a low temperature has a low internal kinetic energy. Energy flowing from the stove to the ice increases the average kinetic energy of the ice molecules and the ice's temperature goes up. The increase in kinetic energy means the jiggling motion of the molecules is increasing. Eventually the molecules have enough kinetic energy that they begin to break free and the solid begins to melt, forming a liquid. At this point energy is flowing into the pan but the temperature of the liquid/solid mixture is unchanging so the kinetic energy is also unchanging even though the ice is melting.

If the inflowing energy is not going into kinetic energy, it must be going into the electrical potential energy between molecules. This makes sense because as the state changes, the positions of the molecules change and potential has to do with position. Because of this, *the liquid has a higher potential energy than the solid.*

After all of the ice has melted, continued heating causes the temperature to rise again. When the temperature hits the boiling point at 100° C, molecules begin to break free and evaporate as a gas. As the state changes from liquid to gas the average kinetic energy of the molecules in the two states again remains the same. Once again *the additional energy input from the stove increases the potential energy of the molecules.*

As a result, solids have the least potential energy, gases the most, and liquids are somewhere in between. Of course solids also have lower kinetic energies than liquids, and liquids have lower kinetic energies than gases. Kinetic and potential energy being the two forms of internal energy, we conclude that solids have the least internal energy, liquids have more than solids and gases have the most internal energy.

### Conduction

In Chapter 9 we discussed conduction as a way that energy is transported through material or between materials that touch. The molecular model of matter readily explains how conduction works.

When a cold pan is placed on a hot electric plate, the pan molecules and the plate molecules come in contact where the two surfaces touch. Both objects are solid so their molecules are not drifting out of place. The higher temperature hot plate molecules are jiggling vigorously while the cold pan molecules jiggle just a little (*Figure 13.9*). As they jiggle, the molecules on the surfaces that touch collide with each other. Molecular collisions between cold, slow-moving molecules and hot, rapidly moving ones speed up the slow ones and slow down the fast ones, transferring kinetic energy to them and causing them to jiggle faster. For this reason molecular kinetic energy, which is heat energy, always flows from a hot object to a cold one. This process continues through the pan itself until it is entirely heated.

It is important to distinguish between the flow of heat and temperature itself. Put a metal spoon and a wooden spoon in the freezer for several hours. Now pick them up. Which *feels* colder? Both are at the same temperature, yet the metal spoon feels colder. What our nerve endings sense and our brains interpret as temperature is really heat flow, and heat flows more

readily to and from metal than wood, although the molecular model does not tell us why.

### Gas Pressure

The molecular model readily explains how gas in a container exerts pressure (*Figure 13.10*). The molecules of a gas, being in constant motion, collide continually with the container walls. Each collision exerts a force on the wall. The gas pressure is then the sum of the collective force exerted by many molecules colliding over a given area at the same time.

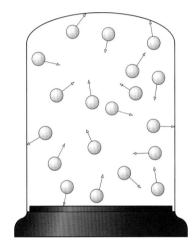

**Figure 13.10**
Gas molecules hitting the wall of a container cause pressure.

Since increasing the temperature of the gas increases the average kinetic energy of its molecules, when the gas is hotter, the molecules hit the wall going faster. Therefore their acceleration at the wall collision will also be greater[1].

_____

[1] A molecule going 300 meters/sec that bounces of the wall at the same speed in one second's time, accelerates by 600 meters/sec² (300 meters/sec into the wall plus 300 meters/

**a) Cold molecules**          **b) Hot molecules**

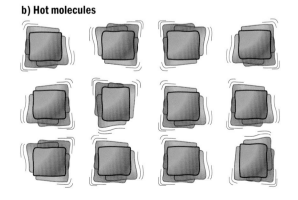

**Figure 13.9**
The effect of temperature on the motion of molecules in solids, using the lumps of green Jello in Figure 13.2. a) In cold molecules, the jiggling back and forth motion is small and molecules can be very close together. b) In hot molecules, the jiggling motion covers more space, and molecules move apart to accommodate the expanded motion.

By Newton's second law increased acceleration means increased force so the average force of a collision will increase. In addition, since the molecules travel faster, they will hit the walls more frequently too. So hotter gases exert more pressure than colder ones. To see if this prediction is accurate, measure the air pressure in your bicycle tire before and after a long ride on a hot road and see how much it changes.

## 13-5 Limitations of the Molecular Model

The molecular model gives us explanations for the states of matter and their densities. It provides us with the insight that temperature is connected to kinetic energy and that changes in internal energy occur when matter changes state.

The molecular model has limitations, however. Notice that nothing has been said about why gases, solids, and liquids respond differently to compression, tension, and shear forces. Also, we have not offered any explanations about why objects differ in color. The molecular model cannot deal with either of those issues. And it does not explain why metals and wooden objects conduct heat differently.

Perhaps the most glaring omission is any discussion of plasmas. The molecular model does not explain why a gas changes state to a plasma when heated to a high temperature. It was the study of plasmas that necessitated the next model, one that considers the internal structure of molecules and admits that they can be broken down into smaller parts.

---

sec away from the wall is 600 meters/sec.) A molecule hot enough to go 500 meters/sec accelerates by 1000 meters/ $sec^2$ by the same reasoning.)

*Your theory is crazy, but it's
not crazy enough to be true.*
Niels Bohr

# 13 STUDY GUIDE

## Chapter Framework

### A. The Molecular Model of Matter
1. Experimental Basis
   a. *Properties of matter*
   b. *Brownian motion*
2. Assumptions
   a. *Tiny particles, called molecules*
   b. *Different matter, different molecules*
   c. *Molecules in constant motion*
   d. *Molecular motion governed by classical motion and force laws*

### B. Explanations from the Model
1. Physical States
2. Differing Densities

### C. New Insights
1. States of Matter and Internal Energy
2. Internal Kinetic Energy and Temperature
3. Relative Order of Internal Energy in States of Matter
4. Heat Flow: Conduction
5. Gas Pressure

### D. Limitations of the Model
1. Doesn't explain color
2. Doesn't explain response to different forces

## Comprehension

### Matching
1. _____ The tiny constituent particles of which matter is composed.
2. _____ A measure of average kinetic energy of the molecules that make up an object.
3. _____ The constant, irregular motion of very fine particles suspended in a fluid and observed with a microscope.
4. _____ The transfer of microscopic kinetic energy between two solid objects (a hot one and a cold one) that are in physical contact with each other.
5. _____ Model that explains the behavior of gases observed by Maxwell.
6. _____ Force per unit area.

a. Molecular Model

b. Heat Conduction

c. Pressure

d. Temperature

e. Molecules

f. Brownian Motion

### True/False
1. _____ Pressure in a hot tire is greater than the pressure when the tire is cold.
2. _____ For a given material, the solid state has a higher internal energy than the gaseous state.
3. _____ Molecules, even in solids, are in constant motion.
4. _____ The molecular model is limited in that it cannot explain the color of an object.
5. _____ Heat is the amount of energy associated with electrical potential energy.
6. _____ In the molecular model, molecules are assumed to move according to the laws of special relativity.

7. _____ According to Maxwell, all of the gas molecules in a balloon are traveling at the same speed.

### Fill in the Blank
1. _____ are the incredibly tiny particles that make up matter.
2. Increasing the temperature of an object _____ the average kinetic energy of the molecules within the object.
3. When a liquid transforms to a gas in a closed container, and both liquid and gas are present simultaneously, the temperature of the substance _____ .
4. Ice and liquid water are present in the container of Figure 13.8 at the same temperature. The _____ of the two states is the same.
5. A cold pan is placed on a hot stove burner. Thermal energy flows from the _____ to the _____.
6. For a given type of material, matter as a _____ has the greatest potential energy.

## Analysis

1. Between two objects, heat always travels
   a) from a cooler to a warmer object.
   b) from a warmer to a cooler object.
   c) randomly between the two objects regardless of their temperature.
   d) Heat doesn't travel between objects.

2. For nearly all substances, the density of physical states increases in which order?
   a) Solid, gas, liquid
   b) Liquid, gas, solid
   c) Solid, liquid, gas
   d) Gas, liquid, solid

3. The average distance *between* molecules in the states of matter (solid, liquid, gas) increases in which order?
   a) Gas, liquid, solid
   b) Liquid, solid, gas
   c) Solid, liquid, gas

4. If a large bucket of water and a small bucket of water have the same temperature,
   a) both have the same total internal energy.
   b) both have the same total molecular kinetic energy.
   c) the average molecular speed is the same for both.
   d) both have the same total energy.
   e) the water molecules in the small bucket are moving faster than those in the large bucket.

5. Heat conduction occurs from a warm room through a closed window on a cold day because

   a) the molecules in the glass window are moving faster than those in the air inside the room.

   b) fast molecules go through the window to the outside.

   c) slow molecules enter the room from the outside.

   d) slow molecules transfer energy to faster ones with which they collide, on the average.

   e) fast molecules transfer energy to slower ones with which they collide, on the average.

6. Evaporation of water from the skin has a cooling effect. This is because

   a) the most massive water molecules escape into the surrounding atmosphere.

   b) water molecules with the greatest speed escape into the surrounding atmosphere.

   c) water molecules with the least kinetic energy escape into the surrounding atmosphere.

   d) the surrounding atmosphere transfers its energy into the water.

   e) the least massive water molecules escape into the surrounding atmosphere.

7. What would Robert Brown have observed if he increased the sample temperature while looking through his microscope? He would have found that

   a) the pollen grains twitch and jerk more rapidly.

   b) there would be no change in the motion on the pollen grains.

   c) the pollen grains twitch and jerk slower.

## Synthesis

1. Using the Molecular Model, explain why gases readily change volume when pressure is applied, while liquids and solids do not change volume appreciably, unless under enormous pressure.

2. Use the Molecular Model to explain each observation:

   a) The density of solid nitrogen molecules is greater than the density of nitrogen molecules in air.

   b) Heat flows from hot objects to colder ones.

   c) Perfume spilled at one end of a room can be smelled at the other end after a few seconds.

3. Your neighbor knocks at your door and asks you to explain something. She bought a helium-filled balloon for her daughter in a warm grocery store. When she put it in her car on a cold January day, the balloon shrank and she thought the balloon had sprung a leak. But the balloon returned to its original size when she took it into her warm house. What explanation can you give based on the molecular model?

4. Figure 13.6 illustrates how the distribution of molecular speeds varies with mass of the gas particles for helium, nitrogen, and argon. Helium atoms have a mass of 4 units, nitrogen molecules have mass 28, and argon atoms have mass 40. Sketch what the graph might look like for oxygen molecules, if oxygen molecules have a mass of 32. The most important characteristics of the distribution are the most popular speed, the fraction of molecules with that speed, and the overall width of the distribution.

5. Using the graph in Figure 13.8:

   a) Identify the portions of the graph where only one state of matter is present (e.g., only solid, only liquid, or only gas). Describe what happens to the temperature during these portions of the graph as time and total energy increase. (If you were looking at a thermometer, what would you see happening?) From your observation of the temperature change, what can you conclude about the kinetic energy of the matter during these processes? That is, does the kinetic energy increase or decrease as the *total* energy increases?

   b) Now look at the segments when two states of matter are present (solid & liquid, liquid & gas). Describe the temperature behavior within these segments as time and total energy increases. What can you conclude about the change in kinetic energy based upon the temperature behavior?

   c) Hopefully, you have identified stages in the process where the kinetic energy is constant but the *total* energy is increasing. How can you explain this? Think about what happens to the average distance between molecules as you go from state to state. What kind of energy is associated with the relative positions of particles?

6. Sketch the time vs. temperature graph shown in Figure 13.8 on a piece of paper and match each description below with the appropriate segment of graph.

   a) Pan containing only liquid water.

   b) Pan containing only ice.

   c) Pan containing only steam.

   d) Pan containing liquid water with ice floating in it.

   e) Pan containing boiling water with steam.

7. The details of Figure 13.8 apply to changes of state for many substances other than water. Pick one of the substances (other than water) in Table 12.1 and sketch a graph like Figure 13.9 for your substance. Things to consider: At what temperatures will you have plateaus? Between what temperatures will you have sloping lines?

# The Nuclear Atom

*When it comes to atoms, language can be used only as in poetry. The poet, too, is not nearly so concerned with describing facts as with creating images and establishing mental connections.*

*Niels Bohr*

## LEARN

- How the gold-foil experiment and atomic spectra led to our understanding of atomic structure;

- The Thomson model of the atom, also known as the plum pudding model, and its limitations.

- The Rutherford model of the atom, also known as the nuclear or solar system model, and its limitations.

- The Bohr model of the atom, also known as the modified solar system model, and its limitations.

The molecular model of Chapter 13 was a triumph of science. It provided a mental image around which to explain states of matter. It established a critical connection between an object's temperature and the kinetic energy of its molecules. Maxwell's equation describing the distribution of molecular speeds, derived from the molecular model, remains very useful for the study of gases even today.

However, as you know, the molecular model says nothing about the internal structure of molecules. Indeed, in the last chapter we asked that you not get too distracted by your knowledge that molecules are in fact composed of atoms. By the mid-to-late 1800s research in chemistry had firmly established atoms as the basic molecular building block. Attention turned to them and the type of structure they had.

In this chapter the models we consider will be models of *atoms*, not molecules. This may appear as a disjointed leap in the development of our discussion on matter, yet it isn't. Molecular structure can be quite complex and is best understood only after the nature of atoms is

comprehended. After these most basic building blocks are described we will return again in Chapter 19 to the discussion of the molecules they build.

Usually, a transition from one model to a new one occurs gradually after many experiments motivate the need for change. Occasionally, however, a new model springs forth immediately from the dramatic and unexpected results of a single experiment. Our understanding of the atom has progressed via both slow, evolutionary processes and quick, abrupt pathways, as you will see.

## 14-1 The Plum Pudding Model

Watch how a toddler explores her world. Chances are that at least one toy gets ripped or chewed open to see what's inside. A good way to understand how something works is to take it apart. To study atoms, experiments were designed to tear them apart and observe the pieces.

In Chapter 4 we discussed how the atom-breaking work of J. J. Thomson and the careful measurement of charged oil drops by Robert Millikan led to the discovery and quantification of the electron. By the beginning of the twentieth century, the following facts had been well established:

1. The atom contains positively-charged and negatively-charged parts.
2. The negative part, the electrons, has the same mass and charge in every kind of atom.
3. The positive part determines the unique nature of the atom. The positive parts of atoms of the same kind are identical with each other but differ in mass from atoms of other types.
4. The mass of an electron is much, much smaller than the mass of the positive parts.

In an article published in 1904, Thomson combined these four observations into the simple model presented in *Figure 14.1*. Thomson proposed that the positive charge of the atom was uniformly distributed, like a cloud, throughout the space it occupied. Electrons were embed-

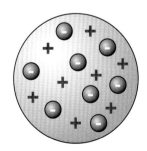

**Figure 14.1**

The plum pudding model proposed by J. J. Thomson. The positive charge is spread diffusely throughout the atom; electrons are sprinkled throughout the positively-charged region.

ded randomly within the positively-charged volume. Each atom contained enough electrons to balance out the positive charge.

Thomson's model came to be known as the "plum pudding" model. Plum pudding, a favorite British dessert, contains bits of plum sprinkled throughout a cake-like base. For Americans who don't eat much plum pudding, a better image might be an oatmeal-raisin or chocolate-chip cookie. The positive charge resembles the cookie dough with the electrons sprinkled throughout like the raisins or chocolate chips.

## 14–2  Rutherford's Gold Foil Experiment

Ernest Rutherford (1871–1937) was a former student of J. J. Thomson who had participated in many gas-discharge experiments with him, gaining expertise in that technology. At about this same time Rutherford learned of high-energy, positively-charged particles, called **alpha particles**. While interesting in their own right (see Chapter 25), Rutherford realized that alpha particles could be used as atomic-sized, high-energy bullets to further break apart atoms as a test of Thomson's plum pudding model.

Rutherford determined to shoot alpha particles at atoms in a razor-thin gold foil. He hypothesized that the rapidly moving alpha particles would slice right through the diffuse positive "pudding" of the gold atoms. An alpha particle would experience only a weak repul-

**Alpha Particle:**
A helium nucleus emitted in radioactive decay.

sion from the diffuse positive charge of the gold atoms as the particle passed through the foil. Attractive encounters of an alpha particle to an electron would also occur only rarely. So nearly all alpha particles were expected to cut straight through the foil. At best, a few might experience a slight deflection from a straight-line flight.

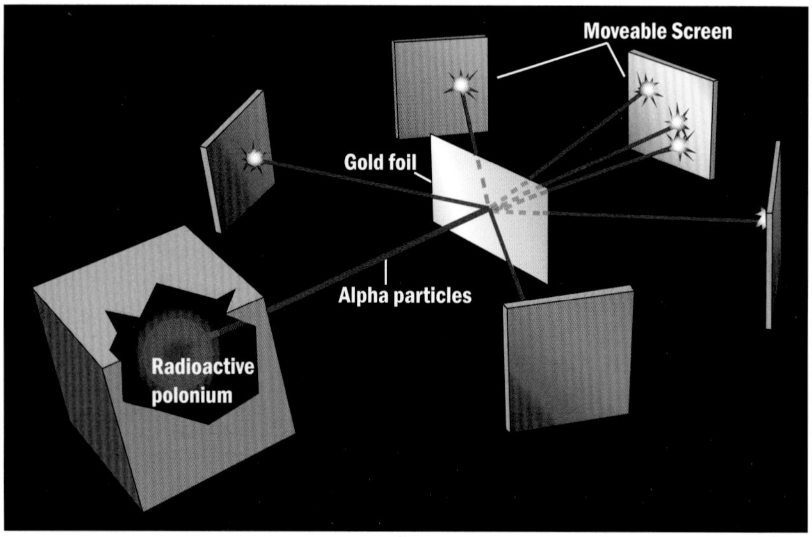

In 1911, Rutherford and two junior colleagues set up an apparatus like that shown in *Figure 14.2*. A sample of a substance called polonium emitted a beam of alpha particles. These particles, moving in a straight line, were directed at an ultra-thin piece of gold foil. A movable screen coated with zinc sulfide, which emits flashes of light when alpha particles slam into it, was moved to different positions around the gold foil. With this arrangement, the investigators could see from the flashes of light how much the alpha particle's flight deviated from a straight line when passing through the foil.

Because the light flashes on the detector screen were weak, the experiments had to be conducted in the dark. An observer would position the screen, turn out the lights and let his eyes adapt to the darkness. Sitting quietly with attention focused on the screen, they counted the blips of light that appeared during a set time interval. Then the process would be repeated, with the screen placed in a new location around the gold foil.

Rutherford was not a patient man, so he convinced two junior colleagues to actually collect the data. Fortunately, his colleagues were both patient *and* meticulous. Given the working hypothesis, the pair might have concentrated their observations at screen locations directly behind or a few degrees on either side of the foil. Instead, they moved the detector to many locations, going almost 360° around the gold foil.

The number and pattern of hits on the screen were counted at each location. Most of the alpha particles were found to behave just as Rutherford expected, hitting the screen behind the foil with small deflection angles. But occasionally, about one in every 8,000 particles, a flash was detected in a most unexpected place: somewhere in *front* of the gold foil!

That alpha particles occasionally reflected backwards astounded Rutherford. He later wrote:

It was quite the most incredible event that has happened in my life. It was almost as incredible

**Figure 14.2**
Rutherford's Gold Foil Experiment. Alpha particles emitted by a radioactive source were shot at a thin gold foil. Particles were detected when they hit a screen and caused the zinc sulfide coating to glow. When the screen was in front of the gold foil, a few particles bounced back and were detected when they hit the screen.

as if you fired a 15-inch (artillery) shell at a piece of tissue paper and it came back and hit you.[1]

## 14-3 The Atom Has a Nucleus

Rutherford and his colleagues analyzed the recoil patterns of the alpha particles. They realized that only one interpretation of the results was consistent with Newton's laws of motion and the electrical force law. To reflect backwards, a particle had to stop and change direction. In doing so it experienced a large acceleration which in turn required a large repulsive force. Such a force could only result if the positive charge of the gold atoms were concentrated in very small, very dense particles. Thomson's plum pudding model was wrong!

The scientists called the dense, positively-charged particle the **nucleus**. Because only a few alpha particles recoiled backward, repulsive encounters with the nucleus had to be infrequent; further proof that the nucleus was small and thus hard to hit. Rutherford concluded that both the mass and positive charge of the atom must be concentrated in the nucleus while the rest of the atom was empty space.

Rutherford's calculations indicated the nuclear diameter was about $10^{-15}$ meters. Other types of experiments found the atomic diameter to be about $10^{-10}$ meters. The nucleus is about 100,000 times smaller than the atom! If the nucleus were a marble placed at the Wilkinson Center on the BYU campus, the outer edge of the atom would extend from the Marriott Center on the north to the Botany Pond on the south.

Rutherford's results required that the atom's mass be concentrated in a very small space which means it has a very high density. The nuclear density is about $10^{16}$ (1 with 16 zeros after it!) grams in a cubic centimeter. That is equivalent to squeezing 90 *billion* 250-lb linebackers into a space with a volume of 1 cubic centimeter.

### Solar System Model

How did Rutherford account for the electrons? He assumed they orbited outside the nucleus through a volume which was the size of the atom itself. In the plum pudding model atomic diameters were set by the extent of the positive "pudding". Electrons have a small size and mass and take up very little space so their physical size could not determine the atomic diameter. In Rutherford's model the diameter is set by the volume through which the electrons orbited.

Rutherford's model resembles a solar system where electrons, like planets, exist in mostly empty space at large distances from a very dense Sun-like nucleus. Held in place by the electromagnetic force, the electrons were thought to orbit the nucleus in elliptical paths just as planets orbit around the Sun under the influence of gravity (*Figure 14.3*). Not surprisingly, this new model was sometimes called the **solar system model** of the atom.

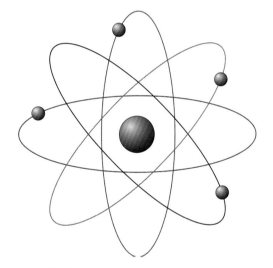

**Figure 14.3**
The Rutherford model of the atom, also known as the Solar System Model.

Scientists quickly became aware that this model couldn't be quite right. James Maxwell had demonstrated that accelerating charges produce light. Electrons moving in elliptical paths are charged particles undergoing accelerated motion. Where was the light that should be produced? And because electrons, like planets, could orbit with any possible acceleration, shouldn't electrons emit light with a continuous spectrum? Furthermore, conservation of energy requires that the radiated energy come from the electron's kinetic energy. Electrons should lose kinetic energy and speed and quickly spiral down into the nucleus.

Atoms don't usually emit light at all. The

**Nucleus:**
The atomic nucleus is the very dense, positively charged center of the atom.

**Solar System Model:**
A model of the atom in which the electrons orbit the small, dense, positively-charged nucleus in elliptical paths. The model was proposed by Rutherford.

[1] Lord Rutherford, "The Development of the Theory of Atomic Structure," (1936 essay), in *Background to Modern Science,* New York: Macmillan, 1940.

atoms in Thomson's gas tubes had to be stimulated with electrical energy and become a plasma to produce radiation. When this happens, as we saw in Chapter 12, these tubes radiate discrete colors or wavelengths of light, not a continuous spectrum. Clearly, a new model was needed to resolve these problems.

## 14-4  Light Spectra

To review from Chapters 11 and 12, white light emitted by the Sun can be separated into all the colors of the rainbow. Newton discovered this using a simple prism (*Figure 14.4a*). Hold a piece of white paper on one side of the prism and direct the separated light onto the paper. You should see that the colors change continuously from red through orange to yellow, green, blue, ending in violet. Exactly where one color ends and the next one begins is impossible to identify. The colors of light change smoothly and continuously from one end of the rainbow to the other in a continuous spectrum.

The plasma in Thomson's discharge tubes also give off light but with a difference. A tube containing neon gives off a bright red-colored light. Hydrogen gives off a reddish light. Mercury gives off a yellowish-blue light. Passing their light through a prism to separate the colors

**Emission Spectrum:**

An emission spectrum is the set of colors of light given off, or emitted by, an object.

yields only a few color bands as shown in *Figure 14.4b*. Here it is easy to distinguish between the red light and the blue-green light since there are no other colors in between. The black regions between the colored lines indicate an *absence* of light energy at those colors.

Recall that spectra like that from Thomson's tubes are called discrete emission spectra. Figure 12.8 in Chapter 12 showed other examples of discrete emission spectra. Because the colors appear as sharp lines in these spectra, we often speak of them as being "emission lines."[2]

### *Hydrogen Emission Spectra*

The emission spectra of atoms can be quite complex. Neon, for example, produces dozens of lines in an intricate pattern. A successful model of the atom must explain this pattern and that of every atom. We start with the simple ones first.

The simplest of all atoms is hydrogen. Hydrogen has several groups or families of emission lines. Only one of these families of lines is located in the visible region (*Figure 14.4b*). The others are in the ultraviolet and infrared regions. A Swedish mathematician named Janne Rydberg (1854–1919) discovered by trial and error a formula that reproduced the frequencies of all of hydrogen's different families of emission lines. The formula, published in 1890, was:

$$f = C\left[\frac{1}{n_2{}^2} - \frac{1}{n_1{}^2}\right]$$

where $f$ is the frequency of emitted light, $n_1$ and $n_2$ are integers (1,2,3,4 etc.), and $C$ is a constant. We often use the letter "n" to represent a variable that is restricted to only be integer values. The subscripts 1 and 2 provide a way to indicate two different integers. Rydberg found that each *family* of spectral lines was indicated by a unique value of $n_2$, and each *line* within that family was indicated by a unique value of $n_1$.

The equation worked incredibly well for the known emission lines in the hydrogen spectrum. Better still, it predicted the frequencies of undiscovered lines that were soon found. Clearly it was teaching us something about atomic struc-

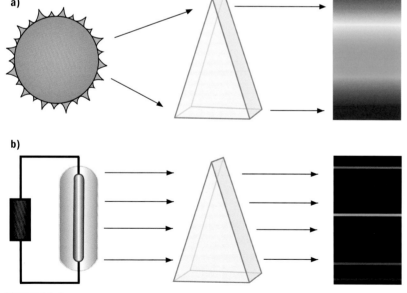

**Figure 14.4**

Comparison of Continuous and Discrete Emission Spectra:

a) Continuous Spectra—The Sun gives off white light. Passing the white light through a prism reveals all the colors of the rainbow. The colors change continuously from red to violet.

b) Discrete Spectra—Gases in discharge tubes give off only a few colors of light. Light from a tube containing atomic hydrogen looks reddish. When the red light is passed through the prism, only four colors are found. The colors are very distinct. The reddish color that our eyes detect is a result of the combination of those four colors.

_____

[2] A mathematical analogy might be helpful. The set of real numbers is continuous. There are an infinite number of numbers between 3.1415 and 3.1316. Integers are discrete. There are no integers between 3 and 4. Another analogy is a course in cooking, where we can use any fraction of a cup of milk, but eggs come only in integers.

ture. However, it would be more than 20 years before a reasonable explanation could be given for why this formula worked.

### Continuous Spectra

Rydberg's formula gave encouraging insight into how atoms were built but further clues were slow in coming. The next critical clue would actually come from a study of continuous spectra.

Hot objects glow at all wavelengths. You have seen an example of this in the heating element of a stove when it glows "red-hot" at a temperature of about 1200 °F. The filament in an incandescent light bulb glows "warm white" at about 4,000 °F, and the visible surface of the Sun glows "white-hot" at around 10,000 °F. Remarkably, the colors in the spectrum of a hot object depend only on the object's temperature, not its material composition. *Figure 14.5* shows the visible part of the continuous spectra for several temperatures.

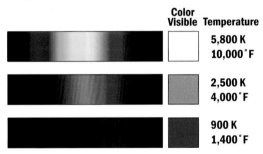

| Color Visible | Temperature |
|---|---|
| | 5,800 K 10,000˚F |
| | 2,500 K 4,000˚F |
| | 900 K 1,400˚F |

**Figure 14.5**
The continuous emission spectrum from hot objects at different temperatures. Black represents the absence of color. The Sun, an incandescent (filament) light bulb, and hot burner represent the different temperatures. Remember that white light is a balance of all the colors. If some colors are missing, or present in excess, the perceived color will not be white.

A number of scientists tried, and failed, to develop an accurate description of the spectrum emitted by hot objects using the physical principles that were understood in the late 1800s. Finally, in 1900, a German scientist named Max Planck developed a description that modeled the observed spectrum accurately. However, to derive his new theory Planck had to make a bold assumption. He assumed that light energy could only be emitted by a atom in a discrete unit called a "quantum" (plural quanta) of energy. The size of the energy quantum is related to the frequency of the light through

$$\text{Energy} = h \times \text{frequency}$$

Hopefully this formula looks familiar. The energy quanta introduced by Planck are the photons discussed in Chapter 11! Planck found that the discrete nature of the emitted light can be modeled by assuming that atoms can only have certain discrete amounts of energy, and when atoms change from a high energy state to a low energy state they emit the energy difference as light.

Planck thought the assumption of quantized energy was not realistic and called the introduction of energy quanta "an act of desperation". He felt sure that a better description would be developed soon. Then in 1905, Albert Einstein used Planck's notion of energy quanta, now called photons, to explain the photoelectric effect.

Acceptance for the quantization notion gradually became widespread. Physicists began to recognize this assumption had far-reaching implications and a new branch of physics, now called quantum mechanics, was born.

## 14-5 Quantization

Two related ideas had emerged. First is that the spectrum of hydrogen could be described by a series of integer numbers in the simple Rydberg formula. Next was that the energy in a photon of light took on discrete values related to the frequency. With this background Niels Bohr (1885–1962), a Danish scientist and colleague of Thomson and Rutherford, set about to solve the problems of the solar system model.

Bohr recognized that the plasma spectra from gas discharge tubes were created by the electrons of an atom. He reasoned that since the light energy in emission lines had discrete colors and thus discrete energies, perhaps other aspects of the electrons were also discrete or "quantized." So he applied the idea of quantization to the angular momentum of an electron. Recall from Chapter 8 that angular momentum is given by:

**Angular momentum = mass × speed × radius**

Bohr postulated that the angular momentum was only allowed to take on "quantized" values given by the formula:

**Angular momentum = n × h**

where *n* is again a positive integer from 1, 2, 3 etc. to infinity and h is Planck's constant. The integer *n* defined here is sometimes called the *quantum number*.

A quantized angular momentum places restrictions on electron orbits and energies. Electrons could only orbit the nucleus in circular orbits with constant radii. Otherwise they could not maintain a specific, fixed angular momentum as required.

Bohr also assumed that the energies of electrons are quantized as well. In his derivation of the allowed values for energies he found that they were inversely proportional to the square of the quantum number **n**. That is:

**Energy is proportional to $1/n^2$**

That Bohr's energies had the same relation to n as the Rydberg formula was encouraging. The Rydberg formula, angular momentum, and energies all had a dependence on discrete integers making it clear that the atom worked in set quantities of energy and momentum. In other words, it was quantized.

## 14-6  The Bohr Model of the Atom

Bohr proposed a model of the atom based on quantization. *Figure 14.6* shows the geometric arrangement of electrons around a positively-charged nucleus according to this model. Electrons orbit the nucleus in circular paths whose radii satisfy Bohr's assumptions.

Electrons never occupy the space between the allowed orbits.

Bohr's quantum number **n** became the label that identifies each possible electron orbit and the energy of an electron in that orbit. The smallest possible value of the quantum number, **n** = 1, corresponds to the allowed orbit having the smallest radius. As **n** increases, it specifies allowed orbits of increasing radius.

The Bohr model has circular orbits at special radii, while the Rutherford solar system model postulated elliptical orbits with no restrictions on the radius. Because of these two differences, the Bohr model is sometimes called the **modified solar system model.**

*Figure 14.7* represents the energy values of electrons in the orbits of the Bohr model. Horizontal lines represent different orbits and are labeled by the corresponding quantum number, **n.** These lines are also called "energy states" since, by the postulate of quantization, any electron in that orbit possesses a specific energy. The lowest energy state, **n** = 1 is at the bottom of the figure. Orbits higher than this have larger radii and their electrons possess greater energy.

### Discrete Emissions

The energy diagram in Figure 14.7 explains graphically how discrete emission lines are created in glowing gas tubes. Suppose a single electron resides in the **n** = 2 energy state. In that

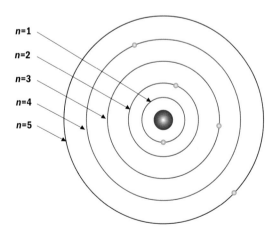

**Figure 14.6**
The Bohr Model of the Atom. Electrons move around the nucleus in circular orbits. (The orbits are not drawn to scale in order to show more than one of them.) The first orbit is many times larger than the nucleus. As the quantum number n increases, the energy of the electron and the radius of its orbit increases.

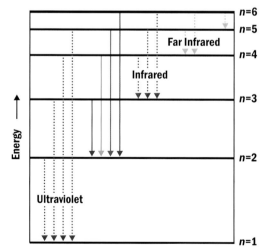

**Figure 14.7**
The energy levels of a Bohr atom. The arrows represent differences between two energy states. They also represent photons that are emitted when electrons jump between states. The colors of the arrows are those of the photons in the emission spectrum of hydrogen. Solid arrows represent visible photons. Dashed arrows represent photons outside the visible region. Reversing the direction of the arrows would give an absorption spectrum.

## ENERGY FORMULAS

When talking about electronic states and electronic energies, two important concepts arise. The first is the absolute energy. The absolute energies identify the ordering or sequencing of the quantum states. They specify which state is lowest in energy, which state next lowest, etc. States which have high absolute energies are identified by horizontal lines high up in Figure 14.7.

The second concept is the energy difference between two states. The arrows of Figure 14.7 represent the sizes of energy *differences* between several pairs of states. Look at the length of the arrow between states n = 6 and n = 5 and then look at the length of the arrow between n = 2 and n = 1. Which arrow is longer? The arrow between n = 2 and n = 1 is longer. That means the energy difference between the first and second states is greater than the difference between the 5th and 6th states. This is a general result: In the Bohr model, energy differences between successive states gets smaller and smaller.

Bohr's energy equation calculated absolute electron energies for a given n state. Bohr recognized that Rydberg's formula calculated energy *differences*. Rydberg's n1 and n2 numbers correspond to initial (n1) and final (n2) quantum numbers of Bohr. Bohr's model also reproduced the value of Rydberg's constant C.

What Rydberg had come up with by trial and error, Bohr derived from a few assumptions and the classical laws of force, motion, and conservation. It was a great success.

state its energy is low, but it is not at lowest state. Now suppose it falls down to that lowest state where $n = 1$. It can do this only by losing energy. The energy that is lost emerges as a photon of light. The energy *difference* between the two orbits determines the frequency and color of that light. In other words:

**Energy of outer orbit – Energy of inner orbit = Energy of emitted photon**

and

**Frequency = Energy of emitted photon / h**

A single emission line is produced when an electron drops from a higher energy orbit to a lower energy orbit. Electrons from large numbers of atoms transitioning between many different energy states creates the entire emission spectrum. The arrows in Figure 14.7 show many possible changes in energy state. The length of each arrow is a measure of the energy difference between the state where the electron started and where it ended. So longer arrows correspond to larger changes in energy and shorter arrows correspond to smaller changes.

The specific emission spectrum of hydrogen can be explained using the general energy diagram of Figure 14.7. Hydrogen has four lines in visible light, those that are shown in Figure 14.4. It turns out that these four lines correspond to the four arrows in Figure 14.7 that stop at $n = 2$. The color of each arrow represents the color of that specific emission line. So violet photons arise when electrons in the $n = 6$ orbit fall down to the $n = 2$ orbit, red photons are produced

when electrons fall from the $n = 3$ to the $n = 2$ orbits, etc. If you recall that violet photons are more energetic than red photons, this assignment should seem reasonable.

The diagram can also explain the emission lines of hydrogen that are found in the ultraviolet and infrared regions. Long jumps from higher states to the $n = 1$ orbit generate ultraviolet photons. Shorter jumps from higher states to the $n = 3, 4, 5$, etc. states generate low energy photons in the infrared or far infrared regions.

### Absorption Spectra

Are you wondering how an electron gets into the higher states in the first place? In Thomson's tubes the energy comes from collisions. When an electric current flows through the gas, energetic electrons collide with atoms kicking their electrons up to higher energy levels. For this reason the higher levels are often called "excited" states since electrons there have extra "excitation" energy. As they fall back down they release this energy as light, creating an emission line.

There is a second way electrons can elevate to higher levels. Consider an electron in the $n = 1$ state. Suppose a photon happens to pass by with just the right energy to kick the electron up to a state with a higher $n$. The electron can absorb that photon and in so doing jumps to the new orbit. Photon absorption is the reverse process of photon emission. The absorption process can be represented in Figure 14.7 by reversing the direction of the arrows.

For this reason there is a correspondence

between an absorption spectrum and an emission spectrum. As shown in *Figure 14.8,* when a hydrogen atom absorbs photons from white light passing through it, the colors removed to form the absorption spectrum are the exact same colors present in the emission spectrum. Again, this is expected because the only difference is the direction the electron jumps between levels; up for absorption and down for emission.

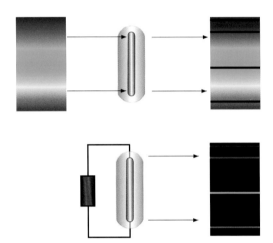

**Figure 14.8**

Comparison of emission and absorption spectra. In an absorption experiment, light from a white source passes through a tube containing hydrogen gas. The hydrogen absorbs red, blue-green, blue and violet photons from the light, leaving black gaps. The lower figure shows a gas discharge tube. A high electrical voltage is applied to the gas and causes it to emit photons. The colors of photons absorbed are the same as the ones emitted in a gas discharge tube.

## Problems with the Model

The success of the Bohr model with hydrogen was close to perfect. This success, though, was not replicated to the same degree with other atoms. The model did not predict the correct numbers of lines in emission spectra of some elements. When the model did get the number of lines correct, the predicted frequencies often did not match the measured ones. Clearly there was still more to be learned.

In forming his model Bohr adroitly sidestepped one critical issue that plagued Rutherford's solar system model. Bohr's electrons are still accelerating charges. Accelerating charges emit radiation. Bohr postulated that radiation was emitted only when electrons changed their orbits. While this assumption enabled him to successfully account for the hydrogen spectrum, there was really no justification for it.

Bohr's model introduced quantization but did not say why the angular momentum should be quantized. Bohr could only say that this assumption led to a successful explanation of the hydrogen spectrum and Rydberg's formula. Having yielded such a spectacular success, the assumption had to be correct. Yet the critical "why" question remained unanswered.

## CAMBRIDGE AND COPENHAGEN

Many of the key experiments in the development of atomic models were done in the Cavendish Laboratory at Cambridge University in England. The Cavendish Laboratory was established in 1874. Its first director was James Clerk Maxwell who made key discoveries about electromagnetic radiation and its wave nature. At the beginning of the 20th century, J. J. Thomson directed the Lab.

Thomson's ground-breaking experiments on the electron made Cambridge the place to be for physicists. Ernest Rutherford came from New Zealand to work in the Cavendish laboratory. He did important gas discharge tube experiments before taking a brief appointment in Canada, where he studied radioactivity, another hot topic of the time. Rutherford moved back to Britain, where he performed the gold-foil experiments with assistant Hans Geiger and undergraduate student Ernest Marsden at Manchester University. Ultimately, in 1919 Rutherford returned to Cambridge as head of the Cavendish Laboratory.

In 1911, Niels Bohr came to the Cavendish Laboratory to work with Thomson. But after meeting Rutherford at a party, Bohr moved to Manchester to study in the Rutherford laboratory. Bohr published his model of the atom in 1913. He returned to Copenhagen and his fame spread throughout the scientific world. Many scientists then came to Copenhagen to work at the institute Bohr established there. In 1943, Bohr fled to England because his Jewish heritage put him at risk during the Nazi invasions. He returned after the war was over.

International travel was surprisingly common among scientists, even before the days of commercial aviation. During the early 20th century England and Germany were seen as the dominant contributors to scientific advances and scientists flocked to both countries for study. The United States replaced them as the leader during the second-half of the 20th century. However, declining university enrollments and public interest in science and engineering in the U.S. in the 21st century may well mean that some new country will claim the role as the leader in the pursuit of scientific knowledge.

## 14–7 Conclusion

As we have emphasized many times, science progresses as new experiments provide new observations. Sometimes the new observations are inconsistent with the explanations provided by old models. When this happens, old models are usually not completely thrown out. Instead, they may be "decorated" when new information becomes available. Or, the old model may be "patched" up like a pair of favorite blue jeans when a hole develops.

The molecular model of matter successfully explained the behavior of collections of atoms acting together. The plum pudding model served as the beginning model for the interior design of the atom. Rutherford's gold foil experiment single handedly overturned the plum pudding model. The solar system model retained the existence of electrons and positive fragments, but the image of a diffuse cloud with embedded electrons morphed into the image of a dense nucleus with electrons in elliptical orbits. Bohr kept the nucleus but quantized angular momentum and came up with circular orbits.

The images of the Bohr and Rutherford models may not seem so different. A circle is just a special kind of ellipse, isn't it? It was the fact that nature operates with discrete quantization rather than continuous energies and momentum that was revolutionary. The ability of the Bohr model to explain so many observations about the hydrogen atom spectra gave it immediate credibility. The old picture of nature had to be discarded. The new picture was, in the words of Alice's Cheshire cat: "Curiouser and curiouser."

# 14 STUDY GUIDE

## Chapter Framework

### A. The Plum Pudding Model
1. Discharge Tube Experiments
   a. *Matter made of positive and negative bits*
2. Description of the Model
   a. *Diffuse positive charge*
   b. *Negative bits embedded throughout*

### B. The Solar System Model
1. Gold Foil Experiment
   a. *Alpha particles*
2. Description of the Model
   a. *Dense positive nucleus*
   b. *Electrons outside nucleus*
   c. *Elliptical orbits*

### C. Emission Spectra
1. Discrete Atomic Spectra of Hydrogen
   a. *Empirical formula with integers*
2. Continuous Spectra of Hot Objects
   a. *Explanation required quantized energy*

### D. The Bohr Model
1. Assumed Quantized Angular Momentum
2. Description of the Model
   a. *Dense positive nucleus*
   b. *Electrons in fixed circular orbits*
   c. *Orbit radius increases with electron energy*
3. Explained Discrete Emission Spectra

## Comprehension

### Matching

a. Nucleus

b. Alpha particle

c. Plum Pudding model

d. Solar system model

e. Discrete spectra

1. ____ Dense, positively-charged center of the atom.
2. ____ Rutherford Model.
3. ____ Spectra in which the colors of light change abruptly and many colors are missing.
4. ____ Thomson Model.
5. ____ Positively charged particle emitted by some radioactive materials (a helium nucleus).

### True/ False
1. ____ The electron has no mass.
2. ____ The red photons found in the emission spectrum of atomic hydrogen are less energetic than the purple photons.
3. ____ The rare, backward reflection of alpha particles convinced Rutherford that the atom consisted of a dense, positively-charged nucleus.
4. ____ In gas discharge tube experiments, positive fragments from different types of atoms are similar to one another.
5. ____ To explain the continuous spectrum, Planck proposed that light could only be absorbed or emitted in discrete amounts.
6. ____ Bohr failed to explain why an accelerated electron does not radiate energy.
7. ____ Rutherford fully expected alpha particles to bounce off the gold foil.
8. ____ The nucleus of an atom occupies more than half of the atom's volume.
9. ____ The color of a hot object is related to its temperature.

### Fill in the Blank
1. The conservation of _____ law explains why photon emission occurs when an electron drops from a high to a low energy state.
2. Thomson's and Millikan's experiments provided strong evidence for the atom's _____ nature.
3. Rutherford's orbits were _____; Bohr's orbits were _____ .
4. An electron with a large value of *n* (quantum number) in the Bohr model is _____ the nucleus and has _____ energy.
5. That nature functions using discrete rather than continuous energy is an assumption of the _____ model.

## Analysis

1. Thomson's gas discharge experiments provide direct experimental evidence for the
   a) Exclusion Principle.
   b) Nuclear Model of atoms.
   c) Bohr model of atoms.
   d) idea that all atoms are made of charged particles.
   e) idea that electrons in atoms behave as waves.

2. In the Thomson (plum pudding) model of the atom, an atom is described as
   a) a positive "pudding" with small lumps of negative charge distributed throughout.
   b) a negative "pudding" with small lumps of positive charge distributed throughout.
   c) a negative "pudding" with one large lump of positive charge in the middle.
   d) a neutral "pudding" with lumps of negative charge around the outside and lumps of positive charge in the middle.

3. In what model do electrons orbit the nucleus so that any orbit allowed by Newtonian physics can be occupied by an electron? (i.e., there are no restrictions on allowed electron energies.)
   a) Quantum model
   b) Thomson or "plum pudding" model
   c) Rutherford or "solar system" model
   d) Bohr or "modified solar system" model
   e) Molecular model

4. White light (containing all visible colors) passes through a gas that absorbs some of the light. The spectrum of light that passes through the gas is then analyzed. That spectrum could best be described as

a) continuous.

b) a discrete spectrum of colored lines.

c) a mostly continuous spectrum that is missing some colors.

d) a discrete spectrum of colored lines that corresponds to the absorbed light.

e) a completely black spectrum.

5. Gases emit light when they are energized by an electrical discharge (a few examples are shown in Figure 12.8). The light results when an electron

a) "jumps" from one energy level up to a higher energy level.

b) "jumps" from one energy level down to a lower energy level.

c) is completely removed from the atom.

d) is absorbed by the nucleus.

6. The figure below shows the energy levels of a Bohr atom. The arrows refer to changes in the energy of an electron in a Bohr atom. Use this figure to answer the next few questions.

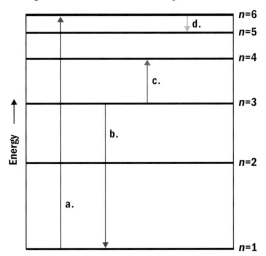

a) Match the labeled arrows with the appropriate description of energy changes.

   i) ____ jump from an excited state to the n=1 state

   ii) ____ jump from an excited state to the n=5 state

   iii) ____ jump from the n=3 state to an excited state

   iv) ____ jump from the n=1 state to an excited state

b) Which arrow(s) correspond(s) to changes that would give rise to an absorption spectrum? To an emission spectrum?

c) At the end of which process (absorption or emission) is the electron farther away from the nucleus? Closer to the nucleus?

d) Which arrow corresponds to the lowest energy photon being emitted?

## Synthesis

1. The experiments of the gas discharge tubes established what about the nature of the atom?

2. Use a qualitative (no numbers needed) time line to map out the sequence of events (experiments) and models that led to the Bohr model.

3. Use the laws of force and motion to explain Rutherford's hypothesis (alpha particles would travel in either straight lines or experience small deflections on passing through the gold foil) based on the Plum Pudding Model. Use these same laws to explain why the results of the gold foil experiments ruled out this hypothesis and required the existence of a dense, small, positively-charged nucleus. (It is the logic of Rutherford's arguments that we are most interested in. You need not give equations.)

4. How can a continuous spectrum be made up from discrete amounts of energy? What role does the size of Planck's constant $h$ play in your answer?

5. What is the relationship between the frequencies present in an emission spectrum and those missing in an absorption spectrum? What law(s) require that there be this type of correspondence?

6. The absorption spectrum at the bottom of this figure was obtained from an unknown material in the gas discharge tube. Compare the absorption spectrum with the known emission spectra for sodium, mercury, and neon gases and identify the unknown specimen.

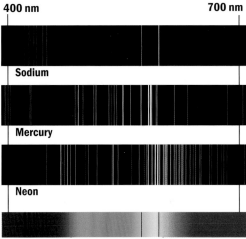

7. Why did Rutherford and Bohr know that electrons couldn't actually be orbiting the nucleus?

# Duality of Matter

*Actually, we need not speak of particles at all. For many experiments it is more convenient to speak of matter waves . . . The two pictures are of course mutually exclusive, because a certain thing cannot at the same time be a particle . . . and a wave . . . but the two complement each other. By playing with both pictures, by going from the one picture to the other and back again, we finally get the right impression of the strange kind of reality behind our quantum experiments.*

Werner Heisenberg

## LEARN

- What experiments show the particle nature of matter.

- What experiments show the wave nature of matter.

- How to relate the probability of locating a small particle to its wave properties.

- The Heisenberg uncertainty principle and how to apply it to predict the results of experiments where the position or momentum of particles is precisely determined.

- The philosophical difference between the quantum mechanical view of nature and that of Newtonian physics.

Back in Chapter 11 we discussed the nature of light and how experiments show that light has both wave and particle properties. We consider this intriguing discovery further in this chapter and consider how it applies to matter. First, let us review.

In 1801, Thomas Young sent a beam of light through two narrow, closely spaced slits. The light diffracted out through each slit making two wave patterns that interfered with each other. Diffraction and interference are wave properties, not particle properties, so this showed light to be a wave.

In 1900, Max Planck, struggling to explain the color of light coming from hot objects, succeeded only by assuming that light is really a stream of small particle-like bundles of energy, called photons. And before this it had been shown in the photoelectric effect that short-wavelength ultraviolet light can knock electrons off a metal surface, but longer wavelength visible light cannot. This happens, Einstein explained later, because photons are

particles and ultraviolet photons have more energy than visible light photons.

The apparent inconsistency between the photoelectric effect and double-slit experiments created a dilemma. Light apparently has both wave and particle properties, either of which can be manifest depending on the experiment being done.

A "self-evident truth" of science is non-contradiction. When two propositions contradict, at least one must be wrong. Has this rule now been violated? No, because there is only one explanation for each experiment. The dilemma is that the explanation shifts depending on the experiment: sometimes light must behave like a particle to explain the results and sometimes it must behave like a wave, a unique and mind-stretching situation.

## 15-1 Wave Nature of Matter

For several years physicists wrestled unsuccessfully with this dual nature, trying to determine which aspect was true and which was an illusion. At length, in an unexpected twist, physics student Louis de Broglie (1892–1987), took a different approach and in his 1924 PhD thesis proposed that wave-particle duality was fundamental not only to light but to *matter* as well!

Matter is tangible with well-defined forms, so it is reasonable to expect its building blocks of electrons, protons, neutrons, etc. to be tangible and well-formed as well. Most people quite understandably visualize these particles as being small balls with tiny mass. Where in this mental image would a wave naturally fit in?

The concept of a wave starts by defining a wavelength. The wavelength of matter, as given by de Broglie, is Planck's constant divided by its momentum. In other words:

$$\mathbf{w} = \mathbf{h/p}$$

where **w** is the wavelength, **h** is Planck's constant and **p** is the momentum.

Planck's constant **h** is a very small number meaning the wavelengths of people-sized things are very small. For instance, the wavelength of a woman walking down the street would be about

**Louis de Broglie**

de Broglie proposed that matter, like light, exhibited a wave-particle duality.

$10^{-35}$ meters, an unimaginably tiny number that is trillions upon trillions of times smaller than anything we know. Even an object of incredibly small macroscopic momentum, like a droplet of water flowing one centimeter per year, would have a wavelength of one thousandth the diameter of an atomic nucleus!

Contemplating wavelengths this small teaches us very little. Recall from Chapter 10 that the diffraction of a wave through a small opening is greatest when the slit is about the same size as the wavelength. Diffraction and interference are most evident when the wavelength is about the same size as the objects the wave encounters. The wavelength of macroscopic objects is much, much smaller than anything encountered in our day-to-day experience so we do not expect to notice the wavelengths of droplets or people or any other common items.

A thrill and challenge of studying extremely small objects is learning something different from what we would intuitively expect based on our experience with the macroscopic world. As Richard Feynman (1918–1988), who received a Nobel Prize for his work in this area, said,

> Because atomic behavior is so unlike ordinary experience, it is very difficult to get used to, and it appears peculiar and mysterious to everyone—both to the novice and to the experienced physicist. Even the experts do not understand it the way they would like to, and it is perfectly reasonable that they should not, because all of direct, human experience and human intuition applies to large objects.[1]

The wave properties of matter are noticeable only when we reduce to the size of atoms or smaller. The wavelength of an electron in a hydrogen atom is about $10^{-10}$ meters, the size of the atom itself. Thus we would expect the wave nature of the electron to be important in describing its motion in or around atoms.

Can we use Newton's equations to describe the motion of an electron in an atom? Newton's equations explain the forces and movement of everyday objects, but when the wave aspect of matter becomes significant, Newton's equations are no longer sufficient. Inspired by the success of the Bohr model and its hypothesis that angular momentum and energy are quantized, a set

of laws of motion pertinent to atomic-sized matter called **quantum mechanics** was formulated independently by Werner Heisenberg (1901–1976) and Erwin Schrödinger (1887–1961) in 1925 and 1926.

## 15-2 Experiments

But can we really see the wave nature of even small particles? Returning again to Young's double-slit experiment, we ask what would happen if the light beam were replaced by a beam of electrons. As mentioned already, the slit spacing needs to be close to the electron's wavelength to create observable interference. Fast electrons have large momenta and, by the de Broglie equation, have wavelengths that are about the size of the space between individual atoms in a solid. A crystal is a solid with a regular arrangement of equally spaced atoms so the gaps between these atoms can function as the slits in a double-slit experiment. Even though there are many more gaps than just two, the result of a beam going through the multiple gaps in a crystal is the same.

In 1927, Clinton Davisson (1881–1958) and Lester Germer (1896–1971) tested de Broglie's hypothesis that matter had a wave nature by passing electrons through a nickel crystal. To appreciate their results, first let's consider at length what is expected when *particles* pass through two closely-spaced slits and contrast that with what is expected when *waves* pass through the same slits.

First consider a "beam of macroscopic particles": bullets shot from a rickety machine gun at two narrow slits cut in a wall (*Figure 15.1*). After passing through the slits, they hit another wall behind the first where the pattern of bullet holes can be examined.

Consider the holes from the bullets passing through the left slit. These hit the second wall

**Werner Heisenberg**

Heisenberg won the Nobel Prize in 1932 for the creation of quantum mechanics, which includes his Uncertainty Principle concerning a particle's momentum and position.

**Quantum Mechanics:**

The branch of physics used to describe the wave properties of light and matter.

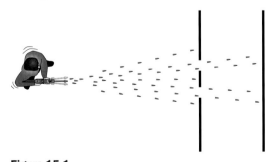

**Figure 15.1**

What kind of results would you expect if you fired a machine gun at a wall with two slits?

**Erwin Schrödinger**

Schrödinger won the Nobel Prize in 1933 for his wave equation that described the behavior of electrons in an atom.

---
[1] Richard P. Feynman, Robert B. Leighton, Matthew Sands, *The Feynman Lectures on Physics, Quantum Mechanics. Vol. III*, Addison-Wesley, Reading, MA, p. 7.

a)

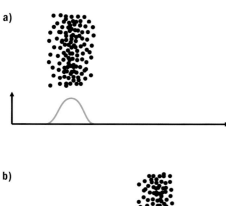

b)

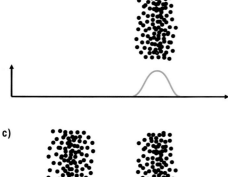

c)

**Figure 15.2**

The resulting pattern of bullet distribution one would expect from the machine gun in Figure 15.2 with:

a) one slit covered,

b) the other slit covered,

c) neither slit covered (patterns combined).

The graphs below each bullet pattern shows the number of bullet holes you would find in the wall behind the slits.

in an area concentrated directly behind this slit. The pattern in the wall would look like the one shown in *Figure 15.2a*. The pattern of bullets which passed through the right slit would look similar, and would be centered behind that slit as shown in Figure 15.2b.

The combined pattern from both slits is just the pattern from bullets passing through the left slit superimposed on top of the pattern from the bullets passing through the right slit. It would look something like the picture shown in Figure 15.2c. The two patterns add together without affecting each other.

The graphs below each of the bullet patterns in Figure 15.2 give the density of holes across the patterns. The peak of the curves is behind the slit center where there are many bullet holes close together. The curves taper off to either side where there are fewer bullet holes spaced farther apart. The red curve in Figure 15.2c is the combined measurement of bullet holes from both

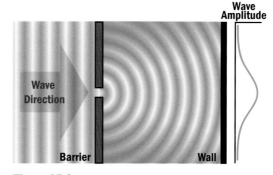

**Figure 15.3**

A water wave passing through a single slit diffracts and spreads out in a fan shape.

slits and is simply the sum of the two curves in Figures 15.2a and 15.2b.

Now consider the behavior of a wave. *Figure 15.3* shows a water wave passing through a barrier with a single slit in it and continuing on to a wall. The wave is traveling from the left to the right of the figure as indicated by the arrow. When the wave hits the barrier it diffracts through the slit, spreading out in a circular pattern. You saw this effect earlier in Figure 10.14b of Chapter 10.

The green curve on the right-hand side of Figure 15.3 shows the amplitude of the wave when it reaches the wall and is analogous to the green curves of Figure 15.2. The amplitude of the wave is largest directly behind the slit and gets smaller away from the center. This is what you would see when light waves are shined through a single narrow slit. The light on a screen would be brightest immediately behind the slit, becoming gradually dimmer to either side.

*Figure 15.4* shows what happens when a water wave passes through two closely spaced

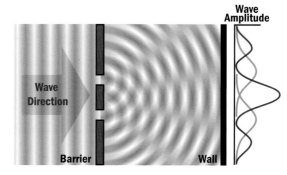

**Figure 15.4**

When a water wave passes through two slits, the diffraction from each slit combine to form an interference pattern. The green curves are the height of the water waves at the edge of the tank from the waves passing through the individual holes. The red curve is the combined height of the waves hitting the edge of the tank. Note that the interference peaks seen in this curve are very different from the ones in Figure 15.2c.

slits. The waves passing through each slit diffract and spread out as before, only now they also interfere with each other creating regions of constructive and destructive interference like we saw in Figure 10.15 from Chapter 10. Constructive interference occurs when the amplitudes of the two waves reinforce each other and add together. Destructive interference occurs in regions where the amplitude of the waves are in opposite directions (one up and the other down) so that they cancel each other out. As before, we have plotted the amplitude of the wave when it hits the wall on the right hand side of the figure. This time, the biggest wave amplitude does not appear behind either slit. Instead, it is biggest *between* the two slits because of interference!

This pattern of wave amplitudes from interfering waves looks different than the bullet pattern from Figure 15.2 because bullets don't interfere like waves do. *Therefore we can determine if electrons travel through slits as waves or if they travel as particles by comparing their distributions at the walls. If they interfere, they must travel as waves.*

The results of Davisson and Germer's double-slit electron-beam experiment are shown in *Figure 15.5*. When electrons pass through slits, they exhibit an interference pattern like water waves. The hypothesis of de Broglie is correct!

Of course the oil drop experiment described in Chapter 4 indicated electrons were particles with a small amount of charge. Whenever we detect them, we always find little particles. In Figure 15.5 the electron detections are small white dots clearly formed by particles. So what we saw for light in Figure 11.16 of Chapter 11,

we also see for electrons. Electrons diffract and interfere like waves having wavelengths predicted by the de Broglie formula. But they are detected like particles.

In summary, electrons, and as it turns out other particles like neutrons, protons, and even whole atoms, have the same wave-particle nature that light has. As with photons, observation of a single electron immediately makes its particle nature clear. However, in double slit experiments the electrons accumulate with diffraction and interference patterns characteristic of their wave nature.

## 15-3 Probability Waves

So what exactly *is* the wave associated with a particle? It certainly does not seem reasonable for it to be a disturbance moving through a medium as discussed in Chapter 10. Those waves travel through ensembles of particles that vibrate in place. In contrast this wave property is associated with *single* electrons.

The double slit experiment in Figure 15.5 provides the same clue we found with light. The build-up of the interference pattern by single electrons, like the photons of Figure 11.16, implies that the "electron wave" tells how likely it is that the "electron particle" will hit various locations on the screen. So we refer to the wave as a **probability wave**, which tells us the *probability* of where the electrons are likely to be detected. An electron has a relatively high probability of being detected in regions where the wave amplitude is large and a relatively low probability of being detected in regions where the wave amplitude is small.

In the double slit experiment with electrons, the probability wave associated with the electrons passing through the slits interferes with itself, creating regions of large probability because of constructive interference and regions of small probability because of destructive interference. Electrons strike the high-probability constructive interference regions more often and avoid the low-probability destructive interference regions.

These probability waves are similar to the **probability curves** like the bell-shaped curve that gives the distribution of grades on a test. The graph of *Figure 15.6* is such a curve and can be thought of as representing the probability for

**Probability Wave:**

A probability curve that moves in time. At a given moment in time, the places where the wave is high are where the object associated with the wave is most likely to be found.

**Probability Curve:**

A curve giving the probability of where an object might be detected. The particle is likely to be found where the curve is high and unlikely to be found where the curve is low.

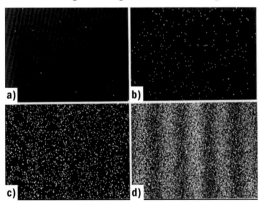

**Figure 15.5**

Result of a double-slit electron experiment performed at Hitachi. Electrons, after passing through two slits, strike a screen, appearing as little white dots. The accumulation of many dots (a to d) eventually forms an interference pattern. Figure courtesy of Hitachi at http://physicsworld.com/cws/article/print/9745.

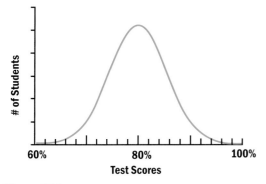

**Figure 15.6**

Bell-shaped curve that might represent a grade distribution on a test.

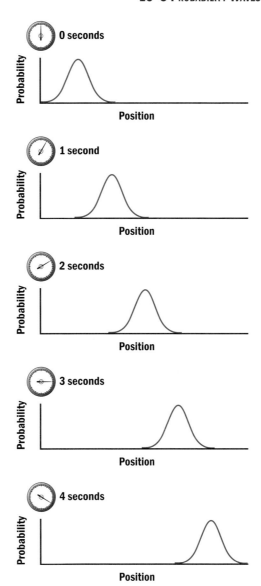

**Figure 15.7**

For a moving electron, the probability of its location changes with time. After 4 seconds, this electron is most likely to be found in a very different location from its starting point.

the grade obtained by an individual student in the class.

To explain, this curve says that the most likely grade earned is 80% because more students received this grade than any other. There is little chance that a student would have been fortunate enough to get a grade of 100%, or unfortunate enough to get a grade as low as 60%.

If a professor predicted the grade of a student picked at random from the class, and knew nothing else about the student, there could be no certainty about that particular student's grade. However, the instructor would know some probabilities based on the curve: The student likely scored close to 80%, and probably did not score above 95% or below 65%.

Similarly, when an electron passes through a double slit, we cannot predict exactly where it will strike the screen. However, we do know the probability of where it will and will not strike: It is likely to strike the screen where the probability wave has a large amplitude and unlikely to strike where the probability wave has a small amplitude. Based on the different probabilities, the experimenter can predict what pattern will be produced when many electrons strike the screen. The curve representing the probabilities of where an electron will strike a screen is called a "probability curve."

Traveling electrons have probability curves that indicate the likelihood of locating them at a particular point in space at a given moment in time. Because the electron is moving, the most probable place to find it advances with the motion. *Figure 15.7* shows what the probability wave of a moving electron might look like. In the figure, the electron starts with a high probability of having a position on the left side of the display. As time progresses the most prob-

able position of the electron moves to the right, being on the far right four seconds after we start our clock.

Measuring a particle's position changes the probabilistic nature of the waves. Before a measurement, the electron has the probability of being anywhere within the probability curve. After the measurement, it has a 100% probability of being in the location where we detected it. Thus, the probability wave goes from a broad distribution like the red curve in *Figure 15.8* to a narrow peak like the blue spike in the same figure.

In other words, before the position is measured, the electron whose probability curve is shown in the figure has a reasonable chance

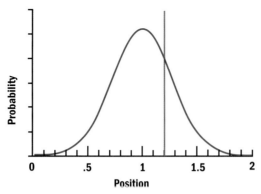

**Figure 15.8**

Probability curves for an electron just before (red) and just after (blue) it is detected at position 1.2. Before being detected the electron has a range of positions between 0 and 2 where it could be detected. After it has been detected, we know exactly where it is (at position 1.2).

of being detected anywhere in the range from about 0.2 to 1.8. After being detected at position 1.2, we know exactly where the electron is. Its probability of being at a position of 1.2 immediately after the measurement is 100%. The probability of being elsewhere is now zero.

## 15-4 Heisenberg Uncertainty Principle

Within the laws of quantum mechanics, probability curves and probability waves describe more than just positions. They also describe a particle's momentum and energy and other properties. As it turns out, these different probability waves are often related to each other. For instance the probability wave associated with an object's momentum is closely related to the probability wave associated with its position. The mathematical equations of quantum

mechanics tell us exactly how to calculate one probability wave once we know the other.

Calculating probable momentum and position leads to an interesting paradox. It is impossible to precisely determine both the position and momentum of a small particle at the same time. This impossibility is called the **Heisenberg uncertainty principle**.

We saw this concept at work back in Chapter 11 when we looked at light diffracting through a small hole (Figure 11.3). If the hole is large, the spot on the screen is fairly sharp and corresponds to the size of the hole. If the hole is small the light diffracts, resulting in a larger diffuse spot on the screen.

We can interpret this effect in terms of the Heisenberg uncertainty principle. The area of the hole puts a firm bound on the uncertainty in the photon's position when it passed through; we know it was somewhere in the hole and nowhere else. When a photon passes through a small hole, its position is determined more precisely than when it passes through a large hole.

Momentum includes the direction of travel as well as speed. So the spread in a light beam reflects the scatter in the momentum values of the photons that make up the beam. If the beam is tightly collimated, the momenta of the photons are similar and well determined. If it is spreading a lot, the direction of the momentum of any particular photon in the beam is more uncertain. Thus, a light beam passed through a small hole has photons with a small position uncertainty, but a relatively large momentum uncertainty. A light beam passed through a large

## ELECTRON MICROSCOPE

High-energy electrons have wavelengths that are much shorter than those of visible light. The shorter wavelength is employed in the design of electron microscopes that create images of objects much smaller than objects visible under conventional light microscopes. Images of objects are limited in their amount of detail by diffraction of light or of electrons at the object's edges. Diffraction of light by objects smaller than the wavelength of light smears the image so that the object cannot be resolved. High energy electrons have a wavelength so short that electron microscope images are limited by the quality of the electron optics rather than the diffraction of the electrons. *Figure 15.9* is an image from an electron microscope that shows a small ($7.5 \times 10^{-9}$ meters wide) iron-platinum particle (dark area) on a carbon support film (light area). The light lines running diagonal across the dark section are planes of atoms that are $2.2 \times 10^{-10}$ meters apart, a distance typical of atomic spacings in solids. This image allows the user of an electron microscope to examine an object that is thousands of times smaller than could be seen through the highest-powered light microscope.

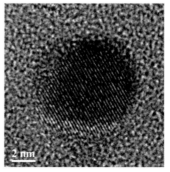

**Figure 15.9**

An iron-platinum particle.

hole has photons with a large position uncertainty, but a relatively small momentum uncertainty.

The inverse relationship between the uncertainty in the position of a photon and the uncertainty in the direction of its momentum is an example of a more general concept. For any particle, its position uncertainty is inversely proportional to its momentum uncertainty. In other words, if we make the position of a particle more certain, we necessarily increase the uncertainty in its momentum. Conversely, if we force the momentum of a particle to be more certain, its position will be made more uncertain.

An example to help understand this effect is a wave in a string. A wave on a string with a well-known position looks like the pulse shown in *Figure 15.10*. Its position is pretty clear but

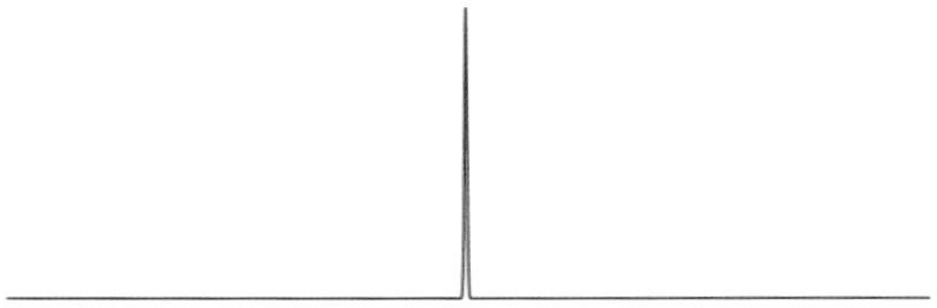

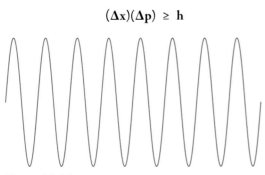

**Figure 15.10**
A pulse wave.

its wavelength is difficult to determine. In contrast the wave shown in *Figure 15.11* has a well-determined wavelength but lacks a precise position because it is spread out all over the string. In the introduction, we learned that de Broglie's relation w=h/p relates the wavelength of a particle with its momentum. Thus, if the wavelength of the particle is uncertain, so is its momentum.

Werner Heisenberg quantified in the Heisenberg uncertainty principle this trade-off in how precisely we can know an object's position and momentum. It states that the uncertainty in position ($\Delta$x) and the uncertainty in momentum ($\Delta$p) are related by the formula

$$(\Delta x)(\Delta p) \geq h$$

**Figure 15.11**
A long wave.

where **h** is the ubiquitous Planck's constant. In other words, the product of the uncertainty in a particle's position and the uncertainty in its momentum is greater than or equal to Planck's constant. This means limiting the range of positions where a particle is likely to be detected makes its momentum less certain. A particle with a narrow range of probabilities for its momentum must have a wide range of probabilities for its position.

The Heisenberg uncertainty principle is not a matter of how carefully or accurately measurements can be made. Rather, it is a fundamental limit on how well two complementary quantities can be determined. It is like a student going to a party the night before an exam. The more time the student spends at the party, the less time they have to study. The more the student studies, the less time they have to party. The student can choose to get a good grade on the exam or have fun at the party, but not 100% of both. Likewise, an experimenter can know a particle's position with high accuracy or how fast it is going with high precision, but not both at the same time.

## 15–5 Philosophical Differences

There is a fundamental difference between motion as described by Newton's laws and motion described by quantum mechanics. Newton's laws provide potentially infinitely accurate descriptions about how objects move. One could, at least in principle, use Newton's laws to know the exact values of an object's position and momentum at any time. Knowing these quantities and what the object interacts with, one could predict exactly where it would be and how fast it would be moving for all times in the future. An extrapolation backward in time could determine where it had been and how fast it had been going at all times in the past.

Quantum mechanics, on the other hand, describes the *probable* location and motion of objects. By its equations, one can predict the statistical results of a number of repeated experiments, but not the precise results of a single experiment. Furthermore, the Heisenberg uncertainty principle says we cannot precisely determine either an object's history or future from measurements made in the present because

## USING THE HEISENBERG UNCERTAINTY PRINCIPLE

A real example of the Heisenberg Uncertainty Principle is the behavior of electrons in "quantum dots." A quantum dot is essentially a very small box within which an electron is confined. If the quantum dot is relatively large, the electron has a position probability wave that is fairly wide. Consequently, the electron's momentum probability wave will be relatively narrow. On the other hand, if the quantum dot is small, the electron has a position probability curve which is narrow. Consequently, their momentum probability waves are relatively wide. So electrons in small quantum dots have a larger momentum range than electrons in larger quantum dots. Experiments on quantum dots have confirmed these predictions.

Another example of the Heisenberg Uncertainty Principle is estimating the energy of the innermost electrons in atoms. In a hydrogen atom, the position probability wave for the electron is much wider than it is for the innermost electron in a uranium atom. The uranium nucleus has 92 times the electric charge of a hydrogen nucleus, pulling the innermost electron about 92 times closer to the nucleus and thus determining its position 92 times more precisely. So the momentum range in hydrogen (with its larger position uncertainty) is much smaller than the momentum range in uranium (with its smaller position uncertainty).

The kinetic energy K of an electron is proportional to its range in momentum squared.

$$K = \frac{1}{2}mv^2 = \frac{(mv)^2}{2m} = \frac{p^2}{2m}$$

This means that the kinetic energy of a hydrogen electron is much lower than the kinetic energy of the innermost electron in a uranium atom. The uranium electron's kinetic energy, proportional to its momentum squared, is about 922 times larger or almost 8500 times as big.

those measurements always have an inherent uncertainty in them.

That the atomic world obeys quantum rather than Newtonian mechanics has philosophical implications. In Newton's deterministic universe, the physical world is akin to a giant machine that continues on its predetermined course once set in motion. In such a universe the future is cast in stone, totally determined by events that were set in motion long ago. Quantum mechanics, however, postulates that interactions do not have exact, perfectly determined outcomes. The range of *probable outcomes* is well determined, but the results of individual encounters are not. So the future is not cast in stone but has an element of randomness in it.

These two views are very different but do converge on the macroscopic level. Probabilities in quantum mechanics behave according to precise mathematical formulas. So they can be used to accurately predict the net results of a large number of events. In other words, a pilot may not know precisely what each component of every atom in an airplane is doing, but because an airplane is made of a huge number of atoms, their collective uncertainty averages to a minuscule amount and he or she can predict with

confidence how the airplane will respond to the various controls.

But are probability curves telling us that the atomic world is truly random? Perhaps particle behavior just appears random to us because we are ignorance of the precise laws governing them. In other words, is measuring the precise position of an electron possible but we don't know how, or is its position truly probabilistic and thus not established until after the measurement?

Two Nobel Prize-winning physicists took opposite sides in this debate at the beginning of the 20th century. Albert Einstein took the view that quantum mechanics required probabilities in its description of experiments because the theory was incomplete. He maintained that the results of experiments only *appeared* to be random because of our lack of knowledge. In other words, the reason scientists don't know exactly where the electron in a two-slit experiment will hit the screen is because there isn't enough information available to them.

Niels Bohr on the other hand argued that the location where an individual electron would hit the screen in a double slit experiment was not determined until the very moment that the electron actually struck. He maintained that experiment was conducted by Alain Aspect (1947–) and colleagues in 1982. Aspect's results were inconsistent with Einstein's "hidden variables" interpretation and consistent with Bohr's idea of things being intrinsically random.

## 15-6 Summary

Matter, as well as light, has both wave and particle properties. Particle properties are evident when matter is detected. Wave properties such as interference and diffraction are evident when objects travel. We use a wave description of how matter moves and a particle description of how matter is detected.

The waves associated with matter give the probability of where the object is likely to be found. The particle properties are evident when the objects are detected as individual "lumps." These lumps can be counted and identified with properties like mass and charge.

The wave properties for macroscopic objects are not evident because their wavelengths are so small. As mass gets smaller wavelength gets larger. To see moving matter diffract or interfere requires experiments with particles whose mass is the size of atoms or smaller.

A particle's position and momentum are "complementary" quantities that can't both be simultaneously determined to arbitrary accuracy. The Heisenberg uncertainty principle states that the product of the uncertainty in these two quantities must always be greater than or equal to Planck's constant.

Quantum mechanics changed our fundamental model of the interactions between the smallest particles in nature. It requires us to consider these interactions in terms of probabilities rather than with the deterministic viewpoint possible using Newton's Laws.

### Selected Sources of Additional Reading:

Richard P. Feynman, *The Character of Physical Law*, The MIT Press.

Brian Greene, *The Elegant Universe: Superstrings, Hidden Dimensions, and the Quest for the Ultimate Theory*, W. W. Norton and Company (1999).

Werner Heisenberg, *Physics and Philosophy: The Revolution of Modern Science*, Perennial (May, 2007)

**Figure 15.12**
Albert Einstein (left) and Niels Bohr at a conference in Brussels in 1930. Einstein and Bohr disagreed on whether quantum probabilities were intrinsically random. (Photo by Paul Ehrenfest.)

the probabilities arising in quantum mechanics were not from a lack of information about the atoms, they arose because atomic-level behavior is random by its very nature. These two views are symbolized by the image at the beginning of the chapter. While the ship is in the fog, we don't know where it is until we see it. Einstein would have said that the ship exists somewhere, but we don't have enough information to know exactly where it is. Bohr, on the other hand, would have said that the exact location of the ship is intrinsically unknowable and that the act of measuring its position causes it to appear someplace.

This issue is largely a philosophical one of the type that is difficult or impossible to resolve. But years after Einstein's death in 1955 it was finally settled. David Bohm (1917–1992) and John Bell (1928–1990) devised an experimental arrangement where the results were statistically different for Einstein's and Bohr's interpretations of the probability wave. Being theoreticians, they didn't actually conduct this difficult experiment, but others did. The most conclusive

# 15 STUDY GUIDE

## Chapter Framework

### A. The Duality of Matter
1. Wave–Particle Duality
2. Wavelength of Matter

### B. Experiments
1. Two-Slit Experiments
2. Low-Intensity Experiments

### C. Probability Waves

### D. Heisenberg Uncertainty Principle
1. Relationship between Position and Momentum
2. Position and Momentum Cannot Both Be Known with Arbitrary Precision

### E. Philosophical Implications
1. Determinism vs. Uncertainty
2. Nature of Quantum Mechanical Uncertainty
   a. *Einstein: due to lack of information*
   b. *Bohr: intrinsically unknowable*

## Comprehension

### Matching

a. Constructive interference

b. Destructive interference

c. Probability curve

d. Probability wave

e. Quantum Mechanics

f. Heisenberg Uncertainty Principle

g. Newtonian Mechanics

1. ____ A probability curve that changes with time.
2. ____ The more you know about position the less you know about momentum, and the more you know about momentum the less you know about position.
3. ____ Phenomenon that creates areas of high probability where the electron will strike the screen.
4. ____ Phenomenon that creates areas of low probability where the electron is unlikely to strike the screen.
5. ____ Postulates a universe where actions do not lead to pre-determined effects.
6. ____ The physical world continues on a predetermined course once set in motion.
7. ____ The likelihood of detecting a particle at a given location.

### True/ False

1. ____ The more you know about an object's position, the more you know about its momentum.
2. ____ Matter has both wave and particle properties.
3. ____ Electrons can form interference patterns, just as light can.
4. ____ It is impossible to predict exactly where an electron will strike the screen after passing through two slits in a double-slit experiment.
5. ____ An object's momentum is the only property associated with probability waves.
6. ____ If moving slowly enough, small objects can have wavelengths that reach macroscopic dimensions.

7. ____ After passing many electrons through two slits, an interference pattern on the screen looks like the probability curve below.

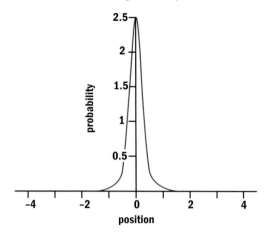

### Fill in the Blank

1. Louis de Broglie proposed that matter has the same _____ duality as light.
2. To see interference patterns in an electron two-slit experiment, the slit's spacing needs to be about the same size as an electron's _____.
3. The product of the uncertainty of an object's position and momentum is always greater than or equal to _____.
4. When an electron is moving (but when not detected) its _____ properties are manifest.
5. When an electron is detected, its _____ properties are manifest.

## Analysis

1. If the speed of a particle increases, its wavelength
   a) decreases.
   b) increases.
   c) stays the same.
   d) could increase, decrease, or stay the same.

2. Which of the following could not form a diffraction pattern in a double-slit experiment?
   a) visible light
   b) x-rays
   c) ultraviolet light
   d) electrons
   e) all of the above could form diffraction patterns
   f) none of the above could form diffraction patterns

3. For which phenomenon would the Heisenberg Uncertainty Principle be a significant consideration in describing motion?
   a) electrons in atoms

b) planets in orbit around the Sun

c) the space shuttle in orbit around Earth

d) billiard balls on a pool table

e) Brownian motion of dust particles in the air

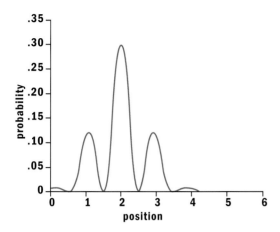

4. The figure above represents a probability curve for an electron. At what position is the electron most likely to be detected?

a) 1

b) 2

c) 3

d) 4

e) 5

5. Macroscopic objects don't show interference effects because

a) quantum mechanics doesn't apply to big objects.

b) they are larger than the wavelength of light.

c) their wavelengths are too short.

d) they can't fit through small slits.

e) they don't have wave properties.

f) the Heisenberg Uncertainty Principle doesn't apply to them.

6. The Heisenberg Uncertainty Principle seems to conflict with the concept of

a) operationalism

b) the quantum theory

c) Newtonian determinism

d) duality

e) mass

7. Electrons passing one at a time through a two-slit apparatus strike a screen. The resulting pattern on the screen after many electrons have struck the screen is

a) a single band of points about as narrow as one slit.

b) a single broad band of points, i.e., broader than the combined width of the slits.

c) a completely random pattern of points.

d) two narrow bands of points about the width of each slit.

e) a pattern of bands where electrons hit separated by areas where no electrons hit.

## Synthesis

1. Explain how the double-slit experiment can show both the particle and wave nature of matter.

2. A proton has a mass that is about 2,000 times as large as the mass of an electron. If a proton and an electron are traveling the same speed, which one will have the larger wavelength?

3. In an experiment called the Stern-Gerlach experiment, a silver atom passing through a magnet will either bend up or bend down. Quantum mechanics can be used to predict the probability of it going up or down, but not what a single atom will do on a trip through the magnet. What experiment could you do to test whether the probabilities predicted by quantum mechanics are correct?

4. Very slow neutrons can have wavelengths as long as a millimeter. Use the Heisenberg Uncertainty principle to explain what a beam of these neutrons will look like after passing through a hole a few millimeters in diameter.

5. How does the wavelength of an electron in an atom compare to an electron which is moving much faster in a particle accelerator?

6. Can a single proton interfere with itself? Why or why not?

7. Your friend argues that she has no choice in her life because the Heisenberg Uncertainty Principle guarantees that everything in this life is random. How would you respond to her?

8. Physicists have recently been able to slow down beams of atoms so that their wavelengths are macroscopic in size. Under these conditions would it be possible to see interference effects with this beam of atoms? Why or why not?

# The Quantum Model of the Atom

*The quantum theory was born in 1900, with the twentieth century, and future centuries will list it among our own's most remarkable achievements. Designed to account for the puzzling behavior of matter at the submicroscopic scale of individual atoms, the theory has enjoyed phenomenal success. It has accounted in a quantitative way for atomic phenomena with numerical precision never before achieved in any field of science.*

N. David Mermin

# 16

## LEARN

- How the quantum model of the atom resolves the problems with the Bohr model of the atom.

- The difference between an orbit and an orbital.

- The shapes of the first three orbitals.

- How orbitals are grouped in shells and which orbitals can be in each shell.

- The relative energies of each shell and of the orbitals within each shell.

- The Exclusion Principle and how it applies when filling atomic orbitals.

In Chapter 15 we noted that Newton's equations were not sufficient to describe the motion of particles like electrons. The rules of quantum mechanics were needed instead. These rules based upon the wave and discrete nature of the atomic world were bold, innovative, and very accurate. They teach us that the wave aspect of matter is real and significant for atomic structure.

Recall that the Bohr model did not answer two very important questions: Why were there special Bohr orbits, and why didn't the electrons radiate when they were in these orbits? The model built on quantum mechanics, the **quantum model**, addresses these questions.

### 16–1 Orbitals

The probability waves describing moving electrons truly do act like waves and, in addition to the diffraction and interference discussed in Chapter 15, can form *standing waves* like the ones presented in Chapter 10. To review, recall that a standing wave forms on a string when a

wave of the proper wavelength travels back and forth on it. The wave traveling to the right meets an identical wave reflecting back from the left and they combine in phase forming a standing pattern (Figure 10.18). The string moves up and down at the antinodes where there is constructive interference but doesn't move at the nodes where the interference is destructive. The nodes and antinodes occur at stationary places and do not drift along the string.

In the same manner, electrons moving about an atom set up standing waves around the nucleus, not in the one dimension of a string or the two dimensions of a surface but in the three dimensions of space. Like their lower-dimension counterparts, these three-dimensional standing waves have nodes and antinodes with well-defined positions.

Because the wave describes the probable location of the electron, the amplitude of the standing wave pattern represents the probability of finding an electron at that location. At an anti-node the probability is highest. At a node the probability is zero.

Since the standing wave pattern is stationary, the probability of locating electrons at any given location doesn't change in time. In other words, the electrons are confined to a static space. Being confined to a static space means the electrons are not accelerating around in an orbit as was visualized in the solar system and Bohr models. If they don't accelerate, they don't radiate and that problem is solved.

This is an important point. However the electrons move, it is not an accelerated motion like that of planets. So the space where they reside should not be called an orbit. We call that space, defined by the anti-nodes of the probability standing waves, an **orbital**.

### Orbital Shapes

Orbital standing waves have different shapes depending upon the number of waves in the pattern and how those waves extend into the different dimensions of space. To explain this further, return again to the one-dimensional string shown in *Figure 16.1*. The string is held firmly at both ends, so the ends don't move and are

**Quantum Model:**

The atomic model incorporating the wave aspect of matter.

**Orbital:**

A standing wave giving the probability of finding an electron in various locations around the nucleus of an atom.

195

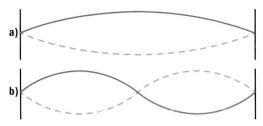

**Figure 16.1**

A stationary string can only have standing waves of certain lengths.

a) Longest possible wavelength for a standing wave in a stationary string.

b) Next longest wavelength for a standing wave.

forced to be nodes. A single wavelength standing wave pattern has one antinode as shown in Figure 16.1a. A wave with two wavelengths, and two antinodes looks like Figure 16.1b. The next shorter wavelength has three antinodes, etc. As the waves get shorter, the number of antinodes increases.

Waves in two dimensions take on shapes that are extensions of their one-dimensional counterparts. The lowest frequency standing wave on a circular drumhead looks like *Figure 16.2*. With some imagination, you can picture this as the string in Figure 16.1a rotated horizontally about its center point. It is just a one-dimensional wave extended to a circular domain.

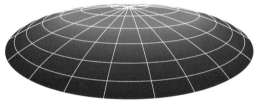

**Figure 16.2**

Lowest frequency wave on a two-dimensional drumhead.

The next lowest frequency wave looks like *Figure 16.3*. You can probably see how this resembles Figure 16.1b rotated in a circle around its highest point. The next vibrational pattern is given in *Figure 16.4*. You can make

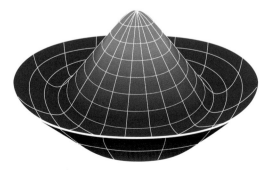

**Figure 16.3**

Second lowest frequency in a circular drumhead.

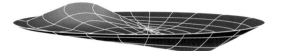

**Figure 16.4**

Third lowest frequency in a circular drumhead.

waves like this if you and your friends hold a circular blanket by the edges and shake it up and down. Notice that a cross section of its middle from left to right *also* resembles Figure 16.1b. The patterns in Figures 16.3 and 16.4 have the same wavelengths, but they resonate differently across the surface.

Extending these standing waves to three dimensions creates a well-known set of shapes called "spherical harmonics." When Erwin Schrödinger developed an equation to describe the standing wave patterns of electrons in an atom he found that the patterns were spherical harmonics. These harmonics are the shapes of the *orbitals*.

An electron in an atom has a fixed wavelength. Fixed wavelengths only set up standing waves at just the right distance from the nucleus. In the quantum model of the atom, Bohr's notion that electrons can only be at certain distances from the nucleus is because at those distances the standing wave pattern just fits around the nucleus. The question of why electrons are limited to discrete orbitals has been answered.

The orbital shapes have names. They are classified by letters: "s," "p," "d," "f," and so on. Why was this sequence of letters chosen rather than "a," "b," "c" etc., which would be a seemingly more natural sequence? It is a historical accident of sorts, and goes back to the early days of atomic **spectroscopy**. Scientists studying emission lines noticed that some were very sharp, others were always present and bright, and others were more diffuse. Scientists labeled these sets of lines "s" for sharp, "p" for principal, "d" for diffuse, and "f" for fine. When quantum mechanics was discovered, they realized that these sets of lines came from different orbitals. The names stuck, and so the first four orbitals are called s, p, d, and f.

The "s" orbitals are spherical in shape as shown in *Figure 16.5*. If we slice through one as in Figure 16.10a we find that the probability is low near the nucleus, peaks at a set distance away, then tapers off at father distances. So it does not have a hard surface as Figure 16.5

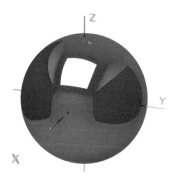

**Figure 16.5**
"s" orbital shape.

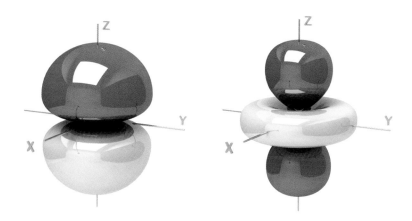

**Figure 16.6**
"p" orbital shape.

**Figure 16.7**
One possible "d" orbital shape.

suggests. To show the shape, we draw in Figure 16.5, and also in Figures 16.6 through 16.9, a surface at the volume in which 90% of the wave amplitude is contained. In a hydrogen atom having a single, unexcited electron, this surface has a diameter of about $10^{-10}$ meters. The Bohr model predicted the atom's diameter to be about this same size.

The spherically symmetric shape of an "s" orbital means that electrons are equally likely to be found in any direction away from the nucleus. Because of this symmetry there is only one kind of "s" orbital.

Remarkably, the probability curve does *not* go to zero at the nucleus itself. This shows how different the idea of an orbital is, for an electron in a Bohr orbit could never visit the nucleus. But they do and we will use this fact in Chapter 25 to understand a nuclear decay process called electron capture.

Next are the "p" orbitals (*Figure 16.6*). The "p" orbitals all have the same basic dumbbell shape with two lobes on either side of a node centered on the nucleus. These nodes can have three possible orientations: aligned with the x-axis, the y-axis, or the z-axis. Each of these three orientations corresponds to a unique type of orbital, so there are three "p" orbitals in the "p" orbital set.

Because, unlike the "s" orbitals, "p" orbitals have lobes, electrons in them are more likely to be found in one direction of space than another. This directionality gives rise to the shapes of atoms and molecules. These shapes in turn dictate the form and construction of crystals and even the rate and types of chemical reactions.

The "d" orbitals have two shapes. One shape is like a dumbbell with a bagel in the center (*Figure 16.7*). The other shape resembles a fat

four-leaf clover (*Figure 16.8*). There are four orientations of this second shape, resulting in a total of five different kinds of "d" orbitals.

Orbitals identified by letters further in the sequence have, as might be expected, increasingly complicated shapes with more lobes and bumps on them. One of the "f" orbitals is shown in *Figure 16.9* as an example.

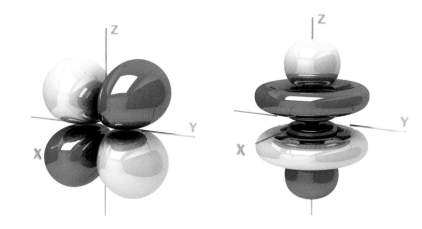

**Figure 16.8**
Another possible "d" orbital shape.

**Figure 16.9**
One of the possible shapes of an "f" orbital.

## THE QUANTUM MODEL IN THE NUCLEUS

The quantum model can also apply to the nucleus of an atom. The protons and neutrons are found in orbitals that have characteristic energies and shapes. However, because of the nature of the strong force and characteristics of the particles involved, the energies and shapes differ from those found in atomic electrons. In the atomic nucleus, the orbitals have diameters of about $10^{-15}$ meters, about 100,000 times smaller than the smallest electron orbital.

## Shells

Different s, p, d, and f orbitals in atoms are created for different numbers of standing waves. Orbitals of the same type have the same general form, but differ in size, energy, and **radial shape**, which is the cross section of an orbital that has been sliced through the center *(Figure 16.10)*. If you imagined that an orbital was a large onion, the radial shape is what you would see when you slice the onion down the middle.

**Radial Shape:**

A cross section of what an orbital would look like if it were sliced in two.

**Shell:**

A group of orbitals having similar energies and sizes.

| Table 16.1 |
| --- |
| Orbital Energies (lowest to highest) |
| 1s |
| 2s |
| 2p |
| 3s |
| 3p |
| 4s |
| 3d |
| 4p |
| 5s |
| 4d |
| 5p |
| 6s |
| 4f |
| 5d |
| 6p |
| 7s |
| 5f |
| 6d |
| 7p |
| 8s |

**Figure 16.10**

Radial shapes of the "1s," "2s" and "3s" orbitals. The colored areas are where the electron has the highest probability of being found. The white areas are where the electron has the smallest probability of being found. The nucleus is in the very center of each of these orbitals.

Consider a set of "s" orbitals. Different "s" orbitals can exist around an atom depending on the number of standing waves as just mentioned. The number of waves denotes the **shell** and it correlates with the amount of energy possessed by the electrons within it. The lowest-energy "s" orbital is called the "1s" orbital because it is in the first shell. It is the smallest of the "s" orbitals and has no nodes in its radial shape. The "s" orbital in the second shell is the "2s" orbital. It is both more energetic and larger than the "1s" orbital. It has one node in its radial shape. The "3s" orbital in the third shell is larger and more energetic still and has two nodes in its radial shape.

Two trends are important to notice. The first is that electrons in higher-numbered orbitals are more likely to be found farther from the nucleus than lower-numbered orbitals. The second trend is that higher-numbered orbitals also possess more energy than lower-numbered

orbitals of the same type. Both of these trends hold true for orbitals with other shapes as well as for "s" orbitals.

Orbital groups are organized into shells with each shell containing only certain orbitals. The first shell has only an "s" orbital. The second shell has "s" and "p" orbitals. The third shell has "s," "p" and "d" orbitals. This pattern continues for increasing shell numbers, with each successive shell having an additional orbital set. *Figure 16.11* is a schematic diagram of the energies of the different orbitals in the first three shells of an atom. The energy spacings are qualitatively (but not quantitatively) correct.

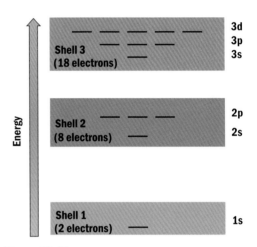

**Figure 16.11**

Energy levels of the first few orbitals in an atom. The number of lines for each orbital indicates the number of orbitals of that kind in the atom.

As we learned in Chapter 9, electrical potential energy decreases as opposite charges are brought closer together. Therefore, the potential energies of the electrons in orbitals closest to the nucleus are the lowest and the energy of electrons farthest away from the nucleus are the greatest. The first shell is then the lowest-energy shell, followed in order by the second, third, and fourth shells. Within a shell, the lowest-energy orbital is the "s" orbital, followed by the "p" orbitals and the "d" orbitals.

The shell diagram in Figure 16.11 has been simplified by excluding shells higher than the third. Beyond the third shell, the orbitals begin to overlap between shells. For instance, the "4s" orbital is actually lower in energy than the "3d" orbital. The actual general order of energies is shown in *Table 16.1*. This order will be discussed further in Chapter 17.

## Spin

Besides their orbital shape and shell, electrons in an atom have a third characteristic called **spin**. The word is a misnomer: they do not actually spin within their orbitals. The spin is the direction of the electron's magnetic field. Each electron has a magnetic field associated with it, just like a bar magnet, and like a bar magnet, this field has a north pole and a south pole. The spin of an electron can point in one of two directions which are called "up" and "down."

## 16-2 Comparing with the Bohr Model

Recall that the Bohr model explains atomic emission spectra as light given off when electrons transition between special stable orbits having different energies. The emitted photon energies matched the energy differences between those orbits. The quantum model is similar in this regard to Bohr's model, except that orbitals replace orbits. The various lines in absorption or emission spectra are still accounted for by the energy differences between electron states in the different orbitals.

For clarity consider some values. The 1s orbital in hydrogen has an energy of –13.6 **electron Volts** (or eV). The energy is negative because the electron is bound to the nucleus and can escape only by obtaining 13.6 eV of energy. The "2p" orbital has an energy of –3.4 eV. If a hydrogen atom has an electron in the "2p" orbital that jumps down to the 1s orbital, it will lose 10.2 eV of energy which is the difference between –3.4 eV and –13.6 eV. We can compute the corresponding wavelength of light for a photon of this energy by using Planck's formula from Chapter 11 and the relationship between wave speed, frequency, and wavelength from Chapter 10. Doing so, we get a value of $1.22 \times 10^{-7}$ meters, exactly the observed wavelength of the emitted light (see *Figure 16.12*).

Next consider again how the two models describe electron motion. As you know in the Bohr model the electrons orbited in circles about the nucleus. This orbital motion kept them out of the nucleus but required that they move at a constant speed and change direction with a constant acceleration. Electrons mov-

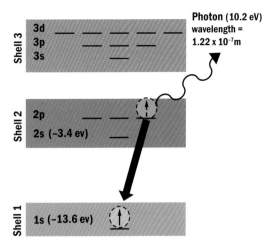

**Figure 16.12**

An electron jumping from the "2p" to "1s" orbital. A photon is emitted with an energy of 10.2 electron Volts and a wavelength of $1.22 \times 10^{-7}$ meters.

ing this way should radiate their kinetic energy away.

The quantum model says that electrons in orbitals reside about the nucleus in the space delineated by the antinodes of the standing wave pattern. We would like to know more about how electrons move as they reside. But to know this we would have to know the electron's position and momentum at the same time to a precision that violates the Heisenberg uncertainty principle. But the quantum model does say that the places where the electron can be found do not change with time. If these places are not changing, then in this sense the electron is neither moving nor accelerating and therefore does not radiate.

## 16-3 The Exclusion Principle

There is no limit to the number of waves that can pass through a point at one time. Waves on the ocean merge and separate all the time. Are matter waves the same? More specifically, does the wave nature of electrons mean an untold number of electrons can occupy the same orbital?

The answer is no. Electrons still have a particle nature and common experience teaches us that two objects, particle or otherwise, cannot be in the same place at the same time. This is codified in the quantum model as the **exclusion principle.** The exclusion principle states that even when two electrons have a probability of being in the same place at the same time, they

**Spin:**

A characteristic of an electron, giving the direction of its intrinsic magnetic field.

**Electron Volt (eV):**

A small amount of energy used to measure energies of particles in atoms and nuclei. It is equal to $1.602 \times 10^{-19}$ Joules.

**Exclusion Principle:**

The rule that two electrons cannot be in exactly the same state in an atom. In other words, no two electrons in the same atom can have exactly the same shell, orbital, and spin values.

cannot be in the same "state." The **electron's state** is defined as its specific shell, orbital, and spin.

An electron's state is like an address. The address has three pieces—the shell, the orbital, and the spin. Think of these as a street number, street name, and city. The exclusion principle essentially says that two electrons cannot have the exact same address. So, for example, two electrons in the same atom cannot be in the first shell in the "s" orbital and both have "spin up."

The exclusion principle provides the rule we use to determine which states in various atoms are filled. An atom of lithium, for instance, has three electrons. Looking at the energy level diagram in Figure 16.11, one can see that the "1s" orbital has the lowest energy and so will fill first. One electron can be placed in that orbital with spin up and another in the same orbital, only with spin down. At that point, any additional electron would have the same "address" as one of the two electrons already there. Therefore, the third electron must be in the orbital with the next lowest energy, the "2s" orbital (*Figure 16.13*).

## Electron State:

The combination of electron shell, orbital, and spin.

### Figure 16.13

The electronic structure of lithium. When filling in an energy level diagram, arrows are used to indicate electrons. Lithium has two electrons in the 1s orbital, one with spin up and one with spin down. It has one electron in the 2s orbital.

We represent the electron occupancy of the various orbitals in atoms with a shorthand notation giving shell number, orbital type, and the number of electrons in that shell. For example, the electron configuration of lithium is $1s^2 2s^1$. The number to the left of an orbital identifies the orbital's shell number, and the superscript to the right gives the total number of electrons in that type of orbital. For "p" and higher orbitals,

the total number of electrons in the orbital set is given, not the distribution amongst individual orbitals.

Consider the electronic structure of oxygen, which has eight electrons (*Figure 16.14*).

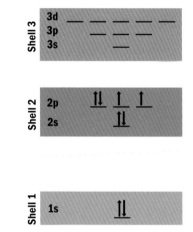

### Figure 16.14

The electronic structure of oxygen. Notice that the electrons fill the orbitals in an energy level spin up first. This is because an electron has slightly less energy when oriented spin up.

From the exclusion principle, two electrons can fit in the "1s" orbital (one spin up and one spin down). Two more electrons can fit in the "2s" orbital (one spin up and one spin down). There are three "2p" orbitals, each of which could hold two electrons, so the remaining four electrons go into these orbitals. So, oxygen has two "1s" electrons, two "2s" electrons, and four "2p" electrons represented as $1s^2 2s^2 2p^4$.

Lastly, consider argon with its 18 electrons (*Figure 16.15*). Applying the exclusion principle, there is room for two "1s" electrons, two "2s" electrons, six "2p" electrons, two "3s" electrons and six "3p" electrons, for a total of 18. In shorthand, this is $1s^2 2s^2 2p^6 3s^2 3p^6$.

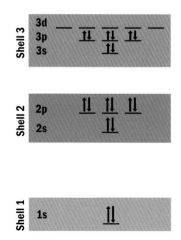

### Figure 16.15

The electronic structure of argon.

## 16-4 Summary

The quantum model removes the problems with the Bohr model by replacing electron orbits with orbitals. Rather than giving the path the electrons travel, orbitals are standing waves giving the probability of where an electron will be found. The problems raised by the Bohr model—why some orbits are special, why these electrons don't radiate, and why electrons don't crash into the nucleus—are all neatly resolved by the quantum model.

Type "s" orbitals are round with only one in the set. Type "p" are dumbbell shaped with three in the set. Four of the type "d" orbitals are clover-leafed shaped with one dumbbell shape with a torus around its middle. There are five orbitals in this set.

Each of these orbitals has a specific energy associated with it. The transitions between orbits allowed in the Bohr model are allowed between the orbitals of the quantum model as well. When an electron moves from a higher-energy orbital to a lower-energy orbital, it releases the energy difference as a photon. The energy of the photon exactly equals this energy difference between orbitals. An electron can also be moved from a lower-energy orbital to a higher-energy orbital by absorbing a photon of the required energy difference.

Electrons in atoms cannot occupy the same states. This, the Pauli exclusion principle, says that only two electrons, each with different spin, can exist in a given orbital. Electrons in atoms fill the lowest energy orbitals in accordance with this principle.

## Chapter Framework

**A. Electron Orbitals**
1. Standing Waves
2. Orbital Shapes
   a. "s," "p," "d," and "f"
   b. *Number of orbitals with each shape in a shell*
3. Shells
   a. *Radial shape*
   b. *Nodes*
   c. *Which orbitals can be in each shell*
4. Spin

**B. Comparing the Quantum Model with the Bohr Model**

**C. The Exclusion Principle**

## Comprehension

### Matching

a. Orbital

b. Shell

c. Spin

d. Exclusion principle

e. s orbital

f. p orbital

g. d orbital

1. _____ The only orbital with a non-zero probability of the electron being in the nucleus.
2. _____ An orbital that looks like a dumbbell.
3. _____ points in the same direction of an electron's magnetic field.
4. _____ A probability standing wave formed by an electron around a nucleus.
5. _____ No two electrons can be in the same state (address).
6. _____ A set of orbitals with similar energies.

### True/False

1. _____ In the quantum model, the nucleus is very small compared to the region where electrons are likely to be found.
2. _____ The orbital shape describes the probability of finding an electron at different angles about the nucleus.
3. _____ Two electrons within the same orbital must have the same spin.
4. _____ There are four different kinds of p orbitals.
5. _____ In the quantum model of the atom, electrons do not accelerate in their orbits around the nucleus as they do in the Bohr Model.
6. _____ Orbitals in the higher-numbered shells are smaller than orbitals in the lower-numbered shells.
7. _____ Electrons in the orbitals in the higher-numbered shells have more energy than electrons in the lower-numbered shells.

### Fill in the Blank

1. The two directions for the spin of an electron are described as _____ and _____.
2. Higher-numbered shells have _____ energy than lower-numbered shells.
3. An electron's state is a combination of its _____, _____, and _____.
4. The shape of the p orbital can have _____ different orientations.

## Fill in the Table

| Shell | Orbital | # of orbitals of this kind | # of electrons in these orbitals |
|-------|---------|----------------------------|----------------------------------|
| 1 | s | 1 | 2 |
| 2 | | 1 | |
| 2 | p | | |
| 3 | | | 2 |
| 3 | | | 6 |
| 3 | d | | |

## Analysis

1. Which of the following orbitals will have the highest energy electrons?
   a) 1s
   b) 2p
   c) 3d
   d) 3s

2. An unexcited atom has its two most energetic electrons in the 3s orbital. How many electrons does it have?
   a) 1 (hydrogen)
   b) 4 (beryllium)
   c) 6 (carbon)
   d) 9 (fluorine)
   e) 12 (magnesium)

3. Which orbitals are possible in the third shell of an atom? (Select all that apply.)
   a) p
   b) f
   c) s
   d) d
   e) g

4. If an electron moves from the 3p to the 2s level in an atom,
   a) a photon will be emitted.
   b) a photon must have been absorbed.
   c) it will be absorbed by the nucleus.
   d) the atomic number will go down by one.
   e) the atomic number will go up by one.

5. Which of the following are possible electronic configurations in atoms? (Select all that apply.)
   a) $1s^3$
   b) $1s^2 2s$
   c) $1s^2 2s^2 2p^5$

d) $1s^2 2s^2 2p^6 2d^2$

e) $1s^2 2s^2 2p^6 3s^2 3p^6 3d^8$

## Synthesis

1. What problems does the quantum model resolve with the Bohr Model? How does it do so?

2. According to the quantum model, why are only certain orbitals possible in atoms?

3. What is the difference between an orbital and an orbit?

4. What is the probability of finding a p electron inside the nucleus? Why?

5. Using arrows to represent electrons, complete the electron energy diagrams at right for the following atoms:

   a) H (1 electron)

   |  |  |
   |---|---|
   | **3d** | __ __ __ __ __ |
   | **3p** | __ __ __ |
   | **3s** | __ |
   | **2p** | __ __ __ |
   | **2s** | __ |
   | **1s** | __ |

   b) Li (3 electrons)

   |  |  |
   |---|---|
   | **3d** | __ __ __ __ __ |
   | **3p** | __ __ __ |
   | **3s** | __ |
   | **2p** | __ __ __ |
   | **2s** | __ |
   | **1s** | __ |

   c) Na (11 electrons)

   |  |  |
   |---|---|
   | **3d** | __ __ __ __ __ |
   | **3p** | __ __ __ |
   | **3s** | __ |
   | **2p** | __ __ __ |
   | **2s** | __ |
   | **1s** | __ |

   d) What similarities do you notice among the patterns of filled orbitals for H, Li, and Na?

6. Which of the following would you expect to have similar atomic shapes? Why?

   a) hydrogen (1s) and sodium ($1s^2 2s^2 2p^6 3s$)

   b) helium ($1s^2$) and boron ($1s^2 2s^2 2p$)

   c) neon ($1s^2 2s^2 2p^6$) and argon ($1s^2 2s^2 2p^6 3s^2 3p^6$)

# The Periodic Table

*The mere accumulation of facts, even an extremely extensive collection, does not constitute scientific method; it provides neither a direction for further discoveries nor does it even deserve the name of science in the higher sense of that word. The cathedral of science requires . . . a design for the harmonic composition of parts and to indicate the pathway by which the most fruitful new material might be generated.*

*Dmitri Mendeleev*

## 17

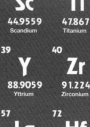

## LEARN

- How oxygen combining ratios led Mendeleev to formulate a periodic table.

- How atomic diameters and ionization energies change periodically with the atomic number of elements.

- To identify families of elements that are grouped together by common or systematic changes in their properties.

- How the quantum model of the atom explains the periodic trends in these properties.

The quantum model of the atom successfully explains the behavior of electrons in isolated atoms, those that are unaffected by the presence of other atoms nearby. However, most atoms are not by themselves. Our food, our bodies, the chairs we sit on, etc., are built of atoms interacting with each other. A successful model of the atom must explain how atoms behave as groups. Here the quantum model excels and is an excellent tool for understanding how atoms interact.

This chapter begins a transition from the study of isolated atoms to the study of interacting atoms; the science of **chemistry**. Atoms form partnerships with other atoms and exchange old partners for new ones. Some atoms dance solo, others in pairs or in lines or even complex formations like the opening ceremonies for an Olympic games.

Chemists refer to the electrical connections between and among atoms as "bonds." Chemical bonds form because the positively charged nuclei of atoms attract not only their electrons, but also the electrons of other atoms. Amazingly,

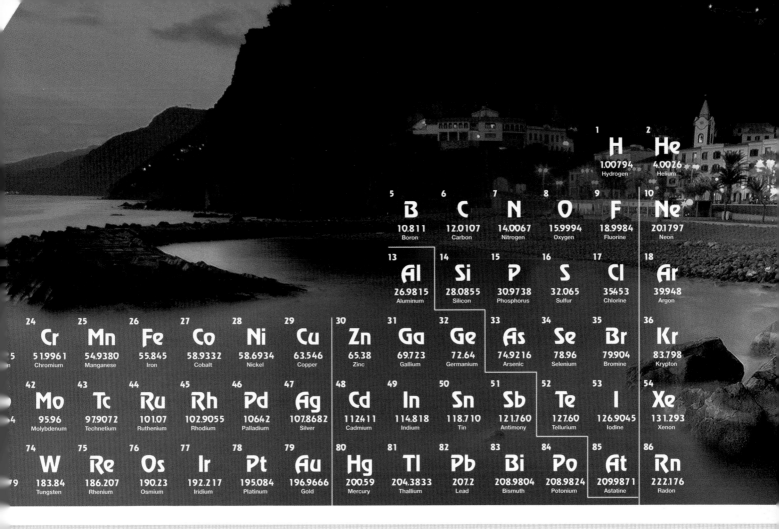

the quantum model explains all of the different ways in which atoms bond. Chapters 17 through 24 introduce the chemistry and bonding of the elements, of simple substances, and even of ones as complex as proteins and minerals.

Medieval alchemists, striving to transmute "base" metals such as mercury into "noble" metals such as gold, laid the first foundations for chemistry. Mystical forces and secret spells were invoked. Gradually, a search for natural laws replaced wizards chanting spells.

Early chemists knew that many substances could be broken down into simpler substances. They called a substance that could not be broken down any further an **element**. We know now that elements contain only one kind of atom, with every atom of the element containing the same number of protons in its nucleus.

During the middle of the 19th century, scientists were discovering many new elements and characterizing their properties as well as the properties of previously known elements. A Russian scientist, Dmitri Mendeleev (1843–1907) was fascinated by these properties. His sin-gle-minded passion led him to make an important discovery: Physical and chemical properties of the elements vary periodically with atomic number. The underlying principle responsible for the patterns remained unknown for more than 60 years. In a great triumph of science, the quantum model of the atom naturally explains many of these observed patterns!

We begin this chapter with a quick look at the early history of chemistry. Then we move to Mendeleev's discovery. We conclude by establishing the connection between the periodic trends in elemental properties and the quantum model of the atom.

Remember that you continue on a journey to learn both how nature works and how science works to understand nature. Mendeleev contributed to both endeavors. Mendeleev's organization of the elements provided a concise way to convey much chemical information. His plan of attack solidified the way scientists approach their tasks and was the first example of using current knowledge to predict the existence of unknown new materials.

**Chemistry:**

Chemistry is the discipline in which atomic interactions are studied.

**Element:**

A substance composed of atoms that have an identical number of protons in each nucleus. Elements cannot be reduced to simpler substances by normal chemical means

## ELEMENT NAMES AND SYMBOLS

The symbol assigned to an element reflects when the element was discovered. Medieval alchemists assigned symbols derived from the original Latin names. Sodium, then called Natrium, got the symbol Na. Gold, called Aurium, appeared as Au. Modern scientists often name an element after its discoverer or the location where the discovery was made. For example, Seaborgium is named after Glen Seaborg and Californium is named in honor of the state in which it was discovered.

**Figure 17.2**
Different combinations of the same elements can produce different compounds. Rust (Fe2O3) and (Fe3O4) are both iron-oxygen containing materials, but the relative amounts of iron to oxygen differ.

### 17-1 Early Chemistry and Chemists

Chemistry developed rapidly in the latter part of the 18th century. In 1789, French chemist Antoine Lavoisier (1743–1794) formulated the law of conservation of mass discussed in Chapter 8. Lavoisier studied how substances react with oxygen. He measured the masses of his starting materials and the masses of the new substances created after the process was over. Lavoisier found that the total mass of the first substance, including oxygen, was equal to that of the substances produced during the reaction. This careful, quantitative, experimental approach established a methodology for many future chemical studies.

In the same era others were studying the decomposition of substances into their elements. They observed that the decomposition of a particular substance always produced the same elements, in the same relative amounts. For example, 100 g of a substance containing cadmium and sulfur always decomposed to give 78 g of cadmium and 22 g of sulfur. Decomposition of a lead-sulfur compound always gave 87% of its mass as lead and 13% as sulfur (*Figure 17.1*). This observation became known as the **law of constant composition**.

Occasionally, different substances were found to contain the same elements, but in different proportions. Rust, an iron-oxygen compound, is 69% iron by mass, but magnetite, another iron-oxygen substance with different properties, is 72% iron by mass (*Figure 17.2*). Gradually, we recognized that changing the proportions of the elements could produce new substances with different properties.

John Dalton (1766–1845), an English school teacher, pulled together many experimental observations to propose what has come to be known as the **Atomic Theory**. We discussed some of these experiments in Chapter 13 when we described the Molecular Model of Matter. Dalton's model stated that:

1) Matter is composed of small indivisible particles called atoms.

2) An element contains only a single kind of atom. Atoms of a given element are identical in every respect, including mass and chemical behavior.

3) Atoms of different elements have different mass and chemical reactivity.

4) Chemical *compounds* are composed of two or more atoms that are joined together in fixed ratios.

**Law of Constant Composition:**

Substances contain a fixed, definite proportion of elements by mass.

**Atomic Theory:**

The model that matter is made up of atoms.

**Figure 17.1**
Illustrations of the Laws of Constant Mass and of Constant Composition.
a) One hundred grams of the orange substance always contain 78 grams of cadmium and 22 grams of sulfur.
b) One hundred grams of the black substance always contain 87 grams of lead and 13 grams of sulfur.

5) Chemical *reactions* are the rearrangement of atoms to form different compounds.

Dalton's assumptions were remarkably correct but, we now know, contained some flaws. Atoms *are* divisible. They contain positively-charged nuclei and negatively-charged electrons. Dalton's second assumption needs refinement. Atoms of elements can differ slightly in mass without significantly affecting chemical behavior. Finally, Dalton's fourth assumption is true for most, but not all substances. Many compounds are known to exist with variable compositions.

Dalton's theory provided a simple way to represent the chemical composition of different compounds. Every element was given a simple one- or two-letter abbreviation. Specifying the elements and the number of atoms identified a compound. For example, the magnesium-oxygen compound can be represented as MgO, with Mg being the symbol for magnesium and O being the symbol for oxygen. Sodium (Na) forms two compounds with oxygen, one has the formula $Na_2O$ and the other is $NaO_2$. The first compound contains two atoms of sodium for every atom of oxygen. The second compound switches the ratio: one atom of sodium is found for every two atoms of oxygen. In Dalton's notation, the subscript *following* an element's symbol specifies the number of that kind of atom in the compound. No subscript after a symbol implies one atom in the formula.

## 17-2 The Development of the Periodic Table

### Families of Elements

By 1850 about fifty elements had been identified. Chemists began to group the known elements into families that shared similar **physical properties** and **chemical properties**. Three important families emerged. Lithium, sodium, and potassium were called *alkali metals*. Beryllium, magnesium, calcium, strontium, and barium were called *alkaline earth metals*. Chlorine, bromine, and iodine made up the *halogen* family.

The eight members of the alkali and alkaline earth families known to Mendeleev are all solids at room temperature. Pictures of alkali metals sodium and potassium, along with rubidium

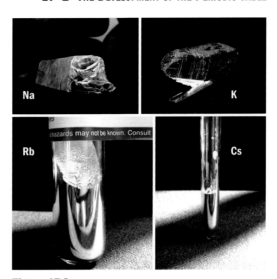

**Figure 17.3**
The alkali metals sodium (Na) and potassium (K) were known to Mendeleev; rubidium (Rb), and cesium (Cs) were discovered later.

and cesium (family members not yet discovered by 1850), are shown in *Figure 17.3*. Alkaline earth metals have a similar luster. Members of both families also conduct electricity easily. The two families differ in their chemical properties, however. The alkali metal elements form compounds with oxygen that contain two metal atoms for every oxygen atom. Oxygen-containing compounds of the alkaline earth metal elements contain one metal atom for every oxygen atom.

The halogen family of elements has more diverse physical properties than the metallic families. Chlorine is a gas, bromine is a liquid that vaporizes easily, and iodine a solid that easily transforms to a gas. They are all colored. *Figure 17.4* shows that chlorine is yellowish-green, bromine red, and iodine purple. The halogens were grouped as a family because each element

**Physical Properties:**
Properties like melting or boiling temperature, density, ionization potential.

**Chemical Properties:**
Properties associated with the chemical reactivity of a material. For example, does a substance combine with oxygen or react with water?

**Figure 17.4**
Three halogen family members: chlorine (yellow gas), bromine (red-orange liquid) and iodine (purple solid) .

**Dmitri Mendeleev**

The Russian scientist and teacher who discovered the Periodic Law and constructed the first Periodic Table.

**Periodic Law:**

The properties of the elements are a periodic function of their atomic masses.

consists of two atoms bonded together. Also, they react similarly with oxygen.

The existence of element families so fascinated the Russian scientist and teacher Mendeleev that the elements became his obsession. With single-minded passion, Mendeleev worked to discover a relationship between an element and its properties. Mendeleev created a card game to detect relationships or patterns. He wrote the known physical and chemical properties of each element on cards. Mendeleev dealt the cards out into rows and columns, playing his own form of Solitaire. Relentlessly he sorted and re-sorted the cards according to different properties, looking for patterns.

### Mendeleev's Process

To illustrate Mendeleev's approach, let's consider a chemical property of the elements called the "oxide combining ratios". The oxide combining ratio is the ratio of an element to oxygen in a compound. *Table 17.1* shows this quantity for the elements known to Mendeleev at the beginning of his studies.

Look carefully at Table 17.1. The elements are sequenced by their atomic masses, but grouped in columns by their combining ratios. What do you notice about the combining ratio as the atomic mass increases? What is the largest value of the ratio? What is the smallest value?

Mendeleev discovered a trend to the num-bers. He had found a repetitive pattern: The oxide combining ratio started at 2 with lithium, then it decreased systematically for a few elements, and then jumped back up to 2 with sodium. The pattern repeated in this fashion as Mendeleev sorted through all the elements.

Mendeleev grouped the elements with the same combining ratios together. This arrangement left several gaps in his table. For example, there was no known element in Column III of Table 17.1 to put between calcium and titanium.

Mendeleev believed that nature would not permit such gaps. Confident that his patterns revealed something fundamental about nature, Mendeleev predicted in 1869 the existence of a new element that would fill the gap. He estimated the physical and chemical properties of this unknown element based on its family members. Nine years later an element with mass of 45, now known as scandium, was discovered. Scandium had an oxide combining ratio of 0.67 and other properties close to those predicted by Mendeleev.

Mendeleev formulated these observations into the **periodic law**:

> **The properties of the elements are a periodic function of their atomic masses.**

Mendeleev's contributions were of two kinds. He contributed scientific knowledge: the periodic law and the first periodic table. The table's structure organized and succinctly conveyed information about element families. Gaps became evident where elements were not yet discovered. Mendeleev recognized that he could use nature's patterns to make predictions about unknown elements and their properties. Chemistry progressed from simple data collection and categorization to a more sophisticated level, one that included predictive powers.

### 17-3 An Improved Periodic Table with More Elements

#### New Elements

In 1861 Mendeleev's first published periodic table contained about 50 elements. By 1900 another 25 elements had been discovered. More than one hundred years later, the total number of elements stands at 118.

### Table 17.1 — Periodic Trends in Combining Ratios

Periodic trends in the combining ratios of elements with oxygen for elements known at the time of Mendeleev. Numbers below the element symbols are the atomic masses.

| Oxide Formula | I. $R_2O$ | II. $RO$ | III. $R_2O_3$ | IV. $RO_2$ | V. $R_2O_5$ | VI. $RO_3$ | VII. $R_2O_7$ |
|---|---|---|---|---|---|---|---|
| Combining Ratio | 2 | 1 | $\frac{2}{3}$ = 0.67 | $\frac{1}{2}$ = 0.5 | $\frac{2}{5}$ = 0.4 | $\frac{1}{3}$ = 0.33 | $\frac{2}{7}$ = .28 |
| | Li 7 | Be 8 | B 11 | C 12 | N 14 | O* 16 | |
| | Na 23 | Mg 24 | Al 27 | Si 28 | P 31 | S 32 | Cl 35.5 |
| | K 39 | Ca 40 | | Ti 48 | As 75 | Se 79 | Br 80 |
| | | Sr 87 | | | | | |

* O does not fit with respect to this particular property. It falls in line if other properties are considered.

The last naturally-occurring element, uranium (element 92), was discovered in 1928. Elements heavier than this are not found in nature but instead are *created* in high-energy laboratories. In these laboratories, protons or light atoms are accelerated to very high speeds and collided into heavier atoms. Sometimes those collisions lead to the formation of new elements. In 1994, scientists at the Institute for Heavy Ion Physics (see *Figure 17.5*) slammed rapidly moving nickel atoms (element 28) into a piece of bismuth (element 83), creating element 111. In 2016, the remaining unnamed elements 113, 115, 117, and 118 were verified as having been created in colliders and given official names and symbols.

**Figure 17.5**

Element 111, named Roentgenium, was discovered in 1994 at the Institute for Heavy Ion Physics at Darmstadt, Germany.

Most of the man-made elements beyond 92 live only for millionths of a second before decomposing into other kinds of nuclei. However, a few heavy elements, like plutonium (element 94), can exist for thousands of years before undergoing changes.

### Improved, Extended Table

Improvements have been made to the periodic table as new knowledge about the atom has become available. Mendeleev first sorted elements according to their atomic masses. However, the number of protons in the atomic nucleus distinguishes one element from another, not their atomic masses. Re-sorting the table by **atomic number** made no significant changes in family structure from Mendeleev's first version and improved the agreement of family properties for a few elements in the middle of the table.

*Figure 17.6* presents the most current version of the periodic table up to element 118. The elements can be broadly classified into two categories: **metals** and **non-metals.** As a general rule, metals occupy the left-hand and middle portions of the periodic table. The black stairstep line running below boron (B), silicon (Si),

**Atomic Number:**

The number of protons in a nucleus. This number defines an element.

**Metals:**

Elements that are good electrical and thermal conductors and can be hammered into thin sheets or drawn into fine wires.

**Non-Metals:**

Elements that do not conduct electricity.

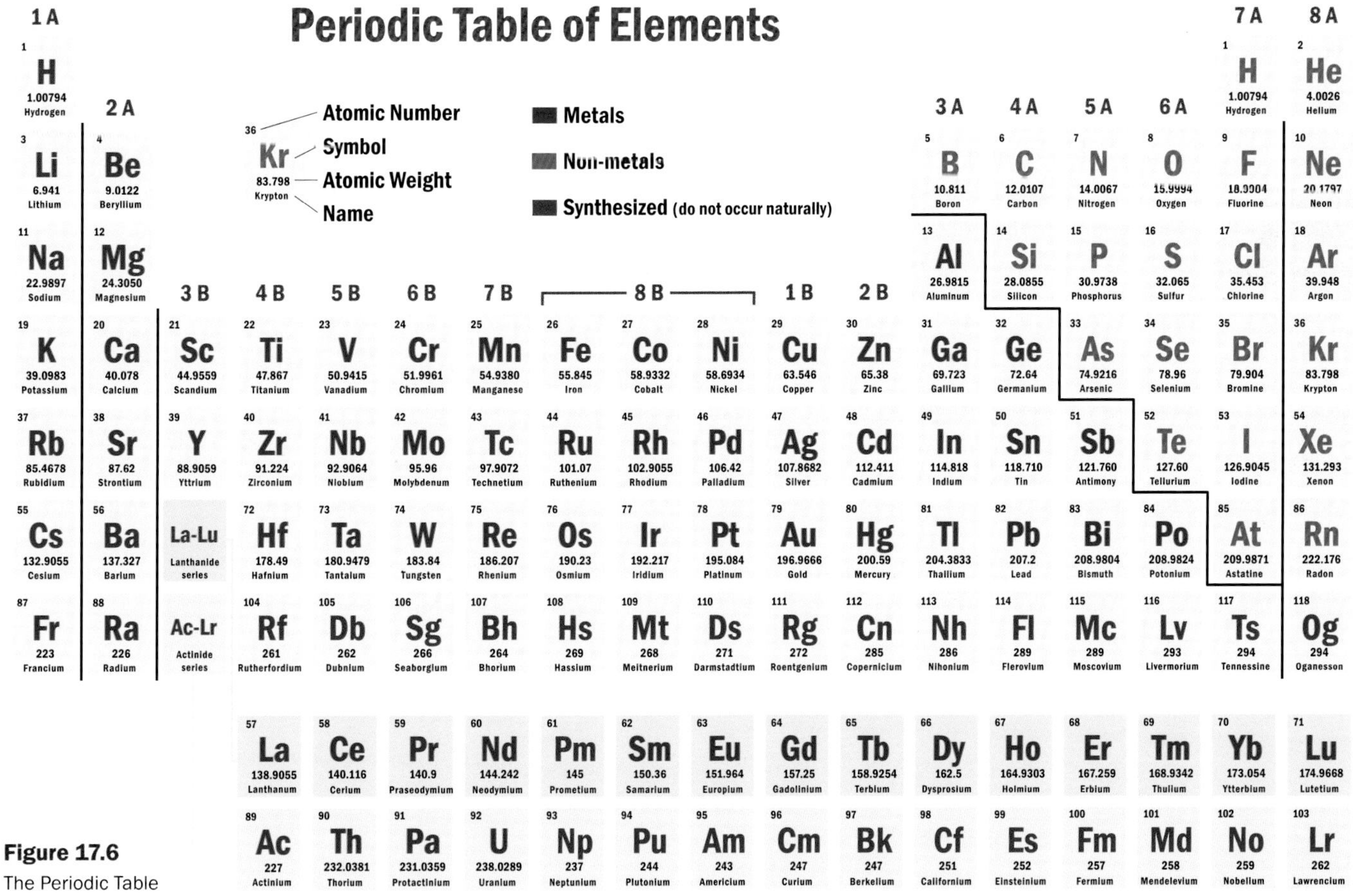

# Periodic Table of Elements

Atomic Number
Symbol
Atomic Weight
Name

■ Metals
▦ Non-metals
■ Synthesized (do not occur naturally)

**Figure 17.6**

The Periodic Table

etc., divides metals from non-metals. The non-metal elements sit on the right-hand side of the table, above and to the right of the black dividing line.

Elements are separated into metals of non-metals based on whether or not they conduct electricity: metals conduct and non-metals do not. About three-fourths of the known elements are metals. All but one metallic element, mercury (number 80), are solids at room temperature. Metals have other properties in common. They are shiny and reflective. They can be hammered into thin sheets and stretched into fine wires. The elements of gold, copper, and aluminum are metals whose properties may already be familiar to you. Metals are studied in greater depth in Chapter 21.

Non-metals show much more variety in their properties. There are non-metal elements that are gases, others that are liquids, and still others that are solids at room temperature. Some are highly colored, while others are colorless. The chemistry of non-metals will be discussed in Chapters 22 and 23.

The modern periodic table structure conveys how the chemical and physical properties of the elements vary. The vertical columns of the periodic table are Mendeleev's **families**, now also called **groups.** The elements of a given family or column have similar properties. For example, the formulas of oxide compounds with elements in the same family will typically be the same. However, the ease or vigor with which the element reacts with oxygen to form the oxide may change as you go down a column.

The horizontal rows of the periodic table are called **periods**. Within a given row, physical and chemical properties change systematically from element to element. A row represents the period or length of the repeating pattern observed by Mendeleev. Moving from the last element in a row to the first element in the next row restarts the pattern.

Some of the family names from early groupings are retained in the modern periodic table. Alkali metals and alkaline earth elements form Columns 1A and 2A, respectively. The halogens make up Column 7A. A new column, 8A, contains the noble gas elements. These elements were not discovered until 25 years after Mendeleev published his first table. The elements with

"A" labels are sometimes called the **main group** elements.

The elements in the large block in the center of the periodic table are collectively referred to as the **transition metals**. Many precious gemstones such as rubies and sapphires owe their colors to the presence of small amounts of transition metals in otherwise colorless substances. Transition metal chemistry is a rich but challenging field. Because of the complexity of transition metals, we shall not study these materials in depth.

Two additional series of elements exist. The lanthanide series contains the elements from 58 to 71. The series gets its name from lanthanum, element 58. The actinide series consists of elements from actinium, element 90, to lawrencium, element 103. All of the actinide series are radioactive. Uranium and plutonium are the two most famous (or infamous) elements of this series.

## 17-4   Periodic Trends in Atomic Size and Ionization Energy

When all the known elements are included, periodic trends of atomic properties stand out with increased clarity. Let us consider two important physical properties, **atomic size** and **ionization energy**. These two properties dramatically portray the trends hinted at by Mendeleev's oxide combining ratios. In addition, these properties will prove useful for further discussions of bonding.

### Atomic Size Variations

*Figure 17.7* plots the size of the atoms, expressed as a volume, against their atomic number. The x-axis is the atomic number of the element and the y-axis is the atomic volume. The graph shows recurring peaks and valleys. The peaks correspond to atoms that have large atomic volume; the valleys show elements with smaller atomic volumes.

Can you identify which family of elements has the largest volume in every period? Now, look just at the trend in the peak volumes. Do these volumes increase or decrease with atomic number?

The atomic volumes peak on members of the alkali metal family. The alkaline earth ele-

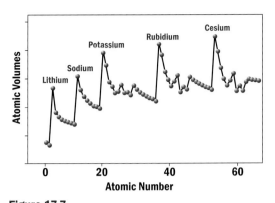

**Figure 17.7**
Atomic sizes vary periodically. This graph shows the variation of the atomic volume with the atomic number. All known elements through element 69 (thulium) are shown here, not just those known to Mendeleev.

ments, just one element to the right in each period, have significantly smaller volumes than their alkali metal neighbors.

Figure 17.7 also shows that the atomic volumes of the alkali metals increase as you go down the column. This same trend is true, but less apparent, for other element families.

### Ionization Energy Variations

First ionization energy refers to the energy required to strip an electron from a neutral atom, thus turning it into an ion. The chemical behavior of an element directly relates to how easily it loses electrons, so this is an important property to understand. We will refer back to this extensively in Chapters 21 and 22.

Like the atomic size, the ionization energy varies periodically with atomic number as shown in *Figure 17.8*. Again we see a set of peaks. In this figure, a peak signifies an element that really likes to hold on to its electrons. That is, to pull away an electron from such an atom

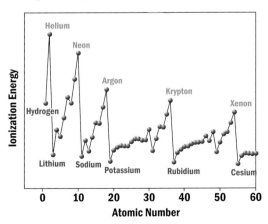

**Figure 17.8**
It takes energy to remove an electron from a neutral atom. This energy, called the ionization energy, varies with atomic number.

requires a great deal of energy. The ionization energy drops immediately following a peak to a minimum value. Atoms with minimum energies lose electrons easily.

Let's look at this figure a little more closely. Which element family has high ionization energies? Which element family tends to have low ionization energies? Looking as a group at metallic elements versus non-metallic elements, how do you characterize the ionization energies of the two groups?

It turns out all metals have low ionization energies. The alkali metals, the atoms with the largest atomic volume, are the easiest to ionize. These low ionization energies are the reason metals are shiny and electrically conducting.

Non-metal elements have large ionization energies. The different ionization energies of the two classes of elements play a significant role in the different chemistry of the two groups.

The highest ionization energies are for the noble gases (helium, neon, argon, krypton, and xenon). Their ionization energies are so high, in fact, that these gases do not tend to interact with other atoms. Only xenon forms chemical compounds at room temperature, while the others can form weak interactions only at low temperatures. Xenon's compound formation occurs even then only with the most reactive element: fluorine.

The appearance, natural state, and chemical aggressiveness of elements vary periodically with atomic number. That so many properties exhibited the same periodicity tantalized scientists for many years after Mendeleev. Surely some underlying fundamental principle could explain everything. The explanation became apparent after Schrödinger and others solved the mathematical equations of the quantum model of the atom.

### 17-5 The Quantum Model Explains the Periodic Table

How does the quantum model explain these periodicities? Let's follow Mendeleev's lead and look for patterns. In the spirit of inquiry consider each question posed below to see if you come up with the answers on your own before you read our answers and explanations.

Look first at *Figure 17.9* to refresh your memory of the ordering of electronic energy levels found from the quantum model. Recall that

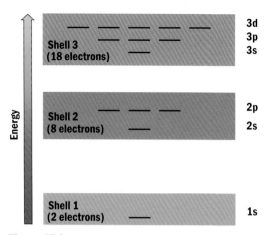

**Figure 17.9**

Simple atomic orbital energy diagram. Remember that each orbital can only hold at most two electrons.

**Electron Configuration Diagram:**

An enumeration of how electrons populate atomic orbitals that is consistent with the "lowest-energy filled first" and "exclusion" principles.

**Valence Electrons:**

One or more electrons in the outermost populated electron shell of an atom. Valence electrons determine an element's chemical reactivity.

each orbital holds two electrons. How many electrons can the first shell of an atom hold?

Now, count the number of elements in the first two periods of the periodic table (Figure 17.6). Row 1 has 2 elements; Row 2 has 8 elements. Do the numbers 2 and 8 seem familiar? How many electrons can the second shell hold?

Perhaps now you think you are onto something. What hypotheses might you form? Suppose you first hypothesize that a connection exists between the rows in the periodic table and electronic shells of the quantum model.

To test this hypothesis, refer to the energy-level diagram of Figure 17.9. Then look at which of its electron orbitals are populated as you go from atom to atom along the first two rows of the periodic table. In assigning electrons to orbitals, remember two principles: 1) electrons populate the lowest energy orbitals first, and 2) no orbital can hold more than two electrons. Energy levels sketched with electrons in

them, often drawn with an up arrow and a down arrow to represent spin, are called **electron configuration** diagrams.

Hydrogen has one electron; it must go into the 1s orbital. Helium has one more electron. Putting two electrons into the 1s orbital fills that orbital up. Shell 1 is complete.

Move down to Row 2. Lithium, the first element of row 2, has 3 electrons. Two electrons must go into the 1s orbital. The third electron of lithium goes into the next available orbital, which is a 2s orbital. Beryllium, atom 4, puts its 4th electron into the 2s orbital. The 2s orbital is now filled.

Each atom along the periodic table has one more electron than the element before it. Hopefully the placement of electrons for elements 5 through 10 is obvious. The set of 2p orbitals are filled next. Boron, atom 5, must put its 5th electron into one of the 2p orbitals. The remaining 5 elements (carbon through neon) each add their additional electron to the 2p orbitals. At atom 10, the 2 p orbitals have 6 electrons. Shell 2 is complete.

*Figure 17.10* shows electron configuration diagrams for the outer-most electrons, called **valence electrons**, of elements 1 through 18. In these diagrams the filled shells below the valence shell are not shown because they do not change once filled.

Looking over your own electron configuration diagrams, or the first two rows of Figure 17.10, you see that in accordance with your hypothesis, rows 1 and 2 of the periodic table do correspond to how electrons fill the first two shells of the quantum model. Furthermore, the

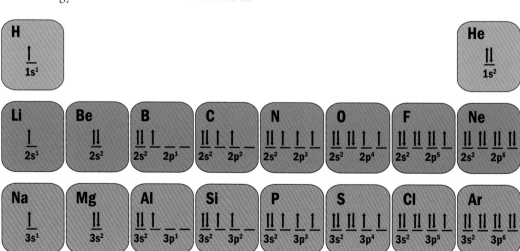

**Figure 17.10**

Valence electron configurations of the elements in rows 1–3 of the periodic table.

two atoms in column 1A each have a single electron in the orbital of the outer, or valence shell. In fact, each member of a group always has the *same* orbital population description for its outer electrons.

Did you notice that the first two noble gases (helium, neon) in Column 8A each have completely filled shells? Nobel gases are unreactive so time for a second hypothesis: Atoms with completely filled shells are unreactive.

Try your two hypotheses out by checking them on Row 3 of the periodic table. Atom number 11, the element sodium, starts off Row 3. Sodium's first 10 electrons fill up Shell 2, so electron 11 must go into Shell 3—specifically into the 3s orbital, because Figure 17.9 tells us that is next in energy.

Working across the third period in the same way you did the second period, takes us to argon. Argon has 18 electrons, eight more electrons than neon. Argon's last electron completes the 3p orbital set.

Now check to see whether the patterns observed earlier are still holding up and whether your two hypotheses still seem valid. Yes, each element of Period 3 has the same outer electron configuration as its family members. Argon, an unreactive noble gas element, has completely filled 3s and 3p orbitals. Both hypotheses seem all right to this point.

But now a problem develops. According to Figure 17.9, Shell 3 can take ten additional electrons; it contains the set of 3d orbitals. But according to the periodic table, moving to atom 19 (potassium) takes you down to a new period!

Time to step back and re-evaluate. Can it be that periods don't correspond to shells after all? Are your hypotheses about reactivity and completely-filled shells completely off-base? Maybe reactivity isn't about filled shells after all. What's going on?

The early atomic scientists, at this point in their own mental exercises, began to scratch their heads. The simple energy scheme developed by Schrödinger and others for atomic hydrogen worked so well for the first 18 elements! What went wrong at atom number 19?

The orbital energy levels of Figure 17.9 were developed without considering the effect of electrons on each other. Repulsive forces between the electrons in an atom changes their energy

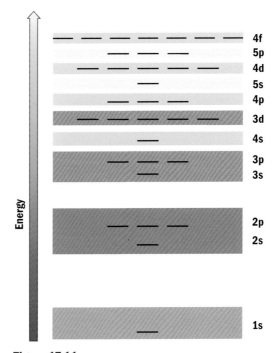

**Figure 17.11**

An atomic orbital energy diagram modified to show the correct ordering of the orbitals in Shells 3, 4, and 5, up to 5p and 4f.

levels. So the quantum model was extended to include this influence that electrons inside the atom have on each other.

*Figure 17.11* presents the revised energy scheme which is appropriate for most atoms. Notice that the 3d orbitals are now higher in energy than the 4s orbital. With this new energy scheme, the outer electrons of potassium and calcium (atoms number 19 and 20, respectively) go in as 4s1 and 4s2, respectively, rather than as 3d electrons. This figure shows the same filling order as Table 16.1.

Following calcium, the first row of transition metal elements appears. The valence electrons of these 10 elements, beginning with scandium, fill in the set of five 3d orbitals. Continuing on, the outer electrons of atoms 31 (gallium) through 36 (krypton) go into the next available orbitals, the 4p orbitals. Krypton's full electron configuration is $1s^2 2s^2 2p^6 3s^2 3p^6 4s^2 3d^{10} 4p^6$. Krypton is another noble gas.

The revised energy scheme restores the pattern of electron configurations for the main group elements (1A through 8A) you observed earlier. All the members of a column have the same valence electron configuration. The quantum number $n$ that identifies the shell of the outermost s and p orbitals locates the row in which the element is found. Your first hypothesis about the connection between shell and periods is correct. .

The second hypothesis relating filled shells with unusual chemical stability has not been significantly improved, even with the energy reordering. The $ns^2\,np^6$ configuration of the noble gases in Group 8A does not always correspond to closed *shells* because the d or f orbital sets in shells where $n$ is 3 or greater are empty. The experimental observation that these elements are chemically unreactive and have high ionization energies suggests that there is something special about that configuration. The quantum model does not easily provide an explanation why. However, knowing that the $ns^2\,np^6$ configuration confers energetic stability enables chemists to make simple predictions about the chemistry of many elements.

Periods 5, 6, and 7 have ten transition metals each. These arise from filling the set of five 3d orbitals in period 5, the set of five 4d orbitals in period 6, and the set of five 5d orbitals in period 7. Period 6 also has the previously described lanthanide series. These fourteen elements come from filling the set of seven 4f orbitals. The actinide series in period 7 are from filling the set of seven 5f orbitals.

The chemistry of these f-electron elements is very complex. Other than to note that these are metals, we will not discuss them further.

## 17–6  Conclusion

The single-minded passion of Mendeleev led him to an important discovery. Periodic patterns exist in the properties of elements. The organizing principle responsible for the patterns is the quantum (wave) nature of the atom.

Periodic patterns arise from the sequential filling of atomic orbitals by electrons and the existence of electron shells. The experimentally-determined structure of the periodic table provided the evidence to improve the simple

quantum model of the atom, and extend it beyond hydrogen. The improved, extended table given in Figure 17.6 shows our new understanding. The quantum model–periodic table connection established that an element's chemical reactivity is determined by its outermost electrons.

Scientists find beauty in simple, elegant ways of understanding nature. From that perspective, the periodic table is like Michelangelo's famous *Pieta* (*Figure 17.12*). The beautifully sculpted statue conveys to even an unfamiliar observer a story of physical suffering and compassionate love. To a religious Christian, familiar with the story of Jesus and Mary, the statue takes on a more profound meaning.

**Figure 17.12**
Michelangelo's *Pieta* (1498, St. Peter's Basilica, Rome)

On one level, the periodic table conveys information about elemental properties. The table also portrays electron configurations and shell structures. New predictions about chemical properties and reactivities become possible. The periodic table is elegant and simple in its conciseness, yet powerfully capable of providing a wealth of chemical and physical information. We shall continue to refer back to it in many subsequent chapters.

*Chemistry is like cooking
(just don't lick the spoon).*
                    popular saying

# 17 STUDY GUIDE

## Chapter Framework

### A. Early Chemistry and Chemists
1. Law of Constant Composition
2. Atomic Theory

### B. The Development of the Periodic Table
1. Families of Elements
   a. *Physical properties*
   b. *Chemical properties*
2. Dmitri Mendeleev
3. Periodic Law

### C. Improved Periodic Table
1. New Elements
2. Sorted by Atomic Number
3. Metals and Non-metals
4. Families or Groups
   a. *Main group*
   b. *Transition metals*
   c. *Lanthanide and actinide series*
5. Periods

### D. Periodic Trends
1. Atomic Size Variations
2. Ionization Energy Variations

### E. The Quantum Model and the Periodic Table
1. Electron Configuration Diagrams
2. Valence Electrons

## Comprehension

### Matching

1. ___ Properties like melting or boiling temperature, density, and color.
2. ___ Good electrical and thermal conductors that can usually be hammered into thin sheets or drawn into fine wires.
3. ___ Two or more different types of atoms that are joined together in fixed ratios.
4. ___ Electrons that are in the outermost, usually unfilled shell of an atom.
5. ___ Elements that do not conduct electricity.
6. ___ Elements that occur in the same row of the Periodic Table.
7. ___ The science of matter and the transformations that it can undergo to form new or different types of matter.
8. ___ Elements in the periodic table which are placed in the same column and have similar chemical properties.
9. ___ A kind of matter that contains only one type of atom.
10. ___ Properties associated with the reactivity of a material.

a. Metals
b. Chemical property
c. Periods
d. Non- metals
e. Chemistry
f. Physical property
g. Element
h. Family
i. Valence electrons
j. Compound

### True/False

1. ___ Dmitri Mendeleev is the father of the Periodic Table of elements.
2. ___ Elements that have similar chemical properties are categorized into periods.
3. ___ Elements with atomic numbers heavier than 92 (uranium) are all man-made elements.
4. ___ Carbon, silicon, and lead belong to the same family.
5. ___ Br (atomic number 35) has five valence electrons.

### Fill in the Blank

1. The two categories of elements are _____ and _____.
2. _____, a missing element, was discovered to fit in between calcium and titanium in the Periodic Table according to oxidation levels.
3. Each metallic element in Column 1A has the _____ atomic volume and the _____ ionization energy of any element in its row.
4. Different substances can contain the same elements but in different _____.
5. According to Table 17.1, the combining ratio of the elements with oxygen in row 3 (Na through Cl) _____ as you go from left to right.

## Analysis

1. List the following atoms in order of increasing atomic volume: nitrogen, oxygen, and phosphorus.
   a) O N P
   b) N O P
   c) N P O
   d) P N O
   e) P O N

2. List Fe, Rh, and Pt in order of increasing density. (They all have about the same atomic volume.)
   a) Pt Rh Fe
   b) Rh Fe Pt
   c) Fe Rh Pt
   d) Pt Fe Rh
   e) Fe Pt Rh

3. Which atom has the lowest ionization energy?
   a) Hydrogen
   b) Helium
   c) Beryllium
   d) Lithium
   e) Aluminum

4. Which of the following statements is false?
   a) Non-metals are found on the right side of the periodic table, metals are on the left side.
   b) Elements in a column are chemically similar.
   c) Li, Na, and K are chemically similar.
   d) Ne, Ar, and Kr are chemically active solids.

5. Match the atoms that belong to the same family. The small numbers to the left of the element symbol indicate the atomic number.

$_{20}$Ca          $_{18}$Ar

$_{03}$Li          $_{12}$Mg

$_{35}$Br          $_{33}$As

$_{10}$Ne          $_{11}$Na

$_{07}$N           $_{09}$F

## Synthesis

1. Describe what advance Mendeleev made to the scientific method by predicting the existence of new elements.

2. The valence electrons of an element have the electron configuration $6s^26p^6$. Identify the element and make a prediction about a) its physical state at room temperature (solid, liquid, gas) and b) its tendency to react with other elements.

3. Write the electron configuration for Calcium (atomic number 20) and for Strontium (atomic number 38). Calcium is important for healthy, strong bones. Strontium is found in the fallout from nuclear explosions. Explain why strontium might be expected to be incorporated into bones along with calcium.

4. Suppose you had three identical test tubes and each one contained a different element, but the same number of atoms. In one tube you had sodium atoms (atomic number 11), in another one you had chromium atoms (atomic number 24) and in the third tube you had mercury (atomic number 80). Which test tube would weigh the most?

5. Refer to Figure 17.7, and decide which of the two elements will have a higher density—potassium (element 19) or calcium (element 20). Use the following questions to guide your thinking: What is the definition of density? Which element has the more massive type of atoms? Which element has the smaller volume?

6. Potassium contains a total of 19 electrons. If the atomic orbital diagram of Figure 17.9 were correct, how many valence electrons would you expect potassium to have? How many valence electrons does the revised set of levels in Figure 17.11 predict?

7. The melting temperatures of the metallic elements of Group 1A are given in the table.

| Element in Group 1A | Melting Temperature |
|---|---|
| Lithium | 180.54 °C |
| Sodium | 97.72 °C |
| Potassium | 63.38 °C |
| Rubidium | 39.31 °C |
| Cesium | 28.44 °C |

a) What trend in melting temperature do you observe as you go down the column?

b) Refer to Figures 17.7 and 17.8 and determine the trend in atomic volume and ionization energy as you go down the column for these elements.

c) Which of the two properties (volumes or ionization energies) shows the same trend as the melting points?

d) Think back to our hypotheses of Chapter 12 regarding melting points (see p. 144). Given those hypotheses, what would you predict about the forces that hold atoms of cesium together in the solid metal compared to the forces that hold atoms of lithium together?

8. The quantum model of the atom offers some insights into the trends in atomic size (Figure 17.7). Consider the following questions and state some observations we can make by comparing the theory with experiment. What type of electron configuration is associated with the largest atomic volumes in a given period? As the $n$ designation of an element's valence electron increases (e.g., 1s1, 2s1, 3s1 etc), what happens to the atomic size of that element?

9. The trend in ionization energy as you go down Group 1A can be explained, qualitatively at least, by the electric force law. Why does it get easier to pull away a valence 6s electron than a valence 3s electron? Hint: which electron is further away from the nucleus, on average?

# The Law of Increasing Disorder

*Nothing in life is certain except death, taxes, and the second law of thermodynamics.*

**Seth Lloyd**

## LEARN

- Irreversible and reversible processes and their effect on the disorder or entropy of the universe.

- To rank various forms of energy in terms of their organization or usefulness to do work.

- The implications of converting energy from one form to another with respect to the law of increasing disorder.

- The implications of the law of increasing disorder on society's long-term energy needs.

The quantum model of the atom is the most detailed and accurate model we have. It has been enormously successful at unifying our understanding of the atom with the discoveries of chemistry. It is truly one of the great triumphs of human thought. But before we further explore its implications, we must consider another aspect of energy, one that is crucial in understanding how energy behaves in molecules and chemical bonding.

In Chapter 9, we learned that there are various forms of energy, and that energy can be converted from one form to another, or even into mass. We also learned that mass and energy (or mass-energy in relativistic processes) are always conserved. In this chapter, we will see that there is a constraint on transforming one type of energy into another. In essence, if energy can be completely converted from one form to another, it cannot be converted back again with perfect efficiency.

Energy may be ranked by "quality," which is a measure of how efficiently it can be transformed through work. Using this ranking sys-

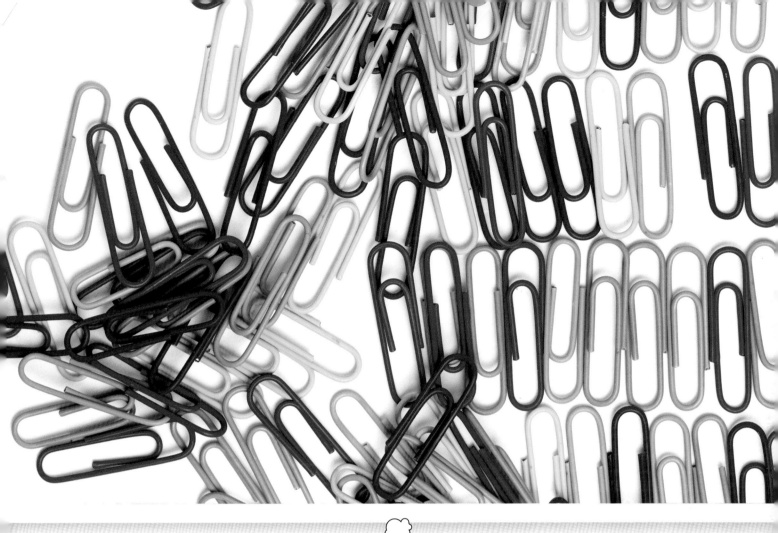

tem we will find that while the *quantity* of energy may be conserved in a transformation, the *quality* of the energy is generally degraded, making it less useful to do work. These observations form the basis of the **law of increasing disorder**, a law that impacts every aspect of life.

In the early 19th century, the invention of the steam engine drove the Industrial Revolution. While crude and inefficient by today's standards, these engines were true marvels of that age. Steam engines used the thermal energy in hot steam, produced by burning wood, coal, and—later—petroleum to do work (*Figure 18.1*). Remember that we defined work in Chapter 9 in terms of the energy required to move an object against a force. In the steam engine, the expansion of hot gases provided the energy that turned crankshafts to propel steam ships or push pistons to drill coal mines.

Scientists and engineers began to study the engine carefully with the hopes of improving its performance. In some cases it was a matter of national pride. (See "Sadi Carnot—Scientist and Engineer.") The investigators wanted to

**Figure 18.1**

The steam engine was a marvelous invention that used thermal energy to do work.

produce an engine that could completely convert into useful work energy all the heat energy available in hot steam.

The reverse process, conversion of work into heat, occurred with no trouble. A simple example of the reverse process is to rub your hands together. Your muscles are doing work, moving

**Law of Increasing Disorder:**

Changes occurring in natural systems always proceed in such a way that the total amount of disorder in the universe is either unchanged or increased. If total disorder is increased, the process is irreversible. Also known as the Second Law of Thermodynamics.

your hands back and forth. The action creates friction, which is manifest as heat. However, all the experiments conducted with the heat engines showed that heat energy could not be completely converted into work. Some heat was always left over.

At about the same time, other experiments were being conducted to understand the operation of another 19th century invention—the refrigerator. Prior to the invention of the refrigerator, an icebox was used to keep food cold for a short time. An icebox worked by conduction; heat flowed from the hot food to the cold ice, melting the ice in the process. The food could never get colder than the ice.

A refrigerator, however, uses work to remove heat energy from a cold object, making the object even colder. (See "A Quick Look at How a Refrigerator Works"). The reverse process, transferring heat from a hot object to a cold one, takes place with no work being required.

The study of these two very different inventions, steam engines and refrigerators, yielded a surprisingly common observation: there was a preferred directionality to processes involving heat. Mechanical energy can be completely converted to heat, but not vice-versa, and heat flows naturally from hot objects to cold ones; to reverse the natural direction requires doing work.

In this chapter we see that many natural occurrences have a preferred or spontaneous direction. These, like the operations of steam engines and refrigerators, have their roots in what we shall state as the law of increasing disorder or the second law of thermodynamics.[1]

## 18-1 Irreversible and Reversible Processes

We are all familiar with events whose effects can't be undone. As a child you probably sang, "All the King's horses and all the King's men couldn't put Humpty together again." If you saw a video clip of a swimmer who suddenly emerged, feet first, from a swimming pool, and arched upward, landing on a diving board, you would probably laugh, realizing the video clip had been played backwards (*Figure 18.2*). We often find humor in the "unnatural." A diver never dives *upward* from a swimming pool. A pet dog or cat never grows younger. Scrambled eggs never spontaneously unscramble. Our experience in everyday life shows us that nature tends to run in one direction.

The examples above illustrate processes that are, in scientific terms, **irreversible**. The described actions do not spontaneously go in a reverse direction. Some irreversible processes can be undone, but these require actions; work that someone or something does to reverse the process.

For example, to imitate the backward-playing video, the diver could be hoisted back up to the diving board with a rope and pulley, but to

---

[1] The first law of thermodynamics (the law of conservation of energy) was discussed in Chapter 8.

**Figure 18.2**
Is this a natural order of events? Notice the splash, which is clearly irreversible.

---

### SADI CARNOT—SCIENTIST & ENGINEER

Carnot was born in France in 1796, the son of a leading government official of the French Revolution. Carnot, while a student at the École Polytechnique, requested permission from Napoleon to allow him and his fellow students to fight in the 1814 battle for Paris. Permission was granted, and they fought bravely, but unsuccessfully. After graduation from the École Polytechnique and additional military service, Carnot took additional courses at the Sorbonne. Carnot also made many visits to factories and workshops to observe how the academic principles he learned at the university were at work in the fledgling French industries. He wanted to improve the performance of steam engines, recognizing that technological prowess could keep France as a world power.

Carnot developed an idealized heat engine based on his observations of real engines. He is credited with making the initial observations that led to the development of the Law of Increasing Disorder. Unfortunately, Carnot died of cholera at the age of 36. Most of Carnot's papers and other belongings were buried with him so his work did not receive recognition until years after his death.

date, no process for unscrambling eggs or making faithful old Fido a puppy again has been discovered.

There are some processes that can occur with equal ease in both forward and reverse directions. Such processes are characterized as being **reversible**.[2] The simplest reversible transformations are the changes in state that we studied in Chapter 12. The state transformations that water undergoes provide good examples of reversible processes and illustrate some key features of reversibility.

[2] Nearly all reversible processes occur only on the molecular level.

Imagine a beaker filled with liquid water and ice cubes at exactly 0° C sitting in a freezer that is exactly at 0° C. If you observe this beaker over time, you will find that the shape of the ice cubes change, but that the total volume (and mass) of ice doesn't change. At this temperature, water molecules on the surface of the ice cube leave and go into the liquid state at the same rate that other liquid water molecules freeze onto the surface of the ice cube. We can represent the process as

$$\text{Ice} <--> \text{Liquid}$$

where the double-headed arrow indicates a reversible process.

**Irreversible:**

An irreversible process is one that goes in only one direction; its effects often cannot be undone. Most processes which occur in nature are irreversible.

**Reversible:**

A reversible process goes both forward and backward at the same time. Reversible processes are relatively rare in nature.

## A QUICK LOOK AT HOW A REFRIGERATOR WORKS

Chapter 13 taught three principles that refrigerators use. They are:

1. When the pressure on a gas is increased, the gas temperature rises; expanding a gas (lowering its pressure) drops the gas temperature.

2. It takes heat energy to evaporate a liquid; condensing a gas gives off heat energy.

3. Heat flows from hot objects to cold ones.

A refrigerator takes advantage of these principles to transfer heat from its interior to its exterior. *Figure 18.3* shows a picture and schematic of the major components that transfer this heat. While designs may vary, all refrigerators must have the same following components:

*Refrigerant*: This is the gas that is compressed and condensed then evaporated and expanded during the refrigeration cycle.

*Compressor*: A pump that circulates the refrigerant and compresses it when outside the refrigerator. It is usually at the back of the refrigerator near the bottom.

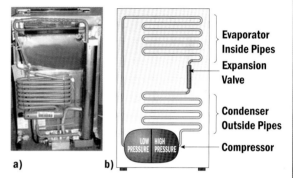

**Figure 18.3**

a) The back of a refrigerator showing the compressor and condenser.

b) A schematic showing the major components of a refrigerator. The yellow color of the compressor represents the region where heat is dissipated into the surroundings around the refrigerator. The blue color of the evaporator indicates the region (usually in the freezer) where cooling takes place.

*Evaporator*: The set of coils inside the refrigerator that becomes cold when evaporation takes place within them.

*Condenser*: The set of coils outside the refrigerator that becomes hot when gas is condensed to a liquid inside them.

*Expansion valve*: The interface where the high-pressure liquid crosses to the low pressure region, expands, evaporates and cools at becoming a low-pressure gas.

The refrigeration cycle starts when the compressor squeezes the refrigerant down to a liquid on the high pressure side of the loop which is outside the refrigerator and colored yellow in Figure 18.3. This compression raises the temperature, allowing heat to flow out of the coils into the room.

On the other end of the condenser pipe is the expansion valve, a tiny, narrow-diameter copper tube. The liquid, at high pressure, is forced through the narrow tube and into the evaporator coils which are inside the refrigerator, often into the freezer section. The liquid refrigerant experiences a large pressure drop as it moves into the larger diameter pipe of the evaporator. Because of the pressure drop, the liquid expands back to the gas state and cools allowing heat to flow from warmer food to the colder evaporator coils. The compressor then pumps the low-pressure gas back outside the refrigerator, and the cycle continues.

In terms of the law of increasing disorder, the key points are:

1. The compressor does work on the gas by compressing it to the liquid state.

2. The expansion process cools the gas and heat naturally flows from warmer contents to the colder gas.

3. Heat is dissipated out into the kitchen environment. The disorder in the dissipated heat is greater than the order within the refrigerator.

**Figure 18.4**
A glass of ice-water is standing on a kitchen counter. Is the melting of the ice cubes a process that can be reversed?

Contrast that example with a glass of water at room temperature into which ice cubes are added. Over time, all of the ice cubes will melt (*Figure 18.4*). No amount of watching will transform the water into ice cubes again. This process is irreversible.

As a third example, consider what will happen if you put warm water into a freezer at a temperature below 0° C. It will freeze. If the temperature is held to below freezing, the liquid to solid transformation is irreversible.

What is the fundamental difference between the three examples? It is the temperature of the water. Reversibility occurs only within a narrow set of experimental conditions such as temperature and pressure. Changing the temperature and/or pressure can alter the irreversibility/reversibility of a process. The specific temperature and pressure at which reversible state transformations occur depend upon the material. In Table 12.1, the melting and boiling temperatures represent the conditions of reversibility for each material. Because reversibility occurs at fixed temperatures and pressures, reversible processes even on the molecular level are relatively rare in nature.

It can be stated with considerable confi-

dence that there are no mechanical processes that occur reversibly. Friction always occurs when two surfaces rub against each other, and this friction causes irreversibility. Some processes, though, like the single bounce of a ball do not create much disorder. We call such processes "nearly reversible". The best way to decide if a process is nearly reversible is to play a film of it backwards in your mind. If it sort of makes sense, like a bounce of a ball, it is nearly reversible. If it makes no sense, like a diver shooting up out of a pool onto a diving board, it is irreversible.

## 18-2 Order and Disorder

There is a fundamental principle that explains the fact that nature has a tendency to run in one direction. The principle has been stated in a variety of ways, one of which is, "If you think things are mixed up now, just wait a while." The key idea is that things tend to get more mixed up as time goes on. Consider *Figure 18.5*, which shows a messy dorm room and the same room after it has been cleaned up. Over time, the cleaned room tends to once again get messed up. It takes work to straighten it up again. Which would your mother prefer to see if she came to visit? Nature, unlike your mother, apparently prefers disorder and chaos.

Let's consider order and disorder on a molecular level. Remember the images the molecular model gave us for how molecules are arranged in the various states of matter. In solids, molecules are arranged neatly in a regular, predictable array, and they take up a relatively small space. In gases, molecules move chaotically throughout the entire volume of their container. The solid state is more ordered, the gaseous state more disordered.

**Figure 18.5**
A room in a state of disorder can be cleaned and organized (with a lot of work). However, over time it will return to a state of chaos.

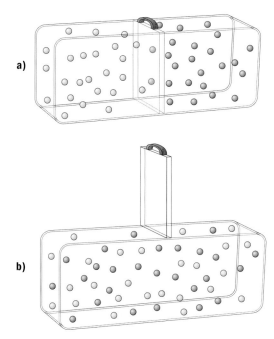

**Figure 18.6**

a) Two kinds of molecules separated in a container.

b) Once the divider is removed and the molecules mix, will they ever spontaneously separate and return to their original state?

Now consider the two images in *Figure 18.6*. Image 18.6a is a container that has two compartments, each containing only one kind of gas. Below in 18.6b is the same container after the divider between the two compartments has been removed and the two gases have mixed. Which image represents the ordered arrangement? Which is the disordered one? Can the process be reversed? Will the mixture of two gases ever spontaneously separate?

Obviously, the molecules in Figure 18.6b are more disordered. Even if you wait a very long time, they never un-mix on their own. Of course, you can do some work and sort out the molecules again, but that is not a spontaneous process. This example illustrates disorder resulting from the various arrangements of molecules in space.

Disorder can also arise from partitioning energy among molecules. Recall the distribution curves in Chapter 13 for the probability of molecular speeds in gases (Figures 13.8 and 13.9). At low temperatures the distribution is sharply peaked, so the molecules in a gas sample all have about the same kinetic energy. At high temperatures there is a much broader distribution of speeds and the energy is dispersed in a more disordered way throughout the molecules. Scientists use the word **entropy** to describe the amount of disorder in a system. Strictly speaking, entropy is the disorder associated with the dispersal of energy throughout the molecules that make up a system. This is often related to the geometric description of the system, such as the chaos of a messy room or the probability of finding a particular type of molecule in a particular compartment of the container. Therefore, the gas in Figure 18.6b has more entropy than that in Figure 18.6a because its particles are mixed throughout a larger volume.

The entropy of a system can be calculated from the mathematical probability of it being in its given state. Such analysis leads to two observations: 1) More disordered systems have a higher probability of occurring, and thus have greater entropy. 2) In general, increasing the temperature of matter increases its entropy.

A messy, disorganized room is not something we are proud of but even so, increasing entropy is not always bad. Increasing entropy makes concentrated energy spread out. This causes heat energy in the Sun to radiate outward and warm our planet. It causes thermal energy in a stove to radiate out and cook our food.

We have used the term *system* without being specific about its exact definition. It is often useful to put a box, either literally or figuratively, around that portion of the world that we want to study. We isolate it, either physically or mentally, from that rest of the world that we don't want to consider. We use the word *system* to denote the stuff inside the box, and *surroundings* to identify everything outside the box that does not interact with the system. Finally, we use the word *universe* to describe the combined environment of the contents of our box (the system), plus everything outside our box (the surroundings).

## 18-3 The Law of Increasing Disorder

Now that we have introduced the concepts of reversible/irreversible processes and disorder, we can formally state the law of increasing disorder as follows:

**A reversible process does not change the total amount of disorder in the universe.**

**An irreversible process increases the total amount of disorder in the universe.**

**Entropy:**

A quantitative measure of disorder. It increases as the disorder increases. It can be calculated mathematically from the probability of obtaining the system in its current state.

Notice that the law has two parts, one for reversible processes, and a second for irreversible processes. In applying this law we must consider the *total* disorder (entropy) of the universe. Mentally dividing our world into the system and the surroundings is a helpful way to keep track of it. An irreversible process going on in the system can decrease its disorder as long as somewhere in the surroundings a compensating process leads to a greater increase in disorder. The net effect of the two processes must be to increase disorder in the universe as a whole.

An example will be helpful to illustrate this idea. Let us consider a refrigerator to be a system (*Figure 18.7*). Placing a newly filled ice-cube tray in the freezer compartment introduces warm water and room temperature air into the system. The freezing compartment is cooled to a lower temperature and eventually the liquid water turns into solid ice. Turning water to ice leads to a *decrease* in the entropy of the system.

If that was all that was happening, the refrigerator would violate the law of increasing disorder. However, something else had to be taking place in the refrigerator at the same time for the ice to form. At the back of the refrigerator, electricity entered the system to drive the compressor, and hot air was dissipated out into the kitchen, increasing its room temperature. Some of that heat is from the now-frozen water, and some is from the compressor. Remember that increases in temperature represent increases in entropy, so there is an increase in the entropy of the system's surroundings.

The refrigerator works because the increase of entropy in its surroundings is greater than the decrease of entropy inside the system, and therefore the total entropy of the universe has increased.

The law of increasing disorder is sometimes erroneously used to argue against the theory of evolution. The claim is that evolution represents a decrease in the entropy of organisms because it leads to them being more organized and complex. This argument ignores the fact that as organisms become more complex they interact with their surroundings in such a way as to increase the entropy of the universe. A simple one-celled organism absorbs nutrients and energy from its environment and uses them to become more ordered. But it also excretes waste products which increase disorder. Humans and more complex creatures do likewise.

In addition to this the Earth "system" constantly receives life-sustaining energy from its surroundings, specifically the Sun. The process that creates sunlight is highly irreversible. The disorder from creating sunlight and getting it to Earth is much greater than any subsequent ordering that takes place on Earth.

The law of increasing disorder provides an important criterion to use in predicting whether a process can take place or not. If the process will increase the entropy of the universe, it just might work. If calculations show that the process will decrease the universe's entropy, don't bother trying it, you will waste your time.

When NASA sent two rovers to Mars, those robots discovered certain forms of iron oxides. The discovery prompted NASA scientists to proclaim that water must have existed on Mars. Fundamentally, this claim is rooted in the

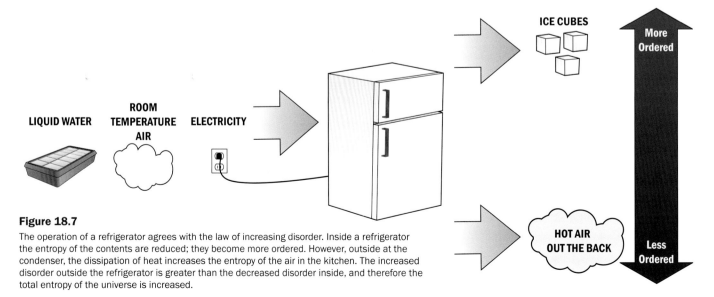

**Figure 18.7**
The operation of a refrigerator agrees with the law of increasing disorder. Inside a refrigerator the entropy of the contents are reduced; they become more ordered. However, outside at the condenser, the dissipation of heat increases the entropy of the air in the kitchen. The increased disorder outside the refrigerator is greater than the decreased disorder inside, and therefore the total entropy of the universe is increased.

law of increasing disorder. Earth-based experiments have shown that, of the possible chemical reactions that could produce these oxides, the only ones that obey the law of increasing disorder require water.

## 18-4 Order and Energy

As stated in the introduction, the law of increasing disorder arose from studies designed to improve the performances of early steam engines. Those studies showed that even in the best-designed engines, not all the energy available from the fuel can be captured, controlled and put to use, like turning the wheels of your car or propelling you uphill. Even the human body, which is among the most efficiently designed "engines," can't completely convert all the chemical potential energy from food into useful work. Some energy is expelled as body heat while additional energy is eliminated in the form of bodily waste products (carbon dioxide, urine, and feces).

The inability to convert all energy into useful work can be explained by the law of increasing disorder. In *Figure 18.8* we see three forms of energy: the **macroscopic kinetic energy** of water molecules going over Niagara Falls, the **electrical potential energy** of electrons flowing through an electrical circuit, and the **microscopic kinetic energy** or thermal energy of water molecules in the Great Salt Lake. In each of these three pictures we see a macroscopic (large-scale) object with an inset that shows a magnified cartoon of the particles involved to illustrate motion at the molecular level.

Water molecules going over Niagara Falls have an overall uniform direction to their motion—they are going downhill. Electrons flowing through a circuit also all travel as a body through the light bulb. The water molecules in the Great Salt Lake are moving around, but they are not going anywhere. Like gas molecules, they undergo random collisions with no net direction to their overall motion.

These are simplified depictions, of course. Water molecules in Niagara Falls do move in directions other than downhill and electrons experience resistance as they flow through wires and collide with nuclei in the passage. Still, the

**Macroscopic Kinetic Energy:**

The kinetic energy possessed by moving objects given by $\frac{1}{2}$mass × (speed)$^2$.

**Electrical Potential Energy:**

The form of energy associated with the relative positions of charged objects. Objects with opposite charges have maximum electrical potential energy when they are separated by greatest distance, but objects with the same charge have maximum electrical potential energy when they are separated by the least distance. This is the type of energy stored in a lightning cloud.

**Microscopic Kinetic Energy:**

The kinetic energy associated with atomic and molecular motions. A stationary object can have microscopic but not macroscopic kinetic energy.

**Figure 18.8**

Illustrations showing the origins on an atomic level of the ordering of different energy types.

a) Water molecules falling over Niagara Falls under the influence of gravity are generally moving downward. Gravitational potential and macroscopic kinetic energy are represented here.

b) Electrons flowing through a circuit are generally moving in the same direction. Electrical potential energy is represented here.

c) Water molecules in the Great Salt Lake, essentially a large pond, move chaotically, with no net organization to their motion. Microscopic kinetic energy is represented here.

| Table 18.1 — Forms of Energy and Their Rankings in Terms of Order | |
|---|---|
| Gravitational Potential Energy and Macroscopic Kinetic Energy |  |
| Nuclear Potential Energy | |
| Electrical (Household) | |
| Chemical Potential Energy | |
| Thermal Energy (also known as Heat or Microscopic Kinetic Energy) | |

general uniformity of motion in a waterfall or electric current is flow that can be harnessed for useful work. When the motion is more random, as with the water sitting in the Great Salt Lake, there is no natural organized flow to tap into.

Nuclear potential energy is a highly organized form of internal energy contained atomic nuclei. Chemical potential energy is the internal energy associated with the electrostatic interactions holding electrons to the nuclei of atoms, atoms together in molecules, and molecules together in liquids and solids. Chemical potential energy is intermediate in organization between electrical potential and thermal energy.

*Table 18.1* summarizes the various forms of energy and their ranking with respect to order. A form of energy can be converted completely into all the forms of energy appearing below it in the table. If we want to convert a less-organized form of energy into a more-organized form, the law of increasing disorder requires that we pay a price. Only part of the lower-ordered energy can be converted upwards and the remainder must be degraded to a lower form, usually heat.

*Figure 18.9* illustrates the application of the Law of Increasing Disorder to a car engine. Engines transform fuel energy into the kinetic

energy of motion. The fuel energy is chemical potential energy stored in the gasoline. As the gasoline burns, it is converted to hot gases. These expand and push on the pistons, giving them ordered kinetic energy. On average about 20% of the chemical potential energy is converted to the kinetic energy of the car. The remaining energy is downgraded to heat expelled as hot gases from the exhaust pipe or dissipated in friction.

As touched upon earlier, life forms are also governed by the law of increasing disorder. Sunlight is energy from nuclear reactions in the Sun. Sunlight is fairly high-quality energy. Plants on Earth absorb the sunlight and partially convert it into chemical potential energy through the chemical reactions of photosynthesis. Then, when the plants die, the complex molecules in the plants decay into simpler molecules with heat as a major by-product, and chemical potential energy is converted to thermal energy. Through biochemical processes in animals (including humans) that consume the plants, the chemical potential energy can be partially converted to higher forms of energy like kinetic energy of movement or the electrical potential energy powering the respiratory pathways of

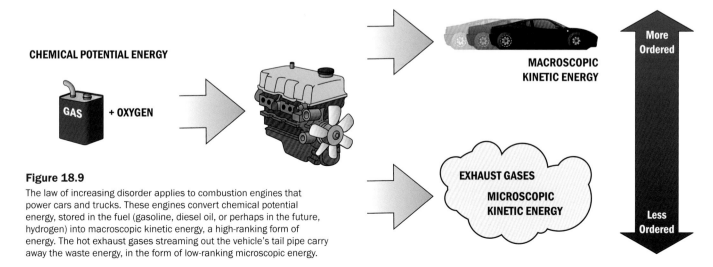

**Figure 18.9**
The law of increasing disorder applies to combustion engines that power cars and trucks. These engines convert chemical potential energy, stored in the fuel (gasoline, diesel oil, or perhaps in the future, hydrogen) into macroscopic kinetic energy, a high-ranking form of energy. The hot exhaust gases streaming out the vehicle's tail pipe carry away the waste energy, in the form of low-ranking microscopic energy.

cells. But always nature, operating according to the law of increasing disorder, takes a toll during the process, and a major portion of the chemical energy stored in the plant is discarded as heat.

## 18-5 Energy Conservation and Social Issues

The law of increasing disorder requires every irreversible process to increase disorder in the universe. If you want to convert energy from a more disordered form to a more ordered one, the law requires some of the energy to be converted downward to an even more disordered form.

Engineers talk about the efficiency of an engine as a measure of the price nature requires for the upward conversion of energy. If an engine were perfectly efficient, all the chemical potential energy stored in its fuel would be converted to the higher quality macroscopic kinetic energy. However, in even the best-designed and well-tuned engine, the law of increasing disorder requires that a fraction of the energy in the fuel be exhausted in a more disorganized form, usually as heat. The more disordered the starting energy is, the greater the amount of energy that will be wasted. You might think of the implications of this law as "You can't win; you can't even break even!"

Some philosophers in the latter half of the 19th century believed that the law of increasing disorder would ultimately result in the end of all life. They reasoned that the universe would eventually run down, as all the useful energy gradually degraded to thermal energy, a state called "heat death." The final stanza of T. S. Eliot's 1925 poem, "The Hollow Men," has been appropriated often enough as a description of this final entropic state that the Wikipedia article for the poem has a See Also reference to the entry "Heat death of the universe." The last lines of the poem are: "This is the way the world ends . . . Not with a bang but a whimper." Sidney Harris has depicted the law of increasing disorder in several of his cartoons. One is shown in *Figure 18.10.*

**Figure 18.10**
How does this cartoon illustrate the Law of Increasing Disorder?

The law of increasing disorder tells us that every irreversible action ultimately impacts the universe's quantity of useful energy. While we can't do much about the eventual death of the Sun, we can consider our use of Earth-based energy sources. To anyone concerned about the availability of the world's natural resources for future generations, prudence and good stewardship of those resources means that human activities should be conducted as efficiently as possible.

# 18 STUDY GUIDE

## Chapter Framework

**A. Law of Increasing Disorder**
1. Sadi Carnot

**B. Irreversible and Reversible Processes**

**C. Order and Disorder**
1. Entropy

**D. Order and Energy**

**E. Energy Conservation and Social Issues**

## Comprehension

### Matching

a. System

b. Entropy

c. Irreversible process

d. Reversible process

e. Surroundings

f. The Law of Increasing Disorder

1. _____ Everything outside what we have defined to be the system.
2. _____ A process that goes in only one direction; its effects cannot be undone. Most processes that occur in nature are this way.
3. _____ A process that goes both forward and backward at the same time.
4. _____ A small piece of the world around which we mentally draw a box and upon which we focus our attention.
5. _____ A quantitative measure of disorder. It increases as the disorder increases.
6. _____ Disorder in the universe increases or stays the same any time a process occurs.

### True/False

1. _____ Increasing the temperature difference between two objects increases disorder and entropy.
2. _____ Irreversible processes are always spontaneous and occur on their own without any intervention.
3. _____ From our current understanding, sometime in the future engineers will design a car that is completely efficient; i.e., a car that creates no additional disorder in the universe.
4. _____ Gravitational potential energy is a more ordered form of energy than electrical potential energy.
5. _____ A salt shaker and a pepper shaker get knocked off the table and break on the floor. Separating the salt and pepper can be considered an irreversible process.

### Fill in the Blank

1. An ice cube melts in a warm glass of water. This is an example of a(n) _____ process.
2. Complete conversion of one energy form to another energy form takes place only if the energy converts to a _____ energy form.
3. The universe is the combination of a(n) _____ plus its _____.

## Analysis

1. Overall disorder remains unchanged in

a) reversible processes.

b) chemical processes.

c) mechanical processes.

d) irreversible processes.

2. If analyzing a fridge in relationship to the rest of the house it is in, what would the fridge be considered?

a) Entropy

b) Surroundings

c) System

d) Both (b) and (c)

3. Which of the following is a reversible process?

a) A man diving into a pool.

b) Water falling down Niagara Falls.

c) A pendulum swinging in a frictionless environment.

d) Scrambling eggs.

e) None of the above.

4. Which of the following processes is closest to an ideal reversible process?

a) A golf ball falls into mud and sticks there.

b) Water evaporates from a glass sitting on the kitchen table.

c) A book sliding on a horizontal table comes to rest because of friction.

d) A ripe peach rots in the Sun.

e) An ice cube changes shape while floating in a glass of water at $0°$ C.

5. An auto engine cannot convert all of its fuel's chemical potential energy into macroscopic kinetic energy because

a) some is destroyed in the conversion.

b) some goes into gravitational potential energy.

c) some converts into mass.

d) some is always converted to heat.

6. The Law of Increasing Disorder places limits on the efficiency of energy conversion. Which of the following is allowed?

a) 100% conversion of thermal energy to kinetic energy.

b) 100% conversion of chemical potential energy to kinetic energy.

c) 100% conversion of sunlight to kinetic energy.

d) 100% conversion of electricity to ambient temperature thermal energy.

e) 100% conversion of thermal energy to chemical potential energy.

7. Of the quantities listed, the one associated with the most disorder is

   a) chemical potential energy.

   b) gravitational potential energy.

   c) macroscopic kinetic energy.

   d) nuclear potential energy.

   e) thermal energy.

8. In an old-fashioned ice box (literally a box containing ice with room for food containers), the food's temperature could never get lower than 0° C. Explain why.

9. In the freezer in your refrigerator, food probably gets down to about −10 °C. What can you conclude about the temperature that the refrigerant gas reaches during the expansion portion of a refrigeration cycle?

10. In the following scenarios, identify which of the two situations is more disordered.

    a) A large, solid chunk of table salt and a beaker of pure water *or* a solution made by mixing the salt and water together.

    b) A solid chunk of ice *or* a container filled with the same mass of water in the gaseous state.

    c) A chamber with two compartments, one containing pure oxygen and the other containing pure nitrogen *or* the same chamber in which the two gases have been allowed to mix.

11. Pure aluminum melts at a temperature of 660° C. When liquid aluminum solidifies at this temperature, is the process reversible or irreversible? What effect does the process have on the total disorder in the universe?

## Synthesis

1. An object slides across the table and comes to a rest because of friction. Explain how there is more "order" in the beginning and more "disorder" at the end of this process.

2. State the Law of Increasing Disorder in your own words.

3. Illustrate the Law of Increasing Disorder by describing an irreversible process.

4. No process can occur in which the total effect results in heat flowing from a cooler object to a hotter object. Why?

5. Stacey drops a bottle of perfume on the floor of a large room. The bottle completely shatters. Ashley smells the perfume on the other side of the room a few seconds later. Using the molecular model of matter and the Law of Increasing Disorder, explain why Ashley smells the perfume on the other side of the room.

6. Do the following for each of the situations below:

   • Describe what would happen to the system.

   • Name and state, in you own words, the fundamental principle that could explain what would be observed.

   • Explain what would happen to the order of the system in terms of the fundamental principle. Be sure to describe the order at the beginning and how it changes with time.

   a) A car is moving along a flat highway. The engine is off and the car coasts to a stop.

   b) A drop of ink is released into a large flask of water.

   c) An ice cube is placed into a pan of warm water.

7. State both the Law of Conservation of Energy and the Law of Increasing Disorder. What happens to the energy and to the entropy when

   a) fossil fuel is burned.

   b) water from behind a dam is used to make electric current and the electric current is used to operate a toaster.

8. A refrigerator causes a transfer of thermal energy from a cooler region to a hotter region. The separation of hot and cold causes an increase in order. The door on the refrigerator is left open.

   a) What happens to the temperature of the kitchen? Explain your answer using the Law of Increasing Disorder.

   b) If the fridge door were shut, order would appear to increase with the separation of hot and cold. Explain how this is possible using the Law of Increasing Disorder.

9. A tractor trailer truck driving down a mountain at 60 mph hour comes to a complete stop when he rounds a bend and sees a line of traffic ahead. The truck's brakes become so hot that they start to smoke. Describe this event in terms of an energy conversion: a) What kind of energy did the truck have coming down the hill. b) What kind of energy did it have when fully stopped. Explain why this process is allowed by the Law of Increasing Disorder.

10. Cars and trucks vary widely in their gas consumption efficiencies. A subcompact car may get 30 miles per gallon of gas consumed while a large, heavy, military-type vehicle now sold for popular use may get fewer than 10 miles per gallon. Discuss the effect on the disorder in the Universe by burning a gallon of gas in the small car as compared to the large military vehicle.

11. Explain how the Sydney Harris cartoon in Figure 18.10 illustrates the Law of Increasing Disorder.

# Atoms, Molecules, and Extended-Bonding Substances

*To see a World in a Grain of Sand*

*And a Heaven in a Wild Flower*

*Hold Infinity in the palm of your hand*

*And Eternity in an hour.*

William Blake, Auguries of Innocence

# 19

## LEARN

- To distinguish between elements, compounds, and mixtures.

- To identify the number and type of atoms in a molecule or extended network structure from its chemical formula.

- How characteristic atomic groupings or fragments give rise to molecular families.

- How bonding types and geometry relate to molecular structure.

- How the various types of spectroscopy and crystallography give elemental and structural information about molecules and compounds.

When physicists talk about matter, they may mean anything from subatomic particles to galaxies. When chemists talk about matter, they usually mean atoms and molecules. Chemists strive to understand exactly how and why atoms combine as they do into intricate molecular structures. Understanding this allows us to take what nature has accomplished and replicate it in a laboratory for our benefit. Or extend it to form substances that are new.

Consider the drug tamoxifen. This treatment for breast cancer was first found as a drug called paclitaxel in the needles of the Pacific yew tree (*Figure 19.1*). But since this tree grows very slowly and cannot be efficiently grown and harvested, chemists pursued methods to synthesize paclitaxel on a large scale. In the process they created the similar tamoxifen molecule with its improved effectiveness against cancer and fewer unwanted side-effects.

Thinking on the molecular scale requires imagination. We have all gazed up at stars, experienced gravitational forces, played with mag-

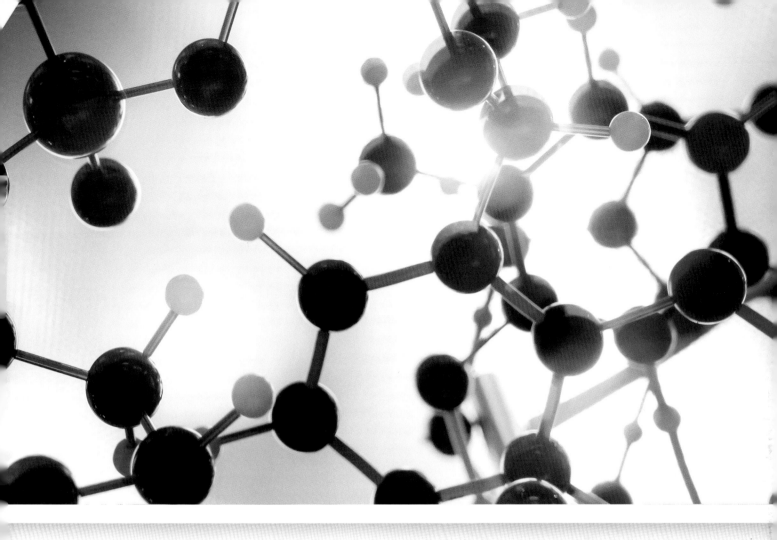

**Figure 19.1**
The branches, needles, and fruit of a Pacific yew tree from which paclitaxel is obtained.

nets, and seen electricity at work. But we do not have the same direct experiences with individual molecules. If this is your first opportunity to learn about these building blocks of matter, be reassured that they are readily understood, and very relevant.

Since molecules are made of atoms, each is identified by a formulaic notation that enumerates the atoms within them. The water molecule, for example, is $H_2O$; two atoms of hydrogen

combined with one of oxygen. But there is much more to a molecule than its parts. How the atoms join together often determines molecular behavior more than the specific atoms. When James Watson and Francis Crick discovered the double helical structure of DNA, for example, they soon recognized that it was its structure that allowed it to function in genetics. The atoms that compose it are important of course, but its structure makes it a functional marvel. In this chapter we consider both molecular constituents and structure.

Someone once said, "Beauty is in the eye of the beholder." Chemists find beauty in the form and structure of molecules. In the opening quote for this chapter, William Blake speaks of seeing the world in a grain of sand and holding infinity in the palm of his hand. The numbers of atoms in a grain of sand or molecules in a handful of sugar border on infinity. The order in the physical world that is the subject of this course is manifested on many levels including that of atoms and molecules. We hope you find beauty in atomic and molecular order.

## 19-1 Classifications of Matter: Pure Substances and Mixtures

### Pure Substances: Elements and Compounds

There is nearly an infinite variety of matter so we start again as we did in Chapter 12 with the method of Aristotle and create categories of matter based on their similarities. First consider the types of "building blocks." A **pure substance** is one with a regular, repeating building block that gives it a defined, fixed chemical composition. This building block may be of one type of atom or many different types. If it is of one type of atom it is called an **element**. If it has more than one type of atom it is called a **compound**.

The atoms in elemental substances may be single and by themselves or joined together but regardless there is only one type. Elemental substances include the helium gas in balloons, liquid mercury in thermometers, and the aluminum foil that covers last night's leftovers.

Compounds are far more common in nature than elemental substances. We mentioned water as hydrogen combined with oxygen. Hydrogen peroxide, a popular disinfectant and bleach, also is hydrogen combined with oxygen. In a water molecule, the ratio is two hydrogen atoms to one oxygen atom; in hydrogen peroxide, the ratio is one to one. Common table salt has one sodium atom for every chlorine atom. Sucrose, the sugar you sprinkled on your cereal this morning, contains carbon atoms, hydrogen atoms and oxygen atoms in the ratio 12:22:11.

### Mixtures: Blends/Composites, Solutions and Alloys

#### Blends/Composites

In our daily lives, we rarely encounter matter that is a pure substance. We deal most commonly with **mixtures** of pure substances. Mixtures are just as the word says: substances physically mixed together with little or no bonding between their molecules.

Mixtures of solids are called **blends** or **composites**. Imagine dumping the contents of a salt shaker and a pepper shaker into a bowl and stirring. You have just prepared a composite mixture. The salt and pepper are blended together but their molecules are not joined. Even though it might be tedious, you could separate them just by physically sorting their grains apart.

You likely wear clothes made of a "blended" fabric. These are different mixes of natural and/or synthetic fibers woven together. Each fiber has a different property such as being stretchy, wrinkle-free, shrink-resistant, etc. Blending fibers into a common weave produces a fabric retaining the properties of the individual components. If the blending is intricate, looking at the fiber with the naked eye may not reveal its "mixture" aspect but imaging through a microscope will.

Foods are complex mixtures of carbohydrates, proteins, fats, vitamins, minerals, etc. If healthy, there is usually a rich variety in the mix. Less healthy foods often lack complexity and incorporate large quantities of fats and simple carbohydrates like sugar.

### Solutions

**Solutions** are mixtures of pure substances, at least one of which is a liquid, with the other components completely dissolved in the liquid. Your favorite soda pop is a solution of water, sugar (about 6–8 teaspoons per 12 oz.), food coloring, flavorings, and carbon dioxide gas to make it fizzy. Milk and orange juice are solutions of nutrients in water together with solid particles that are not dissolved but rather suspended within them as in a composite.

---

**Pure Substance:**

Chemical matter that has a defined, unchanging chemical composition.

**Element:**

A substance composed entirely of atoms having the same number of protons in their nuclei.

**Compound:**

Matter that contains two or more atoms in a fixed, definite proportion. New compounds form when the relative proportions of atoms change.

**Mixture:**

Matter that contains multiple substances. Many mixtures can be physically separated into their pure components.

**Blend or Composite:**

**Solution:**

A mixture containing two or more compounds, at least one of which is a liquid.

---

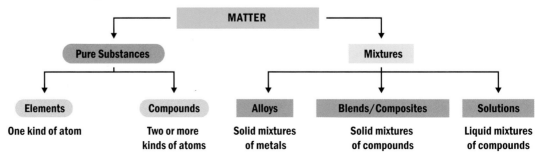

**Figure 19.2**
A flow chart classifying different types of matter.

Unlike pure compounds, the compositions of solutions are not fixed. Solutions of table sugar or of salt in water can have a large compositional range. Dilute solutions contain relatively few ions of sodium and chlorine or sugar molecules while concentrated solutions contain relatively little water and are mostly salt or sugar.

Gases like $CO_2$ often dissolve in liquids only with difficulty. Because of this, sodas are bottled with a large pressure of $CO_2$ above the liquid to increase the solubility. The small amount of high pressure $CO_2$ at the top is what makes the hissing sound when you open a can of soda. When the open soda can stands on the counter or warms up, the dissolved carbon dioxide naturally comes out of the solution, making the soda taste "flat."

## Alloys

**Alloys** form when one or more metals dissolve in each other and then solidify. They are essentially mixtures or compounds with variable composition. So, as with solutions, the relative amounts of the pure substances can vary, sometimes substantially, from one type of alloy to another. Brass, gold jewelry, and stainless steel "silverware" are common alloys.

An alloy can have very different properties from the pure metals that make it up. Pure metals are soft and malleable. Adding small amounts of other metals can produce alloys with a hardness higher than that of the pure metal.

## 19-2 Structural Organization of Matter

The properties of mixtures are derived from the pure substances that make them up. So we turn our attention back to pure substances. We have found that they are naturally divided further into three different classes based upon their atomic-level organization. We call these classes **atomic matter**, **molecular matter**, and **network** or **extended-bonding substances**.

### Atomic Matter

Helium and the other members of the Group 8A noble gases exist as simple atoms whether in a gas, liquid, or solid state. The pictures of Figure 13.3 show the organization in these materials with each ball in those figures representing one atom. The elements of Group 8A in the periodic table always exist naturally as atomic matter.

**Alloy:**
A solid solution of metals.

**Atomic Matter:**
Matter that exists in the solid, liquid, and gaseous states as single atoms.

**Molecular Matter:**
Matter that exists as molecules in the solid, liquid, and gaseous states.

**Network or Extended-Bonding Substances:**
Substances in which every atom or ion interacts strongly with many neighbors. An extended network of linked atoms or ions form. Distinct molecules or ion pairs do not exist in these materials.

## IN THE MARKET FOR A WEDDING RING?

### An Introduction to Buying Gold Jewelry

Pure gold is a very soft metal. Because of its softness, pure-gold jewelry dents or deforms very easily. Adding other metals to pure gold produces a harder substance, one that resists shape changes. For this reason, jewelers use gold alloys rather than pure gold to fashion typical gold rings, pendants, and earrings.

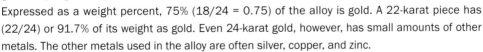

The term karat identifies the amount of gold in the alloy. 24-karat gold is considered to be pure. An 18-karat gold alloy signifies that the fraction of gold is 18/24. Expressed as a weight percent, 75% (18/24 = 0.75) of the alloy is gold. A 22-karat piece has (22/24) or 91.7% of its weight as gold. Even 24-karat gold, however, has small amounts of other metals. The other metals used in the alloy are often silver, copper, and zinc.

In addition to hardness, the color of the gold piece can vary with chemical composition of the alloy. Alloys of gold with platinum or gold with palladium yield "white" gold. Chemical reactivity also varies with composition. A 9-karat gold piece has less than half (by weight) of its metal as gold; typically copper makes up most of the remaining mass. Metallic copper, present in a high proportion in 9-karat rings, can react with the moisture on your skin. The green copper oxide that results can leave an unsightly green circle around your finger. Jewelry pieces with higher gold fractions do not react with skin moisture or oils.

### Molecular Matter

Substances that are always composed of molecules regardless of their state are called molecular matter. Water, a molecular substance, exists as molecules of two hydrogen atoms tightly bound to a single oxygen atom whether as a solid, liquid or gas as illustrated in *Figure 19.3*. At the very high temperatures of plasmas, molecules can be broken apart. But if a substance is molecular for the temperature range of everyday life, it is considered to be molecular matter.

### Network Matter

Magnesium and aluminum, sodium and chlorine in table salt, and the silicon and oxygen of quartz in beach sand represent network or extended-bonding substances. In these substances, every atom or ion interacts strongly with neighboring atoms to form a continuous linked network.

If this classification were based on substances alone then elemental magnesium and aluminum would be classified as atomic matter, like helium, since they have just one type of atom. But it does not depend on the atoms but rather on how they join together. Similarly, you might also expect that sodium chloride would be considered as a molecule of one sodium atom to one chlorine atom. But it doesn't; their bonding is across a network not to individual atoms. In other words, single molecules of magnesium, sodium chloride or quartz do not exist. Rather every atom or ion in these substances bonds with many other atoms that are, in turn, bonded to additional atoms to form a continuous network.

*Figure 19.4* shows the three network solids discussed above with atoms or ions represented as space-filling balls. The magnesium atoms, like all metals, pack together in a simple stacking arrangement that can build outward in the same structure without an end. Sodium chloride packs together in a similar unending fashion only with each positively-charged sodium ion surrounded by six negatively-charged chloride ions and each chloride ion surrounded by six sodium ions. In the quartz, every silicon atom connects specifically to four oxygen atoms, and every oxygen atom connects to two specific silicon atoms. The oxygen atoms bridge between different silicon atoms in an erector set fashion that can again continue forever without an end.

**Ice**
(solid)
$H_2O$

**Water**
(liquid)
$H_2O$

**Steam**
(gas)
$H_2O$

**Figure 19.3**

Water, in each of its three states, exists with distinct molecules.

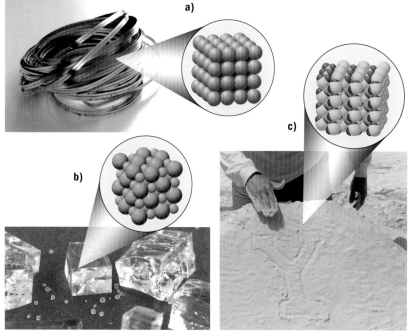

a)

b)

c)

**Figure 19.4**

Examples of extended or network solids. Atoms and ions are shown as space-filling balls.

a) Magnesium (blue-gray balls), a metallic element, is a network solid.

b) Sodium chloride (blue and green balls), an ionic compound is also a network solid.

c) Quartz, the major component of sand has the formula $SiO_2$ (yellow and red balls), but discrete molecules with this formula do not exist in solid quartz.

## 19-3 Chemical Bonds

We have seen atomic structures using tools like electron microscopes for many decades. Yet the three differences in the organization of matter have been known for more than one hundred years, well before modern instruments were invented. How did we recognize these divisions so many years before direct observation was possible?

In Chapter 12 we classified matter by melting and boiling temperatures. Refer back to Table 12.1. Helium and neon belong to the category of atomic matter; hydrogen, nitrogen, water and ethanol typify molecular matter; the remaining substances are network substances. Do you notice the trend in melting and boiling temperatures of each type of matter?

The melting and boiling points tend to group together for a particular type of substance. Atomic substances have very low melting and boiling points; network substances have extraordinarily high ones. Molecular substances tend to have melting and boiling points somewhere in between.[1] This grouping of substances by melting and boiling point characteristics provided the first clues that matter was organized differently in atomic matter, molecular matter, and extended-bonding structures.

In Chapter 12 we made these two hypotheses to explain the relationship between melting and boiling temperatures:

*Hypothesis 1*: The temperature at which a change in state takes place tells us something about the strength of the force that holds the matter together in that particular state.

*Hypothesis 2*: A type of matter whose particles are held together strongly in its solid state will melt at a higher temperature than will one in which the forces between particles are weaker.

Given the distinction between atomic, molecular, and network substances, we can explain these a little better.

The forces between atoms of neon in its solid or liquid states must be considerably weaker and thus of different origin than the strong interactions between magnesium, aluminum, or other metal atoms in their solid and liquid states. The interactions that hold together solids or liquids of nitrogen, water, and ethanol are very likely different as well since they occur between molecules, not atoms. Of these different forces, those between molecules must be stronger than those between the atoms of

atomic matter, but not as strong as the forces between the basic building blocks of extended materials.

Remembering a little more from Chapter 12, we can recognize that the strong forces that hold metals together probably differ from those that hold salts together because while the melting and boiling points of both types of extended solids are comparable, other properties such as electrical conductivity are not.

We use the term **chemical bond** to refer to the attractive forces that hold atoms together in molecules or that hold atoms or ions together in network solids. All chemical bonds arise from electrostatic interactions. Positively-charged nuclei attract electrons, both their own and those of their neighbors, and it is this attraction that creates the bonding of all types.

There are three principal types of bonds: metallic, ionic, and covalent. Metallic and ionic bonds hold network materials together. Covalent bonds hold molecules together. A weak type of bond called van der Waals holds atoms in atomic matter together. And another type, the hydrogen bond, is important in attractions between molecules. Chapters 21-23 explain these types of bonding further.

## 19–4 Chemical Formulas and Structures

### Molecular Formulas

The simplest way to uniquely identify a molecule is by listing its atoms and their relative numbers in a **chemical formula**. Some examples are:

**He**   helium gas—party balloon gas.

$H_2$   hydrogen molecule—potential source of energy in future automobiles.

$N_2$   nitrogen molecule—part of the air we breathe.

$S_8$   sulfur molecule—elemental form of sulfur.

$CO_2$   carbon dioxide—gas produced by burning carbon-based fuels.

**Chemical Bond:**
The attractive force between nuclei and electrons that hold atoms together in molecules or atoms and ions together in network substances.

**Chemical Formula:**
Way to represent the kind of atom and its number in a molecule. The chemical formula of a water molecule that contains two hydrogen atoms and one oxygen atom is given by $H_2O$. The subscript to the right of the atomic symbol indicates the number of that kind of atom in the molecule.

[1] Molecular hydrogen has melting and boiling temperatures lower than neon, an atomic substance, because its mass is very small and melting and boiling temperatures also depend on atomic mass. If its mass were closer to that of neon it's melting and boiling temperatures would be much higher.

$H_2O$    **water**—does this need an introduction?

$H_2O_2$    **hydrogen peroxide**—bleach and antiseptic agent

$C_{13}H_{18}O_2$    **ibuprofen**—a non-steroidal anti-inflammatory agent

$C_{257}H_{383}N_{65}O_{77}S_6$    **insulin**—an enzyme produced in the pancreas

$PtCl_2N_2H_6$    **cisplatin**—an anti-tumor agent

## Table 19.1 — Atomic Color Guide for Figure 19.5

| | | | |
|---|---|---|---|
| ⬤ | Hydrogen | ⬤ | Carbon |
| ⬤ | Nitrogen | ⬤ | Oxygen |
| ⬤ | Silicon | ⬤ | Sulfur |
| ⬤ | Chlorine | ⬤ | Titanium |
| ⬤ | Platinum | | |

**Diatomic Molecule:**

A molecule containing only two atoms of the same kind of element. Hydrogen, nitrogen, oxygen, fluorine, chlorine, bromine, and iodine exist in nature as diatomic molecules.

**Connectivity:**

The details of how atoms connect to one another in molecules or extended structures.

**Double Bond:**

A covalent bond involving two pairs of electrons shared between the two bound atoms. In chemical structure drawings, double bonds are represented by double lines. Double bonds usually involve four electrons, two per bond.

**Triple Bond:**

A covalent bond involving three pairs of electrons shared between the two bound atoms. In chemical structure drawings, triple bonds are represented by triple lines.

A chemical formula strings together the atomic symbols for the elements in the compound. As noted in Section 17.1, a subscript placed to the right of an atom identifies how many times that atom is present in the molecule. The lack of a subscript indicates that only one atom of that element is present in the molecule.

Molecules can be very simple and contain as few as two atoms. Hydrogen and nitrogen exist in nature as molecules of two atoms of the same element. The term **diatomic molecule** is used to identify such molecules. The prefix "di" means "two" so diatomic means "two atoms."

Molecules can also contain large numbers of atoms. Insulin, a protein molecule, contains almost 800 atoms. The largest proteins found in the human body can contain many thousands of atoms.

### Molecular Structure

Molecules have three-dimensional structure and we use different methods, each with their strengths and weaknesses, to illustrate it. In the simplest method colored balls represent atoms and sticks between atoms represent the bonds that connect them. This "ball and stick" model most clearly portrays the details of **connectivity**—how atoms connect to other atoms.

Another method that better reflects the extent to which electron density spreads out from the nuclei is the "space-filling balls" model. This model, used in Figure 19.4, hides structural details that are of interest in this section. So, we will rely on the ball and stick representations for most of our molecular pictures.

A single stick between two atoms represents a single bond. When two atoms are connected by two sticks, it is a **double bond**. We'll learn more about double and **triple bonds** in the next

few chapters. For clarity we use the same color for common atoms according to the scheme given in *Table 19.1*.

This section presents some general types of molecules. Don't worry about memorizing formulas or structures. Approach learning of these molecules like looking at a photo album of your new fiancé's extended family. At first glance you are probably not concerned with small details like Aunt Josephine's exact height but rather look to get a sense of what your new family is like in general. Are they tall or short, dark or blond, old or young? How many of the grandchildren have Grandpa Joe's protruding ears or Grandma Beth's nose? In the same sense ask if the molecules are simple, complex, linear, symmetric, have similar parts, etc.

### Families of Molecules

*Figure 19.5* presents 20 molecules of increasing complexity. Figures 19.5a–d show simple molecules of different structures. Figures 19.5e–t are a sampling chosen to illustrate commonality of parts and structure. Look at these

## MODEL STRUCTURE

The orientation of an atomic group or fragment shown in the picture of one molecule may differ from the orientation shown in another molecule's picture. What matters to a chemist is the number and nature of atoms connected to each other; not whether the fragment is pictured on the right hand side rather than the left hand side of the picture.

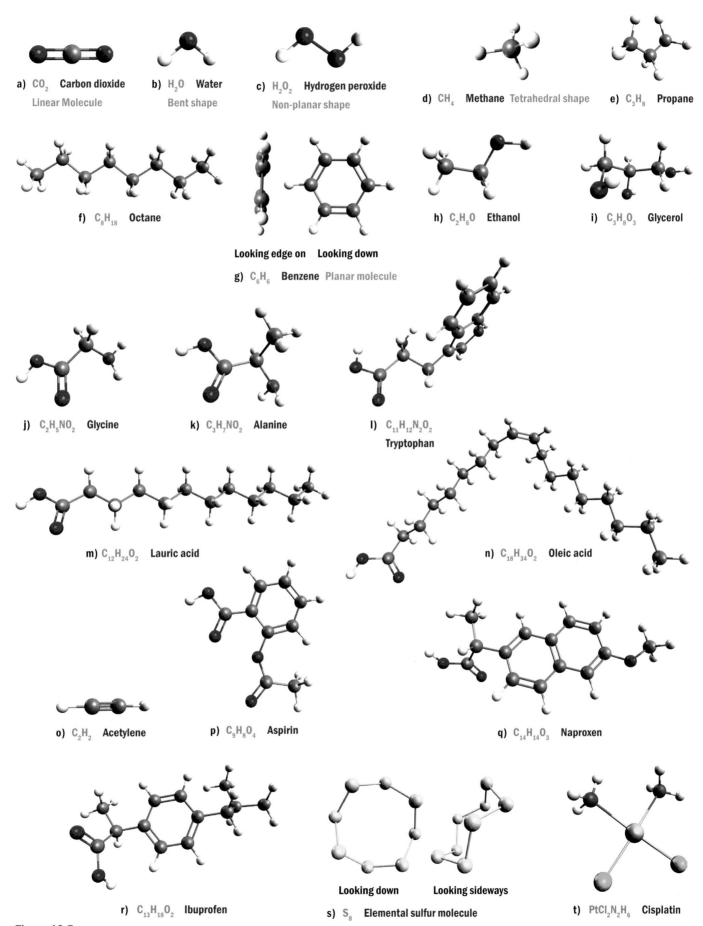

a) $CO_2$ **Carbon dioxide**
Linear Molecule

b) $H_2O$ **Water**
Bent shape

c) $H_2O_2$ **Hydrogen peroxide**
Non-planar shape

d) $CH_4$ **Methane** Tetrahedral shape

e) $C_3H_8$ **Propane**

f) $C_8H_{18}$ **Octane**

Looking edge on    Looking down
g) $C_6H_6$ **Benzene** Planar molecule

h) $C_2H_6O$ **Ethanol**

i) $C_3H_8O_3$ **Glycerol**

j) $C_2H_5NO_2$ **Glycine**

k) $C_3H_7NO_2$ **Alanine**

l) $C_{11}H_{12}N_2O_2$
**Tryptophan**

m) $C_{12}H_{24}O_2$ **Lauric acid**

n) $C_{18}H_{34}O_2$ **Oleic acid**

o) $C_2H_2$ **Acetylene**

p) $C_9H_8O_4$ **Aspirin**

q) $C_{14}H_{14}O_3$ **Naproxen**

r) $C_{13}H_{18}O_2$ **Ibuprofen**

Looking down    Looking sideways
s) $S_8$ **Elemental sulfur molecule**

t) $PtCl_2N_2H_6$ **Cisplatin**

**Figure 19.5**

Images of selected molecules. Balls represent atoms (not to scale) and sticks represent bonds.

figures and answer in your mind the following questions:

1. Are all atoms in the chemical formula of each molecule identifiable in its figure?
2. How many bonds do individual carbon, oxygen, nitrogen, and hydrogen atoms make?
3. What fragments or groupings of atoms are common to many molecules? How common is the grouping of "–CH$_3$" (a carbon atom attached to three hydrogen atoms)? How about the "–O–H" fragment? To which atom(s) do these fragments connect?
4. What structural units are common to the methane (d), propane (e), and octane (f) molecules? A related molecule called hexane (not shown in Figure 19.5) has a formula C$_6$H$_{14}$. Can you sketch its structure?
5. Look at the structure of benzene (g), which has 6 carbon atoms, same as hexane, described above. How does the benzene molecule structure differ from hexane and the molecules similar to it?
6. Glycine (j), alanine (k), and tryptophan (l) are amino acid molecules that make up the proteins in your hair, skin, fingernails, and enzymes. What groups of atoms do these molecules have in common with each other? What is similar and different between them and the organic acids of lauric acid (m) and oleic acid (n).
7. Finally, look at the molecular structures of three common painkillers: asprin (p), naproxen (q) and ibuprofen (r). What atomic fragments do these molecules have in common? Can you find molecular fragments within these molecules that you found in other molecules in Figure 19.5?

Hopefully several patterns were apparent. Carbon atoms naturally make a total of four bonds. They can do so by connecting with four other atoms or by forming two or three bonds with the same atom and then join with as many other atoms as needed to reach a maximum of four. Nitrogen forms three bonds, oxygen two, and hydrogen one.

Just as human families had common characteristics like long straight noses or pointy chins, families of molecules have common atomic groups. For example, the **hydrocarbon** family consists of molecules that contain only carbon

and hydrogen atoms and includes methane, propane, hexane and octane. The **organic acids** all have the fragment

$$-C-O-H$$
$$\|$$
$$O$$

within the molecule. This family includes lauric acid and oleic acid. The amino acid family contains the acid group shown above plus the –NH$_2$ group. This molecular group is called the **amine group** because it is related to ammonia, a molecule with the formula, NH$_3$.

## Geometry of Molecules

Bonding connections determine the geometry of molecules. Some connections naturally make a planar structure, but most create non-planar or bent shapes. Molecules having a carbon/hydrogen backbone naturally have the zigzag layout seen in propane, octane, lauric acid and other molecules in the same families. The ring of the S$_8$ molecule (Figure 19.5s) also has a zigzag shape in contrast to the planar form of the ring of six C atoms in benzene (Figure 19.5g), or in the middle of the ibuprofen molecule (Figure 19.5r).

The number of bonds that an atom can form determines the bonding geometry around it. Carbon atoms can connect to at most four other atoms and when they do this gives rise to a tetrahedral arrangement of the outer atoms as shown in *Figure 19.6a*). The tetrahedron is a four-sided pyramid with triangular faces on all sides. Each of the four outer atoms is located at the corners of the pyramid, with the central carbon atom in the interior.

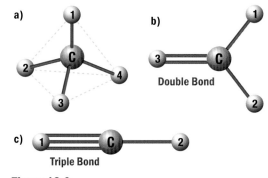

**Figure 19.6**
Geometric arrangement of bonds formed around a central carbon atom.

a) Tetrahedral—four bonds to four different atoms.

b) Planar—four bonds to three different atoms.

c) Linear—triple bond and single bond to two different atoms.

**Hydrocarbons:**

Chemical compounds between the elements carbon and hydrogen. The compounds that make up gasoline are examples.

**Hydrocarbon Molecules:**

Molecules that contain only carbon and hydrogen atoms.

**Organic Acid:**

A molecule that contains the fragment CO$_2$H attached to another carbon atom.

**Amine Group:**

The grouping of NH$_2$ attached to a carbon atom.

When a single carbon atom bonds to three other atoms, it does so by forming a double bond to one atom and single bonds with the other two. This causes two of the bonds to be co-linear and forces all four atoms into the same plane, with approximately 120° angles between the outer atoms (Figure 19.6b). This is why the benzene ring has a planar shape. A carbon atom may also form a double bond each with two other atoms or a triple bond and a single bond, again with two other atoms. In both of these cases the resulting structure is linear (Figure 19.6c).

The nature of molecular bonds is covered in Chapter 23. But here we will say that a single bond is when atoms share a pair of electrons between them as shown in *Figure 19.7* Each atom contributes one electron to the bond. The resulting bond concentrates the electrons in the region between the two nuclei. A double bond is when two pairs of electrons, or four altogether, are shared. As you might expect, a triple bond is when three pairs, or six electrons, are shared.

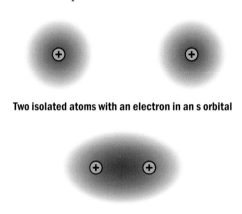

Two isolated atoms with an electron in an s orbital

Two atoms bonded together

**Figure 19.7**
Simple picture of bond formation.

A bond is like blob of negative charge between two positively charged nuclei. This blob attracts the two nuclei, thus keeping them together, but repels other bonds which also have negative charge. This repulsion between bonds keeps them as far from each other as possible which naturally leads to the molecular geometry described above.

### Extended-bonding Substances

Recall that in the network substances that have extended bonding, the chemical formula gives the proportions of the different atoms in the structure and do not represent individual

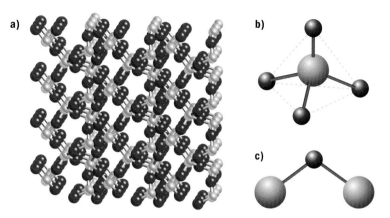

**Figure 19.8**
a) The ball and stick representation of the quartz crystal ($SiO_2$) (orange = silicon, red = oxygen).
b) The tetrahedral arrangement of oxygen atoms around every silicon atom.
c) The connectivity of silicon atoms through bonding with oxygen atoms.

molecules. These atoms pack together in structures that can be as simple as the "stacked marbles" of magnesium shown in Figure 19.4a or the sodium chloride arrangement of Figure 19.4b which is more like a grocer's arrangement of larger grapefruit (chloride) with smaller oranges (sodium) fit into the holes between them.

The model of quartz in Figure 19.4c hints at the complexity that can arise as the basic building blocks become more intricate. This same structure is shown more clearly as a ball and stick representation in *Figure 19.8*. Every Si atom is bonded to four O atoms, and every O atom is bonded to two Si atoms. Since silicon, like carbon, forms four bonds, the oxygen atoms sit at the corners of tetrahedra centered on each silicon atom. The Si–O–Si connections across tetrahedra are bent like the bonds in octane, and for the same reasons.

Because the atoms or ions in extended structures have a regular, repeating bonding geometry, they often form **crystals**. The overall shape of the crystal is set by the shape of the bonds upon which it is built.

Sometimes an extended substance can form crystals with the same chemical formula but a different repeating pattern. $TiO_2$, for example, forms one crystal called rutile and another one called anatase (*Figure 19.9*). White paints and pigments, including those used in sunscreens, consist largely of the rutile form of $TiO_2$. Anatase has electrical properties quite different from rutile and is used in solar cells and other electronic devices.

In Chapter 24, we shall see in more detail how the geometry of the repeating pattern influences the properties of extended solids.

**Crystal:**
A solid with a regular repeating arrangement of molecules or ions.

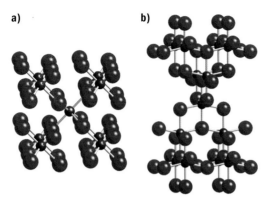

**Figure 19.9**

Two different crystals of $TiO_2$: a) Rutile and b) Anatase. (Red balls are oxygen atoms; black balls are titanium atoms.) The two crystals have different electronic properties. Rutile is the white pigment in paint and anatase is used in solar cells.

**Figure 19.10**

The color in each of these compounds arises from chromium, a transition metal.

## 19-5 Examining Structure

The quantum model of the atom makes measurable predictions about the energies and geometries of bonds formed between different types of atoms. One of the first techniques used to examine bonds was "optical spectroscopy"; which is the previously discussed study of emission and absorption lines from different atoms and molecules. The term "spectroscopy" has since been enlarged and applied to several techniques that are used to identify the elements that make up molecules, to examine how they bond together and to measure the energy of the bonds. Here we present a few of those techniques.

### Electronic Spectroscopy

Bonding alters individual electron orbital energies from what they are in isolated atoms. The resultant energy levels are unique to each molecule so molecules, like atoms, can be identified from their emission or absorption patterns. These patterns create the often unique color of the compound.

Pure compounds containing transition metal elements are often pleasantly colored because many transition metal ions happen to have emission or absorption in the visible region. *Figure 19.10* provides some examples. The colored materials in Figure 17.1 and 17.2 also contain transition metals. Colored glass and gemstones like emeralds and rubies get their brilliant color from small amounts of transition metals incorporated into an otherwise colorless crystal.

Transitions between electron states in colorless substances often do take place but with photon energies in the ultraviolet or infrared. For this reason diamonds will often glow with a blueish color when bathed in ultraviolet light. Colorless, transparent window glass absorbs light in the ultraviolet region which is why it is hard to get a suntan sitting inside a house beside a closed window.

### Vibrational Spectroscopy

Bonds, being based on the non-rigid nature of electron positions, behave like mattress springs, compressing and expanding, like a Slinky® toy. Bonds can also move back and forth in a scissoring-type motion that changes the angle between bonds as shown for a water molecule in *Figure 19.11*. Any flexing of a bond size or position sets up a vibration.

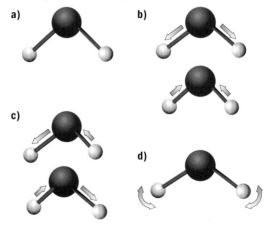

**Figure 19.11**

The three kinds of vibrational motion that the water molecule undergoes.

a) Water in its equilibrium position.

b) Symmetric bond stretch—Expansion (top) and contraction (bottom).

c) Asymmetric bond stretch—One bond compresses while the other expands.

d) Bond angle bend—Scissor motion in and out.

Molecular vibrations usually affect light in the infrared (IR) region. For example, molecules that contain a fragment with a carbon-oxygen double bond

$$\begin{array}{c} \backslash \\ C = O \\ / \end{array}$$

have a strong vibrational absorption in the IR at a wavelength frequency somewhere near $5 \times 10^{13}$ Hz. This absorption is from the C=O bond stretching and compressing. Through this process the molecule removes energy of this frequency from an IR light shined on it and converts it into vibrational energy within that bond.

IR vibrational spectra for aspirin, ibuprofen, and naproxen are shown in *Figure 19.12*. The y-axis gives the absorption of light at each frequency. The deeper the line dips downward, the stronger the substance absorbs light at that frequency.

All three drugs contain the C=O bond and each shows the telltale absorption around $5 \times 10^{13}$ Hz within the region set off by the pair of red lines in Figure 19.12. Each drug also absorbs photons near $9 \times 10^{13}$ Hz. These absorptions arise from stretching motions involving C-H bonds. All three molecules have many of these bonds, and so a strong absorption in this region makes sense.

Other structural features such as –O–H or –NH$_2$ lead to absorptions in different regions of the IR spectrum. Scientists use a table of characteristic absorptions to identify the many different molecular fragments within a molecule. Then they assemble the fragments together as with a jigsaw puzzle to determine the complete molecule.

When the vibrational spectrum is too complicated to completely determine the molecular structure, it can still be used like a fingerprint to identify a known molecule in an unknown sample. Notice that the C=O absorption feature in Figure 19.12 is not exactly the same for all three molecules. Aspirin contains two different C=O groups, and each one has its own absorption. Ibuprofen has only one band, while naproxen shows a band that is partially split into two. These spectral differences can distinguish between these three painkillers if one is suspected of being present.

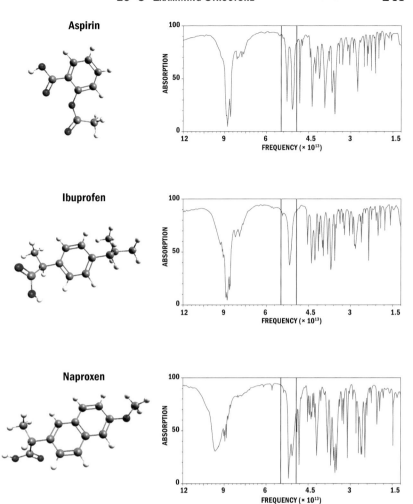

**Figure 19.12**

Infrared spectra of three painkillers. Each dip downward represents an absorption of IR photons of a given frequency due to molecular vibrational motions. The y-axis measures the IR photon absorption. A value of 100 means no photons were absorbed. The x-axis is given in wavenumbers, which is a way to represent photon frequencies. The region between the red lines mark the location of C=O bond stretching motions.

## Mass Spectrometry

One of the first techniques used to prove the existence of molecules was the mass spectrometer, a variation on the gas discharge tubes of J. J. Thompson. Today scientists use many different kinds of mass spectrometer designs, but all employ the same basic operating principle: high energy particles bombard and ionize molecules, causing many of the molecules to fragment into smaller ionized parts. The instrument separates and detects the fragments according to their masses. *Figure 19.13* shows the mass spectra of the same three painkillers discussed above. The y-axis identifies how often a molecular fragment appears and the x-axis gives the mass of the fragment.

The peak with the *largest* mass value must come from the unfragmented molecule. The peaks at smaller mass values are ionized frag-

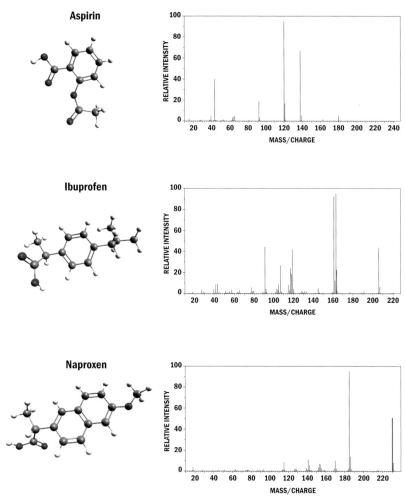

**Figure 19.13**

The mass spectra of three painkillers. The molecular fragment which appears most often is assigned an intensity of 100; other peaks are scaled relative to the intensity (popularity) of the most intense one. The x axis represents the ratio of fragment mass to charge on the fragment. (Most often the charge is +1, but it may be +2 or +3.) The highest mass peak is usually the unfragmented molecule with a charge of +1. Each of these three molecules fragments easily, so the highest mass peak is barely visible.

tor using a wand with a small cloth at one end, then you have experienced this screening technique first hand. Explosives have characteristic fragmentation patterns that the screener can recognize.

## Crystallography

In Chapter 15 we studied the wave nature of electrons and how the gaps between atoms in crystals functioned as slits through which electron beams diffract and interfere. Reversing the experiment, diffraction and interference patterns from electron beams, x-rays or neutron beams can be used to discover the spacing and sizes of the gaps and thus the structure of the crystal.

*Figure 19.14* shows an x-ray diffraction pattern obtained from a small crystal. Each white spot represents a constructive interference point. The dark spaces in between are either the absence of diffraction or the presence of destructive interference.

The pattern and arrangement of the white spots tells how the atoms or molecules are arranged in the crystal. As amazing as it seems, we can extract from the relative intensities of the spots, specific details of what atoms are present, how the atoms are connected to each other, and the distances between them.

ments broken from this molecule. The peak heights are not relevant to this discussion since they are determined by how the molecule was broken apart by the mass spectrometer, not by something intrinsic to the molecule itself.

As with infrared spectra, the fragmentation pattern can be used as a fingerprint to identify a compound. Drug-testing organizations often use this technique to screen for illegal drugs such as steroids or other performance-enhancing substances in athletes. Security screeners at airports use mass spectrometry to detect high energy explosives in carry-on luggage. If your hands or luggage have been swiped by an inspec-

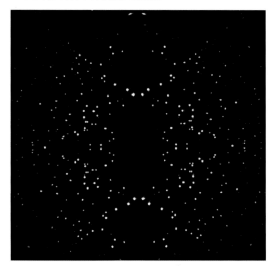

**Figure 19.14**

An X-ray diffraction pattern obtained from a small crystal. White spots locate the regions of constructive interference; dark regions come from destructive interference. The black spindle coming from the top and the black circle in the center are the sample holder and sample, respectively.

At quite uncertain times and places,
The atoms left their heavenly path,
And by fortuitous embraces,
Engendered all that being hath.
And though they seem to cling together,
And form 'associations' here,
Yet, soon or late, they burst their tether,
And through the depths of space career.

James Clerk Maxwell

# 19 STUDY GUIDE

## Chapter Framework

**A. Classification of Matter**
1. Pure Substances
    a. *Elements*
    b. *Compounds*
2. Mixtures
    a. *Solutions*
    b. *Alloys*

**B. Structural Organization of Matter**
1. Atomic Matter
2. Molecular Matter
3. Network Matter

**C. Chemical Bonds**

**D. Chemical Formulas**
1. Connectivity
2. Geometric Arrangement of Atoms

**E. Modern Instrumental Techniques**
1. Electronic Spectroscopy
2. Vibrational Spectroscopy
3. Mass Spectrometry
4. Crystallography

## Comprehension

### Matching

a. Extended or network substances

b. Atomic matter

c. Molecular substances

d. Tetrahedron

e. Linear

f. Chemical bond

1. ____ The geometry around a carbon atom with four single bonds.
2. ____ The geometry around a carbon atom with a triple bond.
3. ____ The attractive interaction that holds atoms together in molecules.
4. ____ The structural organization of water.
5. ____ The structural organization of salts and metals.
6. ____ The structural organization of Group 8A elements.

### True/False

1. ____ Compounds containing transition metals are often brightly colored.
2. ____ Sodium chloride (NaCl) and Magnesium (Mg) are examples of network substances.
3. ____ Molecular substances melt at very high temperatures.
4. ____ In a chemical formula, subscripts are placed to the left of the chemical symbol to indicate the number of that type of atoms in a molecule.
5. ____ Mass spectrometry provides information about the energy associated with motions within molecules.

### Fill in the Blank

Write the chemical formula of these compounds. Refer to Table 19.1 for the atom color guide. Three-dimensional images of the molecules shown in the study guide that you can rotate and manipulate for easier viewing are available at http://ps100.byu.edu. Additional practice questions are also there.

1. Butane—the fuel used in cigarette lighters

   C____H____

2. Acetic Acid—component of vinegar

   C____H____O____

3. Ascorbic Acid—the major component of Vitamin C

   C____H____O____

   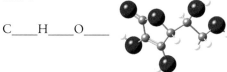

4. Caffeine—a stimulant found in colas and coffee

   C____H____O____N____

   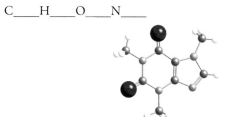

5. The structure of the molecule beta-farnesene is shown below.

   a) How many double bonds are in the compound beta-farnesene (used by many insects to communicate with one another and by plants to protect against insects)? _____
   b) How many bonds does an individual carbon atom form? _____
   c) How many bonds does an individual hydrogen atom form? _____
   d) Is this molecule a hydrocarbon or an organic acid? _____

## Analysis

1. Which of the following is not a compound?
   a) Sulfur dioxide—$SO_2$
   b) Nitrous oxide—$NO_2$
   c) Water—$H_2O$
   d) Oxygen—$O_2$
   e) Rust—$Fe_2O_3$

## Synthesis

1. In Chapter 12, a substance's melting temperature was taken to be a measure of the strength of forces between the units that make up the substance in the solid state. Using examples from Table 12.1, identify the units of matter in an atomic substance, in a molecular substance, and in an extended or network substance. Now, on the basis of the melting temperatures of your examples, infer something about the relative strengths of the forces (chemists talk about interactions) between the units in each type of material.

2. Copper and sodium chloride are both examples of network substances. Compare and contrast the properties of these two substances with respect to some physical properties of the material. Take as your set of properties the following list: a) physical state of the material at room temperature (solid, liquid or gas); b) melting temperature; c) electrical conductivity; and d) color. Which of these properties give you clues that the bonding within copper differs from that within sodium chloride?

3. Shown below are the molecular structures, formulas and portions of the IR spectra for four molecules. What molecular fragment gives rise to the broad absorption (on the left of the spectra) in the alcohols (propanol, butanol and hexanol)? What type of molecular fragments might give rise to the sharp feature on the right?

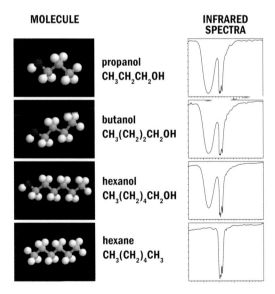

| MOLECULE | INFRARED SPECTRA |
|---|---|
| propanol $CH_3CH_2CH_2OH$ | |
| butanol $CH_3(CH_2)_2CH_2OH$ | |
| hexanol $CH_3(CH_2)_4CH_2OH$ | |
| hexane $CH_3(CH_2)_4CH_3$ | |

4. Figure 19.5 contains pictures of molecules that belong to several different molecular families. Each group of molecules identified below belongs to a different family. Predict what atomic grouping or structural characteristic might be associated with each family.

   a) d, e, and f

   b) h and l

   c) j and k

   d) m, n, p, and r

5. The IR spectra and the mass spectrum obtained from acetic acid are shown below, along with the molecular formula.

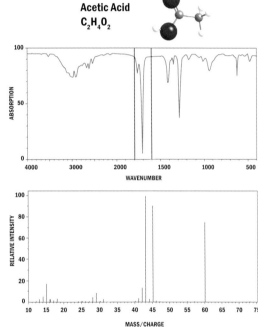

Acetic Acid $C_2H_4O_2$

Predict what molecular feature is responsible for the IR absorption observed between the two red lines. Estimate the mass of an acetic acid molecule from its mass spectrum.

6. Describe the three levels of structural organization of matter—atomic, molecular, and network or extended substances. How are they different?

7. Describe how a forensic scientist would use the techniques of spectroscopy to identify an unknown white crystalline powder found in the locker of a professional athlete.

8. How many atoms of hydrogen are there in each molecule of propane that has the formula $H_3CCH_2CH_3$?

# Principles of Chemical Reactivity

## 20

*Rates of cooking, or growth of muscles, or tightening of muscles, or using the brain—everything involves the speed of some reaction. Understanding these reactions really means getting acquainted with the molecules as if they were your friends and knowing what their nature is and what they will do . . .*

Henry Eyring

## LEARN

- The roles of molecular orbitals, entropy, and energy in chemical bonding.

- To balance simple chemical equations.

- The roles of temperature, energy, and entropy in determining the rates of chemical reactions.

- About chemical equilibrium and how it is governed.

In Chapter 19 we considered matter on an atomic level. The perspective presented was static: matter as unchanging arrangements of atoms, the details of which determine physical properties. The next thing to consider is more dynamic: how atoms change partners creating new molecules or new networks in chemical reactions.

One of the most important advances in the history of humanity was the discovery of how to make and control fire. The energy of fire is locked up in wood and anything that burns. We add a bit of energy to get the fire started and it sustains itself, giving off heat until the fuel is consumed. In the process the chemistry of the fuel changes as bonds are broken and new ones formed. The discovery of fire was really a discovery about chemical reactivity.

We have learned a lot about chemical reactivity since chemistry became a science. We have discovered that the gases on the extreme right side of the periodic table tend not to react. In fact, neutral helium and neon atoms have never been observed to form chemical compounds,

and argon, krypton, and xenon do so only with difficulty. These five gases are found in nature as individual atoms. Because of their low reactivity, they are called **noble gases**.

In contrast to the noble gases, other gases, such as hydrogen, oxygen, and nitrogen, are so reactive that they are not observed as individual atoms, but exist as molecules with pairs of atoms tightly bound to each other.

The metallic elements along the left side of the periodic table—lithium, sodium, potassium, rubidium, and cesium—are all quite reactive. Cesium reacts especially violently (and explosively!) when exposed to water. Because these five elements are so reactive, they are always found in nature combined with other chemical species.

The rates at which chemical reactions take place vary widely. Some reactions are so slow they require time scales of millions to billions of years, while other reactions occur in less than one billionth of a second. Depending on conditions, the same materials can be converted into the same products with widely different rates.

For example, when a tree falls in the forest and begins to rot, the carbon in its wood eventually converts to carbon dioxide over many years. But if that same wood is placed in a fire pit and ignited, conversion to carbon dioxide takes only minutes.

Chemical reactions may seem complex, yet they correlate closely with, and can be predicted from, the periodic table. Ultimately, all can be understood in terms of the quantum model of the atom. In this chapter we will examine some of the basic principles that determine chemical reactivity. You will find that you are already familiar with most of them.

## 20-1 A Brief Introduction to Chemical Bonding

As we learned in Chapter 16, the quantum model of the atom predicts that three-dimensional standing waves—the orbitals—describe the electron probability distributions in atoms. The general shapes of the same types of orbitals are the same for all atoms, although the size of a

**Noble Gases:**

Gaseous elements in the rightmost column of the periodic table (helium, neon, argon, krypton, xenon, and radon) that exist in nature as individual atoms. They are quite unreactive and are very unlikely to form chemical compounds.

particular orbital depends on the nuclear charge and the presence of other electrons. When the total energy (kinetic and potential) of an electron is changed, the probable location of the electron also changes, and is described by a different orbital.

All the positive charge in an atom is concentrated in the atomic nucleus. What happens if two atoms are brought close together? In that case, there are two positively charged nuclei that can attract the atomic electrons. With two nuclei, the single-nucleus standing wave patterns no longer describe the electron probabilities; new and different-shaped orbitals become possible. These new standing wave patterns are called **molecular orbitals**.

If the electrons from the two atoms can achieve a lower energy arrangement in the molecular orbitals than they had when in the atomic orbitals of isolated atoms, the molecular arrangement will occur and the two atoms will stick or "bond" together. This is what happens when, say, two hydrogen atoms come together. They achieve a lower-energy standing wave pattern than is possible for two isolated hydrogen atoms. As they bond, the energy difference is released as photons or heat. Now energy is required to break the bond, because returning to being two free hydrogen atoms is a higher energy arrangement.

Molecular orbitals are more complex than atomic orbitals and tend to be different for every combination of atoms forming a molecule; they don't follow the same simple patterns that atomic orbitals do. Two molecular orbitals for the hydrogen molecule, $H_2$, are shown in *Figure 20.1*. As before, the shapes represent the regions around the nuclei where an electron is likely to

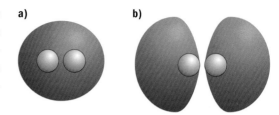

**Figure 20.1**

The two lowest molecular orbitals for the H2 molecule. The lowest energy orbital (a) has high electron density between the two hydrogen nuclei and is therefore a bonding molecular orbital. In the H2 molecule, two electrons occupy this bonding orbital. Going up in energy, the next orbital (b) has a node between the two hydrogen nuclei and high electron density outside the internuclear axis. This is an anti-bonding orbital, but it is not occupied in $H_2$ because the two electrons are in the lower-energy bonding orbital.

be found. Each hydrogen atom contributes its 1s electron to the molecule, and the two electrons go into the lowest available molecular orbital, just as in atomic energy diagrams.

Notice how the lowest energy orbital (Figure 20.1a) differs from the next higher energy orbital (Figure 20.1b). The lowest orbital has high electron probability in the region between the two nuclei, while the next higher one puts most of the electron probability on either side of the atoms, with none in the middle.

More complicated, higher energy orbitals exist for the $H_2$ molecule, but the general principles of molecular orbitals can be grasped from just these two examples. Orbitals that concentrate electron probability density between nuclei contribute to holding the molecule together. These are called **bonding molecular orbitals.** Orbitals that have no electron probability between the nuclei are called non-bonding or **anti-bonding molecular orbitals**, because they either don't contribute to bonding or actually weaken bonds. We can extend these ideas to larger, more complex molecules but the principles behind bonding are the same as for simple

**Molecular Orbitals:**

Standing electron probability waves for molecules. These standing wave shapes and sizes are different from those for individual atoms because of the multiple atomic nuclei.

**Bonding Molecular Orbitals:**

Molecular orbitals that have high electron probability between atomic nuclei in a molecule. When bonding molecular orbitals are occupied by electrons, the high electron density between the nuclei helps hold the nuclei together, contributing to a bond between the atoms.

**Anti-Bonding Molecular Orbitals:**

Molecular orbitals that have low (or no) electron probability between atomic nuclei in a molecule and high electron density in areas not between the nuclei. When anti-bonding orbitals are occupied by electrons, the resulting electron density in the anti-bonding orbital helps pull the nuclei apart, weakening any chemical bond that may exist between them.

## MOLECULAR ORBITALS

Because molecules are composed of more than one atom and therefore have more than one atomic nucleus, the standing wave shapes and sizes of their orbitals differ from those of individual atoms. Each molecular orbital can accommodate up to two electrons, as long as those electrons have opposite spins.

Molecular orbitals may be "bonding," "anti-bonding," or "non-bonding," depending on whether they involve high electron density between atoms (bonding), or not (anti-bonding), or about the same between and not between the atoms (non-bonding). Molecular orbitals are filled with electrons beginning with the lowest energy orbital and working up in energy to account for all the electrons in the molecule. Both bonding and anti-bonding orbitals may be occupied at the same time, depending on the energies of the orbitals and the number of electrons in the atoms.

two-atom molecules: The strength of chemical bonds depends on the orbital energies and shapes and on how the electrons are distributed among the molecular orbitals.

## 20-2 Predicting Chemical Bonding

Whether or not a chemical bond will form depends ultimately on just two things: the energy and the entropy involved. First consider energy. Two materials are likely to react spontaneously if they can achieve a lower energy state; the surplus energy being emitted as light or heat. In these processes the bond energy goes "downhill" from higher to lower values. However, if the process goes "uphill" in energy, energy must be supplied from somewhere. In this case the process will occur only if enough energy is available from the surroundings.

Entropy, remember, is a measure of disorder. You will recall from Chapter 18 that the law of increasing disorder says that in any process the overall disorder, or entropy, must increase. Order may still be increased in a process, but only if there is a reduction in order elsewhere such that the overall disorder increases.

Energy and entropy play against each other in chemical reactivity. A favorable downhill energy change can lead to a reaction even if the entropy is reduced in the process—provided that the release of energy to the surroundings is large enough to maintain an overall positive entropy change for the entire Universe. And a favorable entropy change, one that leads to a local increase of entropy, can enable a process to take energy from its surroundings and go uphill in energy.

As an example, when ammonium nitrate (a compound commonly used as fertilizer) is dissolved in water, the process is uphill in energy. If you hold a glass of water in your hand and add ammonium nitrate, the glass will feel cold as energy is taken in by the process and drawn from your hand. Ice packs used for first aid often use this process to create low temperatures, and under the right conditions it is strong enough to freeze water.

Although the process of dissolving ammonium nitrate is uphill in energy, it is also spontaneous. Why? Because a highly ordered, crystalline material is converted into disordered ammonium and nitrate ions randomly arranged in solution and this greatly increases the entropy. Processes that increase entropy proceed spontaneously just as do those that minimize energy. Since the greater increase in entropy in this process is more significant than the required energy, the ammonium nitrate dissolves, even though it requires energy to do so.

The reaction of sugar with oxygen is downhill in energy and so this releases large amounts of energy as heat. Thus, the products are at lower energy than the starting materials and the surroundings are at higher energy because they receive the released energy. Entropy also increases during this reaction because a highly ordered solid and gas are converted to hot disordered carbon dioxide gas and water vapor. Disorder also increases in the surroundings that receive the large heat release. Both the energy change and the entropy change in the combustion of sugar favor reaction, so this kind of reaction is very likely to take place.

Hydrogen gas will react with oxygen to produce water. At first glance, this looks like an unfavorable process: two disordered gases become a more ordered single gas. However, the product, water vapor, is at much lower energy than the reactant gases, so this energetically favorable reaction releases large amounts of energy into the surroundings. The large energy release causes disorder in the surroundings, so the overall entropy change in the Universe when hydrogen burns is still positive, even though the entropy change for the system (hydrogen plus oxygen) is not.

In general, when the energy and entropy change in the right direction, nature makes chemical bonds. Bonds can be formed in one of three ways. Each of the three ways will be mentioned briefly here, leaving more detailed discussion of each of these important topics for later chapters.

Strong bonds can be formed when a large number of atoms collectively share their electrons. This kind of bonding takes place in metals and is thus called **metallic bonding.** These bonds give metal its strength and are why the gold in Fort Knox does not evaporate into atoms. Chapter 21 explains metallic bonding in more detail.

Some atoms (in particular the metal atoms toward the left of the periodic table) achieve especially low energy electron standing wave

**Metallic Bonding:**
Bonding in metals where large numbers of atoms collectively share electrons.

patterns when they lose their **valence electrons** and become positively charged **cations**. Other atoms (especially the nonmetals toward the right side of the periodic table) achieve low energy electron standing wave patterns when they gain additional electrons to become negatively charged **anions**. When these two kinds of atoms come together, the metal atoms, which need to lose electrons to achieve lower energy, give their "extra" electrons to the non-metal atoms, which need to gain electrons. We call the resulting materials "ionic" because they consist of cations and anions rather than neutral atoms. The attraction these positive and negative ions have for each other is called **ionic bonding**. Common table salt, sodium chloride, is an example of an ionic material. More about ionic bonding will be found in Chapter 22.

When nonmetals interact with each other, lower energy electron standing wave patterns can be realized through *sharing* electrons between the atoms, as in the example of $H_2$ discussed previously. This sharing mode of bonding is called **covalent bonding**, a subject explained in greater detail in Chapter 23. Other common covalent materials include the nitrogen and oxygen molecules that make up Earth's atmosphere and water, on which all known forms of life depend.

## 20-3 Balancing Chemical Equations

Chemical reactions can be described precisely using a mathematical-like notation developed for this purpose. The starting materials, or **reactants**, are written on the left with plus signs indicating which are combining. An arrow or an equal sign (arrows and equal signs are used interchangeably) separates reactants from the material produce by the reaction, or **products**, which are listed to the right of the equal sign. If more than one product is produced, they are again separated by plus signs. Therefore, for the reaction of $H_2$ and $O_2$ to make water, we could write:

$$H_2 + O_2 = H_2O$$

There is a problem with what we have written. While it does accurately present the reactants and products, it tells us nothing about proportions. Remember the law of conservation

of mass from Chapter 8? Mass is proportional to matter so this is a law of conservation of matter itself. On the left (reactant) side of our chemical equation, the oxygen molecule contains two oxygen atoms. However, the water molecule on the right contains only one oxygen atom. Just as in mathematical equations, the equal sign (or arrow) should mean exactly what it says; the matter on the reactant side is equivalent to the matter on the product side. The reaction simply rearranges the atoms (*Figure 20.2*).

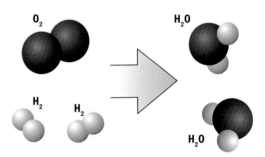

**Figure 20.2**
Schematic representation of the reaction $2H_2 + O2 = 2H_2O$. Note that the number of hydrogen and oxygen atoms does not change in going from reactants to products. Matter is always conserved. The arrangement of the chemical bonds is what changes in the reaction.

Therefore, when writing reactions, it is important to make sure that the number of each kind of atom is the same on both the reactant and product sides of the equation. The process of making sure this is so is called "balancing" the chemical reaction.

How could we balance the reaction for combustion of water above? The easiest way would be to put "1/2" in front of the $O_2$:

$$H_2 + \tfrac{1}{2}O_2 = H_2O$$

The numbers work out this way, but this isn't a very accurate representation of the reaction, because we don't really have half an oxygen molecule. Multiplying everything by two fixes the problem:

$$2H_2 + O_2 = 2H_2O$$

The number to the left on each molecular formula represents the number of molecules present. So now we have four hydrogen atoms contained in two molecules on the left, and four hydrogen atoms contained in the two water molecules on the right. We have two oxygen atoms in the $O_2$ molecule on the left, and two oxygen atoms contained as one each in the two water molecules on the right. We are balanced. This is a good way to describe the reaction. It really does take two molecules of hydrogen for every molecule of oxygen to make water, and for every oxygen molecule used, two water molecules will be produced. Whenever we write a chemical equation, it is important to reflect accurately the relationships between the numbers of each kind of atom or molecule in the reaction by properly balancing the equation.

## 20-4 Rates of Chemical Reactions

We have seen how to predict in general whether or not a chemical reaction will occur, and we have also seen how to reflect conservation of matter in the way we write chemical equations. However, so far nothing tells us about how fast the reactions will go. We can measure **rates of reactions** by monitoring how fast the reactants disappear or how fast products appear.

Consider the favorable reaction of sugar with oxygen to make carbon dioxide and water. How fast does this reaction proceed? Well, it depends. Sugar left out in the air at room temperature reacts only very slowly, so sugar can be safely stored for years and even longer if in containers with the oxygen removed. Sugar taken into the body at 37° C (98.6° F) undergoes the same reaction much more quickly, in a matter of hours. Powdered sugar burns so rapidly as to be explosive under some circumstances. .

Carbon exists naturally in the form of diamond or graphite which is the lead in pencils and the soft lubricant used on the wheels of pinewood derby cars, among other things. The difference in these two forms is just in how the atoms are bound together. Depending on temperature and pressure, carbon will change from one form to another. At room temperature and pressure, the atomic arrangement of carbon atoms in diamond has a higher-energy than in graphite. Going from diamond to graphite is downhill in energy, so why isn't nature making pencil lead out of diamond rings (see *Figure 20.3*)? Fortunately for diamond lovers, even though the reaction is energetically favorable, it is very slow, taking billions of years. So a newly engaged young woman doesn't have to worry about her ring turning into soot.

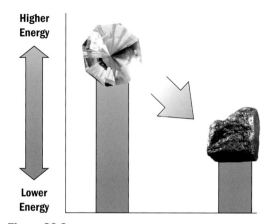

**Figure 20.3**

Diamond, a form of pure carbon, is at higher energy than graphite, another form of pure carbon. Diamond and graphite differ in the way the carbon atoms are bound to each other. If it is downhill in energy from diamond to graphite, why doesn't diamond spontaneously convert to graphite and release the energy?

What controls the speed of a chemical reaction? And why are some reactions explosively fast, while others are glacially slow? First, for two atoms or molecules to react, they must get close enough for their electron orbitals to overlap. An approach this close is called a "collision." Collisions are required for reactions, so collision rates influence reaction rates. In other words, reactions cannot go faster than the reactants can get together.

Collision rates are determined by the concentration or density of the reactant molecules and by their speed, which is determined by the temperature. At higher temperatures molecules collide at greater speeds and more frequently as well so reaction rates nearly always increase with increasing temperature.

However, collision rates do not give a complete explanation. Many reactions go much slower than the collision rate; perhaps only one in 100 or 1,000 or 1,000,000 collisions results in reaction. Why? The energies and entropies involved in a collision also play crucial roles in determining whether or not a collision will help make, for example, the Hope Diamond into a lump of coal.

### Energy and Reaction Rates

Energy is usually required to start a reaction, even when the completed reaction releases energy. It is like a roller coaster ride. The ride won't start until energy is used to pull the coaster to the top of the track, even if the end of

**Rate of Reaction:**

The speed at which reactants are consumed and products are produced in a chemical reaction per unit time.

## Potential Energy Surface:

A diagram plotting the total energy of reactants and products as a function of the "completeness" of a chemical reaction. For all but the simplest reactions, these are multidimensional hypersurfaces that are difficult to visualize.

## Transition State:

The critical point that separates reactants from products on a potential energy surface. Usually this corresponds to the point on the path from reactants to products where the energy is highest.

## Activation Energy:

The difference between the energy of the isolated reactant molecules and energy of the transition state. If the activation energy is added to a set of reactant molecules, it is possible for them to reach the transition state and go on to form products. Reactants with less than the activation energy do not normally form products.

the track is lower than the start. (See *Figure 25.3* in Chapter 25.)

For example, a mixture of hydrogen and oxygen in a balloon at room temperature does not react to produce water unless energy is first supplied in the form of a spark or heat. This is true even though the energy in water bonds is much lower than in the reactant hydrogen and oxygen molecules. There is energy in molecular collisions but at room temperature they are not energetic enough to start the process.

*Figure 20.4* graphs how the energy of reactants and products change with time as a reaction takes place. We call this graph a **potential energy surface** because it is a plot of the electrical potential energy between the reactants. Such plots can be quite complicated if the reactants are many and their energy requirements are complex. The plot shown here is for a simple reaction between a few molecules and illustrates the basic idea well.

For a reaction to proceed, the reactants must first be arranged in a **transition state**. For most reactions this state is reached by breaking existing chemical bonds. In our example, we need to break H–H and O–O bonds in the reactants to free the atoms to recombine differently. Breaking these bonds requires energy. The energy required to form the transition state is

referred to as the **activation energy**. This is the energy from a spark or match.

The curved line—which does look like a roller coaster—shows at the left the energy possessed by the reacting molecules. This energy is elevated by the addition of activation energy then decreases as water bonds having less energy than the original hydrogen and oxygen bonds are formed. The reaction goes downhill energetically as it gives off the energy difference to the surroundings so the line slopes downward to a lower level at the right. .

In reactions of gases, sufficient activation energy often comes from the kinetic energy of the colliding molecules. For these we just mix the gases together and the reaction takes place spontaneously. For liquids and solids the collision rate is often lower and the collisions are not hard enough to start the reaction until we add activation energy through a spark or match.

For fast reactions, the transition state is at the same energy of the reactants or lower. So most of the colliding reactant molecules readily have enough activation energy to go over the transition state "hill". For slower reactions, the transition state is sufficiently higher than the natural reactant state that few molecules have enough activation energy to reach the transition state and react.

### Entropy and Reaction Rates

There is more to reaction rates than energy alone. A collision may be quite energetic, but if the reacting molecules have to collide with a particular orientation, not all collisions will result in product formation.

A key as in *Figure 20.5* is a good analogy. A key must be oriented just right to go into a keyhole, and then must be turned the right way to move the tumblers and open the lock. It doesn't matter how hard the key hits the hole or how hard it is turned if it is oriented wrong or turned the wrong way. Similarly, for many reactions the

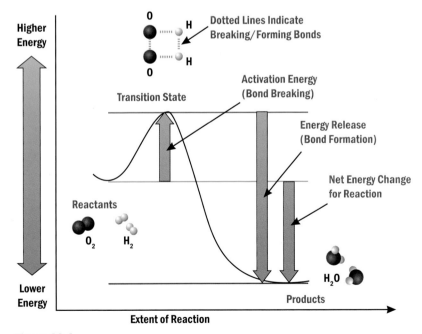

**Higher Energy**

**Transition State**

Dotted Lines Indicate Breaking/Forming Bonds

Activation Energy (Bond Breaking)

Energy Release (Bond Formation)

Net Energy Change for Reaction

Reactants

$O_2$  $H_2$

$H_2O$

**Lower Energy**

Products

**Extent of Reaction**

**Figure 20.4**

Part of the potential energy surface for the reaction of $H_2$ with $O_2$. The $H_2$ and $O_2$ reactant molecules on the left are at lower energy than the transition state, which involves breaking H–H and O–O bonds and formation of H–O bonds. Several additional steps (not shown) are involved in forming the final product: $H_2O$.

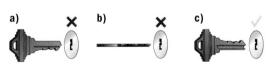

a)   ✗   b)   ✗   c)   ✓

**Figure 20.5**

The key in a) and b) is not oriented properly to enter the keyhole; only c) is positioned to enter, turn, and open the lock. Likewise, in many reactions the molecules must collide with a certain orientation in order for the reaction to occur.

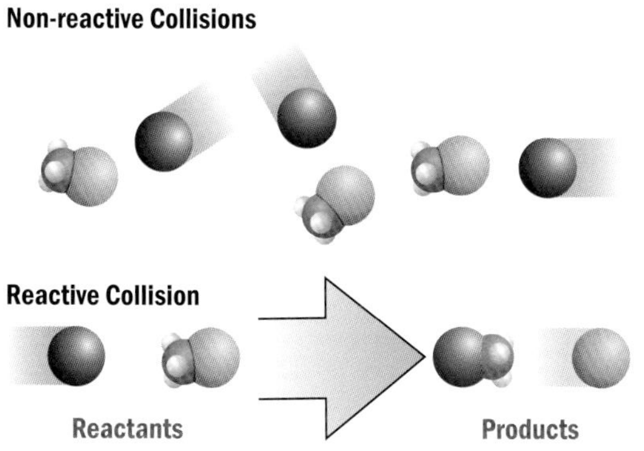

**Non-reactive Collisions**

**Reactive Collision**

Reactants          Products

**Figure 20.6**

In the reaction of iodide (purple) with methyl bromide (gray, white, and pink), the iodide must hit the methyl (gray and white) end of the methyl bromide molecule for the reaction forming methyl iodide to occur. Collisions involving other orientations of the two colliding species do not lead to a reaction; if the orientation is wrong, the iodide just bounces off rather than form methyl iodide.

reacting molecules must fit together properly or no products are formed (*Figure 20.6*).

Collision orientations are random and the transition state is achieved by only a particular, ordered arrangement of the reactants. This is related to entropy since a certain amount of order is required in a collision. The entropy associated with formation of the transition state is called the **activation entropy** because it is required to "activate" the reactants so they can form products.

## Catalysts

Rates of reaction can be significantly affected by the presence of a **catalyst**. Catalysts are chemicals that speed up reactions without being consumed themselves. The reason sugar oxidizes much faster in the body than when sitting on a shelf at the same temperature is because catalysts speed up the reaction.

Life on Earth as we know it would not be possible without the vast array of catalytic molecules, called **enzymes**, which exist and function in various ways in all living organisms. Without catalysts, the reactions of life at room temperature would be too slow to supply energy at the rates needed by living things. Raising the temperature to speed up the reactions that create the proteins, fats, nucleotides, and other molecules of life would not work either, because a higher temperature speeds up the reactions that decompose them as well. Catalysts speed up *specific* reactions for molecules of just the right size and shape. With the right catalytic enzymes, needed

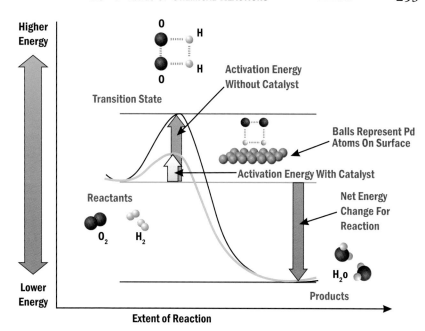

**Figure 20.7**

Potential energy surfaces showing the effect of a catalyst. The catalyst lowers the energy and/or increases the entropy of the transition state, making it easier (and faster!) for reactants to become products. The energies and entropies of the reactants and products are not affected by the catalyst. In this example, the presence of palladium metal causes the H–H bond of $H_2$ to stretch, weakening this bond, which must break to allow formation of water.

reactions are accelerated while reactions that cause destruction are not.

Catalysts work by lowering the energy or increasing the entropy of the transition state, as illustrated by the potential energy surface of *Figure 20.7*. The catalyst lowers the transition state "hill" between reactants and products, without affecting the energies of the reactants or products, as shown on the diagram.

Recall that the reaction of hydrogen and oxygen to form water requires activation energy from a spark. However, in the presence of the metal palladium, the reaction proceeds rapidly without the spark. (See *Figure 20.8.*) Why? Hydrogen molecules interact strongly with palladium atoms on the surface of the metal. These palladium atoms are farther apart than the normal hydrogen-hydrogen distance in the molecule. Strong interactions between hydrogen and palladium atoms stretch and weaken the hydrogen-hydrogen bond enabling it to be broken at a much lower activation energy, one that is achieved by molecular kinetic energy at room temperature. Palladium is not used up in the reaction; it merely acts as a "helper." It can be reused as a catalyst many times as long as its surface remains uncontaminated.

The reaction of glucose with oxygen to produce carbon dioxide and water in living cells is a

**Activation Entropy:**

The difference between the entropy (or disorder) of the isolated reactant molecules and the entropy (or disorder) of the transition state. Frequently, the activation entropy is unfavorable so that colliding molecules do not always react even if they have sufficient energy to react.

**Catalyst:**

A chemical whose presence increases the rate of a chemical reaction without being consumed by the reaction. Catalysts make the energy and/or entropy of the transition state more favorable, without affecting the energies or entropies of the initial reactants or final products.

**Enzymes:**

Protein molecules that function as catalysts in biochemical reactions.

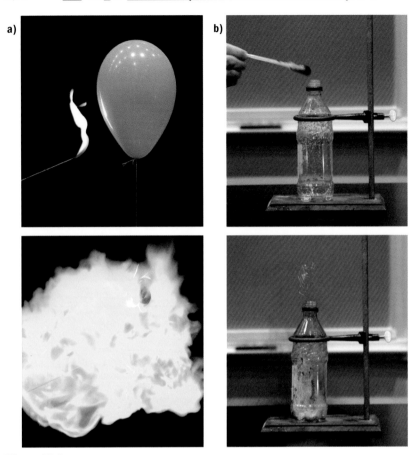

**Figure 20.8**

a) Hydrogen and oxygen mixed in a balloon do not react to form water vapor unless activation energy (in the form of the flame) is applied, even though the water vapor product is at much lower energy than the $H_2$ and $O_2$ reactants. The release of energy from just a few activated molecules forming products supplies energy to activate the rest of the reactants.

b) In the presence of a palladium catalyst, no flame is needed to start the reaction. The catalyst lowers the activation energy so that reactant molecules at room temperature have sufficient kinetic energy to react and become products, explosively releasing more energy.

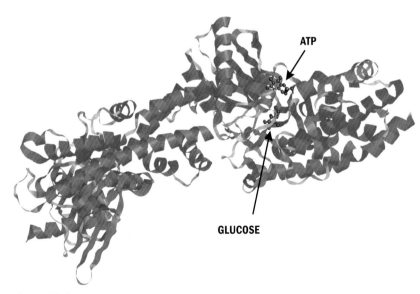

**Figure 20.9**

Hexokinase (depicted as ribbons) is a large molecule that functions as a biological catalyst (enzyme). It binds glucose (a kind of sugar) and ATP so that these two reactants are close together and have the proper orientation to form products. This makes both the energy and entropy of activation much more favorable for the reaction of glucose with ATP than would be the case in the absence of the enzyme.

complex process involving many steps, each sped up by an enzyme. One of the first steps is a reaction between the glucose molecule and a molecule called ATP. The catalyst is a large molecule called hexokinase. The hexokinase is shaped just right to hold the glucose and ATP molecules close together in the right orientation to react (*Figure 20.9*). This makes the subsequent reaction much more likely than it would be if the glucose and ATP had to rely on random collisions alone. When the reaction is finished, the products no longer fit properly to the hexokinase and break free enabling the catalyst to assist in another reaction. Hexokinase only catalyzes the reaction of glucose, not other sugars that have a different shape. And it does not promote decomposition that would be destructive to the living system.

The catalyst hexokinase, like most catalysts, is highly selective. As with the lock and key analogy, it works by taking molecules that have just the right shape and orienting them together so that they fit properly. This is how it changes the entropy requirement of the reaction. Orienting the molecules in a specific way is like a molecular hand positioning a key just so, putting it into a lock and turning. With this ordering, fewer collisions are needed for reaction so the rate increases.

## 20-5 Chemical Equilibrium

Molecules are in constant motion and continually collide with each other as we have been discussing. These collisions can sometimes lead to chemical reactions. What about the reverse process? Can the products react and turn back into reactants? Can water molecules collide in such a way as to break the O–H bonds and re-form H–H and O–O bonds?

The answer is yes. If product water molecules collide with enough energy and the right orientation, it is possible to re-form $H_2$ and $O_2$ (*Figure 20.10*). In a sense, there is nothing special about the direction of a chemical reaction. An energetic collision can build as well as break molecules. Because random collisions are constantly happening, reactions are constantly going on, in both forward (the direction we have written the reaction) and reverse directions.

So a chemical reaction is like a person who is trying to fill the kitchen sink with water from

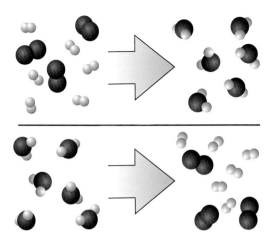

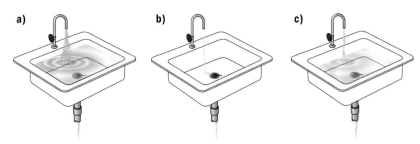

**Figure 20.11**

An analogy to illustrate chemical equilibrium. If the tap flows faster than the drain, the sink fills (a), but if the drain is faster than the tap, the sink never fills (b). If the tap and drain flow at the same rate, the level of water in the sink remains constant, because the system is at equilibrium (c). No net change is observed at equilibrium, even though filling and draining are going on constantly.

**Figure 20.10**

Under the proper conditions, $H_2$ and $O_2$ react to form water (left), but if conditions are changed, it is possible to produce $H_2$ and $O_2$ from water (right).

the tap but can't close off the drain all the way. Whether or not the sink fills up will depend on how fast the water drains out and on how fast the tap puts water in (*Figure 20.11*). If water is put into the sink faster than it can drain away, the sink will fill up and overflow, unless the tap is turned off. On the other hand, if the drain empties the sink faster than the tap can fill it, then all the water put in will go down the drain and the sink will not fill. Similarly, the rates of the reverse and forward reactions determine whether reactants or products accumulate. If the forward rate is faster than the reverse rate, reactants disappear and products form. However, if the reverse rate is faster, products disappear and reactants form; essentially, the reaction runs backwards!

### Forward and Reverse Rates

If the tap on the sink can be adjusted just right, the rate that water flows in will be equal to the rate at which it flows down the drain. In this situation, the amount of water in the sink does not change, even though water is constantly flowing in and out. This is an example of **equilibrium**. The rate of water flowing in and the rate of water flowing out are in balance.

In the same way, when the forward and reverse rates of a chemical reaction are equal, the amounts of product and reactant do not change. We say that the reaction has reached chemical equilibrium and the forward and reverse rates for the reaction are in balance. Even though the reaction may be occurring rapidly, no net change

is observed because the reverse reaction is happening just as rapidly.

In writing reactions, equilibrium is indicated by double arrows, reminding the person reading the equation that the reaction is dynamic and is going in both the forward and the reverse direction. So, for example, at the freezing point of water, where both liquid water, $H_2O_{(l)}$, and ice, $H_2O_{(s)}$, are present at the same time, we could write a chemical equation representing the equilibrium as

$$H_2O_{(l)} \rightleftharpoons H_2O_{(s)}$$

If the amount of ice and water remains constant as is implied in the reaction above, the mixture is at equilibrium. The mass of ice cubes in liquid water at the freezing point does not change, but the cubes do change their shapes over time. Because the equilibrium is dynamic, the ice cubes are melting at the same rate that water is freezing back into ice. The freezing and melting occur at random locations on the ice cubes, so the shapes change as time passes.

### Minimum Energy and Maximum Entropy

In the kitchen sink analogy, the person filling the sink has to adjust the tap just right to balance the flow out of the drain. This may be hard to do. But for reacting molecules, the equilibrium condition is not difficult to achieve. Systems change such as to minimize energy and maximize entropy. For a collection of molecules, the lowest energy and highest entropy state *is* the equilibrium state. Therefore, both energy and entropy behavior favors the establishment of equilibrium.

In the equilibrium ice water example the amount of water in the form of ice can be increased by removing heat energy from the

**Equilibrium:**

The condition where the forward and reverse rates of a chemical reaction are equal, so the system experiences no net change. Equilibrium is also the state of most favorable energy and entropy for a chemical system.

system to slow down the rate of melting. But this action also decreases entropy as the disordered liquid molecules solidify into the regular array of ice crystals. Entropy is increased in the system when heat is added, the rate of melting increases, and more molecules are in the liquid state instead of the more ordered solid state. So maximizing entropy favors turning all the ice to water and minimizing energy favors turning all the water to ice. The system of ice water will adjust the amount of ice and water until it possesses the lowest energy and largest entropy that are simultaneously possible.

All natural systems head toward equilib-rium. The "heat death" of the Universe described in Chapter 18 is the ultimate equilibrium. Fortunately, the rate at which the Universe is headed in that direction is not very fast and the heat death is not an issue that mankind will ever have to deal with.

Energy and entropy play important roles in determining, first, whether or not a chemical reaction will happen and second, if a chemical reaction happens, how fast it will happen. Matter is always conserved in chemical reactions, and this conservation is reflected in reaction equations. Chemical equations are balanced so that the number of each kind of atom is the

## HENRY EYRING'S CONTRIBUTION

Henry Eyring was a brilliant Utah chemist. He was born in 1901 in the Mormon colony of Colonia Juarez, Mexico. He grew up on a ranch there until the Mexican revolution of 1912 forced the family to leave for Arizona. Henry won a scholarship to the University of Arizona, where he studied mining engineering and metallurgy. As a Ph.D. student at the University of California, Berkeley, he turned to chemistry. He taught at the University of Wisconsin, then moved to Princeton where he rubbed shoulders with Einstein and came into his own as a scientific leader. In 1946 he moved to the University of Utah, where he became dean of the graduate school.

Henry Eyring was the first to realize the connection between the energetic and entropic requirements for chemical reaction and the rate of the reaction. He was able to describe these requirements with beautiful mathematics. The resulting "absolute rate theory" he developed is still widely used today.

Eyring was a member of the National Academy of Science, held fifteen honorary doctorate degrees, and won virtually all the prestigious prizes in his field, including the National Medal of Science, the Priestly Medal, the Berzelius Medal in Gold awarded by the Swedish Academy, and Israel's $100,000 Wolf Prize. It is surprising to most chemists that Eyring was not awarded a Nobel Prize, but bone cancer took his life too early for that honor. He served as president of the two most important scientific organizations in his field: the American Chemical Society and the American Association for the Advancement of Science. Eyring published more than 600 journal articles and several influential books, often with the student coauthors' names first. The chemistry building at the University of Utah is named for him.

Eyring has been described as "a truly interesting character." Starting about the age of 60, he ran a 50-yard dash each year, challenging all comers among his students (he did this for 20 years!). He may not have been able to beat all of them, but he never came in last. Occasionally he would welcome visiting scientists by challenging them to a floor-to-table-top jumping contest. Usually he would then demonstrate the feat and take the win by default. He was as comfortable and considerate in talking with and learning from waiters, gas station attendants, and high school students as he was with Nobel laureates.

Eyring was also a man of faith, and made no secret of his convictions. His book, *Reflections of a Scientist* (Deseret Book: Salt Lake City, 1983), describes some of his ideas on science, religion, and life and has been a great source of inspiration for many students. For instance, Eyring once wrote, "If you picked up a watch far from human habitation and found it running, you would ask not only 'Who made this watch?' but 'Who wound it up?' So it is with the universe" (*Reflections of a Scientist,* p. 75). Eyring served in many different capacities in The Church of Jesus Christ of Latter-day Saints and is the father of current LDS apostle Henry B. Eyring.

same on both the product and reactant sides. Favorable reactions involve favorable changes in energy and/or entropy. Fast reactions have low activation energies. Fast reactions also have minimal order requirements in the transition state. Catalysts lower the energy or increase the entropy of the transition state so that the reaction speeds up, but the catalyst itself is not transformed by the reaction. Chemical equilibrium occurs when the forward and reverse rates of reaction are equal, and that equilibrium is the state of minimum energy and maximum entropy for the system. With these fundamental ideas in mind, we are now ready for a more detailed description of chemical bonding.

# 20 STUDY GUIDE

## Chapter Framework

### A. Brief Introduction to Chemical Bonding
1. New standing wave electron probability patterns when atoms bind to form molecules
2. Bonds form if electrons in molecular orbitals are lower in energy than in orbitals of isolated atoms
3. Molecular orbitals may be bonding (high electron probability between atoms) or antibonding (low electron probability between atoms)
4. Placement of electrons in molecular orbitals determines the nature of the bond

### B. Predicting Chemical Bonding
1. Bonds form spontaneously when the energy of the system decreases and/or the entropy of the Universe increases
2. Types of bonding
   a. *Metallic*
   b. *Ionic*
   c. *Covalent*

### C. Balancing Chemical Equations (Conservation of Matter)
1. Writing chemical reactions
2. Atoms are neither created nor destroyed in reactions; balancing the written reaction reflects this.

### D. Rates of Chemical Reactions
1. Reactions occur at a wide variety of speeds
2. Rates increase with increasing temperature because collision rates and energies increase with temperature
3. Many reactions require activation energy to get started
4. Required orientation for reacting molecules is reflected in activation entropy
5. Catalysts decrease energy and/or entropy of activation
6. Enzymes are biological catalysts

### E. Chemical Equilibrium
1. Reactions go both from reactants to products and from products to reactants
2. Equilibrium occurs when the forward and reverse rates of reaction are equal
3. Equilibrium is the state toward which all processes tend, because it is the lowest energy and highest entropy state

## Comprehension

### Matching
a. Activation energy
b. Anti-bonding orbital
c. Bonding orbit
d. Equilibrium
e. Transition state

1. ____ The low energy orbital of the pair of molecular orbitals (MOs) formed when two atomic orbitals combine.
2. ____ The point in a chemical reaction in which the forward and reverse reaction rates are equal.
3. ____ The point in a reaction that separates reactants from products on a potential energy surface.
4. ____ The high energy orbital of the pair of MOs formed when two atomic orbitals combine.
5. ____ The energy that must be put into a system before a reaction can take place.

### True/False
1. ____ The probability waves (orbitals) that describe the possible locations for an electron in a molecule are exactly the same as those for an electron in an isolated atom.
2. ____ Electrons in a bonding molecular orbital are most likely to be found between the nuclei in a molecule.
3. ____ A reaction usually goes faster at higher temperatures.
4. ____ A catalyst is a chemical that is present at the beginning of a reaction but not at the end.
5. ____ A very fast reaction has a very high activation energy.

### Fill in the blank
1. The _____ in a reaction is usually the highest energy point on the path from reactants to products.
2. A _____ lowers the activation energy and speeds up the reaction but is not itself consumed in the reaction.
3. Chemical equilibrium occurs when the forward and reverse rates of a reaction are _____ .
4. Diamonds are, energetically speaking, _____ from graphite.
5. A chemical reaction that would _____ the disorder in the Universe will not occur.
6. Isolated systems achieve _____ when they reach their maximum entropy state.

## Analysis

1. Which of the following equations are balanced?
   a) $2C + O_2 \rightarrow 2CO$
   b) $H_2 + F_2 \rightarrow HF$
   c) $Mg + F_2 \rightarrow MgF_2$
   d) $2H_2O_2 \rightarrow H_2O + O_2$
   e) $2O_3 \rightarrow 3O_2$
   f) $2Fe_3O_4 \rightarrow 3Fe_2O_3 + O_2$
   g) $2Al + 3O_2 \rightarrow Al_2O_3$

2. Hydrogen is burned in oxygen to form water. The chemical equation representing the reaction can be given by
   $$2H_2 + O_2 = 2H_2O.$$
   On an exam, one student writes the equation as
   $$H_2 + O_2 = H_2O$$
   and the other as

$H_2 + O_2 = H_2O_2$

Explain what is wrong with each of these student responses.

3. Atomic chlorine (Cl) is known to be a catalyst for some of the reactions that are responsible for the depletion of ozone $(O_3)$ in the upper atmosphere (also known as the ozone hole). As a catalyst, Cl may

   a) be lowering the activation energy of some reaction involving ozone.

   b) be consumed in the reaction.

   c) form a transition state with $O_3$ in which $O_3$ bonds get weakened.

   d) a and c.

   e) a, b, and c.

4. Characterize the following reactions as occurring with a favorable energy change, a favorable entropy change, or both factors occurring with a favorable change.

   a) $H_2(gas) + O_2(gas) = H_2O$ (liquid)
   Energy given off explosively

   b) $C_3H_8(gas) + 5O_2(gas) = 3CO_2(gas) + 4H_2O$ (liquid)
   Energy given off propane

   c) $C_6H_{12}O_6$ (solid) $+ 3O_2(gas) = 3CO_2(gas) + 6H_2O$ (liquid)
   Energy given off glucose

   d) $NH_4NO_3$ (solid) $+ H_2O$ (liquid) $= NH_4^+ + NO_3^-$ in water solution.
   Energy absorbed (ions are free to move throughout the solution).

Reaction d is the reaction that occurs inside a cold pack that athletes may use to reduce swelling following an injury.

## Synthesis

1. Why does food kept at room temperature spoil faster than food stored in the refrigerator or the freezer?

2. TNT is a well known explosive. It has the chemical formula $C_7H_5N_3O_6$. TNT explodes to form molecules of $N_2$ gas, $CO$ gas and steam (water vapor) + soot (elemental carbon).

   $2C_7H_5N_3O_6$ (solid) $\rightarrow 3N_2(gas) + 7CO(gas) + 5H_2O(gas) + 7C(solid)$

   a) Check to see if the decomposition reaction given above is balanced

   b) Discuss whether this reaction is favored from an energy perspective, an entropy perspective, or both.

   c) As any viewer of old Westerns or Bugs Bunny cartoons can attest, TNT does not spontaneously explode. Often TNT is ignited by lighting a fuse. Explain this observation in terms of transition states and activation energies.

   *Hint:* The molecular shape of TNT is shown at right. Think about what must happen within the molecule to produce such species as CO.

3. Sketch a potential energy diagram for a reaction in which the products are energetically downhill from the reactants but for which there is a high activation energy. Label the reactants, transition state, and the products. On the same diagram indicate how a catalyst affects the activation energy of the reaction.

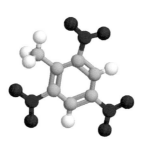

# Bonding in Metals, Alloys, and Semiconductors

*A theory is the more impressive the greater the simplicity of its premises, the more different are the kinds of things it relates, and the more extended its range of applicability.*

*Albert Einstein*

# 21

## LEARN

- How the quantum model of the atom explains the bonding in metals and semiconductors.

- How the properties of metals and alloys such as electrical conductivity, metallic luster, malleability, thermal conductivity, and chemical reactivity can be explained by metallic bonding.

- Why the properties of semiconductors differ from those of metals.

As we learned in Chapters 12 and 17 especially, materials differ widely in their physical and chemical properties. In this and the next two chapters, we return to the quantum model of the atom and consider how it accounts for the defining properties of metallic, ionic, and molecular matter. We start here with metals.

Recall that metals form network solids. The quantum model, originally developed to explain the behavior of isolated atoms, readily explains the strong interactions holding metallic atoms together within the network. It is the bonding in metals that gives rise to their properties.

Materials like germanium, silicon, and arsenic lie on the boundary between metals and non-metals. At times these elements can be induced to act like metals and at other times like non-metals. We consider these in this chapter as well. The quantum model nicely explains their behavior, a behavior that has revolutionized electronics—and our world.

## 21-1 Properties of Metals

Let's review the familiar metallic properties and add a few new ones. As you saw in Table 12.1, metals generally have very high melting and boiling temperatures. Only one metal, mercury, is a liquid at room temperature, and only two others, cesium and gallium, melt at body temperature. In the solid state, metals have high densities. Lead and gold are two familiar metallic elements with especially high densities. Metals are good conductors of electricity.

In addition to these qualities, metals have others in common as well. Consider the following:

**Malleability:** Metals can be hammered, pressed, or rolled into very thin sheets without shattering. Pure gold is especially known for its malleability. It can be rolled into sheets as thin as 0.000003 in. (0.1 micron). At this thickness, the gold foil is only a few hundred atoms thick yet it stays together. Architects and interior designers take advantage of this fact and glue thin gold foil, called gold leaf, on picture frames,

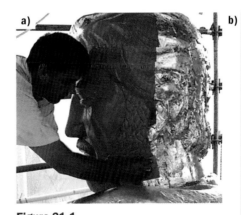

**Figure 21.1**

a) Thin sheets of gold, called gold leaf, are applied to a statue known as the Golden Pioneer.

b) The finished statue atop the Oregon State Capitol Building in Salem.

furniture, vases, and other art decor. *Figure 21.1* shows two pictures of the Golden Pioneer atop the State Capitol Building in Salem, Oregon. The first photo shows the gold leaf being applied to the statue and the second shows the completed statue atop the building.

**Malleability:**

The characteristic of substances that allows them to be worked into desirable shapes or drawn out into wires.

**Opacity:** How many times have you had to unwrap an aluminum-foil-covered bowl in your refrigerator looking for a particular leftover? Even relatively thin pieces of metal are opaque. A person can't see through the metal because light doesn't pass through it.

**Reflectivity:** Every time you check your hair or makeup in front of a mirror, you take advantage of the high reflectivity of metals, usually aluminum thinly coated onto glass. Metals, in addition to being opaque to light, are also highly reflective. Light easily bounces back off their surfaces.

**Thermal conductivity:** A cook stirring a pot of hot soup on the stove uses a wooden or plastic spoon rather than a metal one to avoid getting burned. Metals are good conductors of heat. They heat up much more quickly when they come in contact with something hot than do non-metallic materials.

## 21-2 Bonding in Metals

Four key factors determine bonding within metals. First, bonding involves only an atom's valence electrons. Second, the valence electrons of metals have low ionization energies. Third, metals have few electrons compared to the total number allowed in their valence orbitals. Fourth, electrons will occupy the lowest energy orbitals available to them.

You recall from Chapter 17 that alkali metals have the lowest ionization energies in every row in the periodic table. These metals have only one valence electron. The s and p orbitals in their outermost shells have 7 empty places where electrons could go. Transition metal atoms, which have low-energy d orbitals, have even more free orbitals. Titanium has four valence electrons but room for 14 more.

### Shared Orbitals and Energy Bands

When atoms are close to each other, the electrons on one atom are attracted by the nucleus of the other atom. As mentioned in Chapter 20, the orbital description that was appropriate for isolated atoms doesn't fit the new situation. The standing waves that describe electron states change to reflect the new interactions.

As *Figure 21.2* shows, the energy levels of

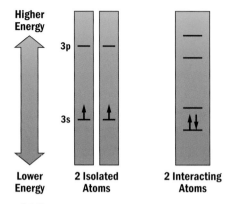

**Figure 21.2**

The formation of molecular orbitals causes the electron energy levels to change. When two sodium atoms get together, the two 3s valence electrons form two new molecular orbitals. One orbital has a lower energy than the atomic orbitals in the isolated atoms. The other has a higher energy. These are the bonding and anti-bonding orbitals. Notice that the 3p orbital shows the same behavior even though there are no electrons in them.

two adjacent metal atoms are different from what they are when isolated. Consider two sodium atoms, each with a single 3s valence electron. The two 3s atomic orbitals in the atoms modify to become two orbitals with one a bit lower in energy and one a bit higher.

The two valence electrons, one from each atom, go into the lowest energy orbital. This is a bonding orbital with a lower energy than the atomic orbitals of the atoms when separated having an electron probability concentrated between the two nuclei. In the higher energy orbital, the electron probability is small in the space between the two atoms. This causes the nuclei to repel one another and no bond is formed. This higher energy orbital is an anti-bonding orbital as explained in Chapter 20.

As the number of interacting atoms increases, a new set of bonding and anti-bonding orbitals is added for each interacting atom. As *Figure 21.3* shows, the lowest energy bonding levels thickly group together as do the anti-bonding levels above them. When the number of atoms is very large—and a gram of a metal easily has more than $10^{20}$ atoms—then the resulting energy levels will be so close together that they behave as a continuous band rather than a discrete set of orbitals.

This example was for the orbitals containing the valence electrons. Similar kinds of energy bands are formed for the other atomic orbitals in the outer shell, even if they don't have any electrons in them. The electrons in a solid piece of metal occupy the lowest allowed energy band

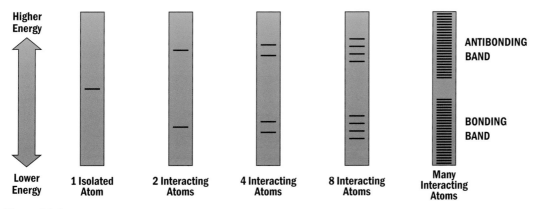

**Figure 21.3**

As the number of interacting atoms increases, the energies of the new molecular orbitals change. This figure shows how the 3s orbital in sodium changes for increasing numbers of interacting atoms. For a large number of atoms, the energy levels form a continuous band of energies.

but there are many other bands just barely above them in energy into which they can move.

*Figure 21.4a* represents the energy band of electrons in a metal. The energy levels filled with electrons are shown as blue lines. The yellow lines represent empty energy levels. Because the levels are very closely spaced in energy, only small quantities of energy are needed to excite electrons up into unoccupied levels.

As you well know by now, orbitals describe the probability of finding electrons somewhere in space. The orbitals associated with metallic energy bands extend over large regions of space, large enough to include many nuclei.

To pose an analogy, consider the seats in a large basketball arena. An electron in an isolated atom could be thought of as being most likely to

be found within a single specified seat. An electron in a metallic network has a probability of being found in any of the seats in a given row. Therefore, it is best to think of these electrons as being shared by all the nuclei, rather than belonging to any particular one. The term **delocalized electrons** is sometimes used to describe them because they are not localized around any one nucleus, but are free to move throughout the metal. Scientists reinforce this image by speaking of a "sea" of electrons that surround the nuclei. In *Figure 21.5* the sea of electrons is represented by the diffuse blue cloud surrounding the nuclei.

**Delocalized Electrons:**

Electrons in metallic orbitals are not confined to be near a specific nucleus, but have comparable probabilities of being around many different nuclei.

**Metallic Bond:**

The chemical bond that binds metal atoms to other metal atoms in forming metal substances.

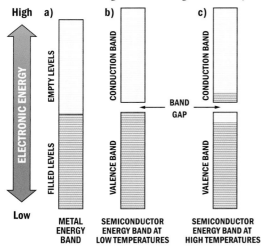

**Figure 21.4**

The electronic band structure in metals and semiconductors.

a) In metals there is a set of energy states so closely spaced that they can be regarded as continuous.

b) In semiconductors, there is a gap between the filled and unfilled levels. At low temperatures all the electrons are below the gap.

c) As the temperature increases, some electrons get thermally excited into the unfilled levels.

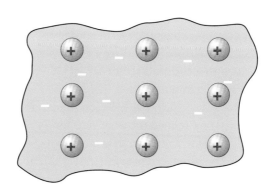

**Figure 21.5**

The distribution of electrons in the metallic-bonding model. The blue region represents the sea of electrons that surround the metallic nuclei. The electrons are said to be "delocalized" and free to move throughout the metal.

The electrons may be like a shifting sea but on average one will always be between the atoms. These atoms, having lost their valence electrons, are ions with a net positive charge. The electrons with their negative charge sit between the ions holding them in place. This type of bonding is called **metallic bonding**.

## 21-3 Metallic Bonding Model Explains Metal Properties

The relatively simple picture in Figure 21.4a and 21.5 of a set of closely-spaced energy levels with delocalized, mobile electrons explains the properties of metals as follows:

**High melting temperature:** In Chapter 12, we hypothesized that strong forces between atoms were present in materials that exhibited high melting temperatures. The metallic bonding model says that these strong forces come from the electrostatic attraction between the mobile electrons and the nuclei. The electron orbitals making up each energy band extend over many nuclei keeping them tightly bonded to each other. It takes a lot of kinetic energy to pull these nuclei away from each other and change the solid metal to a liquid.

**Electrical conductivity:** An electrical current is when charges move under the influence of an electric field. In a metal, the mobile electrons are not bound tightly to any particular nucleus, so they are able to move relatively easily.

**Thermal conductivity:** The same mobile electrons responsible for electrical conductivity also carry kinetic energy. This kinetic energy is heat energy. When one end of a metal piece heats up, the mobile electrons carry the increased kinetic energy rapidly throughout the piece creating a high thermal conductivity.

**Malleability:** Pounding a thick piece of metal into a thin foil requires that the metal nuclei pass over one another. The fluid-like electrons act like a lubricant between the layers of nuclei. They reduce the repulsive forces that would be generated when layers of nuclei, sliding over one another, come into direct contact.

**Opacity:** Given the almost infinite number of energy states and their close spacing, there are always going to be a pair of energy states whose energy difference matches some photon energy in the electromagnetic spectrum. Metals are opaque because they can absorb radiation over the entire visible region of the spectrum, as well as in the infrared and the ultraviolet.

**Reflectivity:** This property is related to opacity. The mobility of the electrons allows them to easily interact with the light waves. Absorption of light causes oscillations in the electrons. Those oscillations in turn radiate light energy. The reflection off a metal arises from this radiation. The different colors of copper, gold, and silver are related to subtle differences in their absorption and reflection properties in the visible region of the spectrum.

## 21-4 Alloys—Metal-Metal Compounds

The requirements for metallic bonding are not overly specific. Any type of atom with a low ionization energy and few valence electrons will form a metallic bond. Because all metals fit this description, metallic bonding can occur between atoms of different kinds of metals. Therefore, it is possible to make metal-metal compounds, called **alloys**, in which one or more types of metal atoms are incorporated into other kinds of metal. White gold, for example, is an alloy of gold and platinum. Brass is an alloy of copper and zinc.

Unlike other kinds of compounds, the compositions of alloys are not required to have fixed ratios. There are useful alloys of lead and tin that range from having relatively few tin atoms, each one completely surrounded by lead atoms, to the reverse; a few lead atoms each completely surrounded by tin atoms.

Two different kinds of alloy structures can be formed, depending on the relative sizes of the different metal atoms (*Figure 21.6*). When the atoms from each of the different alloys are about the same size, one type of metal atom can substitute for another. Like a grocery display of red delicious apples and golden delicious apples, a red apple could occasionally be replaced with a green one and the stack would still be stable. Brass is an example of this type of alloy since copper and zinc atoms have similar diameters.

When the two types of metal atoms differ greatly in size, the smaller atoms can fit into the holes formed by layers of the bigger atoms. This is like a grocer placing cherries in the gaps formed by layers of oranges. Steel, which is an alloy of iron with a few percent of carbon, is an example of the second type with smaller carbon atoms fitting within the network of iron atoms.

Whether an alloy forms at all, and which form it adopts if it does form, is governed by the principles of reactivity outlined in the previous chapter. Taking two pure metals and forming an alloy from them increases the entropy of the metallic system. The random positions of dif-

**Electrical Conductivity:**

A measure of the degree to which a substance conducts an electrical current.

**Alloy:**

A combination of two or more metals into a single homogeneous substance.

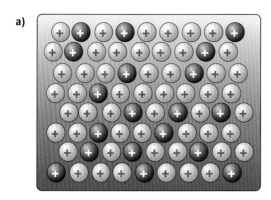

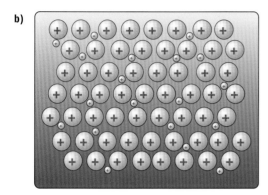

**Figure 21.6**

The two types of alloys.

a) Atoms from two different metals are the same size and can substitute for each other.

b) Atoms from two different metal atoms of very different sizes. Small-sized atoms from one metal can fit into spaces between the other metal's larger atoms.

ferent metal atoms within the alloy lead to an increased disorder.

If the two metals are very similar, then there is little energy change during mixing. Alloys formed from dissimilar metals do release energy into or absorb energy from the surroundings. An alloy that releases energy on formation will be more stable than one that doesn't. For alloys that release energy, disorder increases in both the system and the surroundings.

The properties of alloys are similar in character to those of metals, but may differ in magnitude. An alloy of two pure metals will conduct electricity, but either of the two pure metals will usually be a better conductor. An alloy will often melt at a lower temperature than either of the pure metals from which it was made. The reduction in melting point can be very significant. Lead-tin alloys of certain compositions have much lower melting points than either pure lead or pure tin. These alloys are used as solders—low-melting-point materials used to connect metal pipes or wires together (*Figure 21.7*).

The malleability of pure metals can be a

problem in many applications. Pressure may cause such a piece to thin or flatten. To avoid this, alloys of metals with atoms of different diameters are used. The irregularities introduced by the different sizes make it harder for one layer to slip over another making the alloy less malleable than the pure metals.

Magnesium and aluminum are two of the lightest metals. Strong alloys of both metals are used when reduction of weight is a design consideration. As the automotive and aerospace industries work to prepare lighter, stronger vehicles and planes, alloys based on magnesium or aluminum are becoming increasingly important.

## 21–5 Semiconductors

**Semiconductors** are those elements bordering the black staircase separating metals from non-metals on the periodic table. Their properties are not exactly metallic in nature, nor are they strictly non-metallic either. Because semiconductors are close to metals in most of their properties such as being solids with high melting points and being electrically conductive under certain conditions, so they are sometimes called semi-metals or metalloids.

The computer chips that have revolutionized modern life are built on silicon and germanium semiconductors. Computers, smart phones, televisions, digital music and communications, modern automobiles and LED lights all rely on semiconductor technology. Silicon Valley, a region in central California, got its nickname from the many electronics and computer companies there.

The energy band model used to explain metallic properties also explains semiconductor properties. As Einstein's quote at the opening of this chapter says, a model is more impressive when it can explain a wide range of properties and account for observed differences. In this regard, the quantum model of the atom and its offspring, the metallic bonding model, are impressive in their ability to explain semiconductors as well as metals.

### *Electrical Resistivity*

One way to characterize how easily electricity can flow is through a quantity called **resistivity**. The greater a material's resistivity, the less

**Figure 21.7**

A photo of lead-tin solder (the silvery patches) holding pieces of copper pipe together. A plumber talks of "sweating" the pipe together.

**Semiconductors:**

A solid crystalline substance, such as germanium or silicon, that conducts electricity better than insulators, but not as well as metals. Unlike metals, they become better conductors as their temperature increases.

**Resistivity:**

A measure of the resistance to the flow of electrical current.

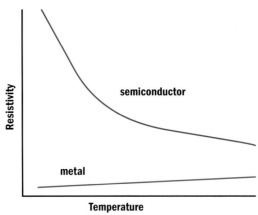

**Figure 21.8**

The electrical resistivity measures resistance to the flow of electricity. The resistivity of metals increases slightly with temperature. Resistivity for semiconductors decreases greatly with temperatures. Unlike metals, semiconductors conduct electricity better at high temperatures.

**Band Gap:**

The band gap is the energy difference between the top of the valence band and the bottom of the conduction band in insulators and semiconductors.

**Valence Band:**

The low energy band of a semiconductor. Unexcited electrons reside here.

**Conduction Band:**

The range of electron energy, higher than that of the valence band, sufficient to make the electrons free to accelerate under the influence of an applied electric field and thus constitute an electric current.

easily current will flow through it. As *Figure 21.8* shows, the resistivities of metals and semiconductors respond very differently to increases in temperature. Metals become slightly more resistive as the temperature is increased while semiconductors become much less resistive with increasing temperature.

In metals, resistivity increases with temperature because of the increased jiggling motion of metal nuclei. This motion deflects electrons as they flow through the lattice. So how can we understand the much more dramatic and opposite-trending behavior of semiconductors?

### Band Gaps

The answer lies in the energy bands. Figure 21.4b depicts the energy bands in semiconductors. They are similar to the energy bands for metals, with one key difference. In metals, the bands associated with the bonding and antibonding orbitals overlap, forming one continuous set of levels. In semiconductors, the bonding and antibonding orbitals form distinct, separate bands. The energy spacing between the bands is called a **band gap**.

A semiconductor band gap is relatively small. In silicon and germanium, the energy width of the band gap corresponds to photon energies in the infrared portion of the spectrum.

At very low temperatures, all of the valence electrons in a semiconductor reside in the lower energy band. This band, called the **valence band**, is completely filled. When the temperature is raised, electrons gain enough thermal energy to jump into the upper or **conduction band**. Fig-

ure 21.4c represents this process by showing the excited electrons as blue lines in that band. The energies where electrons are missing are shown as yellow lines in the valence band.

The excited electrons in the conduction band gain access to a large set of closely spaced, anti-bonding energy levels. Electrons in this band are very conducting, hence its name. Electrical conductivity is also helped by the creation of the empty levels down in the valence band. The electrons remaining in the valence band can also begin to conduct, because there are now empty levels for them to move into.

Semiconductors can also be formed from two different kinds of atoms in a way that parallels the formation of alloys. For example germanium is a natural semiconductor. Gallium (Ga) and arsenic (As) are the elements on either side of it on the periodic table. Gallium has one fewer valence electron than germanium and arsenic has one more. The combination gallium arsenide (GaAs) forms a semiconductor similar in properties to germanium. So does zinc selenide, made of the elements two stations on either side of germanium. And aluminum and phosphorus, the elements on either side of silicon, form a semiconductor as well.

### Optical Properties

Semiconductors have the ability to absorb photons whose energy matches or exceeds the band gap energy. For Ge and Si, whose band gaps are in the infrared, all colors of visible light are partially absorbed, so the semiconductors appear gray. GaAs has a larger band gap than pure Ge, but still one that corresponds to infrared photons, so GaAs also appears gray. The band gap of the semiconductor formed from zinc and selenium corresponds to violet photons. The absorption of these violet photons then gives rise to the yellow color of ZnSe. Still other semiconductors can be created with band gaps in the low frequency end of the ultraviolet region. Such materials are white because all visible colors are reflected rather than being absorbed.

Atoms from other elements having more or fewer valence electrons can be added to semiconductors to refine their conduction behavior to where it can be used to form transistors, amplifiers, and other electronic components. Electrons are added into the valence band of silicon or germanium by doping[1] them with a few atoms of phosphorous, which has one more valence electron than silicon or germanium. Adding aluminum to silicon or germanium creates vacancies in the conduction band because aluminum has one fewer valence electron than the host material.

A semiconductor with vacancies is called a P-type semiconductor, while a semiconductor with extra electrons is called an N-type semiconductor. Doped semiconductors are still electrically neutral. They just have fewer or greater numbers of valence electrons than the pure semiconductor.

### Light Emitting Diodes

Solid-state electronics (e.g., computers, radios, and smartphones) all use transistors, computer chips and circuit boards made of semiconductors. One important semiconductor that is becoming very common is the light emitting diode or LED.

TV remotes use LEDs that emits light in the infrared region. Increasingly, traffic lights are being built from hundreds of red, green or yellow LEDs. The displays on huge TV screens in stadiums or basketball arenas are made from clusters of LEDs, each cluster acting like a pixel on a screen. Examples of LEDs are given in *Figure 21.9*.

A light emitting diode is created by bonding an N type semiconductor directly to a P-type semiconductor to form a single unit. The region where they join is called a **junction**. An electrical circuit is created by attaching the N-type side of a diode to the negative terminal of a battery and the P-type side to the battery's positive terminal as shown in *Figure 21.10*. If the battery supplies a large enough voltage, electrical current will flow from the N-type region (the region with extra electrons) to the P-type region (the region with vacancies).

When an electron crosses the junction and falls into a vacancy, it gives up its extra electrical potential energy by emitting a photon. The color of the photon is determined by the band gap as shown in Figure 21.10b. By choosing the proper semiconductor material, LEDs that emit light from the infrared to the ultraviolet can be prepared.

---

[1] "Doping" is the process of adding small amounts of other atoms.

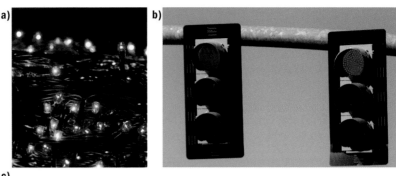

**Figure 21.9**

Several examples of applications using LEDs.

a) LED Christmas lights are gaining popularity for their lower energy use and the reduced heat output, making them safer for use around the home.

b) The LED traffic light on the right is brighter and more economical than the older light on the left that provides light based on gas-discharge tubes.

c) The efficiency and cost savings of LEDs have made massive screens in stadiums, arenas, and even along highways more feasible to build and operate.

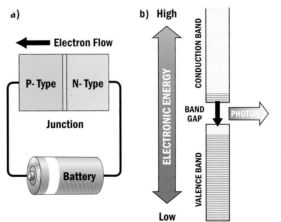

**Junction:**

The interface between two different semiconductor regions in a semiconductor device.

**Figure 21.10**

a) A diagram of a diode, consisting of a p-type semiconductor (one that contains holes in the valence band) and an n-type semiconductor (one that has electrons in or near the bottom of the conduction band) in an electrical circuit with a battery. Electrons flow through the circuit as shown.

b) The relative energies of electrons in the conduction band and that of the holes in the valence band. When an electron falls down into a hole a photon is emitted. The photon color is governed mostly by the band gap of the semiconductor.

## Chapter Framework

A. Introduction

B. A Few Properties of Metal

C. Bonding in Metals
   1. MOs and AOs

D. Metallic Bonding Model Explains Metal Properties

E. Alloys—Metal-Metal Compounds

F. Semiconductors
   1. Resistivity
   2. Band Gaps and Conduction Bands
   3. LEDs

## Comprehension

### Matching

1. _____ Metal-metal compound.
2. _____ Electrons act like a lubricant between layers of nuclei.
3. _____ "Movement of electrons."
4. _____ An electron that is not focused around any one nucleus.
5. _____ Property of absorbing photons throughout the electromagnetic spectrum.
6. _____ Substances that conduct electricity better than insulators but not as good as conductors.
7. _____ The degree to which a substance conducts heat.
8. _____ A measure of resistance to current flowing through a semiconductor.
9. _____ Nuclei surrounded by a "sea" of electrons.
10. _____ How easily light bounces off the surface of a substance.

a. Opacity
b. Reflectivity
c. Conduction
d. Alloy
e. Delocalized electrons
f. Thermal conductivity
g. Metallic bonding
h. Semiconductors
i. Malleability
j. Resistivity

### True/False

1. _____ Light can only be seen through very thin metal.
2. _____ Generally, MOs are low in energy because their electrons will be found between two nuclei.
3. _____ Compositions of alloys are generally fixed in simple ratios.
4. _____ For an alloy to form, the atoms must be different sizes.
5. _____ Often alloys are better conductors than either of the metals, in their pure form, that make up the alloy.
6. _____ Semi-metals are electrically conductive and have high melting points.
7. _____ Semiconductors and metals are very similar in the way each forms alloys.

### Fill in the Blank

1. The _____ model helps answer questions about metals and semiconductors.
2. A difference between metals and semiconductors is caused by the different _____ and _____ of _____ electrons present in the two different types of materials.
3. The _____ electrons act like a _____ between the layers of nuclei when flattening metal with a mallet.
4. The source of differences between semiconductors and metal is caused by _____.

## Analysis

1. Which of the following pair of atoms is most likely to form an alloy?
   a) $_8O$ and $_{31}Ga$
   b) $_{50}Sn$ and $_{82}Pb$
   c) $_7N$ and 17Cl

2. Which of the following is a characteristic of metallic bonds?
   a) brittle
   b) transparent
   c) shiny
   d) low melting temperature
   e) insulator

3. Which of the following is NOT why alloys are useful to us today? Alloys
   a) have lower melting temperatures.
   b) have a higher conductivity rate.
   c) are less malleable.
   d) reduce weight in objects.

4. How do metals and semiconductors change with increasing temperatures?
   a) Metals become less resistive and semiconductors more resistive.
   b) Metals and semiconductors become more resistive.
   c) Metals and semiconductors become less resistive.
   d) Metals become more resistive and semiconductors become less responsive.

## Synthesis

1. Why do elements like Si and Ge form semiconductors but elements like Fe and Cu do not?
2. What is responsible for all the properties of metals?
3. Why is metal opaque?
4. What is the difference with electrons between isolated atoms and metal compounds?
5. Why would automotive industries build cars out of aluminum rather than iron? Than steel?

6. When gold and silver are mixed, the appearance is still that of pure gold. How could you distinguish the alloy from pure gold?

7. Why do metals have high melting points?

8. Why would a sculptor use gold leafing to cover his statue? Answer in terms of malleability, opacity, and reflectivity.

9. What type of atomic particles are influenced in chemical bonding and why?

10. What is the difference between the anti-bonding and non-bonding molecular orbitals?

11. According to the metallic bonding model, how does power flow through a wire?

12. How are opacity and the properties of solids related?

13. Why do alloys have lower melting temperatures than the two metals that form the alloy?

14. Why do metals become less conductive as temperature rises? How is this related to heat conductivity?

15. Silicon has a band gap in the infrared region. What do you predict will be the color of a silicon crystal? Will visible photons be absorbed by a silicon crystal? If so, what color should you see?

16. Would you expect the emission spectrum of an LED to be discrete or continuous?

17. An LED changes colors when it is dipped in liquid nitrogen. It shifts from being red to yellow. What is happening to the band gap of the semiconductor? Is it getting bigger or smaller? What might be causing this effect?

# Bonding in Ionic Compounds

*Ye are the salt of the earth.*

*Matthew 5:13*

## 22

## LEARN

- How the quantum model of the atom explains ionic bonding.

- How ionic bonding explains the properties of salts such as melting and boiling temperatures, electrical conductivity, transparency, and brittleness.

- The most likely ion to form from metals at the far left of the periodic table and non-metals on the far right of the periodic table.

- The formulas of simple salts based on ionic charges and name the salts.

Sharing electrons among many, many atoms in metallic bonding explains why metals have high melting points. In Chapter 12, we noted that two non-metallic substances, sodium chloride or table salt and magnesium oxide, also have high melting and boiling temperatures. These two substances typify the compounds that metals form with non-metals. We call such compounds **ionic compounds** or **salts**, and we call the bonding in these compounds **ionic bonding**.

You may recall that both metals and the ionically-bonded salts are extended bonding substances and therefore may expect them to have many properties in common. But they do not and actually differ significantly from each other. The bonding within them could not be more different and it is the *bonding*, not the resulting network that determines properties. Again, the quantum model of the atom naturally and simply explains exactly why it is so different.

## 22-1 Properties of Ionic Compounds

Ionic compounds have high melting temperatures and boiling temperatures, some so high that they have never been measured. From this we know that the ionic bond, like the metallic bond, is strong. Such similarities, though, quickly end.

Metals all have similar reflective properties, varying often just subtly in color from one element to another. Ionic compounds form non-reflective powders and crystals with a more varied and interesting array of color as shown in *Figure 22.1*. Compounds formed by metals in columns 1A and 2A and non-metals in columns 6A and 7A of the periodic table are colorless. Large crystals of these compounds are transparent as shown in Figure 22.1a. In fact, salt crystals of this type are used as windows in some of the spectroscopy instruments described in Chapter 19. Salts that contain transition metals, those in columns 1B–8B, may be highly colored. Figure 22.1c shows the bright green color of a nickel salt and the brilliant blue of a copper salt.

a)
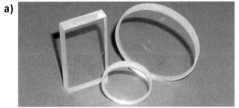

b)

c)

**Figure 22.1**

The transparency of ionic compounds.

a) Instrument windows made of sodium chloride (NaCl) and potassium bromide (KBr).

b) Ionic crystals with imperfections can appear white.

c) Salts that contain transition metal ions may be highly colored.

**Ionic Compound:**

A compound formed between a metal and a non-metal. Ionic compounds are crystalline solids at room temperature. They conduct electricity when molten or dissolved in water.

**Salts:**

Another name for ionic compounds.

**Ionic Bonding:**

The model used to explain the bonding in ionic compounds. Metal atoms lose electrons, forming positive ions. Non-metal atoms gain electrons forming negative ions. In the salt, positive metal ions are surrounded by negative non-metal ions, and vice versa. Because electrostatic forces are strong and long range, each ion experiences attractive interactions with many ions of the other type. The extended interactions give rise to the high melting points.

Figures 17.1, 17.2 and 19.10 show additional colored transition metal salts made from chromium, cadmium, lead, and iron.

All salts are brittle and cannot be easily reshaped. They shatter into many pieces when hit with a hammer. As learned in Chapter 12, salts are ionic conductors. When as a molten liquid or dissolved in water, salts conduct electricity, but dry solid salts do not.

## 22-2 Forming Ionic Compounds

### Key Properties of Metals and Non-metals

To understand ionic compound properties, consider the key differences between metal and non-metal atoms. Metals have large atomic volumes, few valence electrons, and low ionization energies. They easily form positive ions by losing valence electrons. Non-metals, however, have small atomic volumes, many valence electrons, and very high ionization energies. From the high ionization energies considered in Chapter 17, you can infer that non-metal atoms like to hold tightly onto their electrons. In fact, the situation goes further than that. Non-metal atoms have such a strong affinity for electrons that they can pull electrons away from other atoms forming negative ions.

In Chapter 20 we learned that two chemical species are likely to react if the products have lower energy than the starting materials. Like falling balls, they go to the lowest energy condition available to them. The formation of the ionic compound, sodium chloride (NaCl), from metallic sodium (Na element 11) and gaseous

chlorine ($Cl_2$ element 17) illustrates this principle nicely.

*Figure 22.2* presents the energy level diagrams of atomic Na and atomic Cl. Sodium has one valence electron in a 3s atomic orbital; chlorine has seven valence electrons and room for one more to fill its 3p set of orbitals. The Na 3s orbital is higher in energy than the 3s and 3p Cl orbitals. Why should the Na level 3 atomic orbitals be higher in energy than their counterparts on Cl? What factors might explain this observation?

The classical electric force law studied in Chapter 4 states that the force between two charged particles increases when the charge on one particle increases. The force also increases when the distance between the two particles gets smaller. Compared to valence electrons on larger Na, the valence electrons on smaller Cl are closer to their nucleus than are those of Na. Chlorine's set of valence electrons also experience a stronger attraction to their nucleus because the Cl nucleus has 17 protons compared to Na's 11.

These two factors have the same effect: the valence electrons in standing waves around chlorine have a lower electrical potential energy than Na's valence electron. So, when Na atoms and Cl atoms come together, the 3s electron of Na goes downhill energetically by jumping to the Cl atom, giving off energy in the process and satisfying the first principle of chemical reactivity.

What about the second principle, the one that has to do with increasing the disorder in the Universe? The reaction of Na and $Cl_2$ produces

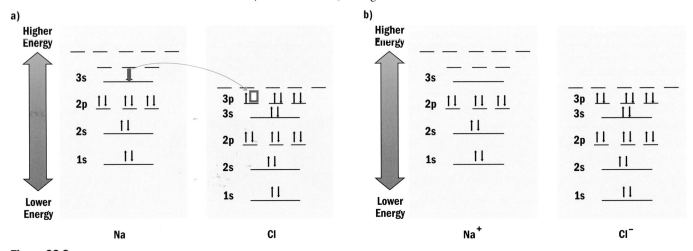

**Figure 22.2**
Electron energy diagrams (not drawn to scale, but showing the relative energies).
a) The transfer of an electron from sodium (Na) to chlorine (Cl).
b) Sodium (Na+) and chloride (Cl_) ions.

an explosive amount of energy, much more than can be represented in Figure 22.2. This energy flows into the surroundings, significantly increasing their disorder. The overall disorder in the Universe increases, making this reaction very favorable.

## 22-3 The Ionic Bond

### Localized Electrons but Extended Structures

Because of the valence electron energy state differences described above, metals easily lose electrons and non-metals easily gain electrons. Metals and non-metals combining to form salts is an arrangement in which one atom completely gives and one completely receives, forming ions in the process. Ionic bonding gets its name because the interaction occurs between ions. Once formed, the positive and negative ions exert attractive electrostatic forces on each other.

In metals, electrons are shared by many metallic ions. In contrast, the electrons in ionic compounds are in atomic-type orbitals localized on each ion. The orbitals do not extend beyond individual ions. The extended, network structure that is found in salts arises from the strong, long-range nature of the electric force. One ion attracts many neighboring, oppositely-charged ions. Each of those ions, in turn, attracts other oppositely-charged ions. Those ions attract still more ions, and before you know it, you have a chunk of salt.

### Structures of Salts

The most energetically favorable arrangement of ions maximizes attractive interactions and minimizes repulsive ones. In the case of $Na^+$ and $Cl^-$ ions, each ion type surrounds itself with ions of the opposite charge. Every ion experiences strong attractive interactions with its neighbors and is shielded from repulsive interactions with ions of its own type. *Figure 22.3a* shows the NaCl structure, where the green balls represent $Cl^-$ ions and the yellow balls indicate $Na^+$ ions.

Many salts have the NaCl structure. Magnesium oxide (a salt made of $Mg^{2+}$ and $O^{2-}$ ions) and potassium bromide (a salt made of $K^+$ and $Br^-$ ions) both form in the NaCl structure of Figure 22.3a. Salts containing ions of the same

charge magnitude but opposite sign (e.g., +1, –1 or +2, –2) and about the same size tend to take on this structure because it represents their most favorable energetic arrangement.

Salts are electrically neutral so the total positive and negative charges must be equal. In NaCl that means there must be one Na atom for every Cl atom. The Ca atom has two valence electrons and naturally forms an ion with a +2 charge. Neutrality is achieved in the ionic compound $CaCl_2$ by Ca combining with two ions of single charged $Cl^-$. The salt $Na_2O$ (from ions $Na^+$ and $O^{2-}$) combines as two $Na^+$ ions for every $O^{2-}$ ion to preserve neutrality. In $Al_2O_3$ it takes two ions of aluminum ($Al^{3+}$) for every three oxide ($O^{2-}$) ions to form a neutral aluminum oxide salt. Later in this chapter we will consider a simple way to predict what combining ratios might be expected for different ionic materials.

Salts with combinations of positive and negative ions other than the 1:1 of NaCl adopt different arrangements of the positive and negative ions. Structures of the 2:1 $Na_2O$ and 2:3 $Al_2O_3$ ionic compounds are shown in Figure 22.3b and Figure 22.3c respectively. One common principle applies in all structures: each ion has ions of the opposite charge as its next-door neighbors.

## 22-4 Ionic Bonding and Ionic Compound Properties

The ionic bond being charged ions held together by electrostatic interactions accounts for the properties described at the beginning of the chapter.

### High Melting and Boiling Temperatures

Electrostatic forces are long-range. An ion can feel the attractive force of oppositely charged ions several neighbors away. The electrostatic force also extends in all directions from an ion rather than being targeted toward its closest neighbor. These two factors are why individual ions interact strongly with many other ions. Because the interaction is strong, a great deal of thermal energy is required to pull individual ions away from their neighbors, hence the high melting temperatures.

Melting destroys the ordered, fixed ionic

**a) NaCl**

**b) Na₂O**

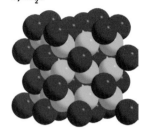

**c) Al₂O₃**

**Figure 22.3**
Structures of ionic compounds. Green balls represent chloride Cl–, yellow balls represent Na+, red ones represent the oxide ion O2–, and blue ones represent Al+3 ions. The ball diameters reflect the relative sizes of ions.

a) The structure of sodium chloride, NaCl.

b) The structure of sodium oxide, Na2O.

c) The structure of aluminum oxide, Al2O3 (corundum).

arrangement of a solid but in the resulting liquid, clusters of ions still cling together. For the substance to boil and become a gas, these clusters must be broken apart, and that requires much higher temperatures still. So ionic compounds have very high boiling temperatures.

### Brittleness

Salt crystals break and shatter when hit with a hammer. They do not bend, flatten, or easily change their shape. Bending, flattening, or changing shape requires layers of ions to slide over each other. As shown in *Figure 22.4*, if one layer of ions moves the distance of just an atomic diameter, positive ions come in direct contact with other positive ions, and likewise for the negative ions. These strong repulsions force layers apart, shattering the crystal.

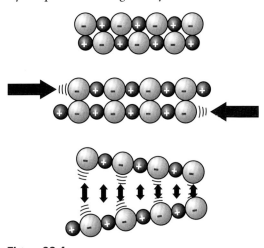

**Figure 22.4**

Hammering on an ionic compound forces ions of like charge to come in contact. The strong repulsive interactions cause the crystal to shatter.

**Electrolytes:**

A chemical compound that ionizes when dissolved in water to produce an electrically conductive medium.

### Electrical Conductivity Varies With State

Electrical conductivity requires mobile charge carriers. All the electrons in both ions of a salt are in standing waves localized on the individual ions. With no mobile electrons and ions that are fixed rigidly in place, solid salts have no way to conduct electricity. But when the salt melts, individual ions become free to move as shown in *Figure 22.5*. Under the influence of an electric force from a battery, the mobile ions become charge carriers whose flow completes the circuit. However ions, being big and awkward compared to electrons, conduct electricity more poorly than metallic electrons.

Likewise, when salt dissolves in water, its ions separate, become mobile, and conduct electricity. Materials that conduct electricity when dissolved in water are called **electrolytes**.

### Transparency

Electrons in salt crystals, being bound in discrete energy levels, are not free to roam in energy bands like they do in metals. For salts made with metals found in columns of the periodic table with "A" designations, the photon energy required to excite an electron to a higher level is in or above the ultraviolet part of the spectrum (*Figure 22.6a*). Lower-energy visible light photons don't excite these electrons to higher levels, are not absorbed, and simply pass through. Therefore salt crystals are transparent.

A crystal block of salt with many cracks or bubbles in it will appear cloudy-white or translucent because the flaws in these crystals scatter

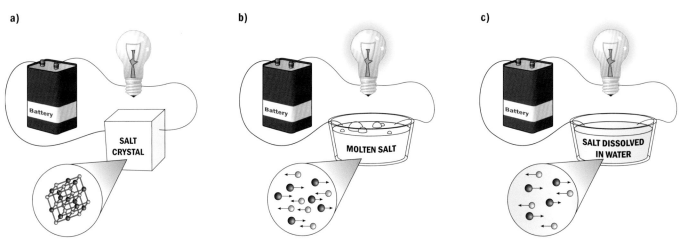

**Figure 22.5**

The conductivity of salts in different states. The blowup shows the arrangement of the ions in each state.

a) Solid

b) Molten (liquid) salt

c) Salt dissolved in water

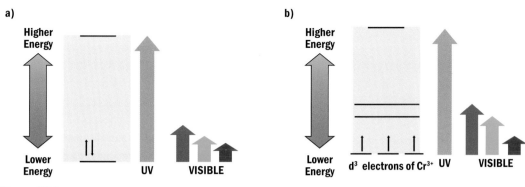

**Figure 22.6**

a) Most salts contain paired electrons and have energy states that are widely spaced apart, matching the energies of UV photons. They don't absorb visible light and are transparent.

b) Transition metal ions often contain unpaired electrons in d orbitals. These give rise to extra energy levels. Electrons can absorb visible light to be excited into these lower states. $Cr^{3+}$ has levels that allow absorption of blue and green photons but not red ones. Rubies are red because of this.

light. Many otherwise transparent minerals in nature appear opaque and white for this reason. (See Figure 22.1b.)

If a salt crystal is ground to a powder it ceases to be transparent. In this case light rays impinging on the powder are refracted and reflected many times by the small powder particles before they emerge. Now light no longer passes straight through as it did with a single crystal. Photons refracting, reflecting, and scattering from particle to particle make the powder appear white instead of transparent.

Some salts containing transition metal ions (the "B" type metals) have a few low-lying electronic states with spacing in the visible energy range. For example, $Cr^{3+}$ has three unpaired electrons in 3d orbitals. These electrons interact with each other and give rise to extra electronic states, as shown in Figure 22.6b. The 3d electrons of $Cr^{3+}$ can absorb both blue and green photons and excite to upper levels in the process. Red photons can't be absorbed and instead are reflected. This is what gives a ruby, a gemstone that contains $Cr^{3+}$, its distinctive rich red color (see sidebar "Rubies and Sapphires").

## RUBIES AND SAPPHIRES

An observer might think that a ruby's chemistry differs greatly from the chemistry of a sapphire because of their different colors. In fact, from a chemical point of view, they are very similar. Both gems are based on aluminum oxide, $Al_2O_3$ (Figure 22.3c). In rubies, a small amount of chromium ($Cr^{3+}$) ions replaces $Al^{3+}$ ions in the salt. This transition metal ion has several closely spaced energy levels that allow it to absorb blue and green light (Figure 22.6b). The red portion of the spectrum is reflected, giving the ruby its red color. The blue color in sapphires arises from a little more complicated source. Impurities of titanium ($Ti^{4+}$) and iron ($Fe^{2+}$) replace $Al^{3+}$ ions. The two impurities, taken together, have a charge equivalent to two $Al^{3+}$ ions. The pairs of ions can be incorporated together, but on different Al sites. Each ion has its own set of closely spaced energy levels, and the combined effect of their absorption of visible photons produces the sapphire's blue color. Other colors sometimes found in a sapphire are caused by different transition metal impurities in the gem.

## 22-5 Predicting Ionic Charges

### The Octet Rule

When the Na atom loses its 3s electron in the Na + Cl reaction, the resulting valence electron configuration becomes $2s^2 2p^6$ which is the same configuration as Ne, a noble gas (see Figure 17.10). But of course it surrounds a positive $Na^+$ ion instead of a neutral Ne atom. The Cl atom gains the electron into its 3p orbitals giving the $Cl^-$ ion the electron configuration of $3s^2 3p^6$, which is the same as the noble gas argon (Ar, element 18).

As noted in Chapter 17, noble gases with the $ns^2 np^6$ configuration ($n$ being a number from 2 for Ne to 6 for Rn) are extraordinarily unreactive. A lack of chemical reactivity implies that this electron configuration has an especially low and stable energy arrangement. It is so stable that the metal and nonmetal atoms in nearly all ionic compounds form ions with the noble gas configuration. This fact leads to the **octet rule** which tells us the most likely charge of the ions that form from each type of atom. The rule states that

> **An atom will most likely form an ion that has the $ns^2 np^6$ configuration of the closest noble gas atom.**

Metals follow the octet rule by losing valence electrons until their outermost shell has the configuration of the noble gas in the row *above* the metal in the periodic table. So Na in row 3 of the periodic table forms a negative ion whose electron configuration looks like Ne in row 2.

Non-metals satisfy the octet rule by gaining enough electrons to fill up their p orbitals. Non-metals form negative ions with electron configurations of the noble gas in their same row. So Cl in row 3 forms a negative ion whose electron configuration looks like Ar, also in row 3.

Elements in each column of the periodic table form ions of the same charge because those in the same column must lose or gain the same number of electrons to achieve a $ns^2 np^6$ configuration. The elements in metallic Groups 1A, 2A, and 3A form +1 ions, +2 ions, and +3 ions respectively. Non-metal atoms from Groups 5A, 6A and 7A form -3 ions, −2 ions and −1 ions, respectively. For metals, the group number conveniently indicates the charge on the positive ion in that column. For non-metals, the negative ionic charge is calculated by subtracting 8 from the group number. Once we know the charges on the ions, charge neutrality dictates how they will combine with oppositely-charged ions to form salts, as explained in Section 22–3 above.

The valence electrons of the transition metal elements in the B columns of the periodic table are in d orbitals and are not expected to follow the simple octet rule. Many of these elements form multiple ions with different charges. Manganese (Mn, element 25) for example, forms ions with a +2, +3, +4, and even +7 charge. As the ionic charge on transition metal ions varies from compound to compound, properties such as color and magnetism change as well as shown in *Figure 22.7*.

**Figure 22.7**
Three different manganese compounds.

The metalloid elements on the border between metals and nonmetals behave in ways befitting their location. Aluminum, in Column 3A, occurs below the dividing line and generally behaves like a metal. Boron, just above it, acts like a metal in its ionic compound with oxygen ($B_2O_3$), but forms non-ionic compounds with hydrogen. Carbon, which has four valence electrons, will neither lose its four valence electrons like a metal, nor gain four to fill its shell like a non-metal. As we shall see in the next chapter, carbon prefers to neither give nor take electrons but shares them instead.

The atoms of both transition metals and metalloid elements gain or lose different numbers of electrons in different chemical reactions, depending on the particular compound that is being formed. There is no simple octet rule for these but they do, of course, react such as to lower the overall electron energies.

**Octet Rule:**
An atom will most likely form an ion that has the $ns2np6$ configuration of the closest noble gas atom.

## Naming Convention

Because the metal and nonmetal atoms forming salts combine in fixed amounts, we can uniquely specify the salt by the two elements involved, so long as the metal is not a transition metal. When speaking of a salt the metal name is given first, leaving it unchanged. The name of the non-metal is then given, but modified by replacing its last syllable with the suffix "ide." Magnesium and oxygen form "magnesium oxide." Calcium and fluorine form "calcium fluoride", etc.

In formulas, the metal symbol is always written first followed by the non-metal as shown in *Table 22.1*. For salts in which the transition metal ion can have variable ionic charges, there is a formal protocol to specify the charge, but we shall not treat it here.

### Table 22.1 — Formulas and Common Names of Salts

| | | | |
|---|---|---|---|
| NaCl | sodium chloride | PbS | lead sulfide |
| KBr | potassium bromide | $Al_2O_3$ | aluminum oxide |
| $MgF_2$ | magnesium fluoride | $BaI_2$ | barium iodide |
| MnO | manganese oxide | $LaCl_3$ | lanthanum chloride |

# 22 STUDY GUIDE

## Chapter Framework

### A. Salts
1. Ionic Bonding

### B. Properties of Metals and Non-metals
1. Atomic Volumes
2. Ionization Energy

### C. The Ionic Bonding Model
1. Localized Electrons
2. Extended Structures

### D. Properties of Ionic Compounds
1. Melting / Boiling Temperatures
2. Electrical Conductivity
3. Brittleness
4. Transparency

## Comprehension

### Matching

a. Salt
b. Ionic Bonding
c. Brittleness
d. Electrolytes
e. Ion
f. Transparency

1. _____ A characteristic of ionic substances, such as salts, that readily shatter when struck a sharp blow.
2. _____ A characteristic of salts that readily transmit light; opposite of opaqueness.
3. _____ The chemical bond that binds metallic ions to non-metallic ions by electrical attraction.
4. _____ A charged particle formed when an atom or molecule loses or gains electrons.
5. _____ A substance formed from the ionic bond of a metal with a non-metal.
6. _____ A chemical compound that ionizes when dissolved or molten to produce an electrically conductive medium.

### True/False
1. _____ Salts can easily be flattened or reshaped.
2. _____ Ionic compounds have extremely low melting temperatures.
3. _____ Molten salts are ionic conductors.
4. _____ Metals easily lose electrons.
5. _____ A salt is electrically neutral as a solid.
6. _____ Electrons like to go to the highest energy condition available to them.

### Fill in the Blank
1. _____ combine with non-metals to form highly-colored compounds.
2. Electrons go to the _____ energy condition available to them.
3. For a given period, metals have _____ atomic volumes, whereas non-metals have _____ atomic volumes.
4. Metals lose _____ to form positive ions.
5. The most energetically favorable arrangement of ions maximizes _____ forces and minimizes repulsive ones.
6. Each ion of an ionic compound has the ions of the _____ charge as its next-door neighbors.

7. When writing down the chemical formula for a salt, the _____ symbol is written first and the _____ is written last.

## Analysis

1. The atomic orbitals for potassium (K) and bromine (Br) are similar to those for sodium and chlorine in *Figure 22.2* in that the potassium atomic orbitals are higher in energy than their counterparts on bromine. Why is this?

   a) Potassium valence electrons are closer on average to their nucleus than bromine valence electrons.

   b) Potassium valence electrons experience a stronger attraction to their nucleus because of a larger atomic volume and smaller nuclear charge.

   c) Bromine valence electrons experience a stronger attraction to their nucleus because of smaller atomic volume and increased nuclear charge.

   d) Bromine valence electrons experience a weaker attraction for their nucleus because there are fewer positively charged protons.

2. The figure below shows the electron energy diagrams for an atom of Mg and two atoms of Cl. Use the figure to answer the following questions.

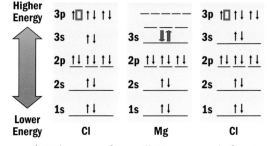

   a) What type of ion will Mg most easily form?

   b) What type of ion does Cl most easily form?

   c) Why does the salt formed between Mg and Cl have the formula $MgCl_2$?

   d) Describe what happens to the electronic energy when a Mg atom gives an electron to each Cl atom.

   e) How does this process increase the entropy in the universe?

3. Figure 22.4 shows two diagrams with arrows.

   a) What type of force (shear, compression, tension) do the arrows in these figures represent?

   b) Which of the two diagrams represents the lower potential energy arrangement of the ions?

   c) Explain your answer.

4. Strontium is a metal found on the left-hand side of the Periodic Table. Using the Periodic Table, determine the ion most likely to form from this metal.

a) Sr (no charge)      c) $Sr^{2+}$

b) $Sr^+$      d) $Sr^{3+}$

5. Phosphorous is a non-metal found on the right-hand side of the Periodic Table. Using the Periodic Table, determine the ion most likely to form from this non-metal.

a) P (no charge)      c) $P^{2-}$

b) $P^-$      d) $P^{3-}$

6. A salt must be electrically neutral. In other words, the positive and negative charges must balance to result in a neutral compound.

a) Use the Periodic Table to determine the most likely charges for ions formed from the following atoms: $_8O$, $_{11}Na$, $_{12}Mg$, $_{16}S$, $_{17}Cl$, $_{19}K$, $_{20}Ca$, and $_{35}Br$.

b) Determine which of the following ionic compounds are likely to be found in nature:

$$K_2S; \ Mg_3O_2; \ CaCl; \ NaBr_2$$

7. Aluminum chloride is an ionic compound with a formula of $AlCl_3$. Which statement is likely to be true concerning the structure of $AlCl_3$?

a) A chlorine atom must be one-third the size of an aluminum atom so the atoms in the compound can pack correctly.

b) Electrostatic forces are impeded by the excess of chlorine atoms, so the bonding structure for $AlCl_3$ is slightly weaker than for a typical 1:1 ratio compound.

c) Al ions are larger than the Cl ions.

d) The ions will arrange themselves in the most energetically favorable arrangements with ions of one charge surrounded by ions of the opposite charge.

8. The correct formula for sodium chloride is:

a) $Na_2O$      c) NaCl

b) $Al_2O$      d) AlO

9. Why does table salt appear white in color?

10. Why do rubies and sapphires differ in color?

## Synthesis

1. Compare and contrast the bonding in metals with that in ionic compounds by selecting the better answer from the pair given for each statement in *Table 22.2*.

a) Using the differences you noted in your answers in the table, explain why metals can be hammered into thin sheets but salts are brittle and shatter into bits when hit with a hammer.

b) Using the similarities you noted in your answers in the table, explain why metals and salts have very high melting points.

## Table 22.2 – Metallic vs. Ionic Bonding

| | Metallic Bonding | Ionic Bonding |
|---|---|---|
| Bonds arise from electrostatic interactions | True / False | True / False |
| Energy levels are widely spaced | True / False | True / False |
| Electrons are localized on atoms | True / False | True / False |
| Strong attractive interactions extend over long distances | True / False | True / False |
| Charge carriers are: | Electrons / Ions | Electrons / Ions |
| Charge carriers are mobile (free to move) | True / False | True / False |

2. The mineral known as beryl has the chemical formula $Be_3Al_2Si_6O_{18}$. To a very simple approximation, the bonding in beryl can be described as ionic.

a) From the positions of the atoms in the Periodic Table, predict the nature of the $_4Be$ ion, $_{13}Al$ ion, and $_8O$ ion in beryl.

b) Given your answers to 2a and the electrical neutrality requirement, guess the form of the $_{14}Si$ ion. Does your answer seem reasonable?

c) Pure beryl is colorless. However, chromium ions, Cr3+ are often found to "contaminate" beryl. You may have heard of this chromium-contaminated beryl as emerald, the birthstone for the month of May. Why does the presence of chromium introduce a green color into beryl?

d) Using Figure 22.6 as a guide, suggest what must happen to the d electron energy levels of the Cr ion when it finds itself in beryl to give rise to a green color.

3. A student was asked to sketch the arrangement of ions in an ionic salt made of +3 and –2 ions. What he proposed is shown in the figure at right, where the red balls represent the –2 ions and the blue balls represent the +3 ions. Does he have the ratio of positive and negative ions correct? Is this the most energetically favorable arrangement of ions? Why or why not?

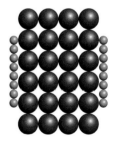

4. What procedure leads to the correct chemical formula for reactants formed in reactions involving compounds held together in ionic bonds?

5. Sketch a diagram showing a possible arrangement of the ions in a salt. Explain what would happen to this arrangement if shear forces were exerted on the salt. Why is the salt brittle? Also, using your understanding of ionic bonds, explain why table salt dissolved in water is an ionic conductor.

6. Describe the octet rule and its impact on the formation of ionic compounds.

# Covalent Bonding and Intermolecular Interactions

*To find truth you have to try and you have to persist in trying. Sometimes it's fun. Sometimes it's hard or boring. But it's always worth it.*

*Henry Eyring*

# 23

## LEARN

- How covalent bonding forms molecules and extended bonding structures according to the quantum model of the atom.

- The cause and relative strength of dispersion forces, dipole-dipole interactions, hydrogen bonds, and covalent bonds

- How bonding concepts explain trends in melting and boiling points.

All types of bonding are essential in giving the world its distinct character. The metallic bond creates the substances that give strength and permanence to buildings, enable modern electronics, and give luster and longevity to jewelry. The ionic bond gives us the beauty of color and crystals and gems. But the bonding that most ties the world and living things together, the one that creates the most diverse attributes of matter, is the one that creates individual molecules, the **covalent** bond.

The properties of metallically and ionically bonded substances do not vary much from other similarly bonded material. All salts are translucent, all alloys are malleable, etc. But when atoms join together in individual molecules, they blend their atomic properties in ways that create discrete units with novel shapes and diverse chemical properties. They may form simple molecules of few atoms or chains of thousands of atoms. They may form gases or liquids or solids. They may be highly reactive or nearly inert. The variety is seemingly endless.

In Chapters 21 and 22, we saw that the

quantum model of the atom explains the properties of metals and ionic compounds. This same model is especially powerful at explaining the bonding that holds molecules together. Further, it gives us the tools to understand the intermolecular interactions that occur *between* molecules as well. In this chapter we will learn about the properties of covalent bonds and intermolecular interactions.

## 23-1 Covalent Bonding

The covalent bond is the bond formed between non-metal atoms. Recall that according to the quantum model of the atom, electrons fill the lowest energy orbitals first. When the lower energy shells are filled, additional electrons occupy higher energy shells. The outermost shell containing electrons is called the **valence shell**. As was emphasized in the chapter on ionic bonding, either filling every orbital in the valence shell or emptying it completely is an especially favorable arrangement.

To review, recall that atoms of metals

achieve filled valence shells by releasing their valence electrons to the sea of electrons that form the metallic bond. The shell below the valence shell now becomes the *de-facto* valence shell and, being filled, its electron energy requirements are satisfied. Non-metals on the other hand fill their incomplete outer valence shell by acquiring other electrons. When non-metal atoms interact with each other, neither is likely to give up electrons because the energetic costs are too high. So non-metal atoms fill their valence shells by *sharing* electrons. It is this atom-specific sharing that creates distinct molecules.

We have already seen an example of this in hydrogen. In Chapter 20 we considered how two H atoms share electrons to form the $H_2$ molecule (Figure 20.1). Since the hydrogen valence shell is the *1s* orbital which can hold only two electrons, an H atom sharing its one electron with another H atom fills each atom's valence shell, a single bond results, and no more bonding takes place.

The hydrogen molecule is the simplest

**Covalent:**

Materials characterized by chemical bonds that involve sharing electrons. Typically, the bonds in covalent substances occur between non-metal atoms.

**Valence Shell:**

The outermost, highest-energy set of orbitals in an atom. The arrangement of electrons in the valence shell determines how the atom interacts chemically with other atoms.

| Name | ethane | ethylene | acetylene |
|---|---|---|---|
| Formula | C₂H₆ | C₂H₄ | C₂H₂ |
| CC bond type | single | double | triple |
| Bond strength (kJ mol⁻¹) | 348 | 614 | 839 |

**Figure 23.1**

Singly-bound, doubly-bound and triply-bound carbon atoms in three covalent compounds of carbon and hydrogen (hydrocarbons). Carbon is represented by the gray balls.

(kJ mol–1 means kilojoules per mole; mole is a standard measure of an amount of a substance.)

**Single Bond:**

A covalent bond involving one pair of electrons shared between the two bound atoms. In chemical structure drawings, single bonds are represented by single lines.

**Double Bond:**

A covalent bond involving two pairs of electrons shared between the two bound atoms. In chemical structure drawings, double bonds are represented by double lines.

**Triple Bond:**

Atoms within a molecule connected by three bonds. For example, acetylene (*Figure 19.5o*).

**Electronegativity:**

A measure of how strongly atoms attract electrons. Both ionization energy (the energy required to remove an electron from a neutral atom) and electron affinity (the energy gained when an electron is added to a neutral atom) contribute to electronegativity. Electronegativity increases from left to right across rows and decreases down columns of the Periodic Table.

**Polar:**

Bonds or molecules having an unequal distribution of charge (one end being positive, the other negative).

**Dipole:**

The separation of positive and negative charge in a polar bond or molecule.

example of covalent bonding, but bonding in more complicated molecules follows the same principles. Electrons are shared so that every atom has a filled valence shell and all the electrons are placed in the lowest energy orbitals possible.

The strength of covalent bonds is described by the amount of energy required to separate the bound atoms. **Single covalent bonds** formed by two atoms sharing a pair of electrons are fairly strong. Large amounts of energy are needed to break this bond and separate the atoms.

Atoms will share until all their empty valence shell orbitals are occupied. If they have enough room they may share two pairs with another individual atom, called a **double bond,** or even three pairs, called a **triple bond**. Triple covalent bonds exist between the nitrogen atoms in N₂ and between the C and O atoms in carbon monoxide (CO). The overall bonding in these molecules is among the strongest known. Quadruple bonds are, in principle, possible between atoms like carbon and silicon but these are very rare because there is insufficient room between atoms to accommodate four shared electron pairs.

*Figure 23.1* shows examples of single, double, and triple bonding represented as single lines, double lines, and triple lines respectively. In these simple hydrocarbons two carbon atoms are bound to each other with hydrogen taking up the remaining sharing requirements.

## 23-2 Bond Polarity

Electrons are not always shared equally in a covalent bond. Often the electrons spend more time nearer one of the atoms than the other. The ability to attract electrons is called **electronegativity.** Atoms that attract electrons well are said to be "electronegative." Electronegativity increases from left to right and from bottom to top on the periodic table. Atoms of cesium (Cs)

are especially weak at attracting electrons. The highly electronegative atoms of fluorine (F) are especially good at attracting them.

When two atoms differ in their ability to attract electrons, the two electrons in the bond will spend more time near the more electronegative atom giving it a small excess negative charge. At the same time, the atom with less electronegativity picks up a small positive charge because the electrons are not around it enough to constantly cancel the positive nuclear charge. This positive charge just balances the excess negative charge on the more electronegative atom and the molecule remains neutral overall.

*Figure 23.2* shows formaldehyde (CH₂O) which is oxygen and hydrogen atoms bonded to a central carbon atom. Because oxygen is more electronegative than carbon, the electron density in the molecule is shifted toward the oxygen atom. Bonds like these with unequal electron sharing are said to be **polar**. Because the bond involves both a negative and a positive "pole," the resulting distribution of charge is called a **dipole**. The greater the charge separation between the poles, the stronger the dipole.

If two *identical* atoms form a bond, as in H₂, N₂, O₂, or F₂, the electrons are always shared

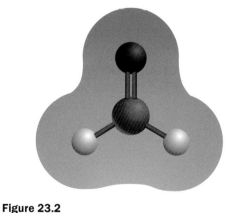

**Figure 23.2**

Charge distribution in the polar molecule formaldehyde (CH₂O). Blue = positive, red = negative. Oxygen is more electronegative than carbon. Consequently, the oxygen end of the molecule is quite negative, and the carbon end is correspondingly positive. The positive and negative charges exactly balance so the net charge on the molecule is zero.

**Figure 23.3**

Charge distribution in the $H_2$ molecule. Blue = positive. Red = negative. The negative charge lies between the two nuclei. The ends of the molecule are positive and the charge is equally distributed between the two H atoms. The negative and positive charges add up so that the net charge on the $H_2$ molecule is zero.

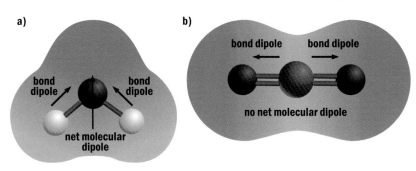

**Figure 23.4**

Arrangement of atoms and charge distributions in two common molecules.

a) Water has a net dipole and is polar. The oxygen end of the water molecule has a partial negative charge (red) and each hydrogen has a partial positive charge (blue); the positive and negative charges add up so the molecule overall has no net charge.

b) Carbon dioxide, despite having polar bonds, has no net dipole because the bond dipoles point in opposite directions and cancel. The oxygens in carbon dioxide have partial negative charges (exactly balancing the positive charge on the carbon).

equally between the two atoms (*Figure 23.3*) regardless of their electronegativity because there is nothing special about one of the atoms that makes it better able to attract electrons than the other atom. Bonds between two identical atoms are called nonpolar.

## 23-3 Intermolecular Forces

In Table 12.1 we listed properties of the covalently bonded molecule ethanol. Its melting and boiling temperatures are in the intermediate range compared to other entries in the table. This is generally true of covalent materials; their melting and boiling temperatures are intermediate between those of pure atomic matter and metallic or ionically bonded substances. Most covalent compounds are relatively easy to melt or boil which means that the **intermolecular** forces between molecules are relatively weak compared to metals and salts but stronger than those between individual atoms.

Recall that the electric force strengthens with increasing charge magnitude and weakens as the square of the separation between the charges. The force between atomic electrons and nuclei is large both because the nuclear charge can be large and the separation between electrons and nuclei is very small.

Distances between molecules are much larger than distances within atoms, so based on this alone the forces between molecules would be expected to be relatively small. But aside from this we ask how can a neutral molecule —with no net charge—be attracted to other neutral

molecules at all? Doesn't there need to be a net charge to feel the electric forces?

### *Dipole-Dipole Interactions*

The polar bonds discussed in the previous section are a good starting point to answer this question. The existence of polar bonds can make the molecule itself polar if they are arranged right. Consider the water and carbon dioxide molecules shown in *Figure 23.4*. Both water and carbon dioxide contain polar bonds. The water molecule is highly polar. In water, the two O–H bond dipoles are bent with respect to each other in a way that their charge separation adds together, yielding a net dipole for the molecule. But in carbon dioxide, the two C=O dipoles point in opposite directions, effectively cancelling each other out. Therefore, even though the bonds are polar, the net polarization in the carbon dioxide molecule is zero (see *Figure 23.5*).

**Intermolecular:**

Between molecules (as opposed to intramolecular, within molecules).

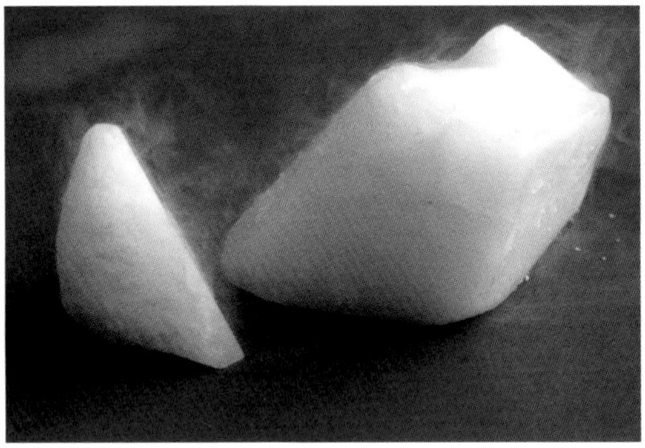

**Figure 23.5**

Because carbon dioxide has no net molecular dipole, its molecules do not stick together well, and consequently its melting point is lower than that of water. This is why dry ice ($CO_2$ in its solid form) is much colder than the average ice cube. This is also why $CO_2$ is difficult to liquify—the molecules do not stick together well enough to easily form a liquid, but will crystallize into a solid if they are sufficiently cold.

Because polar molecules have permanent regions of positive and negative charge, they will attract and repel the corresponding negative and positive regions of other polar molecules. The oxygen end of the water molecule has a small excess negative charge which attracts the slightly positive hydrogen atoms in neighboring molecules. Water molecules therefore stick together quite well, making the melting and boiling points of water much higher than for nonpolar molecules of similar size.

The polarity of water molecules causes them to form extensive networked structures in both the liquid and solid states. A picture of the arrangement of water molecules in ice is shown in *Figure 23.6*. Note how the hydrogen atoms of each molecule are pointed at oxygen atoms

**Solvent:**

A material (typically a liquid) in which another material dissolves.

**Hydrogen Bonding:**

Interactions between hydrogen atoms bound to oxygen, nitrogen, or fluorine with other oxygen, nitrogen, or fluorine atoms. Hydrogen bonds are among the strongest intermolecular interactions.

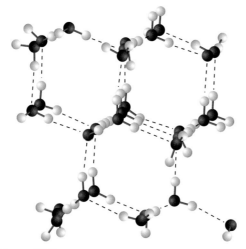

**Figure 23.6**

In this arrangement of water molecules in ice, note how the hydrogen atoms on one molecule point at oxygen atoms on adjacent molecules, leading to the open, hexagonal voids within the ice that contribute to its low density.

on neighboring molecules. The resulting empty hexagonal spaces within the ice give it a density lower than in the more disordered liquid. It is the polarity of water molecules and how they arrange themselves when solid that gives ice a density low enough to float in water.

The polarity of water causes ionic materials to be highly soluble within it. As you know, ionic materials consist of positive and negative ions. When placed in a polar liquid **solvent**, such as water, the positive ions are immediately surrounded by the negative ends of the molecular dipoles of the solvent and the negative ions are surrounded by the positive ends. This close attraction breaks the ionic material apart and disperses it throughout the solvent.

## Hydrogen Bonding

Hydrogen bound to oxygen or nitrogen is highly polarized creating a strong intermolecular force. This force is significant enough to be given a name of its own: **hydrogen bonding**. Hydrogen bonding between water molecules is responsible for the high melting and boiling points of water and for the structure and density of ice as described. Hydrogen bonding is very important in the way many large molecules interact with solvents.

Glucose $(C_6H_{12}O_6)$ is the main sugar that fuels the human body. A chain of carbon atoms covalently bound to each other forms the backbone of this organic molecule (*Figure 23.7*). A number of oxygen atoms, each with one hydrogen attached, are hung from the main carbon scaffold. These hydrogen-bonding groups of atoms and their overall arrangement on the molecule make glucose molecules "sticky" toward each other and also toward the proteins that make up human skin, explaining why pancake syrup is so sticky on your fingers.

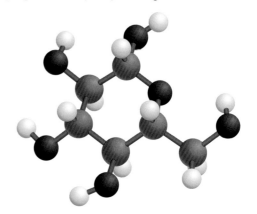

**Figure 23.7**

A glucose (sugar) molecule. The red balls represent oxygen atoms, the gray balls represent carbon, and the white balls represent hydrogen.

Glucose, having many highly polar parts and being overall polar itself, is highly soluble in water. When the water evaporates, interactions between these polar molecules make it energetically favorable to assemble the molecules into ordered lattices (*Figure 23.8*). So sugar, like water, naturally freezes into crystal shapes.

As you would expect with strongly interacting polar molecules, the melting and boiling points of glucose are quite high compared to similar molecules that lack hydrogen bonding.

**Figure 23.8**
Hydrogen bonding interactions in sugar cause the molecules to easily organize into large crystals. Table sugar is sucrose, which consists of a glucose molecule linked to another kind of sugar, fructose.

### Dispersion Forces

Dipole-dipole interactions and hydrogen bonding involve permanent, relatively strong dipoles. Non-polar atoms and molecules are also attracted to each other, albeit weakly. Even helium, the most non-polar material known, interacts with itself enough to condense and form a liquid at low temperatures. What makes helium atoms "sticky" with respect to each other?

The answer lies in the nature of the electron distribution around atoms. Electrons in orbitals do move. We cannot know exactly how they move but they do move. Without this movement there would be no polarized bonds. And for single atoms this movement causes the electron charge density to constantly change and fluctuate within each orbital. As electron density fluctuates, short-lived regions of excess or deficient negative charge form around each atom. When negative and positive regions on adjacent atoms match up, the two atoms are attracted to each other. Because this pairing is energetically favorable, plus-to-minus pairing occurs more often than the pairing of similar charges. The result is that all atoms are "sticky" toward each other to some degree. Intermolecular forces arising from the formation of these temporary dipoles have a number of different names, including "van der Waals forces" and **dispersion forces**. No matter how they are called, they tend to be very weak.

Nitrogen (see *Figure 23.9*), as previously mentioned, forms molecules of two atoms bound together by a strong triple covalent bond. The two nitrogen atoms in the $N_2$ molecule are identical, so the molecule has no dipole. This

**Figure 23.9**
Nitrogen is a purely covalent material and is therefore non-polar. Weak dispersion forces account for the attraction of $N_2$ molecules to each other. Because the intermolecular attraction is weak, low temperatures are required to liquefy nitrogen (liquid nitrogen boils at 77 K or -321 °F).

means that the only force between $N_2$ molecules is the weak dispersion force. Low temperatures are required to liquefy or solidify nitrogen. Only at low temperatures is the kinetic energy of the molecules smaller than the dispersion forces, allowing the molecules to stick together and become liquid or, at even lower temperatures, solid.

We can rank intermolecular forces by the relative amounts of energy required to separate atoms or molecules from each other (*Figure 23.10*). Dispersion forces between atoms or nonpolar molecules are the weakest. These materials have very low melting and boiling temperatures. Interactions between dipoles are roughly ten times stronger and substances with

**Dispersion Forces:**

Weak intermolecular attraction arising from the formation of temporary dipoles in non-polar molecules. Also known as van der Waals forces.

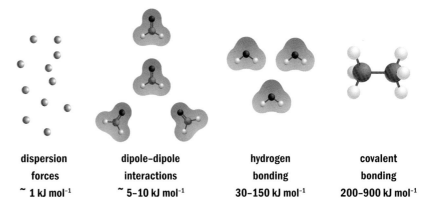

| dispersion forces | dipole–dipole interactions | hydrogen bonding | covalent bonding |
|---|---|---|---|
| ~ 1 kJ mol⁻¹ | ~ 5–10 kJ mol⁻¹ | 30–150 kJ mol⁻¹ | 200–900 kJ mol⁻¹ |

**Figure 23.10**
Relative strengths of molecular interactions. (kJ mol–1 means kilojoules per mole; mole is a standard measure of an amount of a substance.)

dipolar molecules have higher melting and boiling points. Hydrogen bonding is a special case of dipole-dipole interaction, and is about ten times stronger still. For comparison, the covalent bonding within molecules is shown and it is roughly ten times stronger than hydrogen bonding.

## 23–4 Network Bonding

Covalent bonding does not always create molecules. Substances like carbon can bond covalently to form networks or extended bonding substances in the same manner as the ionic and metallic bonds. Diamond and graphite are both forms of covalently bound pure carbon, but the arrangement of their atoms gives them remarkably contrasting properties.

In diamond, each carbon atom has a single covalent bond to each of four neighboring carbon atoms. The result is a 3-dimensional network of strong covalent interactions (*Figure 23.11*). Given this structure, it is not surprising that diamond is one of the hardest known materials. With each of the carbon atoms being held rigidly in place by four strong covalent bonds, it is very hard to deform.

It is also not surprising that diamond has a very high melting point. The network of bonds makes the whole diamond crystal behave as one giant molecule. Melting requires breaking strong covalent bonds, not weaker intermolecular attractions, so when heated it tends to decompose by reacting with surrounding materials rather than melt.

Graphite consists of 2-dimensional networks or planes of carbon atoms held together by covalent bonds (*Figure 23.12*). The various planes of atoms are held together by weak intermolecular forces.

The covalently-bonded planes of atoms behave as giant molecules and, graphite, like diamond, can't easily be melted; it too tends to decompose at high temperatures rather than melt. On the other hand, because the forces between the planes are weak, the planes of

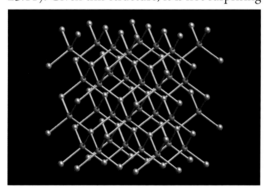

**Figure 23.11**

The arrangement of carbon atoms in diamond. Each atom is covalently bound to four other atoms.

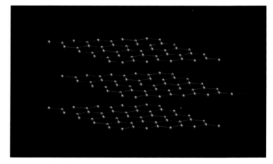

**Figure 23.12**

The arrangement of carbon atoms in graphite. Each carbon atom is bound to three neighboring carbon atoms, forming 2-dimensional covalent networks (planes) of atoms. Weak intermolecular forces hold the planes together.

**Self-ionization:**

The reaction of certain neutral molecules (such as water) with other identical molecules to produce cations and anions.

**pH:**

A logarithmic measure of the concentration of hydronium ($H_3O^+$) ions in water. pH values less than 7 describe acidic solutions, pH = 7 is neutral (that is, the pH of pure water is 7), and pH values greater than 7 indicate the solution is basic.

**Acidic:**

Having a pH value less than 7, meaning that the hydronium ion concentration is greater than in pure water.

**Basic:**

Having a pH value greater than 7, meaning that the hydronium ion concentration is less than in pure water.

## ACIDS AND BASES

Hydrogen bonding in water is so extensive that there is even a weak tendency for water molecules to transfer H+ in the reaction $2H_2O = OH- + H_3O+$ (about one molecule in every 10 million does this in pure water). The ions that form from this **self-ionization** of water, $H_3O+$ and OH–, are called hydronium and hydroxide ions, respectively.

The addition of compounds called acids to water increases the tendency to form hydronium ions. Acids can cause the concentration of hydronium ions in water to vary over many orders of magnitude. Hydronium ion concentration is measured using the **pH** scale, which expresses hydronium ion concentration logarithmically. Thus, a change of 1 in pH corresponds to a factor of 10 change in concentration, a change of 2 pH units corresponds to a 100-fold change in concentration, and so on. Pure water has a pH of 7 and is said to be neutral. Lower values of pH have larger hydronium ion concentrations and are said to be **acidic**. Values of pH greater than 7 have lower hydronium ion concentrations and are said to be **basic**.

The pH of water can have large effects on its chemical properties. For example, the solubilities of many compounds increase, sometimes dramatically, when the concentration of $H_3O+$ increases. Biological processes are especially sensitive to pH. When sulfur oxide gases released during the combustion of coal dissolve in water, they can make the water quite acidic, resulting in "acid rain" that kills trees and fish and dissolves the rock in monuments.

atoms easily slip with respect to each other making graphite soft and suitable as a lubricant.

## 23-5 Molecular Ions

The atoms in some binding situations have too many or too few electrons to accommodate them all. For example a neutral atom with an odd number of electrons bonding with an atom that has an even number cannot have all of them paired. At least one electron will be by itself which is energetically unfavorable.

For covalent bonding to work in such cases, electrons must be lost or gained resulting in a charged polyatomic **molecular ion**. Bonding *within* these multi-atomic ions is covalent, while bonding *between* molecular ions and other ions is ionic.

Molecular ions are common in nature. A few important molecular ions (*Figure 23.13*) include nitrate ($NO_3^-$), sulfate ($SO_4^{2-}$), silicate ($SiO_4^{4-}$), and ammonium ($NH_4^+$). These ions often bond with simple monoatomic ions like $Na^+$, $K^+$, $F^-$, $Cl^-$, etc.

Materials formed from molecular ions have the properties expected for ionic substances. They form crystals, they have high melting points, they conduct electricity when melted or in solution, and they dissolve in polar solvents like water.

The minerals that make up Earth are mostly formed from molecular ions, with v and related ions being the most common. Silicate has the ability to share its oxygen atoms with neighboring silicate groups as will be described further in Chapter 24.

**Molecular Ions:**
Groups of atoms covalently bound to each other that have a net charge because electrons have been lost or gained to facilitate formation of the covalent bonds. Also called polyatomic ions.

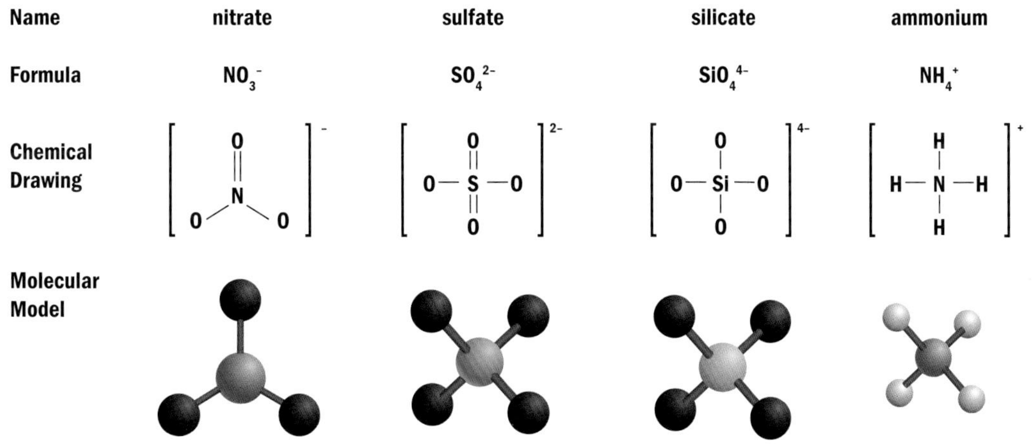

| Name | nitrate | sulfate | silicate | ammonium |
|---|---|---|---|---|
| Formula | $NO_3^-$ | $SO_4^{2-}$ | $SiO_4^{4-}$ | $NH_4^+$ |

**Figure 23.13**
A few important polyatomic ions

## Chapter Framework

### A. Properties of Covalent Compounds
1. Wide range of melting and boiling points
2. Usually electrical insulators

### B. Model for Covalent Bonding
1. Non-metals bond with each other by sharing valence electrons
2. Single, double, and triple bonds depend on the number of shared valence electrons

### C. Molecules
1. Covalent materials exist as individual molecules
2. Each molecule has a shape and has the properties of the material

### D. Bond Polarity
1. Electrons may not be shared equally in a bond
2. The electronegativity of the atom determines how strong electrons are attracted
3. Bonds with unequal sharing are polar

### E. Intermolecular Forces
1. Chemical bonds between molecules are weaker than bonds within
2. Types of intermolecular forces, from weakest to strongest
   a. *Dispersion forces*
   b. *Dipole-dipole interactions*
   c. *Hydrogen bonds*

### F. Properties of Covalent Materials
1. Molecular substances (nitrogen, water, glucose)
2. Network solids
   a. *Diamond, graphite as examples*
   b. *Properties depend on arrangement of atoms*
3. Molecular ions
   a. *Binding within the ion is covalent*
   b. *Binding between the ions is ionic*

## Comprehension

### Matching

1. ____ The chemical bond between two non-metals characterized by sharing of valence electrons.
2. ____ A separation of charge with one positive side and one negative side
3. ____ A material in which another material dissolves.
4. ____ Having a pH value less than 7, meaning that the hydronium ion concentration is greater than in pure water.
5. ____ Chemical compounds between the elements carbon and hydrogen. The compounds that make up gasoline are examples.
6. ____ Ions composed of more than one covalently-bound atom.
7. ____ A covalent bond involving two pairs of electrons shared between the two bound atoms.
8. ____ Bonds or molecules having an unequal

a. Molecular ions
b. Intermolecular force
c. Double bond
d. Polar
e. Covalent bond
f. Hydrocarbons
g. Dipole
h. Solvent
i. Acidic

distribution of charge (one end being positive, the other negative).
9. ____ Forces between molecules.

### True/False
1. ____ Covalent bonding occurs between non-metal atoms.
2. ____ Metal and non-metal substances combine to form molecules.
3. ____ Molecular substances exhibit both covalent and intermolecular interactions.
4. ____ Covalent molecules do not have well-defined shapes.
5. ____ The triple covalent bond of carbon monoxide (CO) is a type of weak chemical interaction.
6. ____ Dispersion forces occur between non-polar molecules.

## Analysis

1. Which type of bonding involves the sharing of electrons?
   a) Ionic bonding
   b) Covalent bonding
   c) Chemical bonding
   d) Physical bonding

2. Which of these substances consists of individual molecules?
   a) Diamond (C)
   b) Graphite (C)
   c) Water ($H_2O$)
   d) Sodium chloride (NaCl)
   e) Hydrogen ($H_2$)
   f) Chlorine ($Cl_2$)
   g) Ammonia ($NH_3$)

3. Which of the following pairs of elements would you expect to be covalently bonded (no ionic or metallic bond)?
   a) $_{27}Co$ and $_{28}Ni$
   b) $_{19}K$ and $_9F$
   c) $_{15}P$ and $_8O$
   d) $_{11}Na$ and $_{53}I$

4. Determine the metal or non-metal nature of C and O. The compounds $CO_2$ and CO exist. What prediction can you make about their properties?
   a) Metallic alloy, conducting
   b) Transparent gas
   c) Metallic alloy, nonconducting
   d) Brittle, transparent solid, non-conducting

## Synthesis

1. What kind of bonding (metallic, ionic, or covalent) do you expect within a hydrocarbon molecule? Why? What kind of interactions (dispersion, dipole-dipole, or hydrogen bonding) do you expect to be important between hydrocarbon molecules? Why? Do you expect relatively high or relatively low boiling points for hydrocarbons?

2. Classify the following bonds as polar or non-polar. For the polar bonds, label which atom is more positive.

   a) The bond between two hydrogen atoms.

   b) The bond between hydrogen and chlorine.

   c) The bond between sodium and chlorine.

   d) The bond between carbon and hydrogen in a $CH_4$ molecule.

   e) The bond between carbon and oxygen in a carbon dioxide molecule.

3. Based on molecular polarities, predict:

   a) How will the solubility of sodium chloride in very polar water compare to the solubility of sodium chloride in moderately polar ethanol? Explain.

   b) Glycerol is a moderately polar solute. In what type of solvent would you expect glycerol to have the higher solubility, in a polar solvent or in a non-polar one? Explain.

4. Both graphite and diamond are forms of pure carbon. Explain why diamond is one of the hardest known substances, whereas graphite is a soft, lubricating material. If both are pure carbon, how can they be so different?

5. Very low temperatures are required to liquefy helium. Based on your understanding of intermolecular forces, explain why this is so.

6. The boiling temperatures of several members of the family of straight-chain hydrocarbons ($CH_4$, $CH_3CH_3$, $CH_3CH_2CH_3$, etc.) and the related family that contains a single –OH group on the last carbon ($CH_3OH$, $CH_3CH_2OH$, $CH_3CH_2CH_2OH$, etc.) are plotted as a function of chain length.

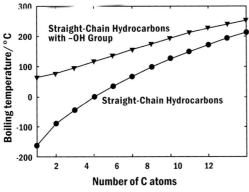

   a) Describe the trend in boiling temperature for each family. (Do boiling points increase or decrease with increasing molecular size?)

   b) For a given number of carbon atoms, which family boils at a higher temperature?

   c) On the basis of the graphs, what might you predict about the boiling temperatures of a straight-chain hydrocarbon and its relative with an –OH containing molecule if both have a very large number of carbon atoms.

   d) The boiling temperature reflects the strength of forces between (not within) molecules in the liquid state. The straight-chain hydrocarbon molecules are non-polar; intermolecular forces are of the dispersion (van der Waals) type. Using the data in the graph, formulate a hypothesis to explain why the larger straight-chain hydrocarbon molecules with more C atoms boil at higher temperatures than smaller molecules.

   e) The –OH containing molecules are polar; they experience hydrogen bonding as well as dispersion (van der Waals) forces. Hypothesize which force is stronger: that associated with dispersion forces or those involved in hydrogen bonding.

   f) Water boils at a very high temperature (100° C) given its small mass. Offer an explanation for this observation based on the hypotheses you have formulated for (d) and (e).

7. Complete the following:

   a) Compare and contrast metallic, ionic, and covalent bonding by selecting the better answer from the pair given for each statement.

| | Metallic Bonding | Ionic Bonding | Covalent Bonding |
|---|---|---|---|
| Bonds arise from electrostatic interactions | True / False | True / False | True / False |
| Electrons are localized on atoms | True / False | True / False | True / False |
| Energy levels are widely spaced | True / False | True / False | True / False |
| Occurs within molecules | True / False | True / False | True / False |
| Explained by the quantum mechanical model | True / False | True / False | True / False |
| Weak intermolecular interactions hold individual particles together | True / False | True / False | True / False |

   b) Using the differences noted in your answers to part a), explain why metals and molecular materials usually absorb light well, whereas salts tend to be transparent.

   c) Using the similarities you noted in your answers to part a), identify which of the fundamental interactions (gravitational, electromagnetic, strong nuclear, or weak nuclear) is responsible for all forms of chemical bonding.

8. Complete the following:

   a) Compare and contrast intermolecular interactions by selecting the better answer from the pair given for each statement.

| | Dispersion | Dipole-dipole | Hydrogen Bonding |
|---|---|---|---|
| Arises from electrostatic interactions | True / False | True / False | True / False |
| Occurs only for polar molecules | True / False | True / False | True / False |
| Occurs only when nitrogen or oxygen atoms are bound to hydrogen | True / False | True / False | True / False |
| Involves short-lived regions of excess charge | True / False | True / False | True / False |

   b) Rank the intermolecular interactions from strongest to weakest.

   c) Using what you know about the relative strengths of the intermolecular interactions, order the following materials from lowest to highest boiling points: ammonia ($NH_3$), nitrogen gas ($N_2$), and nitric oxide (NO).

# Animal, Vegetable, Mineral—
# It's All Chemistry

*Better living through chemistry.*

*the slogan of an American chemical company in the 1970s*

## 24

## LEARN

- How saturated and unsaturated fatty acids differ on the molecular level and how those differences contribute to their physical state at room temperature.

- The major constituent fatty acids in fats compared to those found in oils [saturated vs. unsaturated] and how to categorize them as "good" and "bad" fats.

- The basic building block of silicate minerals.

- How the bonding in asbestos, mica, and quartz gives rise to different properties such as morphology in these materials.

Chemists like to call chemistry the "central science" because atoms and molecules are at the basis of all materials and most natural processes. Do you know that molecules change in your eyes, your nervous system and your brain every time a photon strikes your retina and you "see" blue sky or red tulips? Were you born brunette but are dying to be a blonde? Do you have straight hair but want curly locks? Hair dyes and the products for permanents and straighteners all have their roots (pun intended) in chemical principles. Do you like to climb rocks? Do you know that differences at the atomic level make climbing on sandstone more dangerous than climbing on granite?

In this last chapter devoted to chemistry, there isn't time to delve deeply into all the fascinating areas of biological chemistry, food science, cosmetology, pharmacology, atmospheric chemistry, or geochemistry. So we have selected two areas to highlight, choosing them because they involve families of naturally-occurring materials. Both have important applications in our everyday life.

The first presentation introduces a molecular family called fatty acids and their role in human health. The second focuses on extended network structures of geological minerals. Taken together, these examples illustrate that chemical principles apply across diverse materials. Both also show that our understanding of these principles can lead to new products and better lives.

## 24–1 Fatty Acids

What are fatty acids and why should you care about them? Perhaps you or some member of your family counts calories and worries about the fat content in your diet. As you read the nutrition labels, like those shown in *Figure 24.1*, on your favorite butter, margarine, or cooking oil, you may encounter terms like "saturated fats," "unsaturated fats," and "trans-fats." You might also read that some fats are good, even essential, for your body to function. Advertisements you come across tout the absence of

**Figure 24.1**

Nutrition labels from a) margarine and b) olive oil.

"trans-fats" or the presence of "omega"-fatty acids in products.

Can we make sense of all this? Yes. You now have the tools to understand how fats look and work on the molecular level. This will help you to see why some are desirable to humans and some are not.

### Fats and Oils

Let's begin our study of fats and fatty acids by considering six samples of high-fat substances: shortening, butter, stick margarine, olive oil, canola oil, and a "buttery spread" shown at room temperature in *Figure 24.2*. Notice how some are liquids at room temperature, some are solids, and some are a blend.

Throughout our presentations on bonding we have referred to melting and boiling points as a way to estimate forces between molecules. By cooling down the liquids and heating up the solids, we can measure the temperatures at which these materials undergo the solid-liquid change of state.

*Figures 24.3* and *24.4* show these same substances cooled to the temperature of dry ice (–78° C) and heated to 70° C. At the low temperature of dry ice, all six are solids. At the higher temperature, all are liquids. If you were to monitor the state changes upon cooling, you would notice that the olive oil solidified before the canola oil did. Upon heating, the margarine, then the butter, and finally the shortening liquefied. Starting from the conditions of *Figure 24.3*, with all substances as cold solids, you would get the following ordering of melting temperatures as the substances heated up:

→

| canola oil | olive oil | buttery spread | stick margarine | butter | shortening |

While measuring the melting points of these substances you would also notice something strange. We have noted earlier that water melts exactly at 0° C and copper melts sharply at 1083° C, but our test materials melt over a *range* of temperatures, not at a *single* temperature. Why is this?

Melting point behavior tells something about the purity of a material. Pure substances change physical state at a single temperature. Matter that is a mixture of multiple substances changes its physical state over a broad range of temperature. So, from our observations, we can conclude that each of these six samples is a mixture and not a pure compound.

Of course these foodstuffs can be characterized more fully than by just measuring melting points. Food scientists have identified the various components of each fat or oil by separating each mixture into its components and then using the instrumental techniques described in Chapter 19 to identify each component.

We label fatty substances as **fats** or **oils** on the basis of their melting points, with fats being solid at room temperature and oils being liquid. Current thinking is that oils are better for your health than fats. Fats lead to solid-state

### Fats and Oils:

Fats and oils are substances that do not dissolve in water, but can dissolve in hydrocarbon liquids. Fats are solid at room temperature; oils are liquid at room temperature.

**Figure 24.2**

Six fatty substances as seen at room temperature: a) stick margarine, b) butter, c) shortening, d) a "buttery" spread, e) canola oil, and f) olive oil. Some are soft solids, others are liquid.

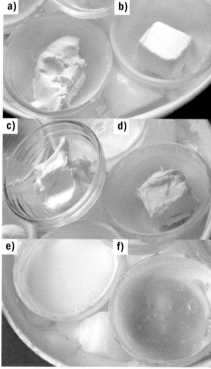

**Figure 24.3**

The state of these test substances when cooled to –78° C. All are solids at this temperature.

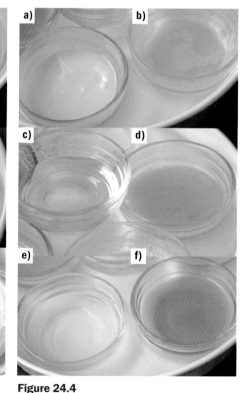

**Figure 24.4**

The state of these test substances when heated to 70° C. All substances are liquid at this temperature.

artery-clogging deposits that cause heart attacks and strokes. Oils with their lower melting temperatures do not appear to be as much of a problem in this regard.

## Triglycerides

All fats and oils contain a molecule called glycerol. *Figure 24.5* shows its structure. Glycerol is a small molecule, containing only three carbon atoms. Each carbon atom has one –OH group attached to it. These groups enable glycerol to react readily with molecules that belong to the family of organic acids.

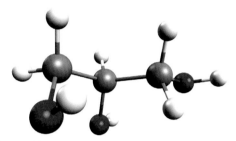

**Figure 24.5**
The molecular structure of glycerol, C3H8O3, which lies at the base of all fats and oils. The atom colors are O red, C gray, and H white.

Remember from Chapter 19 that an organic acid molecule contains the group:

$$\begin{matrix} O \\ \| \\ -C-OH \end{matrix}$$

We shall use the notation –COOH to represent this molecular group for conciseness.

A basic example of a glycerol + acid reaction is shown in *Figure 24.6*. Acetic acid, a simple organic acid found in vinegar, has been chosen to represent a typical organic acid. Each acid molecule "attacks" an –OH group on the glycerol molecule. During the reaction, the H atom on each OH group of glycerol and the entire –OH group on each acid are removed and combined to become water. At this same time bonds form between each organic acid and the glycerol molecule at the sites where the atoms were removed. The product, a molecule containing three acids hooked to glycerol, is called a **triglyceride**. Most fats and oils are triglycerides. A few fats and oils (mono- or diglycerides) have only one or two fatty acids.

If you have ever had your blood analyzed by a doctor, you may have seen your blood triglyceride level included in the report. Since the acid molecules attached to the glycerol in fats

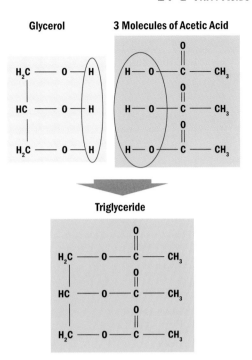

**Figure 24.6**
A simple example of the reaction of glycerol with three acid molecules. Acetic acid is a simple acid; the reaction with fatty acids is similar. The circled atoms are removed in the reaction, and bonds are formed that connect each acid molecule with glycerol.

are different from those found in oils, the nature of the triglycerides found in your blood reflects your diet, especially your intake of fats and oils. In fact, the behavior of triglycerides is dominated by the nature of fatty acids. So let us look at them in more detail.

## Fatty Acids—Saturated and Unsaturated

### Saturated Fatty Acids

The acids most commonly found in fats and oils, called **fatty acids**, contain long hydrocarbon chains with a –COOH at the end. You have already seen two fatty acid molecules: Lauric acid (Figure 19.5m) and oleic acid (Figure 19.5n).

*Figure 24.7* presents names, melting temperatures, molecular formulas, sources, and structures of fatty acids that are important in natural fats and oils. Look first at the molecular structures on the left under the heading of "Saturated Fatty Acids." These molecules are long chains of C atoms linked together in a zig-zag fashion. The –COOH group sits at one end of every fatty acid molecule. Every carbon atom but the two at either end of the molecule is bonded to two H atoms. One molecule in this class differs from another only by the number of

**Triglyceride:**

A large molecule created by reacting three fatty acids with glycerol.

**Fatty Acids:**

A molecule with a long hydrocarbon tail and an acid group –COOH at the other end.

| Saturated Fatty Acids | | Unsaturated Fatty Acids | |
|---|---|---|---|
| **Name** | **Structure** | **Name** | **Structure** |

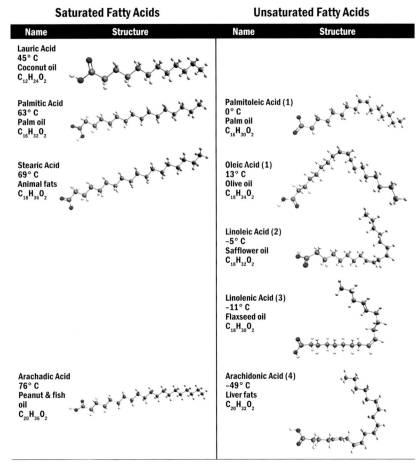

Lauric Acid
45° C
Coconut oil
$C_{12}H_{24}O_2$

Palmitic Acid
63° C
Palm oil
$C_{16}H_{32}O_2$

Stearic Acid
69° C
Animal fats
$C_{18}H_{36}O_2$

Arachadic Acid
76° C
Peanut & fish oil
$C_{20}H_{36}O_2$

Palmitoleic Acid (1)
0° C
Palm oil
$C_{16}H_{30}O_2$

Oleic Acid (1)
13° C
Olive oil
$C_{18}H_{34}O_2$

Linoleic Acid (2)
–5° C
Safflower oil
$C_{18}H_{32}O_2$

Linolenic Acid (3)
–11° C
Flaxseed oil
$C_{18}H_{30}O_2$

Arachidonic Acid (4)
–49° C
Liver fats
$C_{20}H_{32}O_2$

**Figure 24.7**

Examples of saturated and unsaturated fatty acids with their melting points and chemical formulas. Also given are the fats or oils in which these fatty acids are the major component. The number of double bonds are given in parentheses for unsaturated fatty acids.

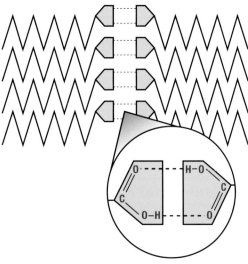

**Figure 24.8**

The packing of saturated fatty acid molecules in the solid state. The zig-zag lines represent the hydrocarbon tails and the blue shapes represent the –COOH group. The dashed lines represent the hydrogen bonds that hold pairs of acid molecules together in the solid. Details of the hydrogen bonds are shown below. The close packing of the hydrocarbon tail leads to the formation of many van der Waals interactions. These forces cause saturated fatty acids to be solids at room temperature.

–$CH_2$ groups. The melting point of a saturated fatty acid increases with increasing chain length.

*Figure 24.8* represents in a simple way how saturated fatty acid molecules pack together in the solid state. The –C–C– chain is shown as a zig-zag line, and the blue shape represents the acid group. Notice how the herringbone structure of each molecule allows them to tightly pack together when solid. Being close together, the dispersion intermolecular forces can hold the molecules more tightly together when solid. As the number of atoms in the molecule increases, more dispersion interactions become possible. It takes more energy to break these interactions, and so the melting point increases as the number of –$CH_2$– units in the molecule increases.

Hydrogen bonding provides additional attraction. The enlargement of *Figure 24.8* shows details of the hydrogen-bonding interactions between the –COOH structures at the end.

## Unsaturated Fatty Acids

Go back to Figure 24.7 and look at the unsaturated fatty acids in the right column. Compare saturated/unsaturated pairs of molecules that contain the same number of carbon atoms such as palmitic and palmitoleic, stearic and oleic, stearic and linoleic, arachidic and arachidonic acids.

The term "saturated" indicates that the molecule contains the maximum possible number of H atoms. The saturated molecule in each pair therefore contains more H atoms than its unsaturated partner.

Recall that C atoms can make four bonds. If H atoms are absent in unsaturated molecules, each C atom still makes four bonds by forming double bonds with the adjacent C atom. Each C atom in a double-bonded pair is bonded to three other atoms; two C and an H. Carbon atoms that form only single bonds are connected to four other atoms; two C and two H. The geometry around a C atom with bonds to four atoms is different from the bonding geometry to only three atoms (Figure 19.6). The change in bonding geometry gives rise to kinks in the molecular structure.

The kinks in the structures greatly affect the properties of unsaturated fatty acids. Consider the melting temperatures of saturated/unsaturated pairs of molecules containing the same number of C atoms such as stearic and oleic acids. The effect of double bonds is to lower the melting point. All of the unsaturated fatty acids are liquids at room temperature. In going from saturated stearic acid to unsaturated oleic acid, the melting point decreases by 56° C even though the molecules differ only by two small H atoms.

Because dispersion interactions are weak, it seems somewhat surprising that removing only two H atoms can lead to such a huge reduction in melting points. Another factor must contribute. *Figure 24.9* identifies that factor—the inability of unsaturated fatty acids to pack tightly together in the solid.

The structural kink introduced at each double bond in an unsaturated fatty acid molecule

**Figure 24.9**

The packing of unsaturated fatty acids in the solid state. Double bonds introduce kinks that prevent the neat, efficient packing found in saturated fatty acids. Because the unsaturated molecules cannot get as close to each other, van der Waals interactions decrease. Thus, the melting points decrease as well, making unsaturated fatty acids liquids at room temperature.

makes tight packing impossible. As Figure 24.9 shows, trying to pack the left-hand side of the molecules closely together forces the right-hand side to either pack less efficiently or to have atoms trying to be in the same space. Overall, the dispersion interactions decrease between

**Trans-fatty Acids:**

A non-natural form of unsaturated fatty acids in which H atoms are on opposite sides of the double bond. Cis fatty acids are the natural form. H atoms are on the same side of the double bond.

## TRANS-FATTY ACIDS—A NEW HEALTH HAZARD?

While unsaturated fats appear to be more heart-healthy than saturated fats, they do have some downsides. The double bonds represent sites of high chemical reactivity, especially to oxygen. Butter left out on a warm kitchen counter goes rancid when the double bonds present in the oleic acid component react with oxygen in the air.

To increase shelf-life and prepare fats with a higher melting point, manufacturers can add hydrogen back into unsaturated fats turning them into saturated fats. A nutrition label on a food product that says "includes partially hydrogenated oil" indicates that these chemically altered fats are part of the product. Shortening, for example, starts out as a liquid oil that is hydrogenated to form a solid containing a high proportion of saturated fats.

Under the conditions in which the hydrogenation process takes place, a second reaction can occur simultaneously. This other reaction causes a change in the bonding geometry around double bonds. All naturally-occurring unsaturated fatty acids have both H atoms on the same side of the double bond (*Figure 24.10a*). During the hydrogenation process, unsaturated fatty acids can be transformed into molecules in which the H atoms are now on opposite sides of the double bond (Figure 24.10b).

The Greek words *cis* and *trans* are used to describe the two types of geometries around the double bond. *Cis* applies to the natural fats in which H atoms are on the same side; *trans* fats, produced during hydrogenation reactions, have H atoms across the double bond.

Trans-fatty acids resemble saturated fatty acids in their overall structure. The molecules are almost linear, with only small kinking at the double bond. *Figure 24.11* contrasts oleic acid (a), which is a cis-fatty acid, with its trans 18-carbon counterpart, elaidic acid (b). Current research suggests that these trans-fatty acids cause even more problems than saturated fats. Trans fats are implicated in diabetes, obesity, cancer, and heart disease. Some studies also suggest that trans fats may displace important polyunsaturated fats in the brain, leading to mental disorders, including dementia. In 2003, the U.S. Food and Drug Administration issued a regulation requiring food manufacturers to include the trans fat content in the nutrition labeling of all products by January 1, 2006.

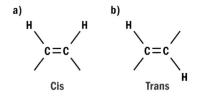

**Figure 24.10**

Unsaturated fatty acids may have both hydrogen atoms on the same side (a) or on opposite sides of the double bond (b).

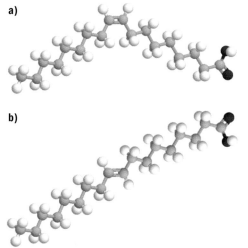

**Figure 24.11**

A comparison of the structure between oleic acid (a) and its trans counterpart elaidic acid (b).

**Saturated Fat:**

A triglyceride containing three saturated fatty acid molecules.

**Monounsaturated Fats:**

Mono = 1 in Greek. Fats containing fatty acids with a single double bond, such as oleic acid.

**Polyunsaturated Fats:**

*Poly* = many in Greek. Fats containing fatty acids with many double bonds, such as linolenic or arachidonic acid.

adjacent unsaturated molecules. This reduction decreases the overall intermolecular attractions which lowers the melting point.

### Triglycerides and Your Health

All of the saturated fatty acids shown in Figure 24.7 are solid at body temperature (37° C). When these fatty acids combine with glycerol to form triglycerides, the triglycerides become **saturated fats** which are also soft, sticky solids at body temperature.

Butter, shortening, and animal fats, all solids at room temperature, are triglycerides with a large proportion of saturated fatty acids. Shortening contains a high percentage of tristearin, the triglyceride formed from the reaction of three molecules of stearic acid (18 carbons) with glycerol. Animal fats contain mixed triglycerides with palmitic and stearic acids. Butter contains a mix of saturated fatty acid triglycerides and oleic-acid-containing triglycerides.

Triglycerides formed from unsaturated fats are usually liquid at room temperature and make up the oils we have considered in the experiments of Figures 24.2 through 24.4. When the triglycerides contain acids with one double bond, they are called **monounsaturated fats**. Those formed from acids with multiple double bonds are called **polyunsaturated fats**. Triolein, formed from glycerol and three oleic acid (18 carbons) molecules, is a monounsaturated fat found in olive oil. Other foods rich in monounsaturated fats include avocados and canola oil. Oils derived from plants (corn, peanut, sunflower) and some fish provide polyunsaturated fats.

Saturated fats belong to the "bad guys" of nutrition. A diet rich in saturated fats leads to increased levels of cholesterol and increased tendencies toward heart disease, obesity, and diabetes. Monounsaturated fats like olive oil appear to have a neutral effect on cholesterol levels, while some polyunsaturated fats (those high in linoleic acid) have been shown to lower cholesterol levels.

Several polyunsaturated fats are considered essential parts of a healthy diet. Two from Figure 24.7, linoleic and linolenic, are important precursors to other essential molecules in human metabolism. Because the human body does not synthesize these acids, they must be obtained in our diet. Arachidonic acid, present in fish

oils, is required for human brain development and function. Some research suggests that Alzheimer's disease and dementia may be tied to displacement in the brain of these natural acids with other acids.

This brief overview of fatty acids shows that the structure of even complex molecules can be explained through basic covalent bonding properties. Molecular structures, in turn, give rise to properties that can have profound influence on our health and well being.

## 24-2 Silicate Materials

Rocks are made of specific compounds that together are called "minerals" as described in Chapter 29. The rock that you pick up on a mountain hike or the stone that you skip along the surface of a lake are generally not a pure mineral but an aggregate of different minerals blended together. Of these, chances are good that many of them are from a specific class called "silicates." The silicate mineral family forms a rich diversity of materials with interesting structures and properties.

The underlying atomic structure of minerals, as with fatty acids, gives rise to properties that are readily discerned with the naked eye. *Figure 24.12* shows images of three minerals based on the silicate ion. Asbestos shown in Figure 24.12a is made up of thread-like fibers. The fibers can be easily separated, but individual fibers are so strong that they can be woven into fabrics or matted into sheets that are fireproof and heat insulating. Unfortunately, very small bits of the fibers of some forms of asbestos can cause cancer if inhaled into the lungs and so care must be taken in handling it.

Mica, shown in Figure 24.12b, is composed of layered sheets of material loosely stuck together. The layers typically have a uniform thickness and one layer separates easily from another. Simply picking at it with a fingernail can provide enough force to separate layers.

The third mineral, quartz, is shown in Figure 24.12c. Quartz cannot be pulled apart easily. To break a quartz crystal into smaller pieces requires much more force than pulling fibers or layers apart with tweezers or your fingernails. Hammers and chisels are required, and the resulting pieces have very irregular shapes.

The chemical elements making up these

a)
b)
c)

**Figure 24.12**
Three mineral specimens that illustrate different crystal morphologies.
a) An asbestos sample composed of fibers.
b) A mica sample composed of layers or sheets.
c) A quartz sample that breaks into irregular-shaped pieces when shattered with a hammer.

minerals are essentially the same but their **morphologies** could hardly be more different. One is thread-like, the second layer-like, and the third one is block-like. What gives rise to this property of a mineral, whether it can be easily pulled apart into fibers or sheets or can only be broken into irregular-shaped chunks by hitting with a hammer?

In the early 1800s, scientists began to appreciate that the morphology of minerals was related to the underlying atomic structure and chemical bonding. Today, with the help of techniques already discussed such as x-ray diffraction and interference, geologists have determined the three-dimensional arrangement of atoms in even very complex minerals. Let's see how this applies to the three minerals of Figure 24.12.

### The Silicate Ion

The building block of all silicate minerals is the silicate ion which has the formula $SiO_4^{4-}$. This ion is a covalently-bonded molecule con-

**Morphology:**
The form or structure of a material. Asbestos, mica, and quartz all use silicates as a common basic building block. However, these building blocks are connected differently in the three materials. They each have different structures. Consequently, they have extremely different physical properties.

## ASBESTOS MATERIALS

The term asbestos refers to a group of six different minerals, all with a fibrous morphology. The fibers of five of these minerals reflect atomic-level structures like those described in the text. The sixth, chrysotile, also known as white asbestos, has an underlying structure that is layer-like, but the layers curl up to form fibers just like a flat carpet can be rolled up to form a tube. In all six minerals, bonding within each fiber is stronger than between adjacent fibers.

The fibers of these six minerals are strong and resistant to heat, light, and most chemicals and microbes. They are also electrical insulators and poor conductors of heat. These properties lend themselves to many important applications, including building materials such as heat insulation, flooring and ceiling tiles, and fire-resistant fabrics. Asbestos has also been used in clutches and brake linings of automobiles and to reinforce concrete on highways.

While the fiber structure of asbestos minerals led to its widespread use in building materials, that structure poses potential health problems. Very small fibers can be sloughed off, like dead skin, from surfaces subjected to repeated mechanical activity. Once in the air, the fibers can be inhaled into the lungs where they can be trapped. Chronic exposure to the fibers has been shown to cause lung cancer and other lung-related diseases. Asbestos miners and construction workers using building materials containing asbestos were found to be at increased risk.

The U.S. Environmental Protection Agency has banned the use of asbestos. Stringent regulations control the remodeling or demolition of building sites shown to be significantly contaminated by asbestos. You may have seen such buildings swathed in plastic wrap and inhabited by workers in protective suits and breathing respirators.

There is some debate amongst geologists and toxicologists about whether all forms of asbestos require such expensive measures. For example, chrysotile fibers, the most commonly used form of asbestos, are not as toxic as the other forms. They may still be safe for some applications and expensive removal of all types of asbestos may be unnecessary.

The story of asbestos provides a lesson in the care with which we should adopt new technologies. It also points out that we should thoroughly investigate problems with technology before taking drastic, expensive remedies.

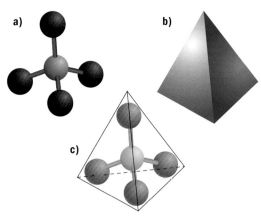

**Figure 24.13**

Three representations of the silicate ion ($SiO_4^{4-}$).

a) In the ball and stick model, the red balls represent oxygen ions ($O^{2-}$) and the blue ball represents a silicon ion ($Si^{4+}$).

b) The tetrahedron, a four-sided figure made up of equilateral triangles, is a simple way to represent the structure of the complex ion.

c) The $Si^{4+}$ ion is hidden in the center, and each vertex represents an oxygen ion.

sisting of a single Si atom surrounded by four O atoms. To satisfy the octet rule for all the atoms, the molecule must acquire four more electrons making it an ion with a negative charge of four units. This negative charge is shared equally among the four oxygen atoms.

The negative charge of the oxygen atoms keeps them as far apart from each other as possible. The resulting structure is a Si atom at the center of a tetrahedron with an O atom at each of its four vertices as shown in *Figure 24.13*. This is the same shape taken by C atoms bonded to four other atoms and for the same reason—it minimizes the electrostatic repulsions between the bonded atoms.

Silicate ions typically pick up their extra electrons from nearby metal atoms turning them into positive ions. These ions are then incorporated into the silicate structure. Like the ionic crystal formed by sodium chloride (Figure 22.3a), the positive and negative ions in silicate

minerals arrange themselves in an orderly fashion so that the total charge in the subsequent crystal exactly balances.

The particular ionic arrangement depends upon the size and charge of the positive ions as well as if and how the silicate ions connect together. Common singly-charged positive ions in silicates are those of sodium and potassium ($Na^+$, $K^+$). Common ions with double positive charges include magnesium, calcium, and iron ($Mg^{2+}$, $Ca^{2+}$, $Fe^{2+}$). Triply-charged aluminum ions ($Al^{3+}$) are also common.

The common mineral olivine is built upon silicate ions held together ionically by doubly charged Mg and/or Fe. The crystal formed follows the pattern of $M_2SiO_4$ where M stands for $Mg^{2+}$ or $Fe^{2+}$. *Figure 24.14a* and Figure 24.14b show the arrangement of positive ions and silicate tetrahedra in $Mg_2SiO_4$ and $Fe_2SiO_4$ and are drawn to scale. The pink balls represent $Mg^{2+}$ ions, the yellow ones represent $Fe^{2+}$ ions, and the blue tetrahedra represent the $SiO_4^{4-}$ ions.

Because the arrangement of ions is very similar in the two structures, it is common to find crystals that contain *both* $Mg^{2+}$ and $Fe^{2+}$ ions. Such a crystal is described by the formula $Mg_xFe_{2-x}SiO_4$. The subscript "x" varies between 0 for all Fe and 2 for all Mg. Notice that the sum of x and 2–x equals 2, so the atomic ratio of positive ions ($Mg^{2+}$ and $Fe^{2+}$) to silicate ions ($SiO_4^{4-}$) is still 2 to 1. A representation of a mixed crystal with a 1:1 ratio of $Mg^{2+}/Fe^{2+}$ is given in Figure 24.14c. Because the diameters of the $Mg^{2+}$ and $Fe^{2+}$ ions are nearly the same, in the mixed crystal one positive ion substitutes for the other without changing the crystal structure. X-ray diffraction studies can reveal whether a given position is preferentially filled by a $Mg^{2+}$ ion or an $Fe^{2+}$ ion, or whether positions are occupied randomly. (See "About Mixed Crystals" in this chapter.)

**Figure 24.14**

The arrangements of positive ions and silicate tetrahedra in one simple mineral shown as a projection. The three dimensional nature of the packing is not illustrated here. a) $Mg_2SiO_4$, b) $Fe_2SiO_4$ and c) a mixed crystal containing both $Mg^{2+}$ and $Fe^{2+}$ ions. Pink spheres are $Mg^{2+}$ ions, yellow ones are $Fe^{2+}$ ions and triangles represent the flattened tetrahedra. The ions are drawn approximately to scale.

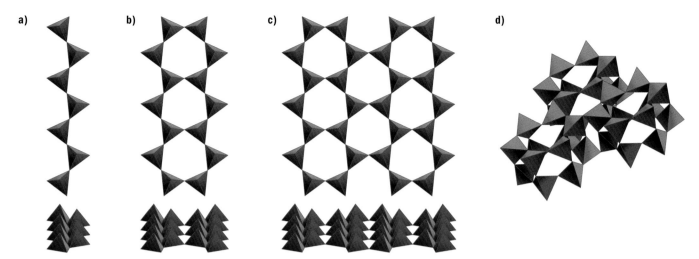

**Figure 24.15**

Silicate ions can link with each other by sharing oxygen ions.

a) Single chains form when two of the four oxygen ions of each tetrahedron are shared individually with two other silicate ions.

b) Double chains form when the single chains string together.

c) Sheets form when three corners of every tetrahedron are shared with three different tetrahedra.

d) Blocks form when all four corners of every tetrahedron are shared with four different tetrahedra in a 3-dimensional structure.

For linkage patterns a), b) and c), two views are shown, one looking down on the tetrahedra, the other looking at them just above edge-on.

When a silicate ion bonds with metal atoms as in olivine, the new material has all of the properties an ionic bond. It is crystalline, transparent, and brittle. It does not conduct electricity or heat and dissolves in water and other polar solvents.

### Connected Silicate Ions

Just as carbon atoms will bond with up to four different atoms in organic molecules, silicate ions will also form up to four bonds with other silicate ions by sharing oxygen atoms. Using the tetrahedral representation of silicate ions where each vertex represents an oxygen atom, *Figure 24.15* shows chains, double chains, and sheets and blocks of silicate structures. Two views are given, one looking down on the tetrahedra, the other looking edge-on at them. Oxygen atoms are shared everywhere vertices touch.

Asbestos is made of single or double silicate chains as shown in Figure 24.15 a) and b). Mica is made of silicate sheets as shown in Figure 24.15 c). Quartz is an entire interconnected block of silicate ions as shown in Figure 24.15 d).

Because oxygen atoms are shared at each link site, the ratio of silicon atoms to oxygen atoms in the structures shown in Figure 24.15 is not 1:4 as it is for isolated silicate ions. Rather, the ratios are 1:3 for chains, 1:2.75 for double chains, 1:2.5 for sheets, and 1:2 for blocks. A more complete list of such structures, together with the chemical formulas and the names of the minerals, is given in *Table 24.1*. Notice how the formulas reflect the given ratios.

As the number ratio of oxygen atoms decreases, so does the overall charge in the structure. In quartz, which shares oxygen atoms at every tetrahedral vertex, the ionic charge is reduced to zero. Quartz therefore does not incorporate metal ions in its structure. The entire mineral is covalently bonded together in a manner similar to the carbon atoms in a diamond. Small wonder that quartz crystals shatter irregularly when hit with a hammer.

The chain and sheet structures, though, still have a net negative charge and so incorporate positive ions into the structures they form. Mica is made up of linked sheets stacked with positive ions between the sheets. *Figure 24.16* shows a simplified representation of mica, in this case

| Table 24.1 — Silicate Structures | | | |
|---|---|---|---|
| **Type of Structure** | **Ratio of Si/O** | **Formula** | **Mineral Example** |
| Isolated tetrahedra | 1:4 | Si O4 | Olivine |
| Double tetrahedra | 1:3.5 | Si2 O7 | Epidote |
| Single chains | 1:3 | Si O3 | Pyroxene |
| Double chains | 1:2.75 | Si4 O11 | Asbestos |
| Sheets | 1:2.5 | Si2 O5 | Mica |
| Framework | 1:2 | Si O2 | Quartz |

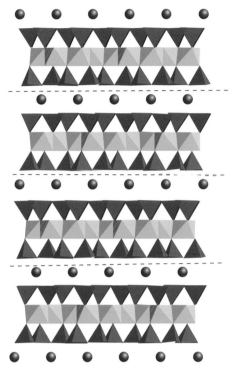

**Figure 24.16**

A simplified view of a mica structure, looking edge-on at the silicate tetrahedra. Two silicate layers (purple triangles) form a sandwich-like layer around the aluminum ions (shown as the blue shapes). Purple balls are positive ions such as K+ or Na+.

The double layer sandwich is tightly-bonded together. Peeling off a mica layer corresponds to breaking the weak interactions of the K+ or Na+ ions, leaving the sandwich unit intact. Possible fracture lines are shown as dashed black lines.

Remember that only a portion of the crystal is shown here. The crystal extends backward through the page and out at each side.

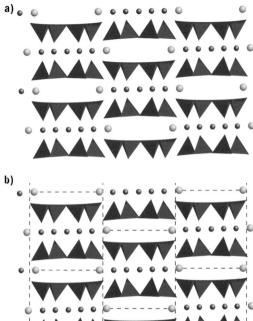

**Figure 24.17**

a) A simplified structure of one form of asbestos mineral showing the edges of double chains and the positive ions that hold them together. Remember that these are chains of silicate ions. In this figure, the chains extend backwards into the page. The small pink balls are small ions such as Mg2+, the larger blue balls represent the large Ca2+ ions. Two sets of double chains form an extended sandwich around the set of small ions. These units are strongly bonded together. The larger Ca2+ ions hold sandwich units together, but only weakly.

b) The same structure, but the black lines mark the weak bonding interactions where the structure will pull apart most easily. Remember that these structures extend back into the page, so that the fracture forms fibers.

bound together by Al, K and Na ions. Other metal ions can be incorporated into it as well just as in olivine.

In Figure 24.16 the teal blue shapes represent $Al^{3+}$ ions, the purple balls represent $K^+$ or $Na^+$ and the purple tetrahedra represent the silicate ions. Notice how the silicate sheets are separated by alternating layers of the two kinds of positive ions. Two silicate sheets are held tightly together by ionic bonding with the small, highly charged $Al^{3+}$ ions forming a sandwich-type structure. Adjacent sandwiches are held together by bonds with the larger +1 ions. Having a smaller charge and a larger diameter, these interactions are relatively weak. Peeling off layers from a piece of mica corresponds to pulling off groups of layers of sandwiches.[1]

Asbestos is made of sandwiches of single or, more commonly double chains held together by positive ions, in this case $Mg^{2+}$ and $Ca^{2+}$. A simplified view is shown in *Figure 24.17*. In this figure the pink and blue spheres represent $Mg^{2+}$ and $Ca^{2+}$ respectively.

The figure is a slice through a bundle of fibers that is oriented out of the page. Each unit of four tetrahedra pointing to four more tetrahedra with five $Mg^{2+}$ ions in between is the cross section of a double-chain fiber. These are ionically bound together strongly by the close proximity of the small $Mg^{2+}$ ions to the unbound O atoms on the chain.

Between these units are fewer, larger $Ca^{2+}$ ions. These ions bind the chains together with a much weaker attraction than the $Mg^{2+}$ ions. The black lines of Figure 24.17b trace the weakly bound interfaces. Parts held together by the strong $Mg^{2+}$ attraction stick together while separations occur along the surfaces held weakly by $Ca^{2+}$.

---

[1] Mica layers and asbestos fibers visible to the naked eye actually consist of many stacks of double-silicate layers and bundles of extended sandwiches, respectively. An individual double-silicate layer of Figure 24.16 or sandwich unit of Figure 24.17 would be too small to be seen.

# ABOUT MIXED CRYSTALS

**Why does nature prefer mixed crystals containing both $Mg^{2+}$ and $Fe^{2+}$ ions in $Mg_xFe_{2-x}SiO_4$ minerals?**

What fundamental principles might be involved in answering this question? What model could be formulated to guide our thinking about it?

Below is one line of reasoning to propose an answer. The reasoning is based on principles and concepts you have seen before. Perhaps you may want to formulate your own answers.

**Relevant Background Information:**

The principles of chemical reactivity suggest that a particular chemical product forms because it is lower in energy and/or higher in entropy than other possible products. The law of increasing disorder tells us that systems which are disordered have higher entropy than perfectly ordered ones. Since ions are involved, principles concerning electrostatic force laws and potential energy might be important.

**Formulation of Two Hypotheses:**

Hypothesis 1: Mixed crystals form because they are of lower energy than the pure crystals.

Hypothesis 2: Mixed crystals form because they have higher entropy than the pure crystals.

**Building a Model to Test the Hypotheses:**

Assume that pure crystals of $Mg_2SiO_4$, $Fe_2SiO_4$, and mixed crystals $Mg_xFe_{2-x}SiO_4$ are held together by ionic bonding interactions of +2 ions with the –4 silicate ion.

Assume that the $Mg^{2+}$ ions and $Fe^{2+}$ ions are about the same size. (Look at Figure 24.14 to see if this is a reasonable assumption.)

**The Analysis:**

Let's consider first whether there might be significant differences in energy between pure crystals and mixed crystals. The answer to the question boils down to whether there will be much difference in energy for the electrostatic interaction between Mg2+ ions and silicate ions from the interaction of Fe2+ions with silicate ions. The charges on the two ions are equal. The structures in Figure 24.14 are drawn approximately to scale and you can see that the distances between ions are about the same in size. Thus, our model suggests that electrostatic energies in the pure crystals and the mixed crystals would be about the same. Therefore, the push to form mixed crystals does not come from energy considerations. Hypothesis 1 no longer seems reasonable.

What about Hypothesis 2? The law of increasing disorder tells us that nature prefers disordered materials. The mixed crystal has more disorder than the two pure crystals, each containing only one cation. (The situation is analogous to the mixing of gases depicted in Figure 18.6.) Because our first hypothesis was judged to be false, it seems that nature's preference for mixed crystals in this family of minerals is due to the higher entropy of the mixed crystals. Experimental tests measuring the relative energies and entropies support our conclusions.

Is this conclusion the same for other mineral families? In more complicated mineral families than the one described here, additional disorder is possible. For example, there can be substitution of aluminum within the silicate tetrahedra. For minerals that form in the presence of water, hydroxide ions ($OH^-$) can sometimes replace an oxide ion ($O^{2-}$). In these minerals, both energy and entropy factors are involved in the specific patterns and mixtures of cations that are formed.

# 24 STUDY GUIDE

## Chapter Framework

### A. Fatty Acids

1. Fats and Oils
2. Triglycerides
3. Saturated and Unsaturated Fatty Acids
4. Triglycerides and Your Health
   a. *Saturated fats*
   b. *Monounsaturated fats*
   c. *Polyunsaturated fats*
5. Trans Fatty Acids

### B. Silicate Minerals

1. Bonding in Complex Inorganic Materials
2. Structure-Property Relationships in Silicate Minerals
3. Minerals with Isolated Silicate Tetrahedra
4. Minerals with Connected Silicate Tetrahedra

## Comprehension

### Matching

a. Silicate ion $(SiO_4{}^{4-})$
b. Saturated fatty acids
c. Asbestos
d. Quartz
e. Mica
f. Tetrahedron
g. Crystal
h. Unsaturated fatty acids

1. ____ Contains C=C double bonds.
2. ____ Contains only C–C single bonds.
3. ____ Best geometric arrangement of four single bonds around a central atom.
4. ____ Building block of many minerals.
5. ____ Organization of matter in which atoms or ions are arranged in an orderly, repeating patterns.
6. ____ Silicate mineral in which all silicate tetrahedra are bonded with equal strength to four other tetrahedra.
7. ____ Silicate mineral that has a super "foot-long" structure.
8. ____ Silicate mineral that has a layer-like structure.

### True or False

1. ____ The melting point of saturated fatty acids increases with increasing number of carbon atoms.
2. ____ An unsaturated fatty acid with the same number of carbon atoms as a saturated fatty acid will generally melt at a lower temperature than the saturated fatty acid.
3. ____ Ionic bonds hold fatty acid molecules together in the solid state.
4. ____ The –COOH group is what makes an organic acid an acid.
5. ____ The silicate ion $(SiO_4)4-$ is flat (planar) with the following structure:

6. ____ The underlying atomic structure of both fatty acids and minerals determines many properties, such as melting point and crystal morphology.
7. ____ Most forms of asbestos form fibers.
8. ____ Crystals of quartz flake off in thin sheets.
9. ____ "Mixed" crystals like $MgFeSiO_4$ are more disordered than either pure $Mg_2SiO_4$ or pure $Fe_2SiO_4$.
10. ____ Fractures occur in crystals along lines or planes containing the strongest bonds.
11. ____ The term "saturated" in saturated fats refers to whether every C atom has as many H atoms as it can hold.

### Fill in the Blank

1. A _____ contains three acids hooked to glycerol.
2. Fatty acids with the maximum number of H atoms are designated _____.
3. A solid is said to be _____ when its constituents are arranged in a definite, fixed pattern.
4. A silicate ion has the geometric shape of a _____.
5. _____ acids have H atoms on opposite sides of the double bond, whereas naturally occurring _____ acids have both H atoms on the same side of the double bond.

## Analysis

1. A triglyceride is made by combining
   a) glycerol and carbonate.
   b) organic acids and glycerol.
   c) glycerol and mica.
   d) asbestos and quartz.

2. Which of the following is **not** a mineral?
   a) Quartz
   b) Mica
   c) Arachidic acid
   d) Asbestos

3. Which of the following is an unsaturated fat?
   a) Palmitic acid
   b) Oleic acid
   c) Lauric acid
   d) Stearic acid

4. Fatty acid molecules consist of a hydrocarbon tail attached to
   a) $-SiO_4$
   b) $-MgFe$
   c) $-CO_2$
   d) $-COOH$

## Synthesis

1. Myristic acid is a saturated fatty acid with 14 carbon atoms. It is about 18 percent of the fat found in coconut oil. Looking at other fatty acids in

Figure 24.7, in what temperature range might you expect this acid to melt?

2. The three labels below have come from different sources of dietary fat.

   a) Predict the relative melting temperatures of the three substances.

   b) Discuss which one is likely to be more heart healthy from the perspective of the fat content.

**a)**

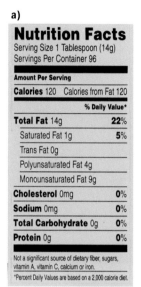

**b)**

**c)**

3. Study the structures of saturated, cis-unsaturated and trans-unsaturated fatty acids and formulate a hypothesis about why trans-unsaturated fatty acids behave more like saturated fatty acids with respect to melting point and artery-clogging tendencies. What experiments might you do to test this hypothesis?

4. Asbestos is a poor conductor of both heat and electricity. Which of the following are reasonable conclusions? (More than one may be possible.)

   a) The electrons in asbestos are delocalized like metals.

   b) The electrons in asbestos are tightly bound to specific atoms or ions.

   c) The electronic energy levels are bandlike.

   d) The electronic energy levels are discrete.

5. Human hair is made up mostly of large molecules called proteins. Based on the principles that you have learned in this chapter, describe what you think the protein molecular structure might look like.

6. The image below is of a silicate mineral. Make a prediction about whether this mineral would appear as fibers, layers, or no regular pattern. Explain your answer. (A three-dimensional image of this structure is available on the website.)

7. The molecular structures, formulas and portions of the IR spectra for four molecules, including two fatty acids, are shown in the figure below. Focus your attention on the regions between the red lines and between the blue lines. Using the IR data for acetic acid and hexane, identify what structural features give rise to the absorption features in the fatty acids.

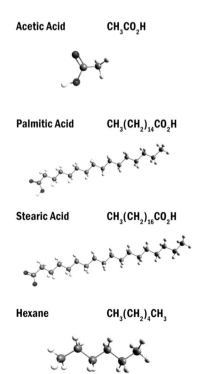

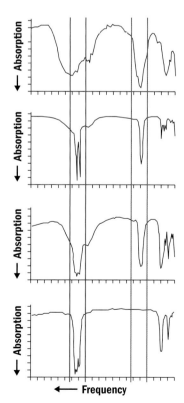

**Acetic Acid**    $CH_3CO_2H$

**Palmitic Acid**    $CH_3(CH_2)_{14}CO_2H$

**Stearic Acid**    $CH_3(CH_2)_{16}CO_2H$

**Hexane**    $CH_3(CH_2)_4CH_3$

← Frequency

# Radioactivity, Nuclear Processes, and Applications

*The discovery of nuclear chain reactions need not bring about the destruction of mankind any more than did the discovery of matches. We only must do everything in our power to safeguard against its abuse.*

*Albert Einstein*

# 25

## LEARN

- The fundamental forces involved in forming a stable nucleus and describe how they influence nucleon mass.

- The processes of fission and fusion.

- How the two forces operating inside the nucleus interact to produce nuclear energy levels.

- Why only certain nuclei are stable, and the processes through which unstable nuclei decay.

- The role of mass-energy and charge conservation in nuclear processes.

- The probabilistic nature of nuclear decay and the concept of half-life.

In the first chapter of the book, four fundamental interactions were introduced. So far we have studied two: gravity and electromagnetism. We learned that these forces are described by two similar equations which we called force laws. We learned how the electromagnetic force, incorporated into the quantum structure of the atom, creates chemical bonds. These bonds, in turn, explain much of our physical world. By any measure, the amount of understanding we obtain from these simple laws and models is astounding.

In this chapter we turn our attention to the remaining two interactions: the strong and weak nuclear interactions. Neither of these are as familiar to most of us because they are very short range. Their influence extends over distances only the size of an atomic nucleus, about 100,000 times smaller than the size of the atom. Even so, they are potent and can produce millions of times more energy than that of chemical bonds.

The gravitational and electromagnetic laws are clear: force decreases with distance

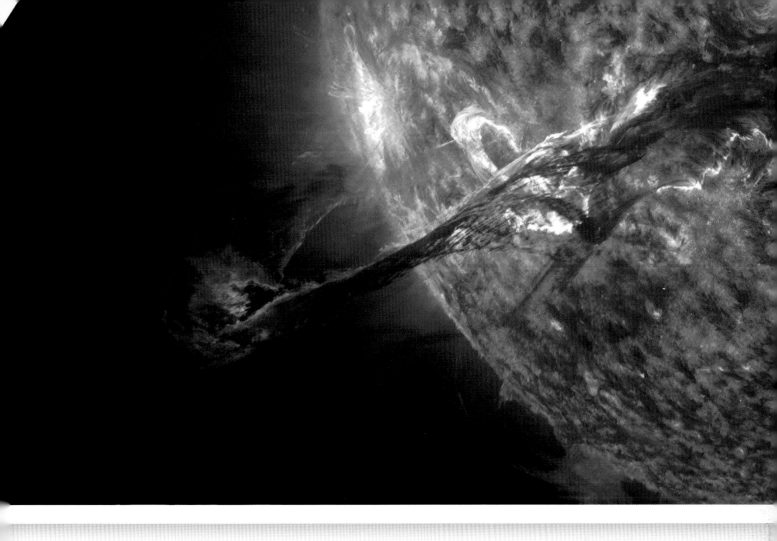

and increases with mass or charge respectively. In contrast, the details of the strong and weak nuclear interactions are vague. Scientists describe them with a theory called quantum chromo-dynamics or QCD. This theory has given us valuable insights, but not enough to write a force law as was done with gravity and electromagnetism. With that surprising limit, we proceed to describe these nuclear forces and their characteristics.

## 25-1 Nuclear Forces and Energy

Before Rutherford discovered the nucleus, no one knew that the **nuclear strong force** existed. It was surprising to learn that all of the atomic positive charge was concentrated in such a small volume. As you know, like charges repel and so the existence of a small positive nucleus meant there had to be some new force, stronger than the electromagnetic force, holding the charged protons together within it. Furthermore, the range of this force had to be extremely short—confined to just the nucleus—because

protons outside nuclei always repel each other and do not feel its attractive influence.

Of course, neutrons are nucleons just like protons, and feel the nuclear interactions as well. So scientists studying the nucleus were faced with the challenge of describing how these two different particles, protons and neutrons, behaved under the influence of both the strong and electromagnetic interactions, the former of which was newly discovered and not at all understood. So we again invoke the method of Aristotle and present observations about the nucleus, classify them, and from them draw general conclusions about what the nuclear forces must be like.

The first key observation is that different nuclei have different mass. Of course, this is because different nuclei have different numbers of protons and neutrons. But when we examine exactly how nuclear mass changes with each element, we find a surprise. In *Figure 25.1*, we plot the total mass of each nucleus divided by the number of protons and neutrons in that nucleus. In other words, Figure 25.1 plots the average

**Nuclear Strong Force Law:**

Scientists are still trying to figure out what the equation for the strong force looks like. Compare this with the Electric Force Law equation: $F = kqQ/d^2$.

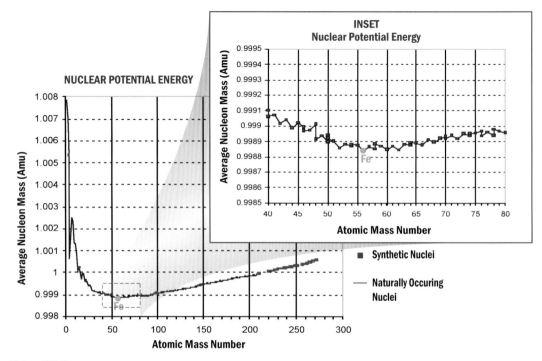

**Figure 25.1**

Graph of average nuclear mass versus atomic mass number. The average nuclear mass is also a measure of the potential energy in the nucleus. The graph is based on isotope masses from the National Institute of Standards and Technology (http://physics.nist.gov) .

**Amu:**

The abbreviation for atomic mass unit. One atomic mass unit = 1.660559 × 10-27kg. This is the average mass of the protons and neutrons in a 12C atom. Because protons and neutrons are so small, it is more convenient to measure their mass in units of comparable size.

mass per nucleon. Surprisingly, this number *changes* as the size of the nucleus changes. How can nucleon masses change from element to element?

In Chapter 9 we learned that mass and energy are related by the equation $E=mc^2$. Changes in energy create changes in mass. This effect is too small to measure for changes in electrical or gravitational potential energy. But changes in nuclear potential energy *are* measurable.

A proton by itself outside a nucleus has a mass of 1.007276 atomic mass units, or **amu**. A similarly isolated neutron has a mass of 1.008665 amu. As a helium nucleus is made of two protons and two neutrons, one would think it should have a combined mass of two neutrons and two protons or 4.031882 amu. However,

the actual mass of a helium nucleus is smaller at 4.001506 amu. The difference—nearly 1% of the total mass—is the binding energy used by the nuclear strong force to hold the nucleons together. But why is the helium nuclear mass *less* if it *includes* energy from binding?

Recall that when an electron is bound to an atom, it *takes* energy to free it. By the same principle, protons and neutrons bound to an atomic nucleus *require* energy to be broken free. In their free state they therefore have more energy than when they were bound. By $E = mc^2$, the energy they lose when they are bound inside a nucleus manifests itself as a lower mass. Figure 25.1 therefore tells us how much mass has become binding energy within each element's nucleus.

A careful look at the graph of Figure 25.1

---

### CHEMICAL VS. NUCLEAR ENERGIES

The energies involved in chemical changes or reactions are roughly a million times smaller than those involved in nuclear reactions. This energy difference is the reason that nuclear power reactors produce much more energy per gram of fuel than power plants using coal or gas. This is also the reason that particles from radioactivity can be dangerous to life, because the enormous energy from a single such particle can disrupt possibly millions of the chemical bonds in living tissue. Similarly, radioactive dating, discussed in this chapter and in Chapter 28, cannot be affected by chemical or environmental factors, because their energy is so much less than the energy of radioactivity.

reveals three other important clues. Let's consider them.

**1. Where is the average nucleon mass highest and lowest?**

In going from lighter to more massive nuclei, the average nucleon mass starts high, decreases, and then increases again. As seen in the inset to Figure 25.1, nucleons in iron atoms have the lowest average mass. Therefore the nucleons in iron are bound with the most energy. This has to mean that the strong force reaches its maximum range of influence at a distance of the diameter of an iron atom nucleus.

To explain why, consider that there are two forces acting in the nucleus, the strong nuclear force and the electromagnetic force. The total energy depends on the relative strength of these forces.

The strong nuclear force is attractive. Recall from Chapter 4 that when attracting objects are brought closer to each other, their potential energy *decreases*. So a nucleus of many nucleons has *less* potential energy from the strong nuclear force than one with fewer nucleons. In other words, if the average number of nucleons stuck to any one particular nucleus increases, the average energy stored in the strong nuclear interaction—and the average nucleon mass—*decreases*.

The electromagnetic force between protons is repulsive. When repelling objects are brought closer to each other, their potential energy *increases*. So a collection of many protons has *more* potential energy from the electromagnetic force than one of fewer protons. In other words, if the average number of protons pushing on any one particular proton increases, the average energy stored in the electromagnetic interaction—and the average nucleon mass—*increases*.

So increasing the size of the nucleus decreases the strong nuclear potential energy and increases the electromagnetic potential energy. Since the strong force is the larger force, the decrease in energy due to the strong force is bigger than the increase due to the electromagnetic force. So, in going from hydrogen to more massive nuclei both total potential energy and average nucleon mass decrease.

However, once you reach a nucleus whose size equals the maximum range of the strong force, adding new nucleons doesn't change the average number of particles stuck to any given

## ISOTOPIC NOTATION

Isotopes of an element have the same number of protons but differing numbers of neutrons. Thus they have differing atomic mass numbers. The number of neutrons can be found by subtracting the atomic number from the atomic mass number. An element's isotope is denoted by writing a superscript on the atomic symbol indicating the amu and a subscript indicating the atomic number or the number of protons of the isotope. For example, the notations $^2_1$H or $^3_2$He indicate isotopes for hydrogen and helium that each have an extra neutron.

nucleon. When you add the new particle, it will only be held to its neighbors that are within range. The nucleons on the opposite side won't be attracted to the newcomer. And the average number of particles stuck to each nucleon stays the same. This means once you've reached the maximum range of the strong force, the only change in energy is the change due to the electromagnetic force. Now the total energy will increase as you increase the size of the nucleus.

The change from decreasing energy to increasing energy happens at iron (56Fe). So, the maximum range of the strong nuclear force has to be about the same size as the nucleus of an iron atom.

Let's review this again, focusing our attention on oxygen ($^{16}$O), iron ($^{56}$Fe), and gold ($^{197}$Au). Each nucleon in the oxygen nucleus is held to all the other 15 nucleons via the strong nuclear force. Eight of these nucleons are protons that all repel one another via the electromagnetic force. Similarly in $^{56}$Fe, each nucleon on the iron nucleus is held to all the other 55 nucleons and there are 26 protons pushing on each other. On the graph the average mass (and energy) decreases from oxygen to iron because the average number of nucleons attracted by the strong force increases by 40, the number of repelling protons increases by 18, and the nucleus is more tightly bound.

In $^{197}$Au, each nucleon in this nucleus is still held to only about 55 of its closest neighbors, only now there are 79 protons repelling each other. So from iron to gold the mass increases because the number of nucleons stuck to one another by the strong force stays the same, the number of protons repelling each other increases by 53, and the nucleus is much less tightly bound.

### 2. How large is the biggest stable atom?

Notice that the graph ends fairly abruptly on the right hand side—the side with the heavy atoms. There are no naturally occurring nuclei with mass numbers larger than 238, and no nuclei at all with masses larger than 281. A nucleus will only form when the forces holding it together are larger than the forces pulling it apart. So the graph tells us that there is a maximum size above which the proton-proton repulsion is stronger than the nuclear strong force and any nuclei larger than this would fall apart. Since the largest atom has about 100 protons, the strong force between two neighboring nucleons must be about 100 times bigger than the electrical repulsion between two neighboring protons.

### 3. How many atoms are there at each mass number?

The chart inset of Figure 25.1 shows that many of the atomic mass numbers have more than one data point above them. This is because even though an element will always have the same number of protons in its nuclei, the number of neutrons in its nuclei may vary from atom to atom. The result is that atoms of the same element can have different mass numbers. Atoms of the same element with different mass numbers are said to be **isotopes** of that element. An isotope of hydrogen having one proton and two neutrons and an isotope of helium having two protons and one neutron each produce a data point at a mass number of 3.

We might expect to find a data point above each mass number for every possible combination of protons and neutrons that total to that number so long as the proton-proton repulsion is not too high. However, this is not what we see in nature. At most we find only a few occurrences at each mass number. For each element there are limited numbers of isotopes with stable nuclei, and a few more unstable nuclei. This fact gives insight into radioactivity and the nuclear weak force to be discussed later in this chapter.

## 25-2 Fusion and Fission

We have related two important ideas about nuclear energy so far. One is the equivalence of mass and energy illustrated by the equation $E=mc^2$ and the other is that nucleons in different nuclei have different amounts of mass. Therefore it is reasonable to conclude, as Einstein did, that if you either combine small nuclei to make a larger nucleus or split the largest nuclei to make smaller ones, the mass that the protons and neutrons lose in the process will be released as energy.

### Fusion

Combining small mass nuclei to make more massive nuclei is called **fusion**. If the mass per nucleon of the more massive nucleus is less than the mass per nucleon of the smaller nuclei, the mass difference is released as energy. The largest nucleon masses are found in the smallest atom of hydrogen, dropping off quickly from there. The biggest change in nucleon mass happens, and the most energy is released, when isotopes of hydrogen having one or two neutrons combine to make helium, as in *Figure 25.2*.

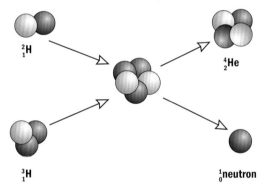

**Figure 25.2**

The fusion reaction: $^2H + ^3H \rightarrow {}^4He$ + neutron. Note that the total number of protons and neutrons doesn't change.

Whenever elements at the left hand side of Figure 25.1 combine to form elements closer to the low-energy nuclei in the middle of the graph, energy is released. There is a difficulty, however, in getting them to combine. As we have seen, the attractive strong force is extremely short range while the weaker, repulsive electromagnetic force is long range. To get the nuclei of two small atoms close enough for the strong force to pull them together, a way must be devised to overcome the electromagnetic repulsion that is keeping the two small atoms apart.

There are several possible ways to do this. One method is to utilize a long-range attractive force larger than the electromagnetic repulsion. There are only four forces. The strong and weak are short range and the electric force is repulsive, which leaves gravity. The gravitational force is

---

**Isotope:**

Isotopes of an element have the same number of protons but differing numbers of neutrons. Thus they have differing atomic mass numbers. The number of neutrons can be found by subtracting the atomic number from the atomic mass number. An element's isotope is denoted by writing a superscript on the atomic symbol indicating the amu and a subscript indicating the atomic number, such as $_1^2H$ or $_2^3He$.

**Fusion:**

A nuclear reaction in which nuclei combine to form more massive nuclei with the simultaneous release of energy.

attractive, but very weak. To have a gravitational force large enough to overcome the electromagnetic repulsion, a huge amount of mass must be gathered. As we will learn in Chapter 33, stars are gigantic clouds of hydrogen gas with enough mass to overcome the electromagnetic repulsion and fuse hydrogen nuclei together to make helium. Obviously, this works well in nature, and solar energy is really nuclear power, but it would not be practical for humans to try to copy this particular fusion reactor design!

A second way to make fusion work is to increase the speed of the atoms. If the atoms have enough speed toward each other to start with, the electric force will slow them down but not stop them before they get close enough for the strong force to take over. Just like the roller coaster in *Figure 25.3*, if the nuclei are moving fast enough to make it over the electromagnetic repulsion hill, they'll fuse and release a lot of energy. This process is similar to how greater energy increases chemical reaction rates.

Kinetic energy of atoms corresponds to heat, so fusion can be made to happen by heating the atoms. Unfortunately, because the nuclei must be brought extremely close together before the strong force can take over—and the electrical repulsion is very large at such short distances—this seemingly simple plan requires temperatures of several million degrees! It is difficult to maintain and control material at temperatures this hot. Several countries have developed working fusion devices that achieve the necessary temperatures for a very short period of time, releasing extremely large amounts of fusion energy all at once. These devices are called hydrogen bombs.

No one has yet come up with a way of sustaining fusion temperatures in a controlled way that doesn't require more energy than the fusion produces. To date there are no fusion reactors that produce more energy than they use. However, an international collaboration is building a very large fusion reactor in France called ITER: the International Thermonuclear Experimental Reactor. Perhaps this machine will help us understand how to produce controlled fusion energy. Fusion would be an excellent source of useful power because of the large abundance of the isotope $^2H$, which can be used as fuel, and because its by-products are harmless.

### Fission

The other way to release nuclear energy is to start with very large atoms and split them into smaller atoms. This is called **fission**. Looking at Figure 25.1, this corresponds to starting with large nuclei at the right hand side of the graph and splitting them into low-energy nuclei in the middle of the graph. With fission, all of the problems with fusion work in our favor. The electric repulsion between protons helps to split the nucleus apart and the largest atoms have the biggest electric repulsion.

As previously noted, the short range of the strong force limits its effectiveness, allowing the electric repulsion to eventually catch up with the strong force as nuclei get larger. The maximum size of stable nuclei is determined by the point where the two forces are roughly equal. In the largest naturally occurring nuclei, the electromagnetic force is nearly as large as the strong force. Only a small amount of additional energy

**Fission:**
A nuclear reaction in which an atomic nucleus, especially a heavy nucleus such as an isotope of uranium, splits into two fragments of comparable mass, releasing energy.

**Figure 25.3**
For a rollercoaster to get back to its starting position, it needs to move fast enough to make it out of the valley and over the hill. Atoms need to be moving fast enough to overcome the electric force before they can fuse.

is needed to break the nucleus apart. Once again it is like that roller coaster, with the most massive nuclei being cars sitting stopped in a very shallow dip high on the track, just waiting for any little push to get it moving. When the nucleus is given the necessary energy it will split into two pieces of approximately equal size, plus a few extra neutrons (*Figure 25.4*).

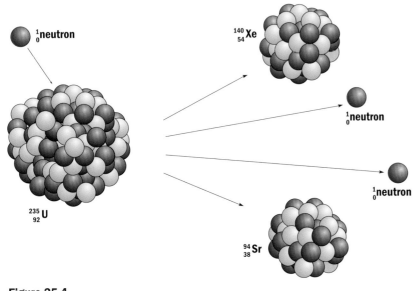

**Figure 25.4**
A fission reaction. A uranium atom absorbs a neutron and splits into 2 medium-sized atoms and some free neutrons. Note that the total number of nucleons remains the same.

**Critical Mass:**

The minimum amount of material necessary for each fission to result in one additional fission.

**Chain Reaction:**

A chain reaction is one that is self sustaining or increasing once it has started. Dominoes knocking each other over is a classic example of a chain reaction.

**Radioactive Decay:**

Spontaneous disintegration of an unstable nucleus accompanied by the emission of ionizing radiation in the form of alpha or beta particles or gamma rays.

If we carefully harness these nuclear reactions, we can use them to produce other forms of energy like electricity. In nuclear power plant fusion, the energy needed to split the nucleus is provided by a free, slow-moving neutron released by a previous fission. When the nucleus of a fuel atom, typically uranium, absorbs the neutron, the neutron's mass decreases, the lost mass is turned into energy, and the energy destabilizes the uranium atom, splitting it and releasing more neutrons that can be absorbed by other atoms. As long as at least one neutron from each fission is absorbed by another uranium atom, making it split, the reaction is self-sustaining. When enough atoms are close enough together and configured so that on average each fission triggers one more fission, the result is the for a **chain reaction**.

Uranium actually releases more than one neutron per fission event. So the reaction rate must be regulated by using inert material that can absorb the extra released neutrons and remain stable, preventing those neutrons from striking uranium atoms. By changing the ratio

of inert material to fuel inside the reactor, the number of neutrons hitting uranium atoms can be increased or decreased. Nuclei of cadmium and boron absorb neutrons extremely well and are used to make rods that control the reaction rate by being moved into or out of the fuel.

While the fission process used in nuclear reactions is fairly easy to control, there are a few significant problems. One is that the elements best suited for energy production are not very abundant in nature. The other is that when these heavy elements fission they produce other elements that are radioactive and poisonous, requiring them to be handled very carefully.

## 25-3 Unstable Nuclei and Radioactive Decay

Turning again to Figure 25.1 we now consider two unanswered questions from our graph of nucleon masses:

1. Why don't all possible isotopes of protons and neutrons occur naturally?
2. Can we manufacture a nucleus that doesn't occur naturally and if so, what happens?

The most common answer to why a seemingly possible situation doesn't happen is that, by the second law of thermodynamics, nature's parts tend to occupy the lowest available energy state. When something is not found in nature, it is usually because there are lower available energy configurations. Just as electrons drop into the lowest available orbital in atoms and molecules, protons and neutrons in a nucleus do likewise. If lower nucleon energy configurations are possible, the nucleus will eventually change to that lower energy state, as long as it can do so without violating any fundamental laws.

A spontaneous process that changes a nucleus from a high-energy state to a lower energy state is called **radioactive decay**. This change always involves emitting high energy photons and/or charged particles. Radioactive decay turns the "parent" nucleus into a "daughter" nucleus with less mass. Because the nuclear force is so large, the emitted particles typically have extremely high energies and can cause damage to anything they hit. It is these emitted particles that make radioactive decay so dangerous.

So the short answer to both the questions posed above is that only the lowest energy configurations of protons and neutrons occur naturally. If we make a nucleus that wouldn't normally exist by firing a neutron or proton into it, it will be unstable, emit energetic particles back out, and change into something that is lower in energy. Let's look closer at the processes of radioactive decay.

### Spontaneous fission and alpha decay

As we discussed above, massive atoms have more mass per nucleon than medium-sized atoms. So massive atoms can undergo fission, split into two medium-sized atoms, and release energy. Returning to the roller coaster analogy, if nuclei really behaved like parked roller coasters, nuclei would never split unless they were given enough energy to push them out of the dips they're sitting in. Unlike the stalled roller coaster, however, nucleons exhibit wave behavior. If a roller coaster gets stuck in a valley, it is obvious to all observers that it is really in the valley. But if small particles like protons or neutrons are placed in a "nuclear energy valley" their locations are not certain. While it is most probable that they will be found somewhere in the "valley," there is a small but real probability that groups of protons and neutrons can be located far enough away from the nucleus that they are effectively out of the valley. Thus, there is a chance that a nucleus will break apart by itself as long as charge and mass-energy are conserved in the process. For most atomic nuclei, this probability is very small, so spontaneous fission is fairly rare.[1]

---

[1] Even so, nuclear bombs use spontaneous fission as their

Referring back to Figure 25.1, we see that the small nucleus of $^4$He, also called "helium-4", has substantially less mass-energy than any of its neighbors. Helium-4 nuclei are so stable that some of the very large nuclei can be thought of as collections of these compact nuclei rather than collections of protons and neutrons.

Atomic nuclei larger than $^{209}$Bi will spontaneously emit helium-4 nuclei as single energetic "particles," so very few nuclei larger than bismuth occur naturally. Once the escaping helium nucleus is beyond the range of the strong force, electrostatic repulsion accelerates it away from the nucleus and it escapes.

A helium nucleus emitted from a heavy nucleus is called an **alpha particle**. Henri Becquerel discovered this process in 1896. This was the first radioactive decay process discovered and was called **alpha decay** after the first letter of the Greek alphabet. These are the alpha particles Ernest Rutherford used in his study of the atomic nucleus. He knew their charge and mass, but at that time didn't understand exactly where they came from.

### Beta decay

Alpha decay explains why large atoms aren't found naturally. So why do only certain specific isotopes occur? Answering this question led to

---

trigger. The uranium or plutonium is kept in segments that are far enough apart that the free neutrons from a spontaneous fission are very unlikely to be absorbed by other fuel atoms, and a chain reaction is impossible. When the bomb is detonated, the segments are pushed together. Neutrons released by any subsequent spontaneous fission will trigger more fissions in a runaway chain reaction.

**Alpha Particles:**

A positively charged particle that is given off by some radioactive materials including uranium, plutonium, and polonium. Alpha particles are now known to be nuclei of helium atoms.

**Alpha Decay:**

The radioactive decay of an atomic nucleus by emission of an alpha particle.

## ALPHA PARTICLES AND SMOKE DETECTORS

Because alpha particles have a large charge, they can't travel very far through matter before they steal a few electrons, lose their energy, and become normal helium atoms. This is the technology behind most smoke detectors. A tiny sample of americium emits alpha particles. These particles travel through the air and hit an electrode where they combine with electrons from a battery, causing a small current. As long as there is a current, all is well.

However, if there is smoke in the room, the alpha particles absorb electrons from the smoke, the current stops and an alarm sounds.

the discovery of the weak nuclear force and our modern understanding of the fundamental particles that make up matter.

The periodic table shows that stable isotopes of atoms with small atomic numbers have approximately equal numbers of protons and neutrons. This changes as atomic numbers increase. Medium-sized atoms have a few more neutrons than protons and large nuclei have substantially more neutrons than protons (See *Table 25.1*).

| Table 25.1 — Neutrons and Protons in Stable Atoms | | | |
| --- | --- | --- | --- |
| Atom | Atomic Number | Atomic Mass Number | Number of Protons/ Neutrons |
| O | 8 | 16 | 8/8 |
| Fe | 26 | 56 | 26/30 |
| U | 92 | 238 | 92/146 |

We may not know a force law for the strong nuclear force, but we do know that protons and neutrons within a nucleus have fairly well-defined energies. These energies can be modeled as the protons and neutrons sitting in energy levels just as electrons do in the quantum model of the atom. Because protons are electrically charged and the neutrons are not, the energy levels are different for these two kinds of nucleons. As you might have guessed, the electrical repulsion between protons gives them higher energies in the nucleus than the neutrons.

The pattern we see for the numbers of protons and neutrons in stable atoms suggests there is a rule in nature requiring the total energy of the protons and neutrons in a nucleus to be about the same. In small nuclei having the same numbers of protons and neutrons, the total proton energy will be greater than the total neutron energy but not so much as to allow room for another neutron. With medium-sized atoms the difference is large enough that most atoms will need a few more neutrons than protons to fill the neutron "energy well" to the same level as the proton energy well. In large atoms the electric force is larger, pushing the proton energy levels much higher than the energies for the corresponding number of neutrons. To fill the energy wells up to the same energy requires filling many more neutron levels and thus adding many more neutrons to the nucleus. These extra neutrons help offset the greater electric repulsion of the protons in heavier nuclei, making them stable.

Spontaneous fission of large nuclei produces medium-sized nuclei with far more neutrons than protons. Remarkably, neutrons in these nuclei will spontaneously change into protons until a stable energy configuration is reached. Processes that change neutrons into protons and, as it turns out, protons into neutrons are known as **beta decay**. Note the following:

- The fact that protons and neutrons can change into one another is evidence that they are made of smaller particles.
- There must be some previously unidentified force that causes the particles to change. This force is the weak nuclear force.
- Charge must be conserved, so a reaction that changes a neutron into a proton must also either absorb a positively charged particle or produce a negatively charged particle. Likewise, a reaction that turns a proton into a neutron must either absorb a negatively charged particle or produce a positively charged particle.

The lowest-mass charged particles in nature are electrons and their anti-matter twins called positrons (see Chapter 3). Beta decay proceeds by emitting and absorbing electrons and positrons. For a nucleus to *produce* an electron or a positron, the difference in mass-energy between the old and new nucleus must be large enough to provide the mass of this particle. This restricts these two decay processes to nuclei that can provide that mass-energy.

The electron-capture process doesn't require any minimum difference in energy because it relies on absorbing an electron that is already there. In Chapter 16 we learned that atomic orbitals are probability clouds describing where electrons can be found. And these orbitals extend down to the nucleus, meaning electrons can actually be within the nucleus. In unstable nuclei, electrons that find themselves in a nucleus can be absorbed into a proton creating a neutron.

If it seems strange to you that a neutron can decay into a proton and electron, you are not alone. In the early days of nuclear research, scientists discovered high energy electrons stream-

**Beta Decay:**

The radioactive decay of an atomic nucleus accompanied by emission of a beta particle.

# THE STANDARD MODEL

Our current understanding of matter is that the fundamental building blocks of normal matter are two types of quarks (up and down) and two types of electron-like particles (electrons and neutrinos), collectively called leptons (from the Greek for light). Quarks combine in groups of three to make protons and neutrons. For each of these fundamental particles there is a matching antimatter particle that has exactly the same mass, but all other characteristics, like charge, are completely opposite. If a matter particle comes together with its antimatter counterpart, they will "cancel out" and their combined mass will be converted into energy. Similarly, when energy turns into mass, it always produces a particle-antiparticle pair.

In addition to normal matter, there are types of unstable, exotic matter made up of two more massive quarks (strange and charm), and two more leptons (muons and mu-neutrinos). There is also a third pair of quarks (top and bottom) and a third pair of leptons (tauons and tau-neutrinos). These heavier particles tend to rapidly decay into their lighter, normal matter counterparts. While a few of these particles occur naturally (muons, for example, are produced in Earth's atmosphere), matter made of these heavier particles is typically created from energy released in collisions in particle accelerators.

Each of the four fundamental forces are related to a specific characteristic of matter. Each force is conveyed between the two objects involved in the interaction by the exchange of small particles called "bosons."

- Gravitational force depends on mass. It occurs because of the exchange of particles called "gravitons." Because there is only one type of mass, the gravitational force is always attractive.

- Electromagnetic force depends on charge. It acts because of the exchange of photons. There are two types of charge: positive and negative. The electromagnetic force can be either attractive or repulsive.

- The strong force is the force that causes quarks to combine in groups of three. It acts because of the exchange of gluons. Because quarks combine in groups of three, there must be three different types of "strong force charge." This characteristic is called "color charge" because it is somewhat analogous to the three primary colors. The nuclear strong force is actually a residual effect similar to an electric contact force. When two nucleons get so close together that the quarks that make up the first nucleon are nearly as strongly affected by the quarks that make up the second nucleon as they are by each other, they will attract each other. This is why the nuclear strong force is so short range.

- The weak nuclear force allows one type of quark or lepton to turn into another type. Charge is typically transferred when the type of particle changes, so this force is currently thought to be closely related to (if it isn't just another manifestation of) electromagnetic force. Theoreticians are currently trying to find a single set of equations that combines both effects.

**Figure 25.5**
Calvin and Hobbes (reprinted with permission of Andrews and McMeel, a Universal Press Syndicate Company).

ing out of certain very heavy isotopes. They were completely baffled by this. Not knowing what else to call these particles, they named them after the second letter of the Greek alphabet—the beta particle.

### Gamma decay

Just as collisions and chemical reactions can excite electrons into higher energy levels, extremely high-energy collisions and nuclear-decay processes can excite protons and neutrons into high-energy levels. Any time protons and neutrons shift from one energy level to a lower level, a photon is emitted just as it is when electrons change energy levels. These photons have extremely high energies and are called gamma rays—named after the third letter of the Greek alphabet. These are the same high-energy gamma rays introduced in Chapter 11.

## 25-4 Radiometric Dating

Decay processes depend on the probabilistic wave behavior of the nucleons, so they are probabilistic in nature. Recall that with the double-slit experiments using photons or electrons it was impossible to predict where any one particle would hit the screen. However, the pattern produced by a large number of particles always averages out from experiment to experiment to be an interference pattern with the same shape.

This same probabilistic nature makes it impossible to predict whether or not any specific nucleus will decay. We can only give the odds that a nucleus will decay within a given time period. But for a large group of radioactive nuclei the probabilities average out and the overall decay rate will always follow a well-determined pattern.

To determine the decay pattern of a particular radioactive isotope, a large sample of the isotope is monitored for several days or weeks. The number of alpha, beta, or gamma decay particles emitted by the sample are counted and the rate of their production is found. By knowing this rate, the researcher can predict the fraction of this material that will decay in any given time period.

Decay rates are measured in terms of **half-life**. One half-life is the time it takes for half of the radioactive nuclei in a sample to decay. After each half-life, half of whatever amount of radioactive material was there at the start will have transformed. So after one half-life, half of the original material remains. After two half-lives half of that or one-fourth of the original material remains. After three half-lives one-eighth remains, etc.

Half-lives are a fixed amount of time so radioactive isotopes can be used as a clock. If it is known how many particles a sample started with, and a measurement is made of how many are left, the number of half-lives that have passed can be calculated. By multiplying the number of half-lives by the length of the half-life we can determine how much time has gone by since the start. As long as you know the starting and ending amounts of the sample, radioactive decay can be used to measure how much time has passed.

Half-lives have a huge range. Some are shorter than a microsecond while others are longer than a billion years. Because many radioactive clocks run slowly, they are particularly well suited to measuring geologic processes. In Chapters 28 you will see exactly how this and other tools have been used to determine time scales for events in Earth's past.

**Half-life:**

The time required for half the nuclei in a sample of a specific isotopic species to undergo radioactive decay.

*Both the man of science and the man of action live*
*always at the edge of mystery, surrounded by it.*

*J. Robert Oppenheimer*

# 25 STUDY GUIDE

## Chapter Framework

### A. Nuclear Forces and Energy
1. Nuclear Strong Force Law
2. Elements and Isotopes

### B. Fusion and Fission
1. Critical Mass
2. Chain Reaction

### C. Unstable Nuclei and Radioactive Decay
1. Spontaneous Fission and Alpha Decay
2. Beta Decay
3. Gamma Decay

### D. Radiometric Dating

## Comprehension

### Matching
1. _____ The minimum amount of mass necessary for one fission to trigger another.
2. _____ A nucleus changes one of its protons into a neutron, or one of its neutrons into a proton.
3. _____ A uranium atom splits into thorium and helium.
4. _____ A nucleon jumps from a high energy level to a lower one and emits a photon.
5. _____ Two hydrogen atoms combine to make a helium atom.
6. _____ A uranium atom splits into xenon and strontium, plus a few neutrons.
7. _____ The amount of time required for 1/2 of the remaining radioactive nuclei to decay.
8. _____ A process where one event always triggers one or more additional events.

a. Alpha decay

b. Fission

c. Chain reaction

d. Critical mass

e. Beta decay

f. Fusion

g. Gamma decay

h. Half-life

### True/ False
1. _____ In the nucleus the strong force between two protons is stronger than the electric repulsion between two protons.
2. _____ The electromagnetic force extends over a longer distance than the strong nuclear force.
3. _____ Charge is always conserved in any nuclear process.
4. _____ Mass changes in nuclear processes.
5. _____ If two large nuclei were to combine, the process would release energy.

### Fill in the Blank
1. Protons and neutrons bound in a nucleus have _____ mass than free protons and neutrons.
2. Oxygen-15, oxygen-16, and oxygen-18 are 3 different _____ of the element oxygen.
3. When an unstable isotope changes into a more stable daughter nucleus and releases energetic particles, the process is called _____.
4. When two nuclei combine to make a larger one, the process is called _____.
5. When a large nucleus splits into two nearly equal parts, the process is called _____.
6. A group of atoms that all have the same number of protons is called an _____.

## Analysis

1. In which of the following nuclear reactions is total charge conserved?

   a) $^{198}_{79}Au \rightarrow {}^{198}_{80}Hg + {}^{0}_{+1}$ positron $+ {}^{0}_{0}$ neutrino

   b) $^{60}_{27}Co \rightarrow {}^{60}_{26}Fe + {}^{0}_{-1}$ electron $+ {}^{0}_{0}$ neutrino

   c) $^{212}_{84}Po \rightarrow {}^{208}_{82}Pb + {}^{4}_{2}He$

   d) $^{198}_{80}Hg + {}^{0}_{-1}$ electron $\rightarrow {}^{198}_{80}Hg + {}^{0}_{0}$ gamma ray

   e) $^{11}_{6}C \rightarrow {}^{11}_{5}B + {}^{0}_{-1}$ electron $+ {}^{0}_{0}$ neutrino

2. Carbon-14 is a radioactive isotope of carbon. Nitrogen-14 is naturally occurring. If you compare the two, what would you expect to find?

   a) A C-14 nucleus has more mass.

   b) An N-14 nucleus has more mass.

   c) The masses of the two are equal.

3. Which of the following nuclear reactions has a proton changed into a neutron?

   a) $^{198}_{79}Au \rightarrow {}^{198}_{80}Hg + + {}^{0}_{-1}$ electron $+ {}^{0}_{0}$ neutrino

   b) $^{212}_{84}Po \rightarrow {}^{208}_{82}Pb + {}^{4}_{2}He$

   c) $^{198}_{80}Hg \rightarrow {}^{198}_{80}Hg + {}^{0}_{0}$ gamma ray

   d) $^{11}_{6}C \rightarrow {}^{11}_{5}B + {}^{0}_{+1}$ positron $+ {}^{0}_{0}$ neutrino

4. Which of the following is true regarding forces in nuclei?

   a) The electromagnetic force is weaker than the strong force, and therefore has no important effects that need to be taken into account in studying nuclei or nuclear energy.

   b) The electromagnetic force, though weaker than the strong force, helps to bind nucleons together into nuclei.

   c) The electromagnetic force acts as a disruptive force in large nuclei, creating repulsions which help in fission.

   d) The electromagnetic force, although disruptive at long range, is attractive at short range and helps keep small nuclei together.

   e) The strong force is short range, and therefore of no major importance in nuclear energy considerations. The electromagnetic force, on the other hand, is very important in fission and fusion reactions.

5. Which of the following would be the best fuel for a fission reaction?

   a) Hydrogen

b) Iron

c) Plutonium

6. Which of the following is the biggest problem with using fusion as a source of energy?

a) The scarcity of fuel (deuterium).

b) The danger of long-lived radioactive wastes.

c) The danger of a runaway reaction.

d) Overcoming the electromagnetic repulsion of particles with like charges.

e) The scarcity of suitable material for control rods.

## Synthesis

1. Uranium has an atomic number of 92. If a uranium atom emits a helium nucleus, what will the atomic number of the daughter nucleus be? What element is that?

2. If you were to combine two carbon-12 atoms in a fusion process, what element would you get? Would this process absorb or release energy?

3. Oxygen-15 is a radioactive nucleus commonly used as a medical dye. Why isn't Oxygen-15 stable? How is it likely to decay?

4. In a fission reaction, Uranium-235 absorbs a neutron and splits into Barium-144, 3 neutrons, and another atom. Use conservation of mass-number and conservation of charge to figure out what that other atom must be.

5. Iodine-123 is often used in medical scans. It has a half life of 13 hours. Approximately what percent of the total amount is left one day after you receive a scan?

6. Explain what evidence led scientists to the conclusion that there were two additional forces, a nuclear strong and weak force, responsible for nuclear processes.

7. Explain how scientists arrived at the conclusion that the strong force is short range.

8. Explain how both splitting atoms apart (fission) and putting atoms together (fusion) can release energy.

9. Why do only certain isotopes occur naturally?

10. Why are there no elements with atomic numbers much larger than 100?

11. What are some of the drawbacks and advantages of fission and fusion as sources of energy? Why is fusion generally considered a preferable potential energy source? Although fusion is preferred, why are all commercial nuclear power plants using energy from fission?

12. Describe the process of beta decay. What roles do conservation of charge and mass-energy play in beta decay?

# Earth's Interior

*Now faith is the substance of things hoped for, the evidence of things not seen.*

*Hebrews 11:1*

## LEARN

- The evidences that support our current model of the interior of Earth, including

  - Direct observational evidence

  - Evidence from meteorites

  - Inferences from Earth's density

  - Evidence from seismic waves

  - Evidence from Earth's magnetic field

- The current models for the compositional and mechanical structures of the interior of Earth.

We have been considering for many chapters the smallest entities we know of: atoms and their constituents. We have modeled atoms and used these models to successfully explain the rich variety of elements and materials in the world. Through our knowledge of electromagnetism and bonding we have manipulated bonds to create unique and useful substances. Our understanding of the strong and weak nuclear forces is less complete but even so we have tapped them to create useful power and frightening weapons. Atoms are much too small to be seen with our eyes yet they are well understood as evidenced by how we use them to our advantage. Clearly we can have faith that there is truth in our models.

Having *faith* that our models contain truth motivates us to reason from them, which in turn leads to more truth. Paul's definition of faith as the "evidence of things not seen" quoted above is the perfect starting point for much of science, but especially for atomic modeling where everything is too small to be seen. And it is particularly true for this chapter as well, which discusses

Earth's interior. Just as no one has seen the interior of a tiny atom, no one has seen the deep, remote interior of Earth. Yet we are certain we know truths about it.

We believe we know what Earth's deepest interior is like by studying physical clues obtainable on Earth's surface. The evidence is so compelling that it eliminates all but a few possibilities. We can be certain, alas, that the center of Earth is nothing like the fanciful description offered by Jules Verne in his 19th century novel, *Journey to the Center of the Earth*. Furthermore, Earth's center bears only a passing resemblance to the interior as pictured by Hollywood in the 2003 movie, *The Core*.

So how do we learn about Earth's interior? What are the evidences that give us confidence in our understanding of this unseen part of our world? The evidences can be divided into five categories:

- Direct observation of rocks from the interior

- Relationships to rocks or meteorites from space
- Inferences from Earth's density
- Evidence from seismic (earthquake) waves
- Requirements for producing Earth's magnetic field

We consider each of these in turn.

## 26-1 Evidence from Direct Observation

When you were a child, you may have ambitiously started to dig a hole in the ground with the intention of digging all the way through to Earth's other side. Sooner or later (probably sooner) you became tired or bored with your project, abandoning it for some other activity. You may never have become aware of how impossible your plan was. Even with the best equipment, latest techniques, and modern methods, we have been able to penetrate only a fraction of one percent of Earth's thickness. The deepest man-made hole is on the Kola Peninsula in Russia. This hole reached a depth of 12 km (7.6 miles)—not very deep, compared to the 6400 km to Earth's center! Nonetheless, the information gathered from such boreholes is still useful.

In addition to rock samples extracted by drilling, there are places where rocks that were formed deep within Earth are now exposed on the surface. By "deep" we mean 24 to 32 km (15 or 20 miles) down, still only a fraction of the distance to Earth's center. Occasionally rocks that may have formed at depths of as much as 450 km are carried upward by ascending magmas and blasted from volcanoes out onto the surface. These rocks give a glimpse into deeper parts of Earth that can't be reached by drilling or other ways.

Examination of all these samples has shown that Earth is not of a uniform composition. The continents are made up of fairly low-density rock such as granite and gneiss, which have average densities of about 2.7 g/cm³. Earth's oceans float on basins of basalt and gabbro that have a somewhat greater density of about 3.0 g/cm³ average. The rock foundations of our continents and oceans are part of Earth's uppermost layer, covering the planet like the peel of an orange. We call this layer Earth's **crust**.

Rock fragments brought to the surface in volcanic eruptions, like the one shown in *Figure 26.1*, are denser (up to 3.3 g/cm³) than the basalts on the ocean floor. They come from a layer below Earth's crust called the **mantle**. Rocks formed in the mantle, when found on the surface, are called **peridotite**. Peridotite contains more iron and magnesium and less silicon and aluminum than the rocks of the crust. Olivine, a silicate material that we talked about in Section

24–2, is the main mineral component of peridotite.

Rock samples from the crust and mantle give us important information, but they do not provide us with a complete picture of the interior because the samples are sparsely distributed over the surface and are still only from relatively shallow layers. We need to look elsewhere for additional evidences.

## 26–2 Evidence from Meteorites

Every day about 100 tons of material are added to Earth's mass by debris falling onto it from space. Most of this material is dust particles that burn up quickly from friction with Earth's atmosphere, then settle as a fine ash onto the surface. Occasionally larger pieces, called **meteorites**, make it through the atmosphere and land intact. There are several types of meteorites, some of which are seen in *Figure 26.2*.

About 85% of all meteorites that have been found are of a type called **stony chondrites**. These are composed of the same basic materials from which Earth and other planets in our solar system were originally made.

A second group of meteorites, making up about 7–8%, are called **stony achondrites**. They appear to be from the upper portions of small planetary bodies (perhaps as big as the Moon or even the planet Mars) that had separated, or "differentiated" into layers and were then broken

### Crust:
The uppermost compositional layer of Earth. It is very thin and composed of two parts: granitic continental crust and basaltic oceanic crust.

### Mantle:
The middle compositional layer of Earth. It is a thick layer made up of peridotite in the upper part and higher density rocks of peridotite composition in the lower part.

### Peridotite:
A rock made up mostly of silicon, oxygen, and the transition metals iron and magnesium. It is denser than the basalt and granite that make up Earth's crust.

### Meteorite:
A rock from space that hits Earth's surface.

### Stony Chondrites:
Meteorites thought to be composed of unprocessed material from the original solar nebula.

### Stony Achondrites:
Meteorites thought to represent material from small planetary bodies that had differentiated into layers and then were broken up.

**a) Iron**

**Figure 26.1**
Photo of mantle peridotite inclusions in basalt from Australia. Olivine contains transition metals that give it the green color. Olivine is a crystalline salt containing mostly Mg, Fe, and silicate ions.

**b) Stony Chondrite**     **c) Stony Achondrite**

**Figure 26.2**
Photos of the three main types of meteorites.

apart by collisions with other small planetary bodies. Some of these achondritic meteorites have chemical fingerprints that identify them as rocks that were ejected from the Moon or Mars when such bodies cratered on their surfaces. **Iron meteorites** (about 6% of all meteorites) also come from differentiated, layered planetary bodies that were later broken apart and scattered.

All these meteorite types help us understand the interior of Earth. Stony chondrites show us the raw material from which Earth was made, while the achondrite and iron meteorites represent the major layers into which a planetary body, like Earth, may differentiate. The very dense iron meteorites should be similar in composition to Earth's central layer, called the **core**, and the stony achondrites should be similar to the peridotite found in Earth's mantle.

## 26-3 Evidence from Earth's Mass and Density

Remarkably, Earth's mass can be found from the acceleration of any object falling on its surface. Recall from Newton's second law that the force F on an object is

$$\mathbf{F} = \mathbf{mg}$$

where **m** is the mass of the object and **g** is the acceleration of gravity. The force **F** arises from the pull of gravity and is the object's weight. This is described by the law of gravitation by

$$\mathbf{F} = \mathbf{GmM/R^2}$$

where **M** is the mass of Earth and **R** is its radius. We have used the radius **R** in the gravitation law instead of the general distance symbol **d** used in Chapter 3 because **R** is the distance **d** between the centers of Earth and the object. If we equate these two expressions for **F**, cancel **m**, and solve for **M**, we get this expression for Earth's mass:

$$\mathbf{M} = \mathbf{gR^2/G}$$

So to find Earth's mass, all we need to know is the acceleration of the object, the radius of Earth, and the universal constant of gravitation. Remarkably, we do not need to know the force of Earth's gravity or the mass of the falling object.

Earth's mass turns out to be a fairly large number, $5.973 \times 10^{24}$ kilograms. This may be nice to know, but why do we care to know it here? We care because if we know Earth's mass then we can calculate its density, and the density in turn will tell us about the rocks that can compose it.

Earth's average overall density is about 5.5 g/cm³. As we noted earlier in this chapter, the rocks that make up Earth's crust have much lower densities; 2.7 g/cm³ for the continental crust, 3.0 g/cm³ for the oceanic crust, and 3.3 g/cm³ for the upper mantle. We can then conclude that rocks in layers lower in Earth's mantle and down into the core must have densities greater than these.

The law of buoyancy tells us that objects more dense than water sink. In a sphere held together by gravity, like Earth, the most dense rocks and minerals will, if allowed, sink to the center. So it is not a surprise that Earth's interior is more dense than its surface.

There are two ways, shown in *Figure 26.3*, that an increasingly dense interior can be constructed. Either (a) the density could increase relatively continuously with depth, or (b) in addition to the crust and the mantle, the density could increase discontinuously in separate,

**Iron Meteorites:**
Meteorites thought to represent the type of material found in Earth's core.

**Core:**
The deepest or central compositional layer of Earth. It is composed mostly of iron.

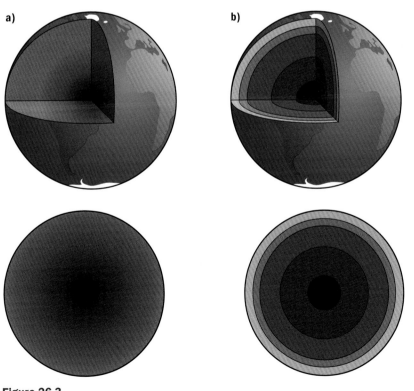

**Figure 26.3**
Models for Earth's interior:
a) gradually increasing density with depth
b) different density layers

## Elastic Rebound:

The point at which stress in Earth's lithosphere is strained to a point where it can bend no further and the lithosphere ruptures and rebounds somewhat like a rubber band that has just been pulled apart.

## Fault:

A break in Earth's lithosphere where rocks on one side of the break have slipped past the rocks on the other side. Faults are created by earthquakes.

## Tectonic Plates:

The brittle, rigid but thin outer part of Earth is divided into sections called tectonic plates.

## Seismic Waves:

Waves produced by earthquakes.

## P-Waves:

Compressional waves produced by an earthquake. They travel the fastest in Earth and so are the first to arrive at seismic wave detectors.

## S-Waves:

Shear waves produced by an earthquake. They are slower than P-waves and so arrive later at seismic wave detectors.

## Focus:

The place inside Earth where an earthquake originates.

## Epicenter:

The point on Earth's surface directly above the focus of an earthquake.

discrete layers. Our determination of the average density does not discriminate between the two models. There are other models that could perhaps be imagined for Earth's interior, but these do not follow Occam's Razor of selecting the simplest explanation that satisfies the observations. If we are to determine which of these two models is most probable, we will need to find some additional evidences.

## 26-4 Evidence from Seismology

Earth's surface is hard and brittle to us, but overall it is actually elastic. When Earth's uppermost layer is subjected to enormous stress or pressure, that layer changes its shape but will rebound elastically when released—just like a balloon when pressed between two hands.

When the stress on this layer is greater than its flexing ability, it will rupture like a rubber band stretched until it breaks. And as a broken rubber band snaps back to its original length and width, when Earth's upper layer ruptures, it returns to its normal form in an **elastic rebound**, illustrated in *Figure 26.4*. The break is called a **fault**. The natural elasticity of Earth's upper layers generally prevents a fault from being more than a few dozen kilometers in length and depth.

Stress on Earth's surface layers ranges from the almost undetectable stress caused by Moon's gravitation to the large, catastrophic stress from the movements of the **tectonic plates**. When the edge of one enormous tectonic plate grinds up against another plate, deep under the surface tremendous pressures are placed on the rock formations of each plate. When mounting pressure finally snaps a section of a plate, shock waves are generated. These waves are called **seismic waves** from *Seismos* which is Greek for earthquake.

Earthquakes simultaneously produce the three different types of waves introduced in Chapter 10—compression, shear, and surface. Each of these, with its own identifiable char-

acteristics, radiates outward from the point of the shift and are measured later at the many earthquake-recording stations dotting Earth's surface. Compression waves travel fastest and arrive at the stations first. They are called "primary" waves, a term that has been shortened to **P-waves**. The shear waves arrive next and are called "secondary" waves, or **S-waves**. It is fortuitous that the P-waves are pressure or compression waves and the S-waves are shear waves, lending a double meaning to the "P" and "S." Both P-waves and S-waves travel through the interior of Earth.

The slowest and last to arrive are the surface waves. Surface waves can cause concrete highways and hard ground to visibly ripple. Surface waves generated by seismic events in the ocean can cause devastating tsunamis. Surface waves, whether far inland or in the ocean, are responsible for most of the damage caused by an earthquake. But since they travel only near the surface, they tell us little about Earth's interior.

The point of origin of an earthquake is called its **focus**. This is the point, often deep below the surface, where the slippage actually takes place. The location of an earthquake referred to in news accounts is the point on Earth's surface directly above the focus and is called the **epicenter** (*Figure 26.5*). The speeds of P-waves and S-waves not only differ from each other but they also change with the properties of the rocks through which they pass. Essentially, the stiffer the rocks, the faster the wave speed. So we gain knowledge about Earth's interior by analyzing the speeds of waves that pass through different parts of it.

As long as seismic waves stay within a medium whose elastic properties are the same in all directions, they will travel in straight lines as shown in *Figure 26.6a*. However, if seismic

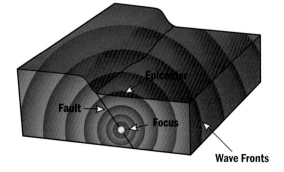

**Figure 26.5**

This diagram shows a fault, and the location of an earthquake epicenter and focus.

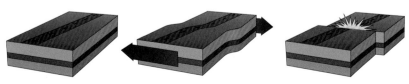

**Figure 26.4**

Earthquakes occur when the elastic limit of the rocks is reached within Earth's lithosphere. Once the stresses are released, the elastic deformation is relieved in a process called "elastic rebound."

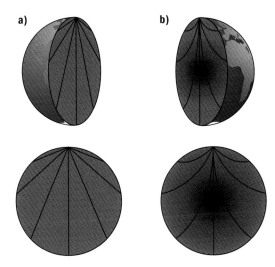

**Figure 26.6**

Paths for seismic waves in (a) a uniform-density Earth and (b) an Earth where the density increases with depth.

waves travel from rocks of one elasticity to rocks of another, or through rocks with elasticity that is gradually changing with depth, their speeds and direction change and they refract—a phenomenon we recall from our previous discussion of wave behavior. This is shown in Figure 26.6b.

The detectors in the grid of earthquake-recording stations are called **seismographs** or **seismometers.** They show that the waves detected farther and farther from an earthquake arrive progressively earlier and earlier than expected if Earth were a uniform-density sphere. This is because, by either model, the waves that travel farther must also travel through greater *depths* than those that travel lesser distances as shown in Figure 26.6. As they go deeper they must be traveling faster. This can only mean that the deeper rock layers are stiffer and the waves refract along curved paths such as those shown in Figure 26.6b. To become stiffer the rock layers must also become more dense which is a second piece of information telling us Earth's interior is more dense than its exterior.

But there is more evidence that must be considered before we flatly state that there is a uniform, gradual increase in rock layer density the deeper we probe into Earth's layers. In the early 1900s, Croatian seismologist Adrija Mohorovicic (1857–1936) compared the travel times of seismic waves arriving at seismometer stations less than 200 km from earthquake epicenters with travel times at stations more than 200 km away. In these data he discovered a **seismic discontinuity,** a distinct and abrupt change in the velocities of seismic waves. This indicated

there was an abrupt change in the rock hardness and density only a few tens of kilometers below the surface. Mohorovicic had discovered that the density of rock changed abruptly with depth.

This discovery challenged the idea that Earth's rock layers change *gradually* from being lighter near the surface to being denser at deeper levels. The boundary between densities is now known as the "Mohorovicic discontinuity," generally shortened (for obvious reasons) to the **Moho**. The Moho is at a depth of 29 to 56 km on average on the continents while only at a depth of about 5 to 10 km under the oceans.

About this same time the German-American seismologist Beno Gutenberg (1889–1960) was puzzling over seismograph records of earthquakes occurring long distances from those stations. He found that in a broad band, 103° to 143° from any earthquake epicenter, *no seismic waves at all were detected.* Beyond 143°, only P-waves were recorded.

*Figure 26.7* depicts the observation and the interpretation. The areas of no seismic waves are

**Seismometer:**

Device that measures ground motion.

**Seismic Discontinuity:**

A place where the velocities of seismic waves change abruptly.

**Moho:**

The seismic discontinuity at the base of Earth's crust.

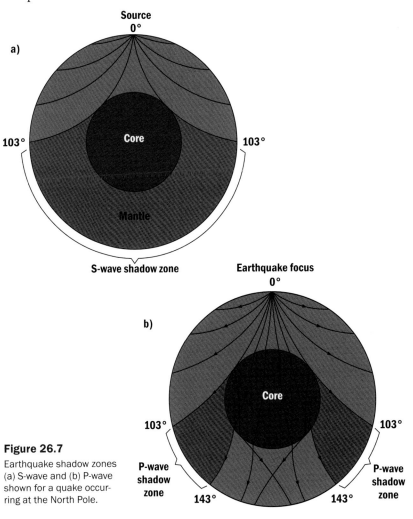

**Figure 26.7**

Earthquake shadow zones (a) S-wave and (b) P-wave shown for a quake occurring at the North Pole.

called **shadow zones**, one shaped like a band for P-waves and one shaped like a cap for S-waves. The P-waves that would have emerged within its shadow zone have been refracted away starting at 103° from the epicenter by a very significant discontinuity and redirected to emerge again beyond 143° from the epicenter. The complete absence of S-waves beyond 103° from the epicenter in its shadow zone indicates that the discontinuity is a boundary between the solid mantle and a liquid layer below, called the **outer core**. This is because S-waves are shear waves, and shear waves can travel only in a solid.

In the 1930s, as seismographs became more sensitive, it was found that a few weak P-waves *did* arrive within the shadow zone. This could only be explained as P-waves reflecting from a discontinuity within the liquid outer core. The additional discovery that P-waves penetrating straight through Earth traveled faster than expected confirmed that there was a stiff, solid volume at earth's center. So the discontinuity is the boundary between the liquid outer core and a solid, denser **inner core**, occurring at a depth of about 5,150 km.

So seismic data show us that Earth is, indeed, a layered planet with a very thin solid upper layer, a thick solid mantle (about 84 percent of Earth's total volume), and a core that is liquid on the outside and solid in the center.

## 26-5 Evidence from Earth's Magnetic Field

Earth possesses a magnetic field that behaves as if the planet has a large magnet within its core. We might then hypothesize that the solid inner core is in fact a large, permanent magnet. However, magnetized iron loses its magnetism when heated to 760°C, a temperature called the **Curie temperature**. Earth's temperature reaches 760° C less than 50 km below the surface, a short vertical distance that is roughly the same as the horizontal distance between Salt Lake City and Provo, Utah. Descending down the additional 3,000 km to the core, the temperature is thought to be *thousands* of degrees centigrade, much hotter than the Curie temperature.

So we must discard the once-popular idea of a magnetized core at the center of Earth. But how then is Earth's magnetic field produced? The only other way we know to create a mag-

netic field is by an electrical current, so perhaps such currents are generating Earth's field. But how could such currents exist in Earth's core?

The answer is that Earth's outer core is liquid iron at a temperature of about 6,000° C at its interface with the mantle above it. It gets increasingly hotter deeper towards the inner core where the temperature is about 6,500° C. This temperature between the top and bottom of the outer core causes convection and iron atoms in the outer core move in great cylindrical cells that also rotate equatorially because of the Earth's rotation.

This liquid iron—an electrical conductor—moves in the presence of the pre-existing magnetic field of the Sun, creating electrical currents. It is these electrical currents in Earth's outer core that generate Earth's magnetic field. This would not happen without the Sun's magnetic field to get the process started, and it would not happen if the outer core of Earth were solid. The easily demonstrated fact that Earth has a magnetic field, therefore, when combined with what we also know about how electrical currents are generated, means that Earth's outer core must be liquid and composed of iron, just as was supposed by the evidence from seismology, meteorites, density, and seismology.

## 26-6 Compositional Layers of Earth

All the evidence we have examined so far shows that Earth, a place of great oceans, snow-capped mountains, and generally temperate climate, is much different deep down inside. Our planet is layered both compositionally and mechanically. First, let's look at the three distinct compositional layers—crust, mantle and core—that we have already identified as Earth's interior (*Figure 26.8, left side*).

### The Crust

We live on Earth's crust, so we know quite a bit about its composition. As we will discuss further in Chapter 29, the continental crust and oceanic crust are significantly different. The continental crust consists of a wide variety of rock types—igneous, sedimentary, and metamorphic rocks of all sorts—but on average it has a granite composition. These rocks consist, in general, of fewer than 20 common minerals, most of which

**Shadow Zone:**

A region of Earth where seismic waves cannot be detected by seismometers.

**Outer Core:**

The upper part of the core that is made of liquid iron.

**Inner Core:**

The lower part of the core that is made of solid iron.

**Curie Temperature:**

The temperature at which a material loses its magnetism.

are **silicates** like those described in Chapter 24. The oceanic crust also consists largely of silicates, but has a higher percentage of other minerals. In contrast with the large variety of rock types found in the continental crust, the oceanic crust is virtually all basalt—a single specific type of rock. As previously mentioned, the average rock density of the continental crust is around 2.7 g/cm³, while the oceanic crust is about 3.0 g/cm³.

### The Mantle

From the Moho layer and below to the outer core is the mantle. Most of Earth's mantle is a compound of silicate minerals called peridotite. Peridotite is a dense igneous rock composed mainly of the minerals olivine and pyroxene. These minerals are high in silicon, oxygen, iron, and magnesium (*Table 26.1*). We can study this composition directly since some chunks of the mantle, you will remember, have been brought to Earth's surface in volcanic eruptions.

Laboratory experiments subjecting the minerals found in peridotite to very high pressures and temperatures show that they are unstable under the conditions of the mantle's lower depths. They undergo chemical reactions and structural changes producing denser minerals at depths of about 270 km and 680 km. Seismic waves speed up at these depths as expected if the minerals there are the ones predicted by the laboratory experiments. Below those depths, the seismic velocities simply increase gradually all the way to the top of the outer core. The percentage of elements in the lower mantle is probably the same as that of the upper mantle given in Table 26.1, but the atoms there have been rearranged through high pressure and temperature chemical reactions to form denser, more stable compounds called **dense oxides**.

### The Core

The density of liquid iron at the extreme pressures at the depth of the core is 10 or 11 g/cm³, and the density of the solid iron within that core is 12 to 14 g/cm³. These densities are the values needed to provide the observed average density of our planet. From this and meteorite samples, we conclude that Earth's core is mostly iron.

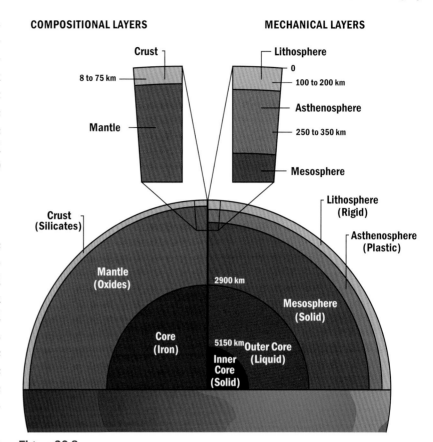

**Figure 26.8**
Earth's interior compositional layers (left side): the crust, mantle, and core. Earth's interior mechanical layers (right side): The lithosphere, the asthenosphere, the mesosphere, the outer core, and the inner core.

The iron core formed during the first few hundred million years of Earth's existence. This formation event, called the "iron catastrophe," greatly changed Earth's nature. When the forming Earth's density and mass reached a critical level, iron, being more dense than the surrounding rock, began to sink towards the center, forming the core. The gravitational potential energy released by iron's downward movement increased the planet's temperature above the melting temperature of rocks, forming a global magma that allowed iron to sink more rapidly, accelerating the formation of the core.

**Silicates:**

Minerals that contain silicon and oxygen bonded together.

**Dense Oxides:**

Minerals that form deep in Earth's mantle due to the enormous pressures.

| Table 26.1 — Composition of Earth's Mantle | |
|---|---|
| Oxygen (O) | 44.8 % |
| Silicon (Si) | 21.5 % |
| Magnesium (Mg) | 22.8 % |
| Iron (Fe) | 5.8 % |
| Aluminum (Al) | 2.2 % |
| Calcium (Ca) | 2.3 % |
| Sodium (Na) | 0.3 % |
| **Sum:** | **99.7 %** |

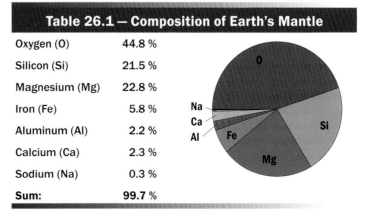

The iron catastrophe heated all rocks to where they could flow, not just the iron. With all rock minerals able to move, the layers of increasing density that we have just identified were formed.

## 26-7 Mechanical Layers of Earth

In addition to the compositional layers of the crust, mantle, and core, Earth's interior can also be categorized in terms of the mechanical or physical behavior of the rocks in those layers (Figure 26.8, right side). Mechanical behavior refers to how the rocks deform when forces are applied to them. Do they behave like solids or liquids? Are they brittle or *plastic*? As before we use the word plastic here to mean non-rigid, deformable, and capable of flowing in response to force or pressure. Silly Putty® is plastic. Think back to Chapter 12 and the discussion on how Silly Putty can easily be formed into a ball and yet can deform and flow on its own. Leave the ball on a table overnight, and it will slowly sag and flatten by morning under the force of gravity.

From the study of earthquake waves, we can determine and map the mechanical properties of Earth's interior layers (*Figure 26.9*).

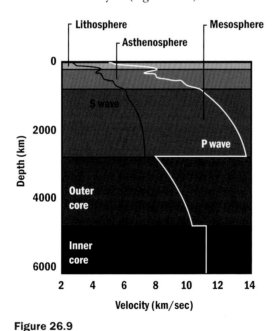

**Figure 26.9**
Velocities of P and S earthquake waves for various depths. Observe how the changes in wave velocity reveal Earth's interior mechanical layers.

### The Lithosphere

Earth's outermost rigid, brittle, skin-like layer is called the **lithosphere**. The lithosphere is a solid rock layer that includes all of the crust layer, the Mohorovicic discontinuity, and the solid uppermost part of the mantle. The lithosphere has, therefore, a quite diverse mineral composition. It is composed of granite in the continental crust, basalt in the oceanic crust, and peridotite in the mantle. The lithosphere is 100 to 200 km thick. The continents and ocean basins are part of the lithosphere which is divided into several large segments, briefly described previously in this chapter, called tectonic plates. These enormous plates are not stationary, but "float" on the softer, partially-molten rock layer of the mantle beneath them. As they move, they collide with and rub against one another.

### The Asthenosphere

The softer, partially-molten rock layer the lithosphere floats on is called the **asthenosphere**. Scientists found that seismic waves traveling through the lithosphere encounter a layer at its bottom through which they suddenly travel more slowly than in either the rocks above or below. This layer is approximately 300 km thick and is sometimes called the **low-velocity zone** for obvious reasons. The top of the low-velocity zone is in the upper mantle and is not a boundary between different types of rock as is the Mohorovicic discontinuity between the crust and the mantle. Rather, it is a boundary between solid peridotite and peridotite that is partially molten—perhaps only 1% to 10% liquid—but enough to make the rock plastic and able to flow.

Because the low-velocity zone is a relatively soft layer, it is called the asthenosphere from the Greek *astheneia,* meaning weak. *Figure 26.10* shows why it exists. The yellow curve shows how temperature increases with depth inside Earth. The blue line defines the melting point of the material at that depth. At depths between about 100 and 450 km below the surface, the temperature curve barely crosses the **melting point line**, indicating that at this combination of temperature and pressure, solid peridotite begins to soften and become more pliable or plastic.

This is an important point. Melting as stud-

---

**Lithosphere:**

The uppermost mechanical layer of Earth, which consists of the crust and the outermost part of the mantle that is too cool to be partially molten. It is brittle and is the only layer in which earthquakes can occur.

**Asthenosphere:**

A soft, plastic, partially-molten mechanical layer in Earth located below the lithosphere.

**Low-Velocity Zone:**

A region of the upper mantle where seismic waves travel slower than expected.

**Melting Point Line:**

A line on a plot of temperature and pressure showing where a substance transitions from solid to liquid.

ied in previous chapters assumed the pressure was the pressure at sea level. But when pressure is increased, the melting temperature also increases. So we must consult graphs like *Figure 26.10* that relate melting to *both* temperature *and* pressure to see if material is solid or liquid.

Peridotite, like most rocks, consists of more than one mineral. Each of the minerals in peridotite has its own melting point at any given pressure, and so the melting point line in the figure only approximates the average of these different melting points. In the asthenosphere, the temperature line crosses the melting point for some but not all of the minerals in the peridotite, resulting in "partial melting," like the room-temperature fats in Chapter 24.

When the temperature curve crosses back below the melting point line with increasing depth, peridotite is again completely solid because of the higher pressure, even though the temperature also climbs as we continue down.

### The Mesosphere

Below the asthenosphere is the lower part of the mantle, which surprisingly has not been given a formal name, although scientists studying the mechanical aspects of Earth's layers sometimes call it the **mesosphere**. This layer extends all the way down to the core. It is solid, not even partially molten, and yet because of the great pressures and temperatures here, the rocks are still plastic, not brittle like the lithosphere. Here the rock still has a peridotite composition, but as previously mentioned the high pressures in this part of Earth's interior have recrystallized the minerals that make up peridotite into more dense silicates and oxides. The high pressures allow the solid rock to flow, but very slowly, at a rate of no more than a few centimeters a year. This flow is caused by temperature and density differences within the mesosphere. Over time this flow has helped Earth to mix and stir itself, allowing the layers we now observe to form.

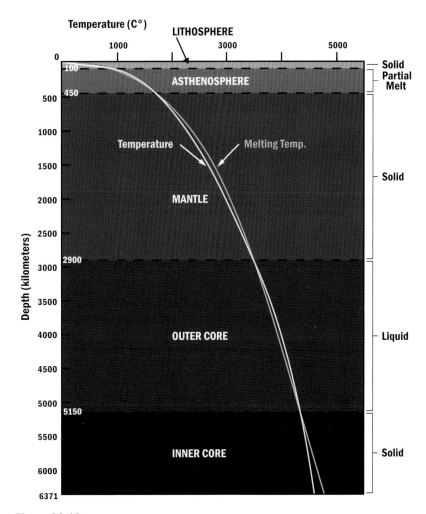

**Figure 26.10**

The yellow and blue lines show the relationship between the melting point of Earth's compositional layers and their respective melting points. Notice how the interaction between temperature and melting point define Earth's mechanical layers.

### The Outer Core and Inner Core

The base of the mantle is where Earth's core begins. This is the one place inside Earth where there is both a change in composition and in mechanical properties. The inner core is slowly growing as iron continues to solidify onto it. By the principles discussed in Chapter 13, changing from a liquid to a solid releases heat energy. The continuing growth of the solid inner core releases an enormous amount of heat, helping to keep the interior of Earth warm.

**Mesosphere:**

The mechanical layer between the asthenosphere and the outer core. It is solid, but still plastic and able to flow.

## Chapter Framework

**A. Earth's Interior—Evidence**
1. Direct Observation
2. Meteorites
3. Earth's Mass and Density
4. Seismology

**B. Composition of Earth's Layers**
1. The Crust
2. The Mantle
3. The Core

**C. Mechanical Structure of Earth's Interior**
1. Lithosphere
2. Asthenosphere
3. Mesosphere
4. Outer and Inner Core

## Comprehension

### Matching

1. ____ The middle compositional layer of Earth. A thick layer made up of peridotite in the upper part and higher density rocks of peridotite composition in the lower part.
2. ____ A break in the lithosphere of Earth along which earthquakes have occurred.
3. ____ The point at which earthquakes originate.
4. ____ A term we use here to describe the mechanical layer between the asthenosphere and the outer core. It is solid, but still plastic and able to flow.
5. ____ Compression waves that arrive before shear waves at seismic wave detectors.
6. ____ A region where an abrupt change in chemical or mechanical properties results in an abrupt change in the speed of seismic waves.
7. ____ Rock made of mostly silicon, oxygen, iron, and magnesium that is denser than the basalt and granite that make up Earth's crust.
8. ____ The _____ of an earthquake is the point on Earth's surface directly above the focus.
9. ____ These are thought to be made of the type of material found in Earth's core.
10. ____ Meteorites that are believed to be similar to the primordial material that formed Earth and other planets in the solar system.
11. ____ The lower part of the core that is made of solid iron.
12. ____ Minerals that contain silicon and oxygen bonded together.
13. ____ The temperature at which a material loses its magnetism.
14. ____ A low-velocity zone for seismic waves composed of partially molten peridotite.
15. ____ A region where seismic waves cannot be detected by seismometers.

a. Curie temperature
b. Mesosphere
c. Stony achondrites
d. Iron meteorites
e. Inner core
f. Silicates
g. P-Waves
h. Mantle
i. Epicenter
j. Shadow zone
k. seismic discontinuity
l. Fault
m. Peridotite
n. Focus
o. Asthenosphere

### True/False

1. ____ The crust is mainly made up of peridotite.
2. ____ The lithosphere is a rigid outer shell of Earth, which consists of the crust and the outer most part of the mantle.
3. ____ The outer core is made up of solid iron rock.
4. ____ The deeper into Earth's center one goes, the more dense rock becomes.

### Fill in the Blank

1. Scientists measure seismic waves using a _____.
2. When the temperature of iron reaches 760°, known as the _____, it loses its magnetism.
3. An earthquake occurs at the _____, and the spot directly above this location, on the surface, is called the _____.
4. The core consists of a _____ iron and nickel outer core layer and a _____ iron and nickel inner layer.
5. The _____ is the seismic discontinuity at the base of Earth's crust.

## Analysis

1. From Earth's average density, we know that
   a) Earth's interior is of uniform density.
   b) density increases as the depth increases.
   c) Earth is a layered planet.
   d) density decreases as the depth increases.

2. What causes the S-wave shadow zone?
   a) The distance is too far to sustain any amplitude.
   b) The waves refract and are directed away.
   c) The waves reflect back to the epicenter.
   d) Shear waves cannot pass through the liquid outer core.

3. From the center to surface, the chemically distinct layers of Earth are
   a) inner core, outer core, mantle, crust.
   b) core, mantle, lithosphere.
   c) inner core, outer core, lower mantle, upper mantle, crust.
   d) core, mantle, crust.

4. Which of the following is one of the important sources of information about the interior structure of Earth?
   a) Sedimentation rates.
   b) Exploration of deep caves.
   c) x-rays.
   d) Earth's magnetic field.

e) Chemical analysis of rocks from the interior.

5. What causes the P-wave shadow zone?

   a) The distance is too far to sustain any amplitude.

   b) The waves refract and are directed away.

   c) The waves reflect back to the epicenter.

   d) Shear waves cannot pass through the liquid outer core.

6. How do we know the composition of the asthenosphere?

7. What are Earth's five mechanical layers called?

8. What evidence do meteorites give us concerning the composition of Earth's interior?

9. When we refer to "plastic" in describing the low-velocity zone, what does it stand for?

10. Explain the difference between the mechanical layers and the compositional layers.

11. If the outer core and inner core are both composed of iron, why is the inner core solid and the outer core liquid?

12. Briefly describe the differentiation of Earth's interior and what this means.

13. Why do seismic waves make abrupt changes in direction and speed when traveling through Earth? Why do the waves travel in curved paths?

14. Describe the differences between S-waves and P-waves.

15. How are the focus and epicenter related?

16. What does *elastic rebound* mean?

## Synthesis

1. What creates a shadow zone? What are the ranges of the shadow zones for S-waves and P-waves? Sketch an example of an earthquake with the different shadow zones generated. Also show in the sketch the curves of each seismic wave according to the layers and density of Earth.

2. List the five sources of information about Earth's interior discussed in the chapter and briefly describe what information is obtained from each source.

3. Draw a picture showing both the mechanical and chemical layers of Earth. Label the drawing and describe each layer of the picture. Explain the relationship between the two types of layers.

4. Figure 26.9 uses the mechanical classification of Earth's interior instead of the compositional classification of Earth's interior when describing seismic waves. Explain why.

5. What is an earthquake? Under what circumstances do earthquakes occur?

6. List the major seismic discontinuities and explain what causes each of them to occur.

7. Look at Figure 26.9. Notice that besides the major discontinuities the waves increase in speed as they increase in depth. After the waves travel through the outer core, does their wave speed continue to increase or decrease as they approach the side of the lithosphere opposite the epicenter? Explain the reasoning behind your answer. Consider the following additional questions to aid you in formulating the correct solution.

   a) What is a wave?

   b) What happens to density as depth increases?

   c) How does density play a key role in the waves' speed?

# Continental Drift and Plate Tectonics

*The important thing in science is not so much to obtain new facts as to discover new ways of thinking about them.*

Sir William Bragg

# 27

## LEARN

- The evidence revealing the fact that the continents were once joined together.

- The concept of seafloor spreading and the magnetic, volcanic, and earthquake evidence that confirms it.

- The parts of the tectonic system, the boundaries between plates, and the evolution of continents over time.

- The basic forces driving the plate tectonic system.

One of geology's most incredible ideas is the theory of continental drift. How could an entire continent, so enormous, hard and unchanging, actually be floating on Earth's surface? This idea was so outrageous that when it was first formally proposed it was openly ridiculed by the scientific establishment of the time. Any and all conceivable "division of lands" ever recorded were political divisions of territory among peoples and nations, not of the land itself.

It is a tribute to the steady method of science, patiently testing preconceived notions step by step, that today the theory of continental drift and plate tectonics is not just an accepted principle of geology, it is *the leading* principle. The realization that the surface of Earth is in constant—if extremely slow—movement revolutionized geology, giving it a coherence and simplicity reminiscent of the revolution in thought caused by Newton's laws of motion or the discovery of atoms. This keystone in understanding the history and present state of Earth's

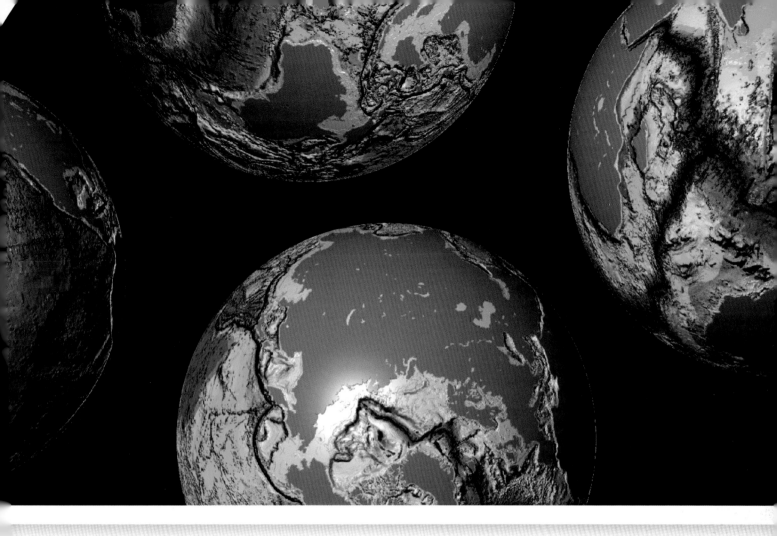

surface permeates every aspect of geologic science.

In this chapter we learn the evidence for continental drift and how this evidence is explained by the theory of plate tectonics. In retrospect it seems so obvious. The continents fit together like a jigsaw puzzle with structures and fossils matching across continental boundaries. Ancient climate, fossil and magnetism patterns make no sense unless the continents were all one land mass 250 million years ago. But other explanations had to be properly considered and discarded before the simple, seemingly outlandish explanation could be embraced.

## 27-1 Evidence for Continental Drift

In 1620, after world maps were completed, Sir Francis Bacon (1561–1626) noted in his book *Novum Organum* that the coasts on either side of the Atlantic Ocean appeared to parallel one another. He may not have been the first to make this observation, for it was readily apparent even on the crude maps of that day. To Benjamin Franklin the apparent relationship of the coast-lines was so striking that he speculated that the surface of Earth might be a cracked shell whose fragments were driven about by the movements of a dense fluid upon which they floated. The German meteorologist Alfred Wegener (1880–1930) used the fit of continents as one of several evidences in his seminal book *The Origin of Continents and Oceans* that laid out a hypothesis that the continents were once together and then split and drifted apart.

Let's look at the geological observations upon which Wegener based his hypothesis.

### Jigsaw Fit of the Continents

The most obvious evidence for continental drift, and certainly one of the most compelling, is the shape of the continental margins. The jigsaw puzzle-like fit of some continents is obvious on a world map and is even more striking when the continents are cut from the map and juxtaposed. *Figure 27.1* shows how well South America and Africa match at the edges of their continental shelves which are the actual edges of the continents. There are a few small areas where the two continents don't fit together very well but these occur primarily where major rivers empty into the sea and deposit their sediment, distorting the shape of the continental edge. Such deposits occurred after the continents separated. In addition, it is probable that some stretching deformation would have occurred along the continental margins as these huge landmasses split and started drifting apart.

South America and Africa are not the only continents that fit together remarkably well at their shelf boundaries. India, Antarctica, and Australia join to them in the south as do North America and Eurasia in the north, strongly suggesting all those continents were once part of a massive supercontinent. Wegener named this large landmass **Pangaea**, a word derived

**Pangaea:**

Pangaea is the name Alfred Wegener gave to the supercontinent that broke up about 200 million years ago to form the continents we have today.

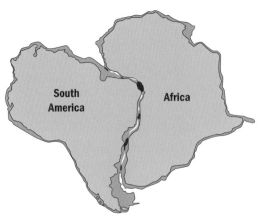

**Figure 27.1**

The fit of the continental shelf margins of South America and Africa. Continents are shown in brown, continental shelves in blue, and the mismatched areas are shown in red. The major mismatch areas are located where large rivers flow into the ocean from one of the two continents. The deltas of these rivers have built up since the time the continents drifted apart.

## ALFRED WEGENER

Alfred Wegener was born and raised in Germany, where he received the best higher education available in the sciences. His interests in meteorology and geology developed as he studied astronomy at Friedrich Wilhelms (today Humbolt) University. After receiving his degree in astronomy in 1905, he took a position as a lecturer in meteorology at the University of Marburg.

Wegener fully embraced challenge and adventure. He spent a winter living on the ice of Greenland. He and his brother Kurt set a world record in ballooning, flying for 52 hours straight. He pioneered the use of weather balloons to track air currents. He published a book, The Thermodynamics of the Atmosphere, which became a standard textbook in meteorology. And he served in WWI, being wounded twice.

He recorded that he first began thinking about a concept that he called "continental displacement" in 1910 when he, like others before him, considered the parallelism of the coastlines across the Atlantic Ocean. At first, he felt the whole idea of continents actually moving was improbable. However, he ran across an old scientific paper that suggested strong similarities between fossils on opposite sides of the Atlantic Ocean. This similarity had been used by the author of the paper to suggest an ancient land bridge between South America and Africa that had foundered and sunk. Wegener thought this was unlikely, but the fossil correlations intrigued him. He began gathering data concerning geologic similarities between unconnected continents, and in 1912 first outlined his ideas about continental displacement in a lecture. He followed that in 1915 with a book, The Origin of Continents and Oceans, in which the comprehensive theory was described.

Wegener theorized that Earth's continents are mobile blocks of land, capable of moving thousands of kilometers around the globe by plowing through the crust, perhaps propelled by the rotation of Earth or tidal forces. He called his idea the "Theory of Continental Drift." Sir Harold Jeffreys (1891–1989), an eminent British physicist with a formidable scientific reputation, made elementary calculations that showed beyond doubt Earth's ocean floor is much too rigid for continents to be shoved through it by any imaginable force. Not knowing that the seafloor was spreading with the continents, this argument carried the day and prevented others from taking seriously the mounting evidence in favor of continental drift.

During his lifetime, Wegener was highly respected for his work in climatology and paleoclimatology (ancient climates), but his theory of continental drift was given a cool reception by his scientist colleagues. Nevertheless, despite the rejection of his original theory and the outright ridicule he received from most of that period's scientific establishment, it is for his ideas about the movements of the continents that he is remembered today. Wegener did not live to see his theory widely accepted. He died from exposure in an ill-fated climatological expedition to Greenland in 1930. It was not until the 1970s that the theory finally gained wide acceptance.

from Greek, meaning "all earth." His vision of Pangaea, as he developed it in the early 1900s, is shown in *Figure 27.2*. Modern refinements of this map have produced remarkably few changes.

### Continental Structure

To better understand how the continents could have fit together, it is helpful to know something about the structural features of continents. All continental structures can be classified as part of a **shield**, **stable platform**, or **mountain belt**. The shields are the ancient geological cores of the continents and contain little sedimentary material. Continental shields are usually surrounded by stable platforms which are basement rock covered by a few hundred feet of sedimentary rock. Bordering on the stable platforms are the mountain belts. The term "belt" is used because they are generally long and narrow like a belt. *Figure 27.3* shows these structures for the North American Continent.

Near the end of the 19th century, Eduard

**Figure 27.2**
The supercontinent of Pangaea as Wegener thought it would have looked near the end of the Paleozoic Era about 250 million years ago, just prior to its breakup.

Suess, an Austrian geologist, noted many structural similarities between Africa, South America and India that suggested these land masses fragmented from a supercontinent. For example there are some shields that end abruptly at continental margins. *Figure 27.4* shows the shield areas of South America and Africa, with the continents arranged for best fit. The shield regions that end at the margin of one continent appear to continue on the adjacent continent, despite the fact that the continents were arranged according to continental shelf margins rather than according to the locations of shields.

The curved lines adjacent to the shields represent the directions of **structural trends** such as mountain belts and zones of deformed rocks.

**Continental Shields:**
The oldest parts of the continents. They represent the roots of very ancient mountains, long since eroded away.

**Stable Platform or Covered Shield:**
An area of the continent where the old rocks of the shield have been covered by relatively flat-lying sedimentary rocks.

**Mountain Belts:**
Regions of the continents where the rocks have been highly deformed by enormous forces. These belts usually lie along the edges of the continents.

**Structural Trends:**
Structural trends are the orientations of major geologic features such as mountain belts, continental shields, stable platforms, and areas of folded and deformed rocks.

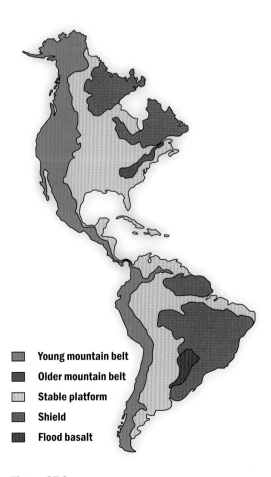

Young mountain belt
Older mountain belt
Stable platform
Shield
Flood basalt

**Figure 27.3**
Map of North and South America showing the major features of the continents.

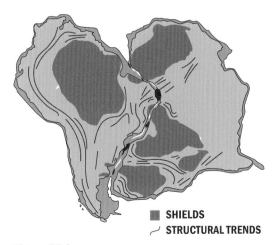

SHIELDS
STRUCTURAL TRENDS

**Figure 27.4**
Structural features of South America and Africa, with the two continents arranged so that the continental shelves match best.

**Paleontologists:**

Scientists who study ancient life preserved as fossils in the rocks.

**Glossopteris Flora:**

An extinct group of seed plants that flourished 250 million years ago. These plants went on to become a dominant part of the flora on the southern part of the supercontinent Pangaea, though they dwindled to extinction after 50 million years.

**Mesosaurus:**

A fresh-water dwelling reptile that lived from 300 to 250 million years ago. It had an elongated head and snout with nostrils near its eyes and a flattened tail used for swimming. Typically it would have been about 1.5 feet long.

**Lystrosaurus:**

A sturdily built, plant-eating reptile (not a dinosaur). Scientists disagree on whether it spent most of its time in water browsing on plants like a modern hippo, or whether it lived mostly on land. An adult would have been about 3 feet long and weighed about 200 pounds.

They are continuous across the continental boundaries as if they had once been connected. The ages of the rocks also match across these boundaries as do tin, iron, and diamond mineral deposits.

These geologic similarities occur for other continents as well. For example, the Appalachian Mountains of eastern North America continue across into the British Isles and Scandinavia when the North Atlantic Ocean is cut away and North America, Greenland and Europe are brought together.

### Paleontological (Fossil) Evidence

In *The Origin of Continents and Oceans* Wegener referred to the similarities of fossils found in widely separated lands. This type of evidence grew stronger as **paleontologists** discovered more and more similar fossils in rocks of the same ages across continental boundaries, particularly in the five southern continents of South America, Africa, India, Australia, and Antarctica. These fossils were of ancient land plants and land-dwelling animals that could not have survived the long journey across the oceans, nor could they have survived in the widely different climates we find on these continents today.

One of the most well known fossils is a group of plants called the **Glossopteris flora** (see *Figure 27.5*). During Wegener's lifetime this flora was discovered in 250 million year old rocks in South America, Africa, India, Australia, and Madagascar. It has since been found in rocks of the same age in Antarctica and the

Falkland Islands. Seeds of these plants could not have been spread across thousands of kilometers of open ocean by natural methods, so Wegener reasoned that these southern landmasses must not have been separated by oceans at that time.

About 250 million years ago, a small freshwater reptile called a **mesosaurus** lived in both South Africa and Brazil (see *Figure 27.6*. Somewhat later, about 200 million years ago, a medium-sized land-dwelling reptile called a **lystrosaurus** left its remains in what are now Brazil, South Africa, India, Antarctica, and China. Neither mesosaurus nor lystrosaurus were capable of crossing large bodies of water, yet their fossils are now separated by oceans.

### Paleoclimatic Evidence

Rocks contain clues about the climatic or environmental conditions under which they formed. For example, fossil plants in sedimentary rocks can often be identified as typical of tropical, subtropical, or temperate climates. Coal beds are the remains of plants that flourished in warm, swampy, coastal environments. Coral reefs flourish only in warm shallow seas found near the equator. Some rocks consist of chemical precipitates, like rock salt, formed by evaporation in poorly circulating bodies of water such as lakes or landlocked seas. Thick deposits of windblown sand may be preserved as sandstones and record the positions of ancient deserts.

Among the most distinctive indicators of ancient climates are the marks and deposits left by continental glaciers—great sheets of ice that

**Figure 27.5**
Fossil leaves from plants that constitute the Glossopteris flora. A fossil of Glossopteris itself is on the left and is about 20 centimeters long.

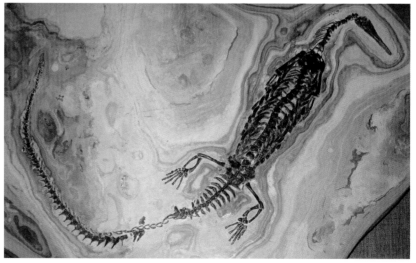

**Figure 27.6**
A fossil Mesosaurus tenuidens (syn. Mesosaurus brasiliensis), from Parana basin, Brazil.

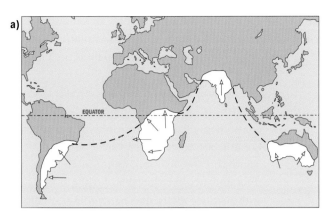
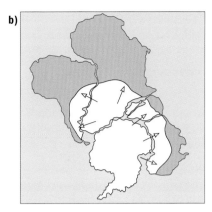

**Figure 27.7**

The present distribution of rocks glaciated by the Permian Ice Age (250 million years ago) (a) and their distribution when restored to the continents pre-drift positions (b). Arrows show the directions of ice movement.

cover thousands of square kilometers. As they move forward during colder epochs and melt and recede during warmer ones they leave characteristic deposits of sediment that can be recognized as glacial in origin (see Chapter 30).

Consider the arrangement of areas glaciated 250 million years ago as they appear on a present day world map (*Figure 27.7a*). Without continental drift it makes no sense. Why was eastern South America cold enough to support glaciers, but not the much higher and therefore colder Andes Mountains on the continent's west coast? Or how could India, sitting across the Equator, have had glaciers? And if India had glaciers, why did they not form in the higher and colder Himalayas where we see them today?

Figure 27.7b shows a portion of Pangaea again with the continents arranged so that their continental shelf margins fit best. In this arrangement the areas of this ancient glaciation form one single region. Not only that, but the directions in which the ice moved, determined by deep grooves left in the glaciated rocks, are now consistent. Wegener viewed this as a remarkable confirmation of continental drift and believed that this **paleoclimatic** evidence could hardly be coincidence.

*Figure 27.8* shows the overall climatic conditions of Pangaea during the late Paleozoic Era, about 250 million years ago, as determined from the rocks of that age. This climatic distribution only makes sense if the continents are moved

**Paleoclimatology:**
The study of ancient climates.

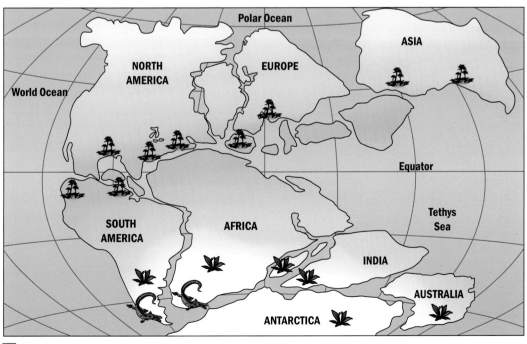

- Glacier
- Low-Latitude Deserts    Coal Swamp    Glossopteris Fossils    Mesosaurus Fossil
- Tropics

**Figure 27.8**

Earth's overall climate picture as determined from the rocks of that age, as well as sample fossil distributions covering the supercontinent of Pangaea during the late Paleozoic Era (Permian Period, 250 million years ago). This distribution of climates and fossils is unexplainable on the basis of the present arrangement of landmasses in the world.

back into their pre-drift positions. It cannot be explained on the basis of their present positions.

### Paleomagnetic Evidence

When volcanoes erupt basaltic lava (see Chapter 29) one of the minerals found in the rock is magnetite, an iron oxide that can be magnetized. As basalt cools on the surface of Earth, the grains of magnetite become tiny recorders. They record the orientation of Earth's magnetic field in a process similar to the recording of music onto a cassette tape. When the basalt has completely cooled, this magnetic orientation is "frozen" into the rock. A basalt sample can lose its magnetic record only if it is heated above the Curie temperature as discussed in Chapter 26.

*Figure 27.9* depicts schematically what is found when the magnetic fields of 250 million-year-old lava flows are measured in South America, Africa, and India. The magnetic records do not give a consistent orientation for the direction to the north magnetic pole. Earth can only have one north pole at a time, therefore, these results do not make sense. But if these landmasses are placed together in Pangaea, then the north arrows frozen in the basalt of each continent all point to a single location. Again, Wegener felt that this was a strong indication that the continents had drifted from locations that were quite different from the positions they currently have.

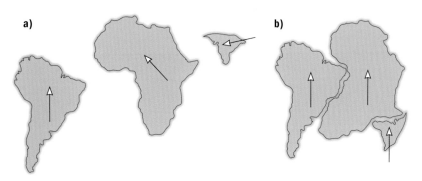

**Figure 27.9**

a) Orientations of the magnetic fields recorded in lava flows of the late Paleozoic Age (250 million years ago) in South America, Africa, and India, with the present orientation of continents;

b) The same magnetic records, with the continents assembled in their pre-drift orientations.

## 27-2 Seafloor Spreading

From the moment Wegener proposed that Earth's continents were once a single supercontinent to the mid-20th century, the small number of advocates and larger collection of critics both concentrated their attention on the continents. This was not because they had no interest in the ocean basins, but because little was then known about the seafloor.

During and after World War II, the U.S. government and other countries with oceanic coastlines became interested in the character of the seafloor. It had been and remained important for our navy to know what the seafloor looked like to better hide their submarines and to know where the enemy might be hiding theirs. At the war's end scientists were interested in using new technology to study the ocean floor for pure research. Industries and businesses of the U.S. and many other nations were interested in its potential natural resources.

The 1950s and 1960s saw considerable effort expended to map the ocean floor in detail. Among the surprising features found during the mapping was a great sinuous ridge that girdled the globe, only rarely poking above sea level at places like Iceland.

In the Atlantic Ocean, the ridge was located almost exactly in the center, equally distant from North America and Europe, and from Africa and South America. The newly discovered undersea ridge's shape was strikingly similar to the shelf margins of the continents on either side. Not only did the continents fit together as Wegener had proposed more than a half century earlier, but this mid-Atlantic ridgeline mimicked the same shape as shown in *Figure 27.10*. This could not be just another coincidence. Scientists who had earlier rejected the theory of continental drift began to look at it again and realize that this was evidence not just for continental drift but also for the mechanism that moved the continents.

Unexpected also was the discovery of a second major feature of the ocean floor: deep trenches—long, narrow, and much deeper than the rest of the ocean basin. Unlike the ridges, these deep trenches were found at the edges of the ocean basins (*see Figure 27.11*).

Between the ridges and trenches the ocean floor was compositionally simple. It was made up everywhere of basalt, covered in places by sediment. This is unlike the continents, which are composed of a wide variety of rock types. Rock ages were found to be very young near the ridges, and older closer to the continents as shown in *Figure 27.12*. The oldest rocks, how-

**Figure 27.11**
Ocean topography off the western coast of South America. Note the lines of underwater volcanoes (seamounts) and the location of the Peru Trench right next to the continent.

**Figure 27.10**
Topography of the ocean floor off the coast of Brazil. Notice the mid-Atlantic ridge with its central rift valley.

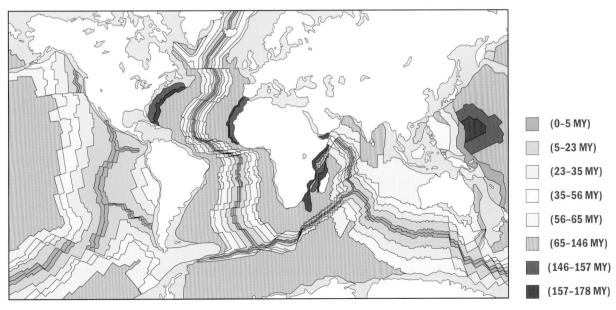

(0–5 MY)
(5–23 MY)
(23–35 MY)
(35–56 MY)
(56–65 MY)
(65–146 MY)
(146–157 MY)
(157–178 MY)

**Figure 27.12**
Ages of the rocks on the ocean floor. Note how the ages get progressively older farther away from the mid-ocean ridges. Also, note that the oldest ocean floor rocks are less than 200 million years old.

ever, were still quite young when compared to rocks on the continents. The oldest rocks on the ocean floor were about 200 million years old, while the oldest rocks thus far discovered on any continent are over 4 billion years old. And no sediment covered the basalts right at the mid-ocean ridges, but it did accumulate to increasingly greater depths farther and farther from the ridges.

Harry Hess of Princeton University proposed in 1960 a theory he called **seafloor spreading**. Hess reasoned that the central rift of the ocean ridge was a fracture where the seafloor was being pulled apart. He proposed that convection currents in the soft and partially molten upper mantle were rising near the mid-ocean ridges then flowing horizontally away from the ridge, pulling the overlying oceanic crust with it. The ridge, he said, is high because hot, buoyant magma rises underneath it. The along the middle of the ridge is created as the ridge is pulled apart and magma erupts along fractures, creating new oceanic crust. This new crust moves slowly away from the oceanic ridge toward the deep ocean trenches, where it descends into the upper mantle to be melted and recycled.

Because the seafloor was created at the ridges and consumed at the trenches, oceanic crust older than 200 million years had been destroyed, making the seafloor so young. Sediment is progressively thicker away from the ocean ridges because it has had longer to accumulate above the older crust. At the ridge itself, the rocks are so young that no sediment has yet built up on top of the basalt.

### 27-3 The Theory of Plate Tectonics

Hess's theory of seafloor spreading provided the mechanism missing from Alfred Wegener's theory of continental drift. Nevertheless, when Hess first presented it in 1960, the evidence was still so tenuous that Hess called it "geopoetry." More scientists were converted to the idea of drifting continents because of these new ideas, but the acceptance was still not universal. It would take additional evidence from studying the magnetism of the seafloor and earthquakes to bring these theories the universal acceptance they have today.

**Seafloor Spreading:**

The theory that the ocean floor grows on either side as the mid-ocean ridge moves apart. The rift created in this process is filled in with basalt as magma squeezes up into the fractures created by rifting.

### Magnetic Reversals and Stripes on the Seafloor

Early in the 20th century, geologists measuring the ancient "frozen" magnetic fields of magnetite minerals in basalts in France discovered some pointed south rather than north. As other old lavas were investigated, it became increasingly clear that Earth's magnetic field was *reversed* when those basalts were created. It was soon discovered that there have been many such reversals with the field alternating between its present direction, the normal polarity, and the opposite direction or reverse polarity. By studying stacks of basalt flows, the sequence of reversals was worked out, complete with absolute dates. It turns out that Earth's magnetic field has reversed its polarity an average of every half million years for the past 65 million years.

Soon after this discovery seafloor geologists mapped the magnetism in basalts at the bottom of the North Atlantic Ocean. They found the magnetic strength to be in stripes—long, narrow bands running parallel to the mid-Atlantic ridge, that alternated symmetrically on either side of the ridge as bands of strong and weak magnetism. Not only was this result completely unexpected, but it also seemed inexplicable, which is a word no scientist likes to use.

In 1963 an explanation emerged, when two British scholars, F. J. Vine, a graduate student, and D. H. Matthews, Vine's supervisor, combined Hess's ideas about seafloor spreading, the magnetic reversals on the continents, and the magnetic stripes of the seafloor into one grand theory we now call the "Theory of Plate Tectonics."

The magnetic strength measured in the stripes on the sea floor is a combination of Earth's magnetic field and the magnetism frozen in the rocks. Vine and Matthews proposed that the stripes of strong magnetism are when Earth's magnetic field and the rock magnetism add together creating a strong field in the magnetometers measuring it. In other words, the strong stripes are those where the ocean basalts have normal polarity magnetism. The weak stripes are where the basalt has a reverse polarity that subtracts from Earth's field leaving the overall signal weak. So the magnetometer surveys found bands of normal polarity and reverse polarity in the seafloor basalts.

Vine and Matthews concluded that as the

basalt lavas were extruded and cooled at the oceanic ridge, they recorded the direction and strength of Earth's magnetic field. As the sea floor spread, these rocks migrated away in either direction from the ridge, allowing newer rock to form that also recorded Earth's magnetic field. As the polarity of Earth's magnetic field changed, the subsequent lavas recorded the opposite polarity. This process is diagrammed in *Figure 27.13*.

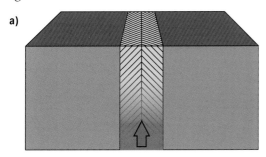
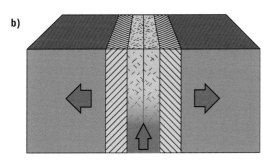
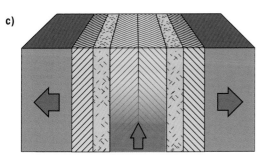

**Figure 27.13**

The development of magnetic stripes of alternating normal and reverse polarity on the seafloor as basaltic lava is extruded at the oceanic ridge and then is pulled to either side as the seafloor spreads. The actual boundaries between adjacent stripes are more complex than can be shown in this generalization.

### *Earthquakes and Plate Boundaries*

Earthquakes do not occur randomly across the surface of Earth. Most of the world's earthquakes occur along ocean trenches and ridges. This is because the brittle lithosphere is being pulled apart at the ridges, and is being bent and sunk back into the asthenosphere at the trenches. Ridges and trenches are plate bound-

aries so earthquake patterns trace the plates that make up the lithosphere.

Using patterns of earthquakes as a guide, scientists have pieced together the plate structure shown in *Figure 27.14*. There are seven major plates, seven to nine secondary plates, and many small pieces at the boundaries called tertiary plates. The largest is the Pacific plate which is also the fastest moving, traveling to the northwest at the speed of seven cm/year, or about as fast as fingernails grow.

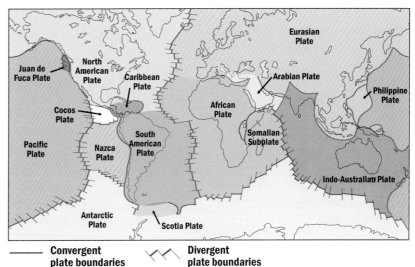

**Figure 27.14**

World map of the major plates and plate boundaries.

## 27–4 Why Do the Plates Move?

So what could move the large plates that are the surface of Earth? The nuclear strong force and weak force are effective only at distances within the nucleus of atoms and thus cannot be responsible. Long-range electromagnetic forces act only between charged objects, and the plates are electrically neutral. This leaves only gravity and the short-range contact electromagnetic forces. There are two locations where gravity and contact generate enough push and pull to move a tectonic plate.

First, along the mid-ocean ridges the plates are higher than the surrounding ocean floor. They are higher because the lithosphere is young and warm and because the hot, low-density asthenosphere is welling up beneath them. Remember from Chapter 6 that when a fluid is heated, it expands, thus increasing the buoyant force and causing it to rise in convection. Even though Earth's asthenosphere is mostly solid (with perhaps 1–5% being liquid), it behaves

## LAKE BONNEVILLE

The Great Salt Lake may seem large, but it is actually a tiny remnant of Lake Bonneville. That was a huge ancient lake that covered most of western Utah, as shown in Figure 27.15. Lake Bonneville grew as Earth warmed at the end of the last glacial period, reaching its maximum size about 16,000 years ago.

The lake drained on the north end, flowing into the Snake River and out into the Pacific Ocean. About 15,000 years ago, a natural earthen dam near Zinda, ID, failed catastrophically. Hundreds of trillions of gallons of water poured through the Snake River canyon in less than a year. The peak flow of this flood equaled the flow in all of the world's modern rivers combined.

In the years that followed, the climate continued to warm and tectonic forces reshaped the landscape. As Lake Bonneville shrank, it reached various levels that were stable for periods of a thousand years or more. The lake's shorelines from these times are still visible today. They form the benches on the east sides of many cities in Salt Lake and Utah counties, and the long flat area around the Point of the Mountain where people like to go paragliding.

Lake Bonneville continued to shrink, cutting off the drainage river on the north. It became land-locked, and the only way for water to leave was through evaporation. Minerals dissolved in river water flowed into the Great Salt Lake basin. The water evaporated and the minerals formed salts—matter with ionic bonds that we talked about in Chapter 22.

The forces that transformed Lake Bonneville into the Great Salt Lake are still at work today. The valleys in western Utah are getting wider as the Pacific, North American, and Juan de Fuca plates shift. Future climate change will also influence the Great Salt Lake because it depends so heavily on yearly rain and snowfall in the mountains.

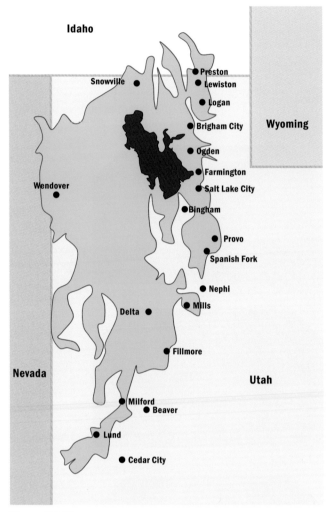

**Figure 27.15**
Lake Bonneville around 16000 years ago. The present day size of the Great Salt Lake is shown in dark blue.

**Figure 27.16**
A view of the mountains in southern Utah County, near Salem. Dirt and rocks washed out of the mountains, creating an alluvial fan before Lake Bonneville was formed. Two shorelines from Lake Bonneville are visible in this picture as broad flat areas at the base of the mountains.

over long periods of time like a very viscous, thick fluid. It may seem strange to think of solid materials flowing like fluids, but given thousands or millions of years and the right temperature and pressure conditions, solid rocks will flow. This upwelling of the asthenosphere at the ridges elevates the plates giving them gravitational potential energy. As the force of gravity pulls on these elevated areas, gravitational potential energy converts to kinetic energy and the plates slowly slide away from the ridges down toward the trenches. This force is called **ridge push** and is shown in *Figure 27.17*.

A second force acts on the plates at the oceanic trenches where lithosphere is being destroyed. Old oceanic lithosphere is cold and dense, unlike the warm, young lithosphere at the ridges. As warm lithosphere moves away from the ridge, it cools and contracts. The contraction of the lithosphere reduces the volume of the plate, making it denser and lowering the buoyant force. At first, this drop in the buoyant force just makes the oceanic lithosphere sink lower into the underlying asthenosphere even though it continues to float. But when the gravitational force on the lithosphere exceeds the buoyant force, the plate then founders and sinks. As it sinks it pulls the rest of the plate down with it. We call this force **slab pull** and it is also shown in Figure 27.17.

There are forces that resist the plate motion as well, which are also shown in Figure 27.17. These are mantle resistance which is friction with the mantle against the sinking plate, collision with other plates, and transform fault friction which is friction between plates sliding past each other. As long as the forces driving plate motion are greater than or equal to the forces resisting plate motion, they will continue to move.

## 27-5  Parts of the Tectonic System

The plate tectonic system can be subdivided into three main subsystems, based on how adjacent plates interact. These are **divergent plate boundaries**, also called spreading zones, **convergent plate boundaries** or collision zones, and **transform boundaries**. Spreading zones are places where plates are pulling apart, collision zones are places where they are pushing against

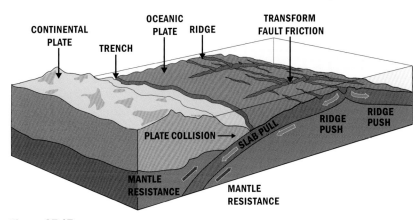

**Figure 27.17**
Forces driving and resisting plate motion.

each other, and transforms are places where they are sliding past each other.

### Divergent Plate Boundaries: Spreading Zones

Divergent plate boundaries are where two plates pull away from each other. The most common type of divergent boundary is the mid-oceanic ridges introduced earlier. As previously mentioned, when two oceanic plates move apart, they open up a great rift or crack in Earth's ocean floor, allowing room for liquid magma from the asthenosphere to flow in and solidify. The magma cools into basalt and in the process creates new oceanic crust. Volcanoes are common along an oceanic rift, but because most of them erupt under water, we rarely see them. Occasionally, enough material erupts under the ocean surface to produce an island that rises, hot and steaming, above the surface of the water. The island of Iceland sits astride the Mid-Atlantic ridge and is the site of frequent eruptions of basalt. The ridge itself is visible on it as a long split. (*Figure 27.18*).

**Figure 27.18**
The visible result of plates pulling apart in Iceland.

**Ridge Push:**

Helps move Earth's plates. The ridge is high and has gravitational potential energy that is converted into kinetic energy as the plate moves.

**Slab Pull:**

Helps move the tectonic plates. As an oceanic plate becomes old, cold, and dense, it sinks back into the mantle, pulling the rest of the plate along with it.

**Divergent Plate Boundaries:**

Boundaries where two plates are splitting apart from each other.

**Convergent Plate Boundaries:**

Boundaries where two plates are colliding with each other.

**Transform Boundaries:**

Boundaries where two plates are sliding past each other.

Oceanic ridges are the sites of frequent earthquakes. But because the lithosphere at the ridge is thin and warm (making it weak), and because the plates are pulling apart rather than colliding, earthquakes tend to be small and shallow. These earthquakes do not produce tsunamis and are generally not dangerous.

Divergent boundaries also occur on continents. One of the best examples of a spreading zone is in eastern Africa (*Figure 27.19*). Here we find the African Rift Valley, a long valley filled in places by deep long lakes such as Lake Malawi and Lake Tanganyika and connected to a narrow arm of the Red Sea. Arabia and part of eastern Africa are perched on a tectonic plate that is slowly moving away from the rest of the African continent. Violent and dangerous eruptions as well as strong and destructive earthquakes occur all along the rift valley. Earthquakes are stronger in continental spreading because continental lithosphere is thicker, colder, and more brittle than the young, warm lithosphere found in oceanic spreading zones.

As spreading continues along a continental rift, eventually the continent is split apart and a new ocean basin forms. In east Africa this has already started where the Red Sea now fills part of the rift and the crust beneath the sea is new oceanic crust. In fact the Atlantic Ocean started as a continental spreading zone about 200 million years ago as North and South America drifted away from Europe and Africa (*Figure 27.20*).

## Convergent Plate Boundaries: Collision Zones

Earth is not growing in size so the creation of new oceanic lithosphere at divergent boundaries requires that older oceanic lithosphere be destroyed somewhere else. The places where this destruction occurs are the convergent plate boundaries where two plates are colliding. Rugged, spectacular mountains, explosive volca-

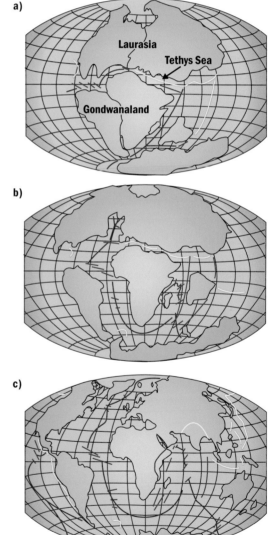

**Figure 27.20**

The history of plate movement during the last 200 million years.

a) Pangaea, 200 million years ago.

b) Plate movement, 100 to 50 million years ago. The Atlantic Ocean is formed as North and South America drift westward.

c) Plate movement 50 million years ago to the present.

**Figure 27.19**

A continental divergent plate boundary in eastern Africa.

noes and huge earthquakes are common here. Even though old ocean lithosphere is destroyed, material is created from which continents are born, and continents, once created, do not easily disappear. We will divide our discussion of convergent plate boundaries into three boundary sub-types: ocean-ocean collisions, ocean-continent collisions, and continent-continent collisions.

**Ocean-Ocean Plate Collisions**

In a collision of two oceanic plates, one plate will dive under the other and sink into the asthenosphere in a process called **subduction**. In general, the plate that subducts and sinks is older, colder, and, therefore, denser than the plate on top. As a plate subducts, it rubs against the overlying plate sometimes causing enormous earthquakes that often produce tsunamis.

A massive earthquake occurred in December 2004 along the collision zone between the Indian-Australian plate and the Asian plate, near the northern end of the island of Sumatra. The quake generated a tsunami with waves up to 50 feet high, smashing against the low-lying coasts of Indonesia, Sri Lanka, India, Thailand, and countries as far away as the east coast of Africa. Scientists manning earthquake early-warning systems had adequate time to send out warnings of the coming of the waves. However, systems to pass on such warnings locally were not in place in this part of the world at the time and an estimated 300,000 people were killed in one of the worst natural disasters in recorded history. In March 2011 a similar earthquake along the Pacific and Eurasian plates in northern Japan created a massive tsunami that killed nearly 20,000 people and rendered 350,000 homeless.

Over the millions of years that plate material travels from a divergent boundary, where it was created, to a convergent boundary, where it is destroyed, it lies beneath the ocean soaking up water. During subduction the sinking plate heats up and releases this water into the overlying wedge of mantle. This lowers the melting temperature of the mantle wedge which begins to melt (*Figure 27.21*). The melted portion is warm and buoyant and rises to the surface, creating a chain of volcanoes along the collision zone. These chains are usually arc-shaped and have come to be called **volcanic island arcs**. The Aleutian Islands, the West Indies, the islands of

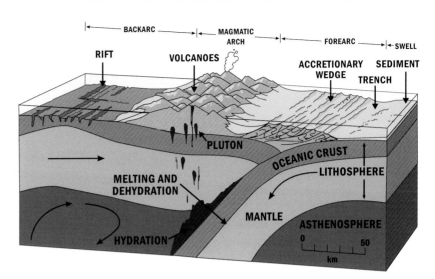

**Figure 27.21**
A diagram of an ocean-ocean plate collision.

Indonesia, Tonga and the Marianas are all volcanic arcs formed above a subducting plate. The volcanic rock that forms these island arcs is less dense than the basalt of the ocean crust. Its composition is more like the rocks in the continents. In fact, we believe that these island arcs are the material from which continents are built over many millions of years.

Unlike the volcanoes that form at divergent boundaries, these volcanoes are extremely violent and explosive, largely because the erupting magma contains more water and is more viscous than magma erupted at divergent boundaries. Eruptions of volcanoes at collision zones have produced some of the world's most deadly natural disasters. They often include earthquakes, tornadoes, tsunamis, spectacular lightning, complete darkness over wide areas and thick deposits of volcanic ash. Those who have witnessed the awesome power of these eruptions do not easily forget them.

**Ocean-Continent Plate Collisions**

When an oceanic plate collides with a continental plate, it is always the oceanic plate that subducts. The continents are made of low-density rock that will not sink. However, sometimes slices of the down-going oceanic lithosphere are scraped off onto the continent, leaving a folded and deformed record above sea level of what the oceanic plate had been like.

An ocean-continent collision can create mountain belts and volcanoes. These volcanoes come up through the edge of the continent from subducting oceanic material. (*Figure 27.22*). The

**Subduction:**

What geologists call the process that occurs at the trenches where old oceanic lithosphere is sinking back into the mantle. The trench area is also called a "subduction zone," and as the plates sink they are said to be subducting.

**Volcanic Island Arc:**

A chain of volcanoes, shaped like an arc, that form at some convergent plate boundaries.

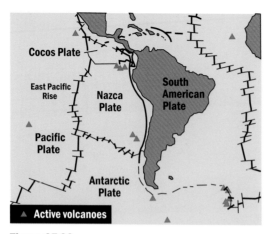

**Figure 27.22**
Active volcanoes, plate tectonics, and South America.

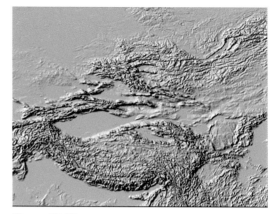

**Figure 27.23**
Digital relief map of the Eastern Himalayas.

material erupted onto the continents is unlikely to ever subduct again, and so causes the continents to grow. The mountains and volcanoes of the Andes in South America and the Cascade volcanoes in North America are good examples of formations in this type of collision zone.

Large earthquakes and explosive volcanoes are characteristic of ocean-continent plate collisions, just as they are of ocean-ocean plate collisions. During the eruption of Mount St. Helens in Washington State on May 18, 1980, the blast was described as "almost beyond comprehension, 500 times greater than the 20 kiloton atomic bomb that fell on Hiroshima and moving outward at velocities of over 300 miles per hour." An eyewitness who viewed the blast reported the following:

> I looked east toward Hanaford Lake and Fawn Lake and that area—it looked like that whole mountain range had just exploded. As the blast cloud approached it looked like a boiling mass of rock—and just as high as you could see. Trees were picked up and thrown into the air at the leading edge of the cloud ... The cloud approached with a roaring noise. As it passed overhead, a tree began to fall and within seconds there were no trees left.

### Continent-Continent Plate Collisions

Continents are made of low-density rocks that are so buoyant they will not sink into the mantle. What happens when two unsinkable objects collide? When a continent reaches a subduction zone and collides with another continent, the subducting oceanic edge may try to pull the continent with it, but because of its low density it cannot sink. Instead, the continents

plow into each other like two cars in a head-on collision. Continents that were once separate land masses become welded together. The edges of the plates and anything in between crumples into a huge mass, creating the highest mountain ranges on Earth. The best modern example of this type of collision is the Himalaya Mountains, which have formed as India collides with Asia (*Figure 27.23*). The Appalachian Mountains in the eastern United States are an example of a mountain belt, now mostly eroded away, that formed in an ancient collision between North America and Africa.

In the deeper parts of a continent-continent collision, rocks are changed by heat and pressure to folded and sheared metamorphic rocks (see Chapter 29). In the upper parts of these collision zones the rocks are less metamorphosed and remain brittle. During deformation they may crack along faults, producing large earthquakes. The impact of India into Asia has affected a large part of the Asian continent and has produced some of the world's most destructive earthquakes. In July 1976, a large earthquake struck the Tangshan area of China. Even though the earthquake only lasted for about 15 seconds, it killed over 250,000 people.

The one striking difference between continent-continent collisions and the other collision types is that there are no volcanoes. Because no plate is sinking into the mantle and melting, no volcanoes form.

### Transform Plate Boundaries

The oceanic ridges are not smooth continuous ridges but instead are formed from relatively straight, short segments that are offset from one another by cracks or faults (see Figure 27.16).

# THE AWESOME POWER OF VOLCANIC ERUPTIONS

Ivan Orloff, an Alaskan Eskimo, wrote the following to his wife during the 1912 eruption of Katmai volcano in the Aleutian Islands:

*We are awaiting death at any moment. A mountain has burst near here. We are covered with ash, in some places ten feet and six feet deep. All this began on June sixth. Night and day we light lanterns. We cannot see daylight. We have no water, the rivers are just ashes mixed with water. Here are darkness and hell, thunder and noise. I do not know whether it is day or night. The earth is trembling . . . It is terrible. We are praying.*

In 1902, Mt. Pelée on the West Indies island of Martinique erupted (*Figure 27.24*). A Mr. Thompson, assistant purser on board a ship that was approaching the harbor when Mt. Pelée exploded, later wrote down what he observed:

*I saw St. Pierre destroyed. It was blotted out by one great flash of fire. Nearly 40,000 people were killed at once. Of eighteen vessels lying in the Roads, only one, the British steamship Roddam escaped and she, I hear, lost more than half on board. It was a dying crew that*

a)

b)

**Figure 27.24**

Harbor of St. Pierre, Martinique prior to (a) and after (b) the eruption of Mt. Pelée.

*took her out. Our boat, the Roraima, arrived at St. Pierre early Thursday morning. For hours before we entered the roadstead, we could see flames and smoke rising from Mt. Pelée. No one on board had any idea of danger. Capt. G. T. Muggah was on bridge and all hands got on deck to see the show. The spectacle was magnificent. As we approached St. Pierre, we could distinguish the rolling and leaping red flames that belched from the mountain in huge volumes and gushed high into the sky. Enormous clouds of black smoke hung over the volcano. The flames were then spurting straight up in the air, now and then waving to one side or the other a moment, and again leaping suddenly higher up. There was a constant muffled roar. It was like the biggest oil refinery in the world burning up on the mountaintop. There was a tremendous explosion about 7:45 soon after we got in. The mountain was blown to pieces. There was no warning. The side of the volcano was ripped out, and there hurled straight towards us a solid wall of flame. It sounded like a thousand cannon.*

*The wave of fire was on us and over us like a lightning flash. It was like a hurricane of fire. I saw it strike the cable steamship Grappler broadside on, and capsize her. From end to end she burst into flames and then sank. The fire rolled in mass straight down on St. Pierre and the shipping. The town vanished before our eyes.*

*The air grew stifling hot and we were in the thick of it. Wherever the mass of fire struck the sea, the water boiled and sent up great clouds of steam. The sea was torn into huge whirlpools that careened toward the open sea. One of these horrible, hot whirlpools swung under the Roraima and pulled her down on her beam end with the suction. She careened way over to port, and then the fire hurricane from the volcano smashed her, and over she went on the opposite side. The fire wave swept off the masts and smokestacks as if they were cut by a knife.*

*I saved my life by running to my stateroom and burying myself in the bedding. The blast of fire from the volcano lasted only for a few minutes. It shriveled and set fire to everything it touched. Thousands of casks of rum were stored in St. Pierre, and these were exploded by the terrific heat. Burning rum ran in streams down every street and out into the sea.*

*Before the volcano burst, the landings at St. Pierre were crowded with people. After the explosion, not one living being was seen on land. Only twenty-five of those on board [out of 68] were left after the first blast."*

These faults are the transform plate boundaries. Along these boundaries the plates are neither colliding nor diverging. Rather, they are simply sliding past one another (*Figure 27.25*). Volcanoes do not form along transform boundaries, because nothing is being subducted and no rifting is occurring.

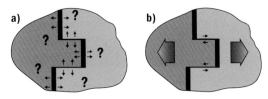

**Figure 27.25**

a) At first it may appear that segments of oceanic ridge (thick lines) have separated from each other along a transform fault (thin lines).

b) Actually, a transform fault is a boundary that separates two plates that are moving laterally past one another (small arrows). The large arrows show the motions of the plates.

Not all transform faults are short. The famous San Andreas fault in California connects a segment of oceanic ridge in the Gulf of California with a segment at the south end of the Juan de Fuca plate. In doing so, it slices off a sliver of California several hundred kilometers in length. While most of the state is part of the North American plate, that sliver rides on the Pacific plate. As the two plates move past one another, strain builds up wherever the fault binds and is released in the earthquakes that are so common in California. Some of these earthquakes can be fairly large and destructive.

## 27-6  Hot Spot Trails

The Hawaiian Islands are one of several linear island chains in the Pacific that do not fit into the plate tectonic picture laid out so far. They are volcanic yet are nowhere near any plate boundaries. The currently active volcanoes in the Hawaiian Islands are on the island of Hawaii, at the southeast end of the chain. As one proceeds up the chain to the northwest, successive islands are inactive and progressively older (*Figure 27.26*). How did this chain of islands form?

It turns out that a single heat source has produced *all* the volcanoes in the chain. The heat source is a **mantle plume** rising from deep in Earth, perhaps from near the core-mantle boundary, which has remained almost stationary while the Pacific plate moves over its top. We call these rising plumes of hot rock **hot spots**. As the plate moves over the hot spot a volcano is created and remains active for a period of time. Then, because the volcano is moving along with the plate, it passes beyond the hot spot and becomes extinct. At the same time a new volcano arises over the hot spot to replace it. In this manner a chain of volcanoes is created on top of the plate with only the volcano that sits over the hot spot being active. Trails of volcanism left on a plate as it moves over a mantle plume are called **linear island chains**.

## 27-7  Evolution of the Continents

We return now to Pangaea. This is not "the beginning" of Earth nor even the original super

**Mantle Plume:**

A buoyant mass of hot rock rising through Earth's mantle. As it nears the surface of Earth, some of the plume melts and erupts at the surface forming a "hot spot."

**Hot Spots:**

Volcanoes that result from the lithosphere moving over a mantle plume. Hawaii is an example of an island-formed hot spot. As the plate moves over the mantle, a line of volcanic structures (such as the Hawaiian chain of islands) marks the passage. The trail of volcanism is called a hot-spot trail.

**Linear Island Chains:**

A chain of volcanic islands created when an ocean plate moves over a hot spot.

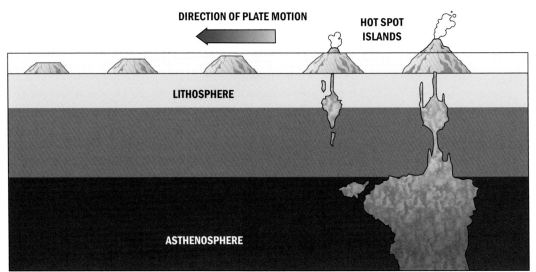

**Figure 27.26**

A linear chain of hot-spot volcanoes is formed as a plate moves over a mantle plume.

## POSTSCRIPT: A COMMENT ON THE WAY SCIENCE WORKS

All the evidence that accumulated during the first half of the 20th century in favor of the idea of continental drift is pretty impressive. Any individual observation might be accepted as merely coincidence, but all the data, when considered as support for a specific idea, is indeed imposing. Yet for half a century after Wegener proposed Pangaea and its breakup, the theory met with open opposition from most scientists, all of them trained in good scientific research methods and some of them considered especially eminent in their disciplines. Hindsight is always available and crystal clear to those of a later generation, so it is easy for us to be critical of the scientists who rejected continental drift. That judgment may cause us to overlook some of the important strengths inherent in the methods of science.

Wegener's treatment at the hands of the scientific establishment is reminiscent of Galileo's treatment at the hands of the religious establishment. It is clear that some of the opposition was not necessarily about Wegener's theory, but was instead aimed at the presumption of Wegener, a well-trained meteorologist who had wandered well beyond the perimeter of his own field, to propose radical ideas in a discipline for which his formal educational credentials did not qualify him. On the other hand, Jeffreys was, in fact, absolutely correct when he announced that continental movement through the oceanic rocks could not possibly have occurred. Had he or someone else not challenged this proposed mechanism, and if it had been widely accepted, it would still have been incorrect; truth is, after all, not determined by majority vote. Thus, sending the proponents of continental drift "back to the drawing board" to come up with a more convincing mechanism was not a penalty, but a reasonable scientific requirement.

Alfred Wegener

Despite occasional statements that science and scientists are not always completely objective, science is an intensely personal endeavor to those engaged in it. Each scientific issue of any consequence is represented by a number of differing viewpoints, each with its own group of proponents. New developments or proposals put forth by one group are scrutinized and tested by the other groups, and weaknesses are exposed while strengths are admitted. Instead of tearing science down, this process builds it by preserving only the theories and ideas that are most consistent with observation. Eventually, those theories that can withstand the most rigorous testing come to be accepted even by those who initially disagreed.

Sir Harold Jeffreys

Even then, it is recognized that good theories are no more than close approximations to the truth, needing constant testing and additional study for possible refinement. (Consider, for example, that Newtonian mechanics and gravitation were considered accurate descriptions of nature for nearly three centuries, until quantum mechanics and relativity revealed them to be only very good approximations.) Thus, if the methods of science are often painstakingly slow, they are at least self-correcting, and serious errors are eliminated, as long as old ideas are honestly questioned and those found lacking are replaced by better ones.

continent but is a landmass that came together by the process of plate tectonics as a single event in the long history of events on Earth. The same forces that split Pangaea apart are the forces that originally assembled it. Geologists estimate there have been at least six major periods of continental building and separation since Earth originally formed. The construction of Pangaea was a relatively recent event, happening only about 300 million years ago. All the features we see on the ocean floors, as well as the present plate configuration have formed since Pangaea broke apart about 200 million years ago. How

did the continents first come to be and can we determine their histories?

Each continent has followed a unique and complex course of development, but the broad outlines of the general evolution of a continent can be understood by focusing on North America. *Figure 27.27* is a map of North America showing generalized ranges for the ages of basement rocks in various parts of the continent. Basement rocks are those that underlie the younger sedimentary cover and are the oldest ones for that location. A consistent pattern is clear: The most ancient rocks are in the shield

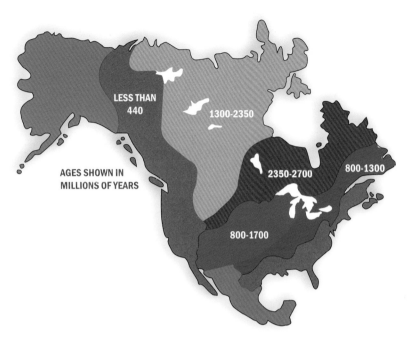

**LESS THAN 440**

**1300-2350**

**2350-2700**

**800-1300**

**800-1700**

AGES SHOWN IN MILLIONS OF YEARS

**Figure 27.27**
A map of North America showing generalized ranges of ages for the continental "basement" rocks. Notice that the ages become younger from the shield toward the margins of the continent.

## Continental Accretion:

The process by which continents grow. When continents collide with island arcs or with other continents, new material may be added and the continent grows.

with the ages becoming younger toward the continental margins.

This age distribution suggests the following general history: The continent originated as a small landmass a few billion years ago likely assembled from volcanic island arcs produced at subduction zones. Other continents were, of course, forming too, and so continental collisions would have occurred. These would have welded "foreign" rocks onto North America—some of which would have remained after subsequent continental rifting. There is good geologic evidence that much of the southeastern United States was part of the African continent before the assembly of Pangaea. When the supercontinent rifted apart it did not break again along the same suture, but left part of the African continent attached to North America. The idea that continents have grown by addition of material at convergent boundaries is called **continental accretion.** By this process the continents have reached their current shapes and sizes.

Like nearly all things scientific, the final chapter on the reconstruction of ancient plate motions has not yet been written. Much work is still being done on pre-Pangaea plate motions. Of course lingering questions do not invalidate the broad aspects of the theory. As we know, all theories require revisions or adjustments— fine-tuning—over years of testing. For example, the fossil remains of a dinosaur called titano-saurus are found in South America, Africa, and India. No problem, right? Wrong. By the time this dinosaur shows up in the fossil record, the landmasses were too far apart for titanosaurs to migrate. Could these fossils be similar but not actually identical? Possibly. Or perhaps there is another answer that will bring more surprises— and possibly offer new puzzles—when we discover it.

*It must have appeared almost as improbable to the earlier geologists, that the laws of earthquakes should one day throw light on the origin of mountains, as it must to the first astronomers, that the fall of an apple should assist in explaining the motions of the moon.*

*Sir Charles Lyell*

# 27 STUDY GUIDE

## Chapter Framework

### A. Evidence for continental drift
1. Alfred Wegener
2. Fit of the continents
3. Continental structure
4. Paleontological (fossil) evidence
5. Paleoclimatic evidence
6. Paleomagnetic evidence

### B. Seafloor spreading
1. A mid-ocean ridge with a central valley
2. Deep ocean trenches

### C. The theory of plate tectonics
1. Magnetic reversals and stripes on the seafloor
2. Vine and Matthews
3. Patterns of earthquakes

### D. Why do the plates move?
1. Ridge Push
2. Slab pull

### E. Parts of the tectonic system
1. Divergent plate boundaries (spreading zones)
2. Convergent plate boundaries (collision zones)
   a. *Ocean-ocean plate collisions*
   b. *Ocean-continent plate collision*
   c. *Continent-continent plate collisions*
3. Transform plate boundaries

### F. Hot spot trails
1. Linear island chains
2. Reference points for absolute motion

### G. Evolution of the continents
1. Accumulation of smaller plates over time
2. Continental accretion

## Comprehension

### Matching

1. _____ The source of the forces that move the tectonic plates around.
2. _____ The study of ancient life preserved as fossils in the rocks.
3. _____ Structures formed on ocean crust when a plate moved over a hot spot.
4. _____ The term used to identify the point within Earth where an earthquake starts.
5. _____ The supercontinent that broke up at the start of the Mesozoic Era to form the continents we have today.
6. _____ Structures formed when two ocean plates collide.
7. _____ The theory that the ocean floor moves as the mid-ocean ridge separates.
8. _____ The orientations of major geologic features such as mountain belts, continental shields, stable platforms, and areas of folded and deformed rocks.
9. _____ The study of ancient climates.
10. _____ An extinct group of plants that flourished from the Permian through the Triassic periods.

a. Pangaea
b. Seafloor spreading
c. Glossopteris flora
d. Paleomagnetism
e. Paleontology
f. Structural trends
g. Island arcs
h. Ridge push and slab pull
i. Linear island chains
j. Paleoclimatology
k. Focus

11. _____ Magnetism preserved or fossilized in rocks. It can often tell us about changes in the orientation of rock bodies after their formation.

### True/ False

1. _____ Scientists widely accepted the theory of continental drift when Wegener proposed it.
2. _____ Criticizing scientific theories helps refine them.
3. _____ Wegener based his theory only on the fit of the continents.
4. _____ Basalt can lose its magnetic orientation if it is heated above the Curie temperature.
5. _____ Continental rock plows through the ocean crust when continents move.
6. _____ Faults like the San Andreas form when two continents diverge.
7. _____ Island arcs colliding together formed the original continents billions of years ago.

### Fill in the Blank

1. _____ evidence, from the pre-drift era, indicates that certain areas of the world supported cold, arctic environments.
2. The polarity of Earth's magnetic field switches from _____ polarity to _____ polarity several times every million years.
3. The ocean floor is mostly composed of _____ covered with deposits of _____.
4. The average ocean floor depth is _____ near continental edges than at oceanic ridges.
5. The coasts on either side of the Atlantic Oceans appear to _____ one another.
6. _____ rise through Earth's crust, creating hot spots.
7. The most deadly volcanoes and earthquakes are found at _____ boundaries.
8. Colder, older, _____ ocean plates _____ under warmer, younger ocean plates.

## Analysis

1. The occurrences of the Glossopteris flora in Permian rocks of South America, Africa, Antarctica, India, and Australia is evidence that
   a) these plants lived in the southern hemisphere since the Permian Period.
   b) these plants can survive in a wide variety of climates.
   c) the southern landmasses have separated since the Permian period.
   d) the southern landmasses have become closer since the Permian period.

2. Which of the following is not evidence for continental drift?

a) Changes in Paleozoic trilobites in North America and Europe.

b) Mountain ranges that cross continental boundaries.

c) Glaciated Permian rocks on several continents.

d) The geometrical fit of North America and Australia.

3. The alternating stripes of strong and weak magnetism found in rocks of the seafloor

a) parallel the oceanic ridges.

b) are perpendicular to the ocean ridges.

c) are oblique (at an angle to, other than perpendicular) to the ocean ridges.

d) are too far for the oceanic ridges to judge their relationship.

4. Convergent plate boundaries do not involve

a) subduction zones.

b) mountain-building events.

c) creation of new oceanic lithosphere.

d) creation of linear island chains.

5. Among the following choices, an earthquake would least likely occur

a) in a young fold mountain belt.

b) in a continental shield.

c) at a transform fault.

d) along the ocean ridge system.

6. Where would a volcano be least likely to occur?

a) Northern California

b) Maine

c) East Africa

d) Japan

7. How does a study of earthquakes and seismic waves provide evidence in favor of the plate tectonic theory?

a) The pattern of earthquake activity corresponds to plate boundaries.

b) Wave velocities are related to plate motion.

c) Seismic studies have determined the boundary between the mantle and the core.

d) Seismic waves power continental drift.

e) Earthquakes are regarded as the energy source for tectonic plate motion.

8. A converging plate margin bisects the Mediterranean Sea. What will be the probable outcome of this situation?

a) The Mediterranean will shrink.

b) A mid-ocean ridge will soon begin to emerge within this area.

c) The water body will grow longer as a result of shear transform faulting.

d) The water body will grow wider.

e) A rift valley will appear in the middle of the Mediterranean.

9. When attempting to fit the continents together, we use the continental shelves rather than the coastline, Why?

10. How does paleomagnetism support the theory of continental drift?

11. What first led scientists like Alfred Wegener to believe that the continents once formed one large continent?

12. What two pieces of evidence indicate that the seafloor is spreading at the oceanic ridges?

13. What was Pangaea?

14. What evidence did Wegener and his supporters gather to strengthen their claim about continental drift?

15. How did evidence of glaciation in the Southern Hemisphere support the continental drift hypothesis?

16. Why do fold mountain belts have long, narrow features?

17. Explain how an ocean plate moves.

18. Why do island arcs tend to be larger than islands in island chains?

19. What causes the elevated position of the oceanic ridges?

## Synthesis

1. You stumble across a time travel device and find yourself stuck in a debate between Alfred Wegener and Sir Harold Jeffreys, with a large audience attending the debate. They ask you the following questions, how would you answer them?

a) What is meant by continental drift?

b) What evidences and observations do you have to support the idea of continental drift? (Name and describe five.)

c) Are there any major problems with the idea of continental drift? Is so, what are they?

d) What does seafloor spreading mean and how is it different from continental drift?

e) What evidences and observations do you have to support the idea of seafloor spreading? (Name and describe two.)

f) How can the seafloor spread when Earth maintains a constant size?

2. Where does the lithosphere form? Where is the lithosphere destroyed? Why must the creation and demolition of the lithosphere occur at the same rate?

3. What are the basic elements of the plate tectonic model? How does it resolve the problems unexplained by earlier ideas of continental drift and seafloor spreading?

4. Describe the differences in the type and duration of volcanic activity in island chains and island arcs? Explain these differences

5. Explain how a continent like North America may have formed.

6. What natural disasters are associated with plate tectonics? Why?

# Geologic Time

*Man is enabled to find sense in this chaos of experience and discover the meaning and measure of this incomprehensive flux of perpetual "flourishing and perishing" which we call Time.*

K. Bhaskaran Nair

# 28

## LEARN

- What uniformitarianism means.

- The techniques used by scientists to determine the relative ages of events in Earth's history:

  - Original horizontality

  - Superposition

  - Inclusions

  - Cross-cutting relationships

  - Faunal Succession

- How scientists use radioactivity to determine the quantitative or absolute ages of events in Earth's history.

- To appreciate the vastness of geologic time.

When scientists speak of the time since the formation of Earth or since the creation of the universe itself, they often describe it as "deep time." The concept of deep time like the theory of plate tectonics is one of the great ideas of science. It is referred to as "deep" because the span of time is enormous—almost incomprehensibly vast. Understanding, visualizing, and conceptualizing the whole idea of deep time is not intuitive. The 80 to 100 years of our own lives is a long period of time to us. Even our grandparents and great grandparents are so far in the past they appear to have lived in a different age, a time beyond our reckoning. Compared to deep time, these are but fleeting moments.

Our best estimate of Earth's age is 4.6 billion years. If you made a movie of Earth's history and viewed one year of it every second, how long would it take to see the entire production? If you didn't pause to go out for popcorn, and kept watching 24 hours a day, you could watch it all in just over 145 years! All of recorded human history would only be one hour of this!

Because Earth's creation was so long ago, the record of early Earth history is difficult to read. It is like an ancient manuscript written in a different language, with most of the pages damaged or missing, particularly those from the deepest epochs. To the credit of many persevering scientists, some of this early history has been deciphered, but there is still much to learn. The last one billion years can be read and understood more clearly than the first 3.6 billion years. Over these last billion years, fewer of Earth's rocky pages are missing and the language seems more familiar because we find signs and structures in those rocks that are similar to features in rocks today. Extrapolating from what transpires now, we learn what once was and what processes created the changes.

## 28-1 Understanding Time

To understand Earth's history we first make assumptions about time and if it affects the laws of nature. We introduced the most fundamental assumption of time as the concept of "time sym-metry" in Chapter 1. This "self-evident truth" asserts that the passage of time does not affect the laws of nature. They operated the same in the past as they do today. Geologists call this concept **uniformitarianism**. Guided by this principle we apply the laws governing the world today to the study of Earth's past and to predict its future.

Another self-evident truth that helps us interpret Earth's history is **Occam's Razor**. Recall this says that if more than one explanation is possible, we should choose the simplest one that satisfies all of the evidence. For events deep in Earth's past, we do not have the luxury of doing the experiment again, so we must rely on Occam's Razor to help us choose the best explanation for what we see now. With this in mind, let us look at Earth and see if we can come up with some simple ways to determine the origin and sequence of past events recorded in the rocks.

To place events in their proper sequence, we can either first position them in relation to other events, or we can determine a numeric

**Uniformitarianism:**

The idea that the laws of nature do not change with time. This idea is also called the principle of "Time Symmetry."

**Occam's Razor:**

The rule that where two or more explanations exist for the same physical phenomenon, we should choose the simplest one that satisfies all of the observations.

353

age. Suppose you are setting up a date with a friend. You might say, "Let's get together after our Physical Science class tomorrow." Or you might instead say, "Why don't we get together at 12:15 pm tomorrow." In the first example, you have given your friend a relative time frame (get together after class) while in the second example you have given a numeric value (get together at 12:15 pm). Scientists who study past events use both of these measures of time. The first we call **Relative Time** and the second **Absolute Time**, although a better name might be quantitative or numeric time, because it is a quantitative estimate of the time, from then until now. Both of these measures of time are extremely valuable in understanding the history of our planet.

## 28–2  Relative Time

To determine the relative ages of events, we use simple but powerful tools called the "Principles of Relative Dating." They all rely heavily on Occam's Razor, and they help us pick the simplest explanation for a sometimes complex series of events. Five of these principles are:

1. Original horizontality
2. Superposition
3. Inclusions
4. Cross-cutting relationships
5. Faunal succession

### *Principle of Original Horizontality*

Much of what we learn about Earth's past comes from sedimentary rocks—rocks formed out of sediments laid down on Earth. (See Chapter 29). Sedimentary rocks form on Earth's surface and often hold clues—ripple marks, bones, and other evidence—that tell of past events. Guided by time symmetry, we observe how and where sedimentary rocks are forming today and extrapolate this knowledge to our study of sedimentary rocks formed in the past. Sedimentary rocks forming today are almost always deposited in layers that are nearly horizontal. This is the principle of original horizontality:

**Sedimentary rocks are deposited in horizontal layers.**

How can we apply this to understanding events in the geologic past? Let's take an exam-

**Relative Time:**

The determination of the sequence in which events occurred, relative to each other.

**Absolute Time:**

A numeric or quantitative measure of time.

**Figure 28.1**
Folded limestones in Rock Canyon near Provo, Utah.

ple from Rock Canyon in the mountains east of Provo, Utah. Rock Canyon's walls are composed mostly of sandstone and limestone layers that are not horizontal but rather are uplifted and bent (*Figure 28.1*). The principle of original horizontality says they were formed horizontally, so something happened after the sedimentary layers were deposited that rotated them from their original horizontal position. Therefore we can confidently identify at least two events at Rock Canyon and place each event in its correct order. First, the rocks were deposited horizontally. Secondly, they were tilted so that they now are no longer horizontal. With this simple observation we have the beginnings of a geologic history of Rock Canyon.

### *Principle of Superposition*

Observing the formation of sedimentary rocks in modern lakes and ocean basins has also taught us that variations in the deposited sediment create different types of layers. Changes in the composition or size of the grains being deposited, or even in the type of matrix or binding material cementing the grains together, can create a unique layering.

Sedimentary layering occurs naturally in oceans and lakes, where fine sand, coarse sand, rocks, and other materials are brought in by streams and rivers. Of course the oldest layers, the ones that formed first, are always on the bottom of the stack. The layers that were more recently deposited are found closer to Earth's surface.

This is the principle of superposition:

**In a stack of sedimentary layers, the oldest layer will be on the bottom and the youngest on the top.**

In *Figure 28.2*, two prominent sedimentary units in Rock Canyon, a dark brown one and a lighter rusty orange one, are shown. The brown rock unit is called Mineral Fork Tillite, and the rusty orange unit is called Tintic Quartzite. The principle of superposition tells us the brown Mineral Fork Tillite is older because it is underneath the Tintic Quartzite.

Unfortunately this principle is not perfect and there are places where the sequencing is reversed by an event that uplifted the oldest layers and bent them over to be on top. Situations like these are discovered when other clues within the rock layers tell us which way was originally up.

### Principle of Inclusions

If you were to carefully examine a piece of the Tintic Quartzite from the outcrops in Rock Canyon, you would see that the quartzite contains small, rounded grains and pebbles of quartz held inside the rock matrix (*Figure 28.3*). Where did these pebbles and grains come from? How did they become part of the rock?

The simplest explanation is that they came from the same types of places where rounded pebbles and sand grains are formed today: beaches, rivers, and deserts. They did not grow in the rock, but are **inclusions** within it. Of course pebbles and grains of sand we see today are loose and not cemented together. To be within a rock, a process had to take them and bind them. For that to happen, the pieces within the rock must be older than the rock that they are now included in. We may not be able to tell the specific formation where these inclusions came from without further study, but we can be sure that they are older and bring with them an earlier history. This is the principle of inclusions:

**Tintic Quartzite**

**Mineral Fork Tillite**

**Figure 28.2**
Layers of tan Tintic Quartzite atop brown Mineral Fork Tillite in Rock Canyon near Provo, Utah. The dashed yellow line indicates the boundary between the layers.

**Solid materials (like pebbles and grains of sand) enclosed within another solid (like quartzite) are older than the rock that encloses them.**

In our brief study thus far of the geology of Rock Canyon, the scientific principles we have used allow us to identify the following events, from the oldest to the youngest:

1. Deposition of the Mineral Fork Tillite
2. Formation of the sand grains found in the Tintic Quartzite
3. Deposition of the sand grains found in the Tintic Quartzite
4. Cementing of the sand grains into rock
5. Tilting of the rock layers to their present position

**Inclusion:**

Rock, fragment of rock, or fossil enclosed within another rock.

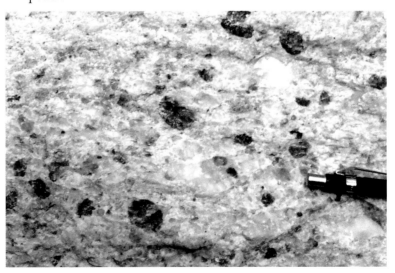

**Figure 28.3**
Small dark pebbles and white grains of sand can be seen in this close-up of the Tintic Quartzite.

**Figure 28.4**
Fossil ammonites that once lived in a shallow sea near what is now the town of Schliefhausen, Germany, during the Jurassic Period approximately 180 million years ago.

**Figure 28.5**
Dark inclusions in a lighter gray granite in the Merced River Gorge near Yosemite National Park, California.

**Ammonite:**

The name given to the fossil-shell remains of animals that lived in the oceans millions of years ago, but are now extinct. They were squid-like animals whose closest modern-day relatives are the nautilus.

**Fault:**

A break in Earth's lithosphere where rocks on one side of the break have slipped past the rocks on the other side. Faults are created by earthquakes.

Another example of the principle of inclusions can be seen in *Figure 28.4*. This figure shows fossil **ammonites** found in a limestone formation. The fossils must be older than the rock because they are included in it. *Figure 28.5* shows yet another example of this principle. This picture shows dark inclusions in granite found near Yosemite National Park in California. Granite forms from magma, which is molten rock deep in the earth that occasionally spurts through volcanoes and other types of cracks in the surface. The dark inclusions are pieces of older rock that were entrapped in the magma before it cooled into the solid granite.

### Principle of Cross-cutting Relationships

We now wash the fine sand, the coarse sand, and the cooled magma off our hands and sit down at an imaginary dinner table, where a beautiful, but equally imaginary pumpkin pie has just been placed in front of us. For purposes of understanding the next scientific principle, imagine that the pie has been cut into six sections. We all have had experience with pie, so we can easily deduce that someone has cut the pie

*after* it was baked. The marks left by the knife that cut the pie can easily be seen in the otherwise smooth surface of the pie.

The same kinds of marks can be found in nature. *Figure 28.6* shows a small **fault** cutting through the Mineral Fork Tillite and the Tintic Quartzite in Rock Canyon. Sedimentary rock layers form horizontally, and if those horizontal layers are disrupted or cut across by something like a fault, then the fault must have happened after the rock layers were formed. This is the principle of cross-cutting relationships:

**Rocks are older than the features (such as faults) or rocks that cross-cut them.**

Let's go back and look more closely at the dark inclusions found in the Yosemite National Park granites discussed earlier. *Figure 28.7* shows a close-up of one of the dark inclusions. Can you see the crack cutting across the dark inclusion

**Figure 28.6**
Small faults (blue) displacing the layering between the Tintic Quartzite and darker Mineral Fork Tillite in Rock Canyon near Provo, Utah.

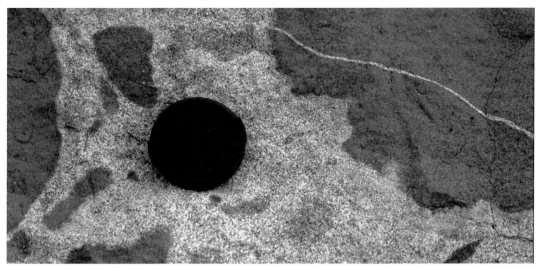

**Figure 28.7**
Close-up of dark inclusions in granite shown in Figure 28.5. Note the camera lens cap for scale. In this photo you can see a crack in the dark inclusion (upper right) that is filled with lighter granite. You can also see the "ghosts" of some dark inclusions that have almost been completely assimilated into the granite.

and how it has been filled with lighter-colored granite? Now we have two evidences that the darker inclusions are older than the granite. First, the dark inclusions are surrounded by the granite and second, the dark inclusions are cross-cut by fractures filled with the granite.

### Principle of Faunal Succession

In 1796, while working on a project building canals to transport coal to market, an engineer named William Smith (1769-1839) began recognizing distinctive layers in the rock uncovered by the excavations. He further realized that each layer of sedimentary rock contained a unique group of fossils. Once a fossil in these layers disappeared from rock above a boundary in the sequence, it was never to reappear higher in the sequence. In other words, extinction lasts forever. This observation of Smith's has been repeated world wide at millions of locations, and is called the principle of faunal succession. This coming and going of fossils in the geologic record allows geologists to put the layers in order from oldest to youngest based on the remains of once living organisms.

Let's look at the rocks in Rock Canyon and find out what fossils they contain. *Figure 28.9* (next page) is a geologic map of the Rock Canyon area, showing both the Mineral Fork Tillite and the Tintic Quartzite. The Mineral Fork Tillite does not contain any fossils and the Tintic Quartzite contains only traces of fossil life.

The Tintic Quartzite is the metamor-

phosed remains of a beach deposit. On top of it are the Ophir Shale and Maxfield Limestone. This sequence of rocks, a quartzite on the bottom, a shale in the middle, and a limestone on the top, reveal a rise in sea level. As these layers were deposited by a rising ocean we find fossil **trilobites** and trilobite fragments preserved with the sediment (*Figure 28.8*). Trilobites changed their shapes through time and the ones we find in the Ophir Shale and Maxfield Limestone formations differ in shape from trilobite fossils found in younger layers. Higher up on the can-

**Trilobites:**
A common animal that lived in Earth's oceans during the Paleozoic Era. They are most closely related to the modern Horseshoe Crab.

**Figure 28.8**
Fossil trilobites collected from the Wheeler Shale near Delta, Utah.

yon walls are younger layers of rock containing fossil corals and shells. As we go from older layers to younger layers we find the trilobites vanish and later so do the corals and shells.

South of Rock Canyon is Slide Canyon (located on the lower right hand side of the map in *Figure 28.9*) where we find the same trilobite fossil types in the same order as they are found a few miles away in Rock Canyon. Even when we go several hundred miles out into western Utah, these same patterns are found. The principle of faunal succession allows us to correlate rock

### GEOLOGIC MAP OF THE "Y MOUNTAIN" AREA, EAST OF PROVO, UTAH

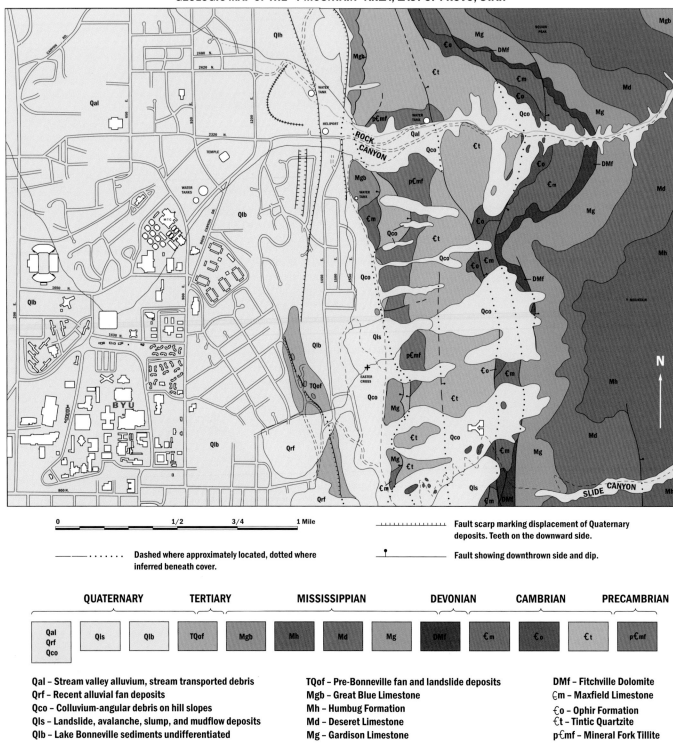

| | | | | | | | | | | | | |
|---|---|---|---|---|---|---|---|---|---|---|---|---|
| **QUATERNARY** | | | **TERTIARY** | **MISSISSIPPIAN** | | | | **DEVONIAN** | **CAMBRIAN** | | | **PRECAMBRIAN** |
| Qal Qrf Qco | Qls | Qlb | TQof | Mgb | Mh | Md | Mg | DMf | €m | €o | €t | p€mf |

Qal – Stream valley alluvium, stream transported debris
Qrf – Recent alluvial fan deposits
Qco – Colluvium-angular debris on hill slopes
Qls – Landslide, avalanche, slump, and mudflow deposits
Qlb – Lake Bonneville sediments undifferentiated

TQof – Pre-Bonneville fan and landslide deposits
Mgb – Great Blue Limestone
Mh – Humbug Formation
Md – Deseret Limestone
Mg – Gardison Limestone

DMf – Fitchville Dolomite
€m – Maxfield Limestone
€o – Ophir Formation
€t – Tintic Quartzite
p€mf – Mineral Fork Tillite

**Figure 28.9**

Geologic map of the Rock Canyon and Y Mountain areas near Provo, Utah. The different rock formations can be identified using the key at the bottom of the figure. The absolute age of these formations is listed in Figure 28.15.

units from place to place, based upon the same patterns of fossils in the rocks. The principle of faunal succession states:

> **Within stacks of sedimentary rocks, there is a pattern of change in the types of fossils the layers contain. The fossils can therefore help us determine the relative age of different layers.**

### Unconformities

As mentioned in the introduction, one of the challenges in reading Earth's history as recorded in the rocks is that the record is incomplete. It's like trying to make sense of a novel after someone has ripped out every third page, or even occasionally large sections. You might still be able to follow the general trend of the story, but you would miss many important details.

This is exactly what it is like for geoscientists trying to read the history of Earth. We find in some places that sedimentation stopped, so nothing was recorded for a particular interval. In other places the sedimentary layers which formed many feet below the surface of the ocean were lifted high above sea level where erosion or some other natural event destroyed all or part of the layers. These gaps in the geologic record are **unconformities**. In a novel with missing pages, the unconformities would be identified by missing page numbers, or by the frayed remains of a torn out page. In the rock record unconformities are recognized by noticing that certain fossils are missing, or by the worn off edges of rock layers (*Figure 28.10*). It is important to recognize these unconformities so that we know how complete the rock record is at any given location.

### Using the Principles of Relative Time

Now that you have been introduced to the principles that help us place events in a proper age sequence, let's apply them to a world-famous geological landmark, the Grand Canyon. *Figure 28.11* is a cross-sectional view or vertical slice down through the rocks of the Grand Canyon. How many events can you recognize? Can you determine a relative sequence for these events? Can you recognize any unconformities? Do you think that it is possible to explain everything in the cross-section as having formed in just one

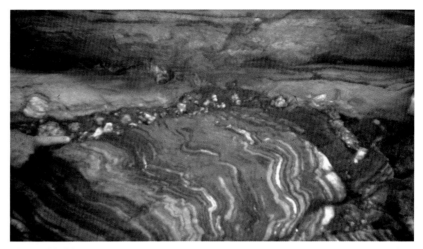

**Figure 28.10**
The "Great Unconformity" in the Grand Canyon between the Cambrian Tapeats Sandstone (top) and the Precambrian Vishnu Schist (deformed, metamorphosed sediments at bottom). Note the finger pointing at the layer of pebbles along the unconformity. These pebbles are pieces of eroded and broken Vishnu schist.

event? After carefully examining Figure 28.11, consult *Figure 28.12*, where we walk through the events that led to the Grand Canyon's formation.

## 28-3 Absolute Time

The remarkably simple principles of relative dating allow us to determine the relative ages of events in Earth's past fairly easily and without any expensive equipment. However, sometimes we would like to know not just the relative sequence of events, but the times at which those events occurred. Determining absolute time is essential if we are to establish a quantitative measure of when events occurred in the geologic past.

**Unconformity:**
A break or gap in the geologic record.

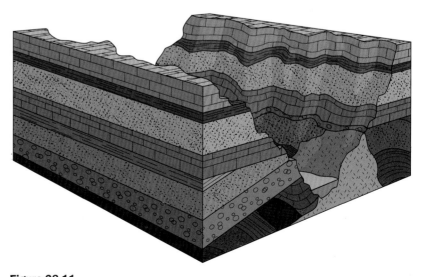

**Figure 28.11**
Block diagram showing the rocks that make up the Grand Canyon. To see how these rocks came to be arranged in this way, look at the sequence of events in Figure 28.12.

**Figure 28.12**

Sequence of events that created the Grand Canyon in Arizona. The ages given are absolute times determined by various methods.

1 - Deposition of layers of sediment (shown in brown shades) in an ocean about 1.8 billion years ago.

2 - Folding, metamorphism (alteration), and uplift of sediments to create a mountainous region and form the Vishnu Schist from the sediments about 1.7 to 1.6 billion years ago.

3 - Intrusion of Zoroaster Granite (red) between 1.6 and 1.4 billion years ago.

4 - Erosion of the region back to sea level between 1.4 and 1.2 billion years ago.

5 - Deposition of a new set of sedimentary layers in an ocean between 1.2 and 1.0 billion years ago. These layers are now called the Grand Canyon Supergroup (shown in green shades).

6 - Tilting and uplift of the region creating a new highland or mountainous area about 1 billion and 740 million years ago.

7 - Intrusion of the Cardenas Basalt (purple) about 1 billion years ago.

8 - Erosion of the region back to sea level and formation of the "Great Unconformity" between 740 and 550 million years ago.

9 - Deposition of Paleozoic, Mesozoic, and Cenozoic sedimentary rocks (orange shades) between 550 and 20 million years ago.

10 - Uplift of the region and cutting of the Grand Canyon by the Colorado River over the last 20 million years produce the canyon we see today.

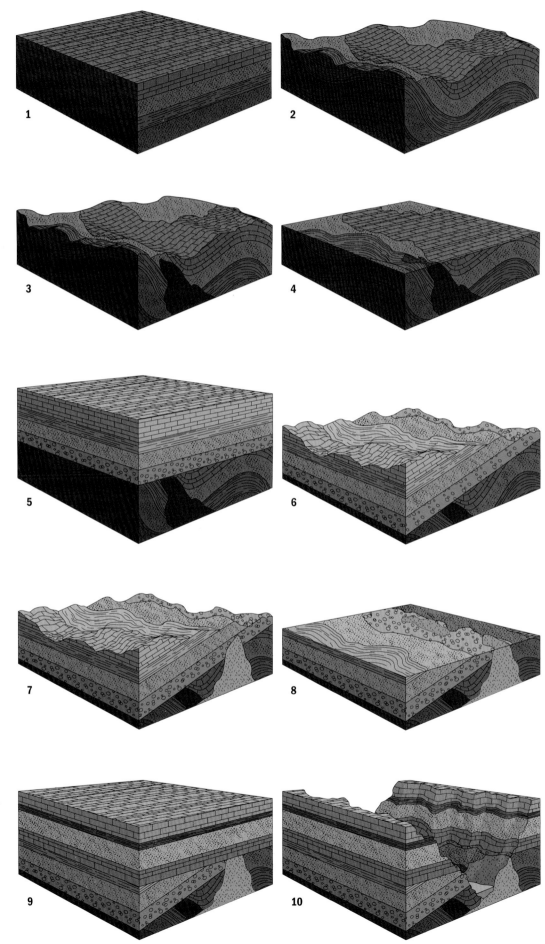

### Earth's Age

One important event that bounds all others is the formation of Earth and the Solar System. How long ago did this occur? What methods might be used to give us an age?

James Ussher (1581–1656), an Anglican Bishop in Ireland, believed that the days of creation mentioned in the Bible were periods of 24 hours each. He used the Biblical genealogies and chronology to determine that Earth was created in 4004 BC. (A short time later a Biblical scholar at Cambridge, Dr. John Lightfoot, identified the exact time of creation as 9:00 a.m. on October 30 in that same year!) If their calculations are correct, Earth today would be about 6,000 years old.

Even though 6,000 years is a long period in terms of human events and lives, this seemed much too short a period of time to other people. One of the most prominent of these was James Hutton (1730–1797). Hutton studied the rocks around his home in Scotland and came to a much different conclusion than Ussher. Hutton proposed the radical idea that the age of Earth was essentially infinite. He stated that he could see "no vestige of a beginning, no prospect of an end."

Other scientists and naturalists attempted to measure the age of Earth using the principle of uniformitarianism discussed at the start of this chapter. Each of these attempts used the observed rates of processes to estimate Earth's age. Georges Leclerc, Count of Buffon (1749), assumed Earth was molten hot when created and calculated the age to be about 100,000 years based on experiments with the cooling rates of cannonballs. In 1846, Lord Kelvin used similar reasoning but more careful experiments to estimate that the age was somewhere between 10 million and 100 million years old.

These estimates seemed too young for many researchers who were literally breaking new ground in their studies of the rocks and fossils they found deep under the surface and high on the mountains. By the late 1800s, additional estimates of Earth's age had been produced by calculating the amount of salt that had accumulated in the oceans (about 100 million years) and by estimating the time it would take to deposit all of the accumulated thickness of sedimentary rock layers found around the world (between 3 million and 1,500 million years).

All of these estimates were based on calculations developed from basic ideas which themselves had problems. The cooling age calculated by Lord Kelvin was only accurate if Earth had no internal sources of heat to keep it warm. We know today that radioactive decay at Earth's core creates considerable heat. The calculation of the saltiness of the ocean did not consider how much salt had precipitated out of the ocean. We now know that a considerable amount of salt has precipitated. Finally, even the thickest piles of sedimentary rocks contain numerous unconformities, so these rocks only represent a portion of the total time that has passed.

A major scientific breakthrough took place in the late 1800s and early 1900s when the phenomenon of radioactivity was discovered and studied by Henri Becquerel and Pierre and Marie Curie. Although they did not estimate the age of Earth themselves, other scientists soon did, coming to the startling conclusion that Earth was 4.6 billion years old! It was the start of a new age of accurate and reliable estimates for Earth's age and for events that had occurred during Earth's long history.

### Radioactive Dating

As mentioned in Chapter 25, radioactive decay takes place at a rate that is unique yet constant for each radioactive isotope. As experiment and observation revealed the nature of radioactive decay, it became apparent that it could be used as a geologic clock—a way to measure the age of any rock that contained radioactive isotopes.

Consider the radioactive uranium isotope $^{238}U$ which we will write as uranium-238. It is called a **parent isotope** and it decays to a **daughter isotope** that is also radioactive. This isotope then decays to yet another radioactive isotope, and so on through a complex series of alpha and beta decays that finally cause the original uranium-238 to become lead-206, a stable isotope that undergoes no further decay. The entire uranium-238 to lead-206 decay sequence has a half-life of 4.5 billion years.

The graph of how the parent isotope diminishes is the same for all radioactive isotopes, the only difference is the value of the half-life. A representative curve is given in *Figure 28.13*. The vertical axis shows the fraction remaining of the original parent isotope. At "time

**Parent & Daughter Isotopes:**

The result of radioactive decay, in which one element decays to form another element. The element we start with is called the parent and the new element formed in the decay process is called the daughter.

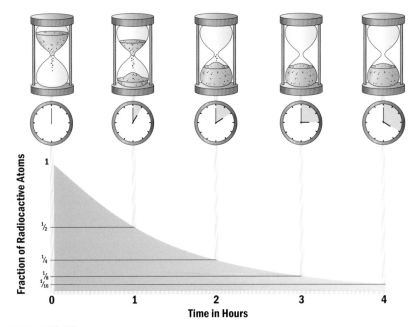

**Figure 28.13**

Decay curve for radioactive isotopes. Unlike some other "clocks," radioactive decay is not linear but exponential. Sand grains fall through an hourglass in a linear fashion. This means that if it takes 1 hour for 500 grains to fall, then it will take two hours for 1,000 grains. With radioactive decay this is not the case. For example, suppose you have 1,000 radioactive atoms and 1,000 grains of sand in an hourglass. You leave them and come back in one hour and find that 500 atoms have decayed and 500 grains have fallen. When you return in another hour, 500 more grains of sand have fallen, but you still have 250 radioactive atoms left. Only one-half of the 500 atoms that remained after the first hour decayed in the second hour. Each hour that passes produces a similar result, with one-half of the radioactive atoms that remained decaying. For this hypothetical example, one hour would be the half-life of the radioactive atoms.

zero" there is no daughter product yet, so the fraction is 1. After one half-life, the fraction is one-half because half of the original parent is left. Likewise, after two half-lives, the fraction is one-fourth, and so on. If we had some way of determining how much uranium-238 there was originally in a rock and how much is left at present, we could divide the latter by the former to obtain the fraction. We could then draw a horizontal line from that value on the vertical axis, intersect the decay curve, and draw a vertical line from that intersection to the horizontal axis, where we would read the age of the rock.

You may have recognized that this proce-

dure requires the assumption that the original rock had no lead-206, so that all of that isotope now present can be ascribed to uranium decay. This assumption is not always valid, but there are ways to determine how much of the lead-206 is original and to correct for that.

The radioactive isotopes that are useful as geologic clocks must have a half-life long enough for there to be a measurable amount of the parent isotope left. The parent isotope must also be relatively abundant in common minerals so that a rock will contain enough of it to be useful. The most commonly used parents and daughters isotopes are listed in *Table 28.1*, along with their half-lives. For greater accuracy, two or more isotopic systems are used on the same rock whenever possible to verify the results.

Observe in Table 28.1 that carbon-14 has a very short half-life compared to the other parent isotopes. It is also different from the other clocks in that it only dates objects that have once been alive. Carbon-14 is produced naturally in the atmosphere, and is part of every living organism. While it is alive, an animal or plant continuously replaces the chemistry of all of its body parts, including the carbon-14. When the organism dies, however, the carbon-14 in the dead animal's body is no longer replaced. If we analyze a dead organism, the amount of carbon-14 remaining reveals how long ago the organism died. After about a dozen half-lives, there is not enough carbon-14 left to measure accurately, so that method can measure times as far back as ~70,000 years. This isotopic clock is thus useful for archaeological dating but not for determining the age of Earth.

When we use radiometric dates we are dating events in time. But what exactly are these events? In the 1920s the geologist Norman Bowen began working on experiments to determine the order that silicate minerals formed in magma. He found that the minerals formed in a certain order as the magma cooled. In a cooling body of igneous rock, the mineral olivine was observed to form first, followed by pyroxene and others, and finally quartz at the other end of the series (*Figure 28.14*). In other words, he found that different parts of the same rock were created at different times.

When we use the tool of radiometric dating, we are determining when the individual mineral reached its "closure temperature", or the

| Table 28.1 — Isotopes Used in Absolute Dating | | |
|---|---|---|
| Parent Isotope | Daughter Isotope | Half-life (years) |
| rubidium-87 | strontium-87 | 47.0 billion |
| thorium-232 | lead-208 | 14.1 billion |
| uranium-238 | lead-206 | 4.5 billion |
| potassium-40 | argon-40 | 1.3 billion |
| uranium-235 | lead-207 | 713 million |
| carbon-14 | nitrogen-14 | 5,730 |

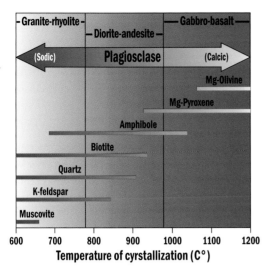

**Figure 28.14**

Bowen's reaction series. Minerals that crystallize at higher temperature are on the right. The high temperature minerals, the first ones to crystallize in a mass of magma, are most unstable at the Earth's surface and quickest to weather because the surface is most different from the conditions under which they were created while the low temperature minerals are much more stable because the conditions at the surface are much more similar to the conditions under which they formed.

temperature when daughter products begin to accumulate in the crystal. Daughter products are forming continually, but they can migrate from the rock. At closure the mineral becomes a closed system and the formed daughter isotopes no longer escape. Bowen's work showed that each mineral has a different closure temperature. So when we look at the radiometric dates from a granite, the dates will be different for various minerals in the rock, because they closed at different temperatures while the rock cooled.

Finally, one widespread misconception about isotopic dating is that the ages obtained by these methods represent the ages of the elements that make up rocks or minerals. This is not the case. The ages obtained by these methods represent **events**, not the age of the elements. We can illustrate this by briefly discussing an isotopic dating method called **fission-track dating**.

In fission-track dating, the isotope of interest is uranium-238. When certain minerals crys-

**Event:**

A happening that occurs at a particular point in space and at a definite time.

**Fission-track Dating:**

A type of radioactive decay clock that uses the trails or tracks created by uranium fission decay to determine the age of geologic events.

## FISSION-TRACK DATING

How do we date a rock or mineral using fission tracks? And what does the age mean when we have obtained it? Let us use, as an example, granite from Little Cottonwood Canyon located in the Wasatch Mountains east of Salt Lake City. This granite was quarried by the first settlers of Salt Lake City and used to build the LDS Salt Lake Temple. The granite is composed mostly of quartz, feldspar, and biotite, with small amounts of zircon, sphene, and apatite. These are minerals that contain enough uranium-238 to be useful in isotopic age determinations. In the laboratory, a sample of granite is crushed and processed through a series of mineral separation techniques to obtain a concentrate of the uranium-bearing minerals. The minerals are then glued to a glass slide, carefully polished, and the fission tracks are revealed by etching the mineral with acids or bases. The tracks found in a mineral grain are counted and this number is used, along with data on the amount of uranium-238 in the grain and the isotopic decay rate, to calculate the age of that rock specimen. The fission tracks tell us how much daughter product was created by the decay process, the amount of uranium-238 represents the amount of parent isotope remaining, and the decay rate (or half-life) allows us to link these two pieces of information into an age.

The fission-track ages we obtained from apatite grains in the Little Cottonwood granite ranged from about 6.5 million years (MYR) to about 11 MYR. This range in age for the granite is substantial and may appear to be evidence of the failure of isotopic dating systems. These differences in age obtained on the same rock body have been used by some to attempt to discredit the whole idea of geologic time and the science behind it. As students of the scientific method, how then do we explain the discovery of such widely differing ages on the same rock body? Which age is right?

Simply put, all the ages measured as described above are "right." They are each telling us something about the cooling history of the granite. The apatite fission-track ages on the temple granite change systematically from 6.5 MYR near the base of the Wasatch Mountains (at about the 5000 ft. elevation) to 8 MYR at about the 7000 ft. elevation, to 11 MYR at the 11,000 ft. elevation. This change in age with elevation shows that the Wasatch Mountains have been forming along the Wasatch fault for millions of years. Movement of the fault has caused the valley to drop away, exposing the mountains and the granite. Temperatures deeper inside Earth are warmer, and so as the granite was brought closer to the surface it cooled. When the apatite grains in the granite cooled below about 100°C (closure temperature), they began to preserve fission-tracks. Before the apatite's cooled below 100°C, uranium atoms were still decaying and producing tracks, but the tracks were not stable because the temperature was too high. Only when the mineral cooled below 100°C did tracks begin to accumulate in the apatite grains. The reason the apatite fission-track ages are older at the top of the mountain than they are at the bottom of the mountain is because the top of the mountain cooled below 100°C about 11 MYR ago, while the rocks at the bottom of the mountain cooled below that temperature only 6.5 MYR ago.

**Geologic Column:**

A chart that shows the subdivisions of geologic time.

**Period:**

A subdivision of geologic time. Smaller than an era, but still several tens of millions of years long.

**Eras:**

The largest subdivision of geologic time.

tallize from liquid magma, they contain trace amounts of uranium-238. With the passage of time, the parent isotope uranium-238 decays to produce a daughter isotope, usually by emitting an alpha particle, but occasionally by spontaneous fission.

When a uranium-238 atom decays by spontaneous fission, the atom breaks into two positively charged, highly energetic fragments. These fragments crash through the mineral that contained the uranium-238 atom leaving a trail of ionized atoms. These trails are called fission tracks and older rocks have more tracks than younger rocks. The number density of fission tracks gives us the rock's age.

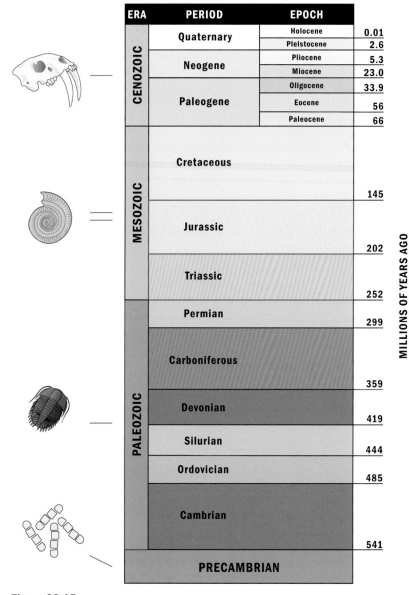

| ERA | PERIOD | EPOCH | MILLIONS OF YEARS AGO |
|---|---|---|---|
| CENOZOIC | Quaternary | Holocene | 0.01 |
| | | Pleistocene | 2.6 |
| | Neogene | Pliocene | 5.3 |
| | | Miocene | 23.0 |
| | Paleogene | Oligocene | 33.9 |
| | | Eocene | 56 |
| | | Paleocene | 66 |
| MESOZOIC | Cretaceous | | 145 |
| | Jurassic | | 202 |
| | Triassic | | 252 |
| PALEOZOIC | Permian | | 299 |
| | Carboniferous | | 359 |
| | Devonian | | 419 |
| | Silurian | | 444 |
| | Ordovician | | 485 |
| | Cambrian | | 541 |
| PRECAMBRIAN | | | |

**Figure 28.15**

Geologic Column showing the main subdivisions of geologic time into "eras" and "periods." Each of the periods are characterized by different assemblages of fossils.

## 28-4 Geologic Column

As the science of geology developed in the early 19th century, it became possible to define various divisions of rocks by the fossils they contained. Often these divisions were given names based on geographic or historical features of the areas in which they were described. For example, the Cambrian, Ordovician, Silurian, and Devonian rocks were named after the Roman name for Wales, two ancient British tribes, and the English county of Devonshire, respectively. Cambrian rocks were identified as those in which the earliest, very abundant fossils of marine invertebrates were found; the presence of certain key fossils identified other rocks as Ordovician, or Silurian, or Devonian, and so forth. In this way the **Geologic Column**, as shown in *Figure 28.15*, evolved.

The Geologic Column is divided into **periods**, which are grouped into four **eras**—the Cenozoic, the Mesozoic, the Paleozoic, and the Precambrian. The first three literally mean recent life, middle life, and ancient life, the names referring to the similarity (or dissimilarity) between modern life forms and the fossils in rocks of those ages. The Precambrian Era is characterized by very rare fossils—mostly impressions of soft-bodied creatures, single-celled organisms, and other very primitive life forms. The Paleozoic Era is characterized by abundant marine invertebrates (trilobites, sponges, corals, mollusks, etc.). However, fish, amphibians, and reptiles, as well as land plants, also appear in the fossil record of this era. Reptiles of an astonishing variety flourished during the Mesozoic Era which was the age of the dinosaurs. This era also saw the emergence of birds, small mammals, and flowering plants. We live in the Cenozoic Era, and the fossils found in Cenozoic Era sedimentary stone layers which are still being formed testify that we, and animals with many of our same characteristics, dominate this period of geologic history, making it the age of the mammal.

The Geologic Column evolved from relative dating techniques first before isotopic clocks were developed, so none of its developers knew how long any of the periods were or even if they were of similar length. It was primarily the use of fossils and the principle of faunal succession that enabled geologists to identify rocks as belonging to a particular period of geologic time like the

Devonian, for example, well before the absolute age of that period was known. With the ability to determine absolute ages, the Geologic Column has become a quantitative tool with known ages for the major divisions and many of the minor subdivisions. It is used in many aspects of geology, and has become the calendar to which the history of Earth is referenced.

# 28 STUDY GUIDE

## Chapter Framework

### A. Understanding Time
1. "Deep Time"
2. Earth's estimated age
3. Time symmetry, or uniformitarianism
4. Occam's Razor

### B. Relative Time
1. Principle of Original Horizontality
2. Principle of Superposition
3. Principle of Inclusions
4. Principle of Cross-Cutting Relationships
5. Principle of Faunal Succession

### C. Unconformities

### D. Absolute Time and Age of Earth
1. Various historical methods
2. Radioactive isotopes and half-life
3. Carbon-14
4. Fission-track dating

### E. Geological Column
1. Eras and periods
   a. *Cenozoic*
   b. *Mesozoic*
   c. *Paleozoic*
   d. *Precambrian*

## Comprehension

### Matching

1. ____ A subdivision of geologic time. Smaller than an era, usually several tens of millions of years long.
2. ____ A type of radioactive decay clock that uses the trails or tracks created by uranium fission decay to determine the age of geologic events.
3. ____ Determining the sequence in which events occurred relative to each other.
4. ____ The largest subdivision of geologic time.
5. ____ A chart that shows the subdivisions of geologic time.
6. ____ A break in the earth where rocks on one side of the break have slipped past the rocks on the other side.
7. ____ A numeric or quantitative measure of time.
8. ____ The idea that the laws of nature do not change with time.
9. ____ The time required for half of the parent isotope to decay to the daughter isotope.
10. ____ A common animal that lived in Earth's oceans during the Paleozoic Era.
11. ____ Fossil shells of animals that lived in the oceans millions of years ago, but are now extinct.
12. ____ A break or gap in the geologic record.
13. ____ Something that has happened in Earth's history.

a. Relative time

b. Absolute time

c. Era

d. Unconformity

e. Half- life

f. Period

g. Fault

h. Trilobite

i. Fission- track dating

j. Event

k. Ammonites

l. Geologic column

m. Uniformitarianism

## True/False

1. ____ Our best estimate for the age of Earth is 4.6 million years.
2. ____ The principle of superposition lets us determine the absolute ages of layers in a stack of sedimentary rocks.
3. ____ Daughter isotopes are the products of decay of radioactive elements.
4. ____ Half-life is the time it takes for one-half of the radioactive parent isotope to decay.
5. ____ An era is a smaller subdivision of geologic time than a period.

## Fill in the blank

1. Time symmetry or _____ is the idea that the laws of nature do not change with time.
2. The _____ teaches us that when one solid is enclosed within another solid, the enclosed or included solid must be older.
3. An _____ is a gap or break in the rock record.
4. The divisions in the geologic column are based upon the _____ they contain.
5. The pattern of fossils found in rocks can help us to determine their ages according to the principle of _____.

## Analysis

1. Which of the following principles is not used in relative dating?
   a) Principle of Inclusions
   b) Principle of Faunal Succession
   c) Principle of Superposition
   d) Principle of Isotopic Decay
   e) Principle of Cross-cutting Relationships

2. A sedimentary rock layer lies on top of a lava flow. The lava flow has been dated at 44 million years. Both the sedimentary rock layer and the lava flow are cross-cut by a dike of igneous rock that has been dated at 27 million years. The layer of sedimentary rock has an age of
   a) more than 44 million years.
   b) somewhere between 44 and 27 million years.
   c) less than 27 million years.
   d) halfway between 44 and 27 million years at 35.5 million years.

3. To be useful as geologic clocks, radioactive isotopes must occur in
   a) very few rocks and have long half-lives.
   b) very few rocks and have short half-lives.
   c) many rocks and have long half-lives.
   d) many rocks and have short half-lives.

4. A fault that cuts through a group of sedimentary rock layers is

   a) younger than the layers.

   b) older than the layers.

   c) either younger or older than the layers depending on its absolute age.

5. Uranium-238 has a half-life of 4.5 billion years. If a mineral has 200 uranium atoms when it is forms, about how many of these atoms would be left after 9 billion years?

   a) 200

   b) 100

   c) 50

   d) 25

   e) Impossible to determine from the information given.

6. A moon rock contains equal amounts of uranium-238 and its decay products. How many half-lives have gone by since the rock solidified?

   a) 1/2 of a half-life

   b) 1 half-life

   c) 2 half-lives

   d) 3 half-lives

   e) Impossible to determine from the information given.

7. What can you conclude from this cross section?

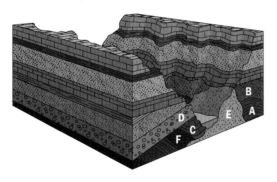

   a) E must be the oldest since it is at the bottom of the other rocks

   b) It is impossible to know whether F is older or younger than E

   c) E is cross-cutting A, B, and C; therefore it is younger than all of them

   d) D must be an igneous rock because they are almost always deposited in horizontal layers

   e) None of the above

8. Why are the periods in the geologic column not equal in length?

9. What two factors limit the usefulness of carbon-14 dating?

10. How are relative dating and absolute dating different in concept?

11. Describe why the same decay curve can be used for any radioactive isotope, regardless of the length of its half-life.

12. Explain why the principle of uniformitarianism is critical in geology and how we use it to understand the history of Earth.

13. Name and state the five principles of relative dating.

14. Create your own Geological Column showing the four eras and representative life forms found in the rocks of each era. Indicate on your Geologic Column the absolute dates of the beginning of each era as determined from radiometric dating.

15. Describe two early methods for dating Earth's age. List a weakness of each method. What was Earth's age according to these methods?

16. When you use radiometric dating methods to determine an absolute age, what does that age actually mean?

## Synthesis

1. Describe the general process of radiometric dating. What makes radiometric dating the most reliable method of dating? What limitations are there to radiometric dating techniques?

2. Explain what unconformities are and provide examples of the geologic processes that cause them.

3. Create a sequence of events that describes the geologic history you can determine from the cross-section below. Your sequence should include the deposition of rock layers, tilting and erosion of said layers, and formation of faults in their proper order. Explain which methods of relative dating you used to arrive at your conclusions. A and B are both sedimentary rocks. C is a fault.

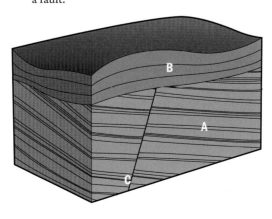

# Earth Materials

*This world, after all our science and sciences, is still a miracle; wonderful, inscrutable, magical and more, to whosoever will think of it.*

*Thomas Carlyle*

# 29

## LEARN

- The rock cycle and how rocks migrate between the three main types: igneous, sedimentary, and metamorphic.

- What minerals are and some examples.

- Where and how igneous rocks form, including the roles of pressure, temperature, and chemistry.

- Physical and chemical weathering and how each leads to sedimentary rocks.

- What metamorphism is and how it alters rocks.

We intuitively appreciate that Earth is a rocky planet, but what exactly are rocks and why are they the way they are? We have already touched upon this somewhat in Chapter 28 since sedimentary layers are the basis of most of the relative dating techniques. The powerful principle of faunal succession led to the geologic column only because skeletons of once-living creatures were fossilized inside certain types of rocks as they formed. In this chapter we consider rock formation itself and the materials from which rocks are made.

### 29-1 The Rock Cycle

We place rocks into three broad, interrelated categories: **igneous, sedimentary**, and **metamorphic.** Molten rock is known as **magma.** Igneous rocks form when magma cools and solidifies (*Figure 29.1*). Sediment is material removed from already existing rock by chemical and physical processes then transported and deposited in another location. Sedimentary rock is sediment that has been compacted and

### Igneous:

The type of rocks produced when melted material solidifies.

### Sedimentary:

The type of rocks created from sediments weathered from other pre-existing rocks.

### Metamorphic:

The type of rocks produced when pre-existing rocks are altered without melting by pressure and heat.

### Magma:

Rock in a liquid state.

**Figure 29.1**

Fine-grained, black basalt lava flows on the island of Hawaii. The basalt cooled quickly as it poured out onto Earth's surface. The Hawaiians called this type of lava "pahoehoe."

369

a) Shale    b) Limestone    c) Sandstone

**Figure 29.2**

Three common types of sedimentary rocks.

cemented together (*Figure 29.2*). Metamorphic rock is preexisting rock of any type that has been heated or compressed with enough energy to recrystalize the minerals within it without melting the rock. (*Figure 29.3*).

These categories are straightforward to define but of course there are more details to consider. Sedimentary and metamorphic rocks, by their very existence, require other solid earth materials to come before them. Sediment cannot be eroded and deposited if there were nothing to be eroded. Metamorphic rock is the recrystallization of a pre-existing **protolith** (proto=precursor; lith=rock). And igneous rocks form only because something first melted. Although separated into different categories, all rock types are linked together and can convert to other types in what is called the **rock cycle**.

*Figure 29.4* illustrates the transformations within the rock cycle. It shows that igneous rock can be eroded at Earth's surface to form

**Protolith:**

A pre-existing rock from which other rocks are formed.

**Rock cycle:**

The transformation of igneous, sedimentary and metamorphic rocks from one type to another.

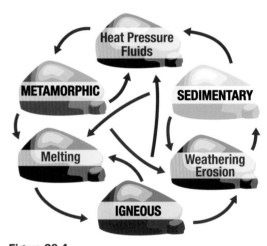

**Figure 29.4**

The rock cycle. All three types of rocks can transform into the other two rock types or into another version of the same type.

sedimentary rock. Sedimentary rock can then be heated and recrystallized into metamorphic rock. Metamorphic rock can in turn be melted into magma and re-solidified to form igneous

a) Marble

b) Gneiss

c) Slate

**Figure 29.3**

Photos of a) marble, b) gneiss, and c) slate, three common metamorphic rocks.

rock again. Any of the three rock types can be processed into the other two or into another version of the same type.

The basic laws of chemistry and physics already discussed govern the behavior of the rock cycle. For example recrystallization in metamorphic rocks is driven by the minimization of energy and maximization of entropy. Magma rises to the surface and cools because of buoyancy. Chemical bonds dictate how minerals form. The science of rock formation is, to a large degree, the study of physics and chemistry applied to the materials that make up our planet.

## 29-2 Minerals: Building Blocks of Rocks

All materials are built of elements. The ten most common elements in Earth's crust ordered by mass are oxygen (46.1%), silicon (28.2%), aluminum (8.2%), iron (5.6%), calcium (4.2%), sodium (2.4%), magnesium (2.3%), potassium (2.1%), titanium (0.6%), and hydrogen (0.1%). These account for 99.8% of the crust's mass. The other 80 naturally occurring elements in the periodic table are present only in trace quantities. Earth itself contains a great amount of iron but nearly all of this is in the core, not crust.

The elements join naturally to form sets of extended bonding substances which together are called **minerals**. There are a number of definitions for the word "mineral". You are probably familiar with "mineral water" in which certain chemical elements are dissolved. Mineral is used as a synonym for ore and also for specific nutrients in our diet. These many definitions compel us to be more precise and we start by first simply stating that in geology minerals are building blocks of rocks and are therefore what most of Earth is made of.

Minerals build rocks but not all materials in a rock are classified as minerals. For our purposes a mineral has the following characteristics:

1. Is naturally occurring
2. Is an inorganic solid
3. Has a fixed or narrowly limited chemical composition
4. Has a definite internal crystal structure
5. Exists within a defined range of pressure, temperature, and moisture

To illustrate these criteria we ask "Is ice a

**Figure 29.5**
Ice forms crystals like this snowflake, showing that it does have internal crystalline structure.

mineral?" It occurs naturally, it is inorganic, and it has a fixed chemical composition of $H_2O$. We all know that ice melts at 0°C, so it exists within a definite temperature range. And it has structure. *Figure 29.5* is a photograph of a single snowflake. Although we often hear that no two are alike, all snowflakes have common features. They all have six arms or sides that arise from linking $H_2O$ molecules together in a regular crystal structure or pattern. Ice is, in fact, a mineral by our definition and glacial ice would be considered a rock!

What about the glass in a window? This is *not* a mineral because it fails two of our five definitions. First, humans manufacture window glass. Second, it does not have atoms that are bonded together in a regular pattern. The atoms are bonded irregularly which is, in fact, a key characteristic of glass. Minerals all exhibit a regular molecular structure.

Thousands of different minerals have been identified, although the list of *abundant* minerals in the crust and mantle is surprisingly small and limited to several dozen. Five common minerals, are shown in *Figure 29.6*. Four of these are silicates. The silicate mineral family is the most abundant mineral group in Earth's crust making up as much as 90% of it. Within this family are many different individual minerals or groups of minerals like feldspar, pyroxene, and mica (Figures 29.6c–e).

As described in detail in Chapter 24, all sili-

**Minerals:**
The basic building blocks of rocks.

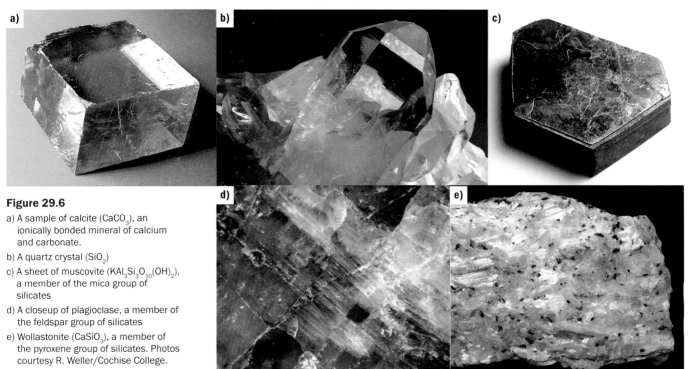

**Figure 29.6**

a) A sample of calcite ($CaCO_3$), an ionically bonded mineral of calcium and carbonate.

b) A quartz crystal ($SiO_2$)

c) A sheet of muscovite ($KAl_3Si_3O_{10}(OH)_2$), a member of the mica group of silicates

d) A closeup of plagioclase, a member of the feldspar group of silicates

e) Wollastonite ($CaSiO_3$), a member of the pyroxene group of silicates. Photos courtesy R. Weller/Cochise College.

cates contain the molecular ion $SiO_4^{4-}$ as isolated entities or linked together into single chains, double chains, sheets, 3-dimensional networks, and other complicated structural mixes. Single silicate units combine with magnesium and iron to form olivine, the most common mineral in the upper mantle. More complicated structures combine with aluminum, fluorine, beryllium, potassium, calcium, sodium, and other elements to form the common minerals of feldspar and mica as well as crystals like topaz and garnets or gems like emeralds (*Figure 29.7*). Plagioclase is a feldspar mineral that, although you may never have heard of it before, is one of the most common minerals in Earth's crust. Silicate minerals are supremely important in the study of the solid earth.

**Figure 29.7**

a) Closeup of Olivine (($Mg,Fe)_2SiO_4$) crystals. The metal combined with the silicate can be either magnesium or iron.

b) Topaz ($Al_2SiO_4(F,OH)_2$) crystal.

c) Spassarite ($Mn_3Al_2(SiO_4)_3$), a member of the garnet group.

d) Emerald ($Be_3Al_2(SiO_3)_6$) a type of beryl crystal. (Same source as figures 29.6)

## 29-3 Igneous Rocks

Most people learn at an early age that igneous rocks are cooled magma. The magma is nearly always a mixture of silicate tetrahedra and other ions. If that were the only important aspect of them we could stop our study of igneous rocks here. However, nearly all of humanity lives on continental crust and igneous processes are critical to continental formation. Magma generated in the mantle and ascending into the crust is the fundamental process by which the continents have grown and continue to grow. Much of this ascending magma has been recycled and reformed repeatedly into sedimentary and metamorphic rocks, then back to magma. No magma? No crust.

A first question to consider in understanding igneous rocks is how originally solid material, perhaps from the mantle, melts to form magma. Or course things melt because they get hot but that is not the entire story for mantle rocks. Recall that, as illustrated in Figure 26.10, the mantle can stay solid as temperature increases if pressure also increases sufficiently at the same time.

When we considered changing states in Chapter 12, we found that substances had a unique melting temperature. At that time we considered only conditions at Earth's surface where the pressure is constant and uniform. In Chapter 26 we refined this concept to understand the state of material inside Earth where pressure is higher. We learned that the crust above the asthenosphere and the mantle below it are both solid while the asthenosphere between is partially melted. And the outer core is liquid while the inner core is again solid. Because melting is determined by both pressure and temperature, the state of material inside Earth can change from solid to liquid to solid again with depth even though the temperature gets progressively hotter with depth.

*Figure 29.8* refines this concept further. Carefully examine the axes. As with Figure 26.10 pressure increases downward with increasing depth. Temperature increases toward the right. Now examine the red curved zone. The area to its left represents a range of pressure and temperature for which the earth's mantle is solid. The temperature here may be hot enough to melt rocks on Earth's surface, but the mate-

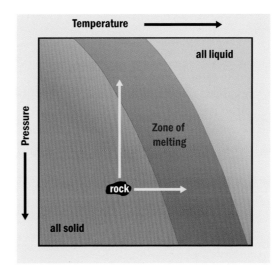

**Figure 29.8**

The relation between state, temperature, and pressure in the mantle. The red area defines the zone of melting for mantle rocks. The sample rock is currently solid, but the yellow arrows show how either an increase in temperature or a decrease in pressure can move the rock into the melting zone.

rial is nonetheless solid because of the increased pressure. The area to the right of the red zone represents pressures and temperatures at which the mantle is completely melted. Within the red zone are pressures and temperatures for which both magma and solid mantle exist together. Magma becomes a greater fraction of the mix of magma and solid mantle the closer we get to the right edge of the zone. In other words, the mantle does not melt at one temperature and pressure—it melts over a range of temperature and pressure combinations. This is expected since, like the fats of Chapter 24, rocks are a mix of different materials each of which has a different melting temperature.

Next examine the sample rock in Figure 29.8. It sits in the pressure/temperature region where material is solid. Increasing the temperature moves the rock to the right and into the melting zone. Likewise, if the pressure is decreased without raising the temperature, the rock moves upward and into the melting zone. In other words, decreasing the pressure alone can cause the material there to melt. This is how magmas are formed at hot spots and beneath mid-ocean ridges. Mantle rising as a *plastic solid*—not a liquid but still able to flow—melts upon reaching places of lower pressure.

In addition to decompression, solid rock can melt into a magma if the chemistry of the rocks change. Figure 29.8 shows the melting curve for rocks of a specific chemistry. The melting zone of rocks of a different chemistry have a different location and shape.

One way to change the rocks' chemistry is to add water. *Figure 29.9* shows a blue curve representing the melting zone when water is added to the rocks. Notice how the curve has altered in shape and location from Figure 29.8. Notice also that while the rock from Figure 29.8 has not changed temperature and pressure, it is now located in the melting zone. So if water is injected into the mantle, the rock melting temperature is altered without changing either pressure or temperature. Previously solid rocks will now be in the melting zone and will form magma.

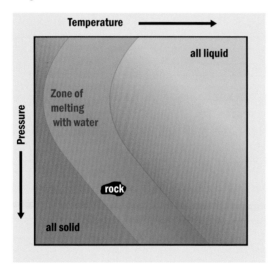

**Figure 29.9**

The relation between state, temperature and pressure in the mantle. The blue area defines the zone of melting when water is added, which is markedly different from that shown in Figure 29.8. This is because the water changes the rock chemistry and alters the curve. The sample rock is in the same location as in Figure 29.8, but is now located in the zone of melting.

This is how melting happens at subduction zones. When oceanic crust descends down into the mantle it brings with it minerals that have water bound in their crystal lattices. When these minerals heat up, they break down and release the water. This less-dense water rises from the subducting ocean crust into the overlying mantle (refer back to Figure 27.19) lowering the melting temperature of the rocks at that location, which then melt.[1]

Processes in the mantle are responsible for

creating most of the igneous rock on Earth's surface. Rising mantle in a plastic solid plume or beneath a spreading ridge ascends because it is a little hotter and less dense than the mantle around it and feels a buoyant force. When it crosses the "beginning of melting curve," magma forms spontaneously as pressure drops. As we learned in Chapter 18, for this process to occur naturally, entropy must increase and it does as molecular bonds in solid rock are broken to form less-ordered liquid.

The buoyancy of hot magma compels it upward from the mantle through the crust and sometimes all the way to the surface. Magma that is less dense than the crust or mantle that surrounds it will always float toward the surface where it may cool to form rocks. Magma that erupts at the surface cools quickly before crystals of significant size can form. The rock may be completely made of crystals, but they can be so small that you cannot see them without a microscope as in *Figure 29.10b.*

**Figure 29.10**

a) A sample of granite showing the crystalline structure. The colors show white plagioclase feldspar, gray quartz, and black biotite mica.

b) A sample of basalt. Unlike granite its crystals are very tiny.

---

[1] This also explains why volcanoes at subduction zones often erupt violently. The magma is full of water that boils out vigorously when the magma decompresses at the surface.

If magma does not make it to the surface, it will slowly cool within the crust until solid. If it solidifies at a slow enough rate, crystals will grow within it and may become large as seen in Figure 29.10a. Therefore, something as seemingly unimportant as the size of grains in an igneous rock tells us about where and under what conditions it formed into a rock.

Magma solidified beneath the surface of Earth forms **plutonic** rocks, named after Pluto, the Roman god of the underworld. Magma that erupts through Earth's surface and cools in the atmosphere as in Figure 29.1, forms **volcanic** rocks, named after Vulcan, the Roman god of fire. Granite is a common plutonic rock, and basalt a common volcanic rock (Figure 29.10).

Remember from Chapter 20 that activation energy is required before a reaction will proceed. Therefore activation energy forms a barrier against the reaction taking place. The lower the activation energy, the more common the reaction.

If the energy barrier for the formation of a particular mineral, say olivine, is small, many such crystals will form as it cools. Small olivine crystals will be abundant and large ones rare because it is energetically easier to form many small, new crystals than a few large ones. The gem variety of olivine, called peridot (the August birthstone) is valuable not because the mineral itself is rare, but because its crystals are rarely large.

## 29-4 Soil and Sedimentary Rocks

Nature is the ultimate recycler. Natural chemical and physical processes erode rocks to create sediment which is then transported and deposited elsewhere. Today's sand on the beach or silt in a river delta is the residue of yesterday's igneous, sedimentary, and metamorphic rocks. What will that sediment be a million or a billion years from now? It may be compacted and cemented to form new sedimentary rock. Then via the rock cycle, it may eventually be melted or metamorphosed into new igneous or metamorphic forms or eroded to again become sediment.

Sediment is created through weathering. The mechanical breakup of rocks by **physical weathering** is usually accomplished by water flow and especially ice freezing and melting in fractures (*Figure 29.11a*). In regions where the temperature rises above and below freezing many times every year, water expanding into ice creates large contact forces that wedge fractures open. In mountainous regions this can cause large masses of rock to fall and accumulate as cone shaped collections of debris called **talus** (Figure 29.11b).

In forming talus, contact forces exerted by expanding ice first remove a piece of rock from a cliff face. The gravitational potential energy of the rock is converted to kinetic energy as it falls. When the rock strikes the ground, the kinetic energy is converted to internal energy

**Plutonic:**

Pertaining to igneous rocks formed beneath Earth's surface.

**Volcanic:**

Pertaining to igneous rocks formed on Earth's surface.

**Physical Weathering:**

Breaking down rocks through physical processes like freezing and thawing.

**Talus:**

A sloping mass of rocky fragments at the base of a cliff.

a)

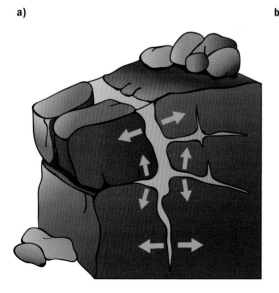

b)

**Figure 29.11**

a) Physical weather comes from water in cracks expanding as it freezes, enlarging the cracks and breaking down the rocks into smaller and smaller fragments.
b) Rocks pried loose through physical weathering form streams of talus down a slope in Cathedral Valley, Utah.

and the rock is further broken. Does this sound familiar? It should. The more-ordered forms of kinetic and potential energy are spontaneously being converted into the less-ordered form of internal energy which includes heat. Finally, although water, ice and gravity are the most important agents of physical weathering, blowing wind can weather rock surfaces and the roots of trees and shrubs growing in fractures can pry rocks apart.

A second type of weathering is **chemical weathering.** Many minerals, especially those in igneous and metamorphic rocks, are **metastable**. This means they were thermodynamically stable with maximized entropy when they formed at elevated temperatures and pressures, but are *not* stable at the lower pressures and temperatures of Earth's surface. Metastable minerals will convert to something else *if* they can overcome the energy barrier required for that reaction. Think of the carbon in a beautiful, expensive diamond. It formed under extreme pressure and temperature and is only metastable at Earth's surface. Powdery graphite is the stable form. If you want to prove this you could take a diamond, leave it under vacuum in a high-temperature furnace overnight, and recover a lump of graphite the next day. The heat of the furnace overcomes the energy barrier that prevents this from happening spontaneously.

Chemical weathering reactions dissolve rocks and minerals to produce new, stable minerals at Earth's surface. Acids promote this type of weathering and water in soils and shallow rocks is often acidic because of the following reaction with carbon dioxide ($CO_2$):

$$H_2O \; + \; CO_2 \; = \; H_2CO_3$$

(water) + (carbon dioxide) = (carbonic acid)

So when $CO_2$ is dissolved in water it generates carbonic acid ($H_2CO_3$) (carbonated drinks are acidic for this reason). There is $CO_2$ in the atmosphere and microorganisms in soil. Plant roots produce $CO_2$ in the soil. In fact $CO_2$ is often 25 or more times higher in soils than in the air we breathe making moisture in soil acidic in many instances.

Carbonic acid creates a reaction called **dissolution**. Here is an example of dissolution with the mineral calcite ($CaCO_3$):

$$CaCO_3 + H_2CO_3 = Ca^{2+} + 2HCO_3^-$$

(calcite) + (carbonic acid) = (calcium bicarbonate)

This reaction says that carbonic acid in water transforms calcite into free calcium ions and in the process changes into bicarbonate ($HCO_3^-$). Marble and limestone are made of calcite. Acidic groundwater flowing through marble or limestone dissolves their calcite and carries the resulting calcium and bicarbonate ions away, creating caves for spelunkers to explore. Within already formed caves, this same water can drip and evaporate creating and depositing calcite as stalagmites and stalactites (*Figure 29.12*).

## Chemical Weathering:

Breaking down rocks through chemical processes like acidic reactions.

## Metastable:

A mineral that is unstable when subject to temperatures and pressures different from those of its formation, but not liable to spontaneously change.

## Dissolution:

To break apart or dissolve in solution.

**Figure 29.12**

Caves are carved in limestone formations through chemical weathering. Minerals are first dissolved from the rocks creating caverns, then precipitated back as stalagmites and stalactites.

Silicates too react with acidic water. The silicate mineral plagioclase breaks down as follows:

$$2NaAlSi_3O_8 + 2H_2CO_3 + 9H_2O = 2Na^+ +$$
$$2HCO_3^- + 4H_4SiO_4 + Al_2Si_2O_5(OH)_4$$

(Na-plagioclase) + (carbonic acid) + (water) =
(dissolved components) + (clay minerals)

In this reaction carbonic acid in water combines with plagioclase to 1) release two chemical species that stay dissolved ($Na^+$ and $H_4SiO_4$), 2) neutralize the carbonic acid by again forming $HCO_3^-$, and 3) form a brand new clay mineral. The new clay is thermodynamically stable at Earth's surface, whereas the plagioclase it was produced from was metastable. Remember our example of the diamond? If you take a crystal of plagioclase and keep it dry, it will remain unchanged forever. However, if you add necessary reactants like water and carbonic acid it will begin to break down into more stable clay.

Just think, the clay used to make the bowl that held last night's Ramen noodles may have started out as plagioclase crystals in granite that cooled deep under the earth. Erosion stripped off the overlying rock and brought the granite to the surface. Weathering reactions turned the plagioclase into clay and streams transported and deposited the clay somewhere else. The material that made your bowl may have originated in the mantle, been born in the bowels of the crust, and recycled by weathering reactions at the surface.

The minerals from chemical weathering dissolved in water may precipitate out to form sediment that can later become rock. Limestone, gypsum, and halite which is natural rock salt, are common examples of this. Chemical and physical weathering also create rock fragments of varying size called **clasts** which can congregate in clastic sediments. Examples of clastic sediment turned to rock are sandstone and shale.

Most clasts will not stick together on their own. To form sedimentary rock they must be buried, compacted, and cemented together by minerals precipitating from ground water into the empty spaces between the grains. Think of sand castles you made at the beach when you were little. To get the sand to stick together you had to get it wet and compact it. The water acted as a "cement," at least until it evaporated, providing a contact force that held the grains together. All clastic rocks require cement.

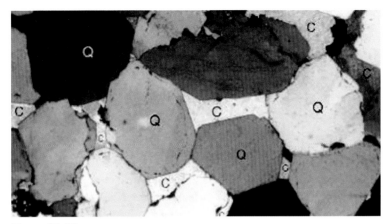

**Figure 29.13**
A microscopic view of a slice of sandstone. The particles marked "Q" are clasts of quartz. The irregularly shaped areas marked "C" are volumes filled in by calcite, cementing the clasts together.

*Figure 29.13* is an image of sandstone taken through a microscope. Grains labeled "Q" are quartz clasts and "C" is a mineral (calcite in this case) cementing the quartz grains together. The calcite was deposited to form sandstone when the sand was compacted and buried with groundwater. What was once loose sand at the beach is now solid rock.

Clastic sedimentary rocks are classified according to the size of their grains. If a rock contains clasts >2 mm in diameter, it is called "conglomerate." Rocks with grains <2 but >1/16 mm are called "sandstones." Rocks with grains <1/16 and greater than 1/256 mm are "siltstones", and "shale" is rock with particles <1/256 mm.

Whatever their origin, chemical or clastic, sediments are deposited by water or wind, into horizontal layers called **strata** (*Figure 29.14*).

**Clast:**

A grain of rock material weathered from a pre-existing rock.

**Strata:**

A layer of material, often one of several layered upon one another.

**Figure 29.14**
A view of the Grand Canyon showing sedimentary rock deposited in a variety of strata. Note the fingers of talus in the lower level, created by weathering of the upper strata.

Typical strata contain different layers as the size or kind of material that is deposited changes. As mentioned in Chapter 28, if the layers we see are no longer horizontal we know that some sort of tectonic activity like folding or faulting has disturbed them.

Sedimentary rocks are valuable and useful. The vast majority of the energy we consume is derived from fossil fuels, and virtually all fossil fuels are formed in and extracted from sedimentary rocks. Eighty percent of the electricity in the U. S. is generated by burning coal and natural gas. The U.S. also uses about 19 million barrels of crude oil every day.

## 29-5 Metamorphic Rocks

Metamorphism literally means to change (meta) form (morphology). In modern English we use these root words improperly. We say that one thing "morphs" into another. However, it would be more correct to say that rock A "metas" into rock B. As mentioned in the introduction, metamorphism is the recrystallization of a rock *in the solid state* at elevated pressure and temperature. If it melted, the end product would be an igneous rock instead. Recrystallization happens spontaneously as energy barriers against the transformation are overcome, total bond energies lower, and entropies increase.

Now an important question could be: How do metamorphic rocks experience elevated pressure and temperature? Temperature commonly increases with depth in the crust at a rate of about 20°C for every kilometer[2]. Typical continental crust is 40 km thick, so rocks at the base of Earth's crust have temperatures of about 800°C. Rocks begin to metamorphose at about 200°C, so most of the rocks in the continental crust are metamorphic by virtue of being deeply buried.

Thus, we didn't really ask the right question. We should have asked how deeply buried rocks get to the surface. The answer lies in plate tectonics. Collisional forces at convergent plate boundaries push crust material upward in mountain belts which then erode from the top down. Eventually the overburden is removed

**Foliation:**
The structural or chemical arrangement into layers of materials in a rock.

and metamorphic rocks are exposed at the surface. Folding and faulting at these boundaries also brings rocks from great depths to the surface where they are exposed without direct erosion. So, in addition to the igneous activity of convergent boundaries, we may think of the crust above subduction zones as "factories" where metamorphic rocks are made and exposed (see Figure 27.19).

Because metamorphic rocks are altered from a pre-existing type, every metamorphic rock has a protolith that it was before metamorphism. We usually know or can make educated guesses of these precursors. Marble has limestone and slate has shale as protoliths, for example.

Many metamorphic rocks exhibit layering within them which tells us something about the forces that produced the rock. The layering can be compositional such as bands of different colored minerals or it may be structural such as how the rock fractures. This layering is called **foliation** and should not be confused with the layering of strata in sedimentary rocks. Metamorphic rocks without layering are considered "non-foliated."

*Figure 29.15a* is a specimen of metamorphic gneiss. Foliation is clearly evident as alternating

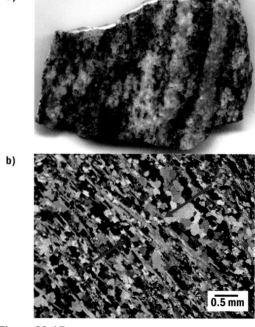

**Figure 29.15**

a) A sample of gneiss showing compositional foliation as different colored stripes.

b) A closeup of a different sample showing structural foliation. The blue lines trace the distribution of muscovite crystals which have been drawn into that configuration by side pressure indicated with the red arrows.

---

[2] This increase in heat with depth is due primarily to two factors: a) heat transfer from the deep earth by conduction and convection, and b) heating through radioactive decay from natural isotopes of uranium, thorium, and potassium.

pinkish and grayish stripes. Figure 29.15b is an image of a different metamorphic rock taken through a microscope to reveal granular details. The gray grains are quartz and the vibrant blue, yellow and pink grains are foliated mica crystals. The red arrows show the direction pressure was applied to the rock to create that foliation. The direction of foliation reveals the magnitude and direction of past, unbalanced forces within the earth where the rock was altered.

Minerals in a metamorphic rock tell us the equilibrium temperatures and pressures present when the rock formed. Foliation tells us the direction that unbalanced forces were applied. Using radioactive dating techniques discussed in Chapter 28, we can learn exactly when the metamorphism and foliation occurred. Meta-morphic rocks can then teach us the history of these changes which in turn teaches us about past tectonic activity. They can even teach us about ancient mountain ranges that have been completely eroded away except for the exposed metamorphic rock of their roots.

The rock cycle and weathering processes combine to give Earth's surface a remarkably rich and beneficial variety. The rock cycle produces thousands of species of varying hardness, strength, and utility. Weathering shapes and converts these into even more forms. Chemical weathering causes the minerals in rocks to dissolve and be transformed into new, stable minerals in soil. Without weathering, there would be no soil. Without soil, there would be no life. We are fortunate for all these processes.

## Chapter Framework

### A. The Rock Cycle
1. Three types of rock: igneous, sedimentary, metamorphic
2. Rocks transform between these types in the rock cycle

### B. Minerals: Building blocks of rocks
1. Thousands of minerals on crust but most are silicates
2. Minerals defined as being
   a. *Naturally occurring*
   b. *Inorganic solid*
   c. *Fixed or narrowly defined chemical composition*
   d. *Definite internal crystal structure*
   e. *Stable against change*

### C. Igneous rocks
1. Formed from magma
2. Melting and solidifying in subduction zones depend on temperature, pressure, and water abundance
3. Crystal size and structure depend on cooling rate
4. Plutonic rocks form beneath surface, volcanic rocks form on surface

### D. Soil and sedimentary rocks
1. Rocks are broken down through physical and chemical weathering
2. Physical weathering is driven by water and ice
3. Chemical weathering is driven by acidic reactions
4. Sediment lithifies when cemented together by minerals

### E. Metamorphic rocks
1. Altered without being melted
2. Most continental rocks are metamorphic
3. Foliations reveal transformation history

## Comprehension

### Matching

a. Chemical sedimentary rocks

b. Chemical weathering

c. Extrusive rock

d. Gneiss

e. Magma

f. Metamorphic rock

g. Mineral

h. Protolith

i. Strata

j. Talus

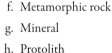

1. ____ Metamorphosed granite
2. ____ Molten rock
3. ____ Igneous rocks that cool and solidify on Earth's surface
4. ____ A naturally occurring, inorganic solid with a chemical formula
5. ____ Causes minerals in rocks to dissolve
6. ____ Contain minerals that precipitate out of water
7. ____ Rock that forms from heat and pressure
8. ____ Layers of sedimentary rock
9. ____ A rock that is metamorphosed
10. ____ Cone shaped masses of rock debris

### True/False
1. ____ Rocks are composed of minerals

2. ____ Igneous rocks with large crystals cooled quickly
3. ____ Water that freezes and melts in cracks results in physical weathering
4. ____ Wind is the primary driving force of sedimentary rocks
5. ____ Forces were applied perpendicular to foliation of metamorphic rocks

### Fill in the Blank
1. The _____ describes how one rock turns into another.
2. Continents are formed by the ascension of _____ into the crust.
3. Marble is metamorphosed _____.
4. Sandstone, siltstone, and limestone are examples of _____.
5. The ocean crust is made of _____, which is a/an _____ rock.

## Analysis

1. From Earth's average density, we know that
   a) Earth's interior is of uniform density.
   b) density increases as the depth increases.
   c) Earth is a layered planet.
   d) density decreases as the depth increases.

2. Which is not a characteristic of minerals?
   a) Naturally occurring
   b) Organic solid
   c) Solid
   d) Homogenous chemical composition

3. Sedimentary rocks are primarily formed by
   a) Water
   b) Wind
   c) Magma
   d) Pressure

4. Assuming the pictures are to the same scale, which of the following igneous rocks probably cooled the slowest?

a)

b)

c)

d)

5. What direction was the applied force during the formation of the metamorphic rock below?

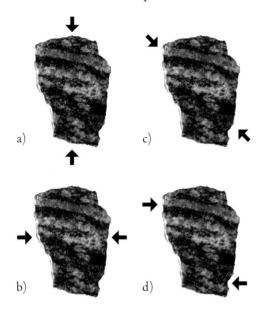

a)

b)

c)

d)

6. As depth beneath Earth's surface increases, what happens to pressure and temperature?

   a) both increase

   b) both decrease

   c) pressure increases, but temperature decreases

   d) temperature increases, but pressure decreases

7. When you chemically combine water with the minerals that make up a rock, what happens to the minerals?

   a) Their melting temperatures decrease.

   b) They become more plastic.

   c) They form colored stripes.

   d) They become better conductors.

   e) They become more dense.

8. How do the origins of igneous, sedimentary, and igneous rocks differ?

9. What does the size of a crystal say about an igneous rock?

10. Describe the two different types of igneous rocks.

11. What part of a metamorphic rock tells the age of metamorphism?

12. Briefly describe the rock cycle.

13. How does part of the mantle melt to form magma?

14. What are the two most important agents of physical weathering?

15. How do clasts stick together to form clastic sedimentary rocks?

## Synthesis

1. Volcanoes that occur near subduction zones are known for their violent, explosive eruptions. While those that are found at hot spots and divergent plate boundaries typically have relatively mild eruptions. Why?

2. Continents are composed primarily of granites which formed at subduction zones, while the ocean floors are composed of basalt formed at diverging plate boundaries. How would you expect the average density of ocean crust to compare to continental crust? Explain your reasoning.

3. When you compare samples of granite and basalt (see images at right), one has large visible crystals and the other doesn't. Explain why.

4. Use the graph in Figures. 29.8 and 29.9 to explain why the presence of water at subduction zones is important to the volcanic activity that occurs.

5. Granite is formed by the subduction of basaltic ocean plates. But granite and basalt have different chemical compositions. Use the graphs in Figures 29.8 and 29.9 to explain why.

6. What are chemical and physical weathering?

7. Explain the differences between chemical and clastic sedimentary rock.

8. Explain the role of water and carbon dioxide in the formation of chemically deposited sedimentary rock.

9. Explain the role of water in the formation of clastic sedimentary rock.

10. Metamorphic rocks form deep in the Earth's crust. How do they get to the surface where we can see them? What locations would be good places to go looking for metamorphic rock?

11. In order to form metamorphic rock, the rock must be at high pressure and temperature. But the temperatures are not high enough to even partially melt the rock. Since none of the rock is liquid, explain in terms of activation energy why the high temperature is necessary.

12. Explain why rocks would change chemical composition when they experience high temperatures and pressures in terms of entropy and energy.

13. Compare and contrast the following pairs of rocks. (See the images.)

    a) Granite and Rhyolite

    b) Rhyolite and Basalt

    c) Granite and granitic gneiss

    d) Limestone and marble

Granite

Basalt

Rhyolite

Granitic gneiss

Limestone

# Surface Processes

# 30

## LEARN

- The major parts of the hydrological system.

- The processes that move water though these parts.

- The causes of erosion and deposition by water and by ice.

- The nature of groundwater and its connection to the other parts of the hydrological system.

Living organisms remain healthy by constantly remaking their structure to heal wounds and replace dead tissue. If this process were to stop, the organism would die. Earth's surface is not a living organism, yet like one, its structure too is slowly, constantly being remade. We have seen that plate tectonics heaves the crust up and down, making it anew in some places and destroying it in others. Other processes, touched upon briefly in Chapter 29, scour and reshape the rocks and soil on Earth's surface as well and so, in a figurative sense, keep it alive.

The many systems that modify and shape Earth's surface include streams, shorelines, glaciers, groundwater and wind. In this chapter we investigate these and how they are driven by fundamental principles of chemistry and physics including convective heat transfer, buoyancy, energy transformation, and changes of state.

## 30-1 Hydrological Cycle

Water is the key agent in modifying Earth's surface. Its *role* is straightforward—streams and

rivers erode land from some places and deposit it as sediment in others. But its *behavior* is complex. Where does the water in a stream come from? Why don't they dry up? Why is there water running in the Provo River in August long after all the snow at its headwaters has melted? To answer such questions we need a basic understanding of the **hydrological cycle**.

*Table 30.1* lists the main parts, or **reservoirs**, of the hydrological cycle and the percentage of Earth's water tied up in each. The term "reservoir," not to be confused with a man-made lake, is appropriate because each part is like a reservoir holding different amounts of moisture.

*Figure 30.1* illustrates how water travels between several reservoirs. It evaporates from oceans and lakes and transpirates from plants into the air where it is carried overland by convective wind currents, cools, and falls as rain or snow. It then flows over and under the ground, eroding as it travels. Eventually it ends up back in the ocean to cycle over again.

The greatest percentage of Earth's water is in the oceans with salt and other minerals dis-

| Table 30.1 — Reservoir Water | | |
|---|---|---|
| Reservoir | % of Total | Residence Time |
| oceans | 97.5 | 3000 yr |
| ice | 2.0 | 10,000 yr |
| groundwater | 0.5 | 1 month to >10,000 yr. |
| lakes | 0.02 | 100–200 yr. for large lakes |
| streams | 0.001 | 20 days |

solved in it. The largest reservoir of fresh water is in the form of ice with the vast majority of this in the ice sheets of sparsely populated Greenland and essentially unpopulated Antarctica. Glaciers in the Himalayas and Alps contain water sufficient to sustain rivers upon which some populations depend. The most important reservoir of fresh water for human use is the 0.5% that is groundwater. The reservoir of water in lakes and streams, so critical for life and weathering, is so small that if we were to round our figures in Table 30.1 to one decimal place, they would not even show up. The erosional significance of lakes and streams comes not from the volume of water

**Hydrological Cycle:**

The movement of water through the various reservoirs on or near Earth's surface.

**Reservoir:**

A place or state where water can reside within the hydrological system.

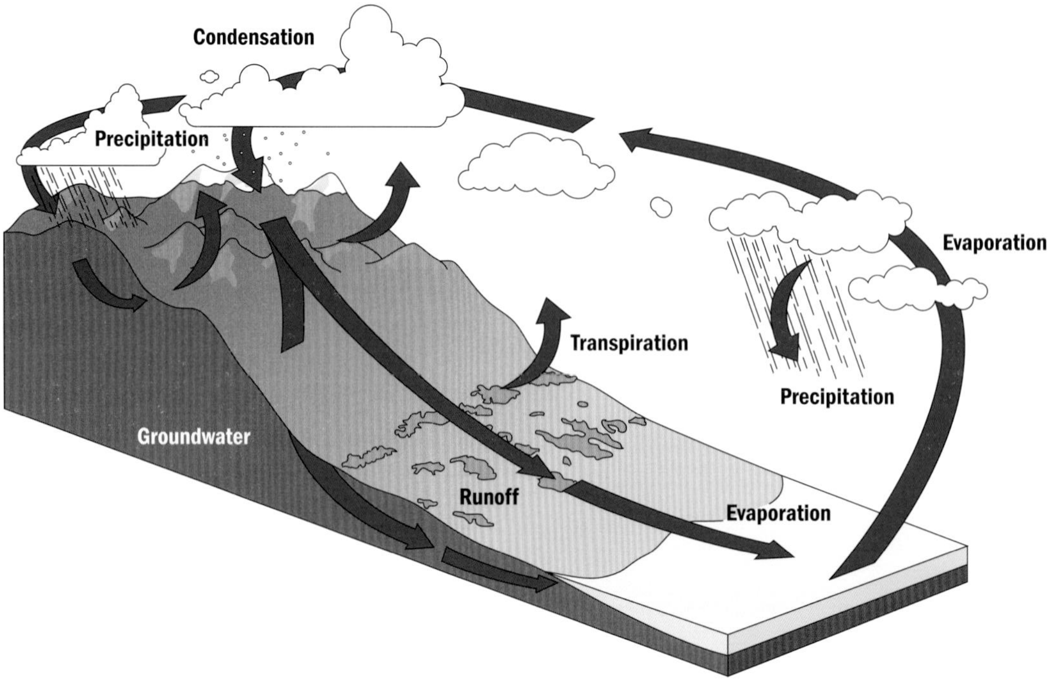

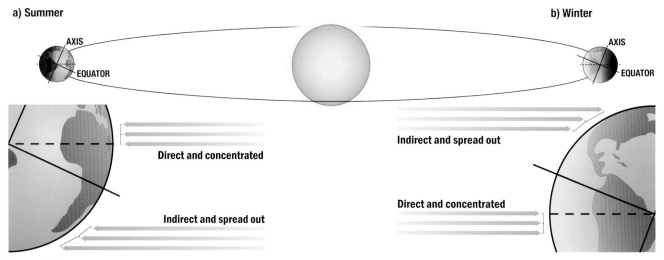

**Figure 30.1**

The hydrologic system showing the main pathways for movement of water. Evaporating water rises because of buoyancy forces and returns to Earth because of gravity. On Earth's surface, gravity acts on both ice and water creating flowing glaciers, rivers, and movement of groundwater.

they contain at a given time but from how much water is constantly cycled through them.

Solar heating and how it varies in different places on Earth drives the hydrological cycle. Our single Earth experiences hot summers, cold winters, and moderate tropical weather simultaneously at different locations because sunlight strikes these places unequally. In northern summer, Earth's rotational axis points toward the Sun concentrating its light there, making it hotter. (*Figure 30.2*) At the same time the south-

ern hemisphere tilts away from the Sun, causing incoming radiation to be spread out over a larger area, diluting its energy and bringing about winter. Six months later Earth's orbital motion causes the tilt to be in the opposite direction and the north and south exchange seasons.

The tilt of Earth's axis affects the seasonal heating of the northern and southern latitudes but has relatively little effect on the heat of the tropics. Being centered on the equator, tropical radiation is similarly strong all year producing

**a) Summer**                                                                                          **b) Winter**

AXIS

EQUATOR

**Indirect and spread out**

**Direct and concentrated**

**Indirect and spread out**

AXIS

EQUATOR

**Direct and concentrated**

**Figure 30.2**

The tilt of Earth's axis causes the angle at which sunlight strikes its surface to alternate depending on Earth's orbital position.

a) In summer, sunlight reaching the southern hemisphere is more diluted than sunlight striking the northern hemisphere because it is spread over a larger area on Earth's surface.

b) In winter, the situation is reversed. The change in sunlight concentration creates the different seasons and drives the hydrological system.

two results. First evaporation is enhanced and steady over the equatorial oceans. Second, the atmosphere near the equator is warmer, less dense, and more buoyant than air at higher latitudes. As a result moist tropical air rises highest into the atmosphere at the equator as shown in the "Hadley cells" of *Figure 30.3*. This rising air expands and cools causing the water vapor within to condense into drops and fall back as rain making the tropics both warm and wet. It is a good idea to both wear shorts and take an umbrella when visiting Hawaii.

Rising tropical air divides and expands northward and southward to latitudes of about 30° in both directions. Along the way the air cools further, becoming denser and descending to lower elevations. As it descends it eventually reverses flow and migrates back to the equator in the equatorial trade winds, completing the circular flow of the Hadley cells. These circulation cells are convection cells driven by radiation from the Sun as discussed in Chapter 6. They and the mid-latitude cells redistribute heat energy and water from the equator to the poles.

The water that is thus transported up from the equator rains down on the continents. Water on the surface flows to lower places as gravity pulls it downward, converting the gravitational potential energy of higher elevations into the kinetic energy of moving streams at lower elevations. Some of this water seeps into the ground where it flows in response to differences in pressure. Water falling as snow and building up as snow and ice on land flows too but under the influence of both gravity and pressure.

Because water flows, it is continually changing from one reservoir to another. **Residence time** in Table 30.1 is the typical length of time a parcel of water spends in each reservoir. Typical water molecules in the ocean spend about 3,000 years there before being removed by evaporation and transferred to a continent. In contrast, water will be in a stream an average of just 20 days and in an ice sheet for more than 10,000 years.

There are practical reasons for caring about residence times. In the US, about 50% of our fresh water is derived from the ground. Some cities like Tucson and San Antonio rely entirely on groundwater. Polluting an aquifer with a long residence time, or pumping water out of it at a faster rate than it is naturally replenished will destroy or use up a critical resource.

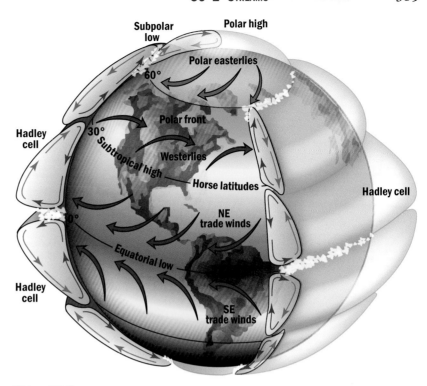

**Figure 30.3**
Air circulation patterns. Greater solar heating at the equator creates the Hadley cells which bring moist air from the tropics to mid-latitudes. This moisture falls upon the continents as rain.

Flowing liquid water in streams and ice in glaciers have greatly modified most of the surface of the continents. Flowing groundwater too, despite being usually out of our sight, modifies and erodes Earth's surface and subsurface in places.

In Chapter 27 we discussed the tectonic system. The hydrological cycle, driven by solar heat, is essentially at war with this system which is driven by interior heat. Plate tectonics builds mountains while the hydrological system tears them down. Let's us consider in greater detail how the surface is worn away.

## 30-2 Streams

As with the term "reservoir" we also use the term **stream** in a generic way. A stream is any system of flowing surface water with a headwater and an endpoint. Streams differ greatly in size and flow pattern and include everything from a great river like the Amazon to a desert arroyo that is dry except during a flash flood.

A typical stream system is illustrated in *Figure 30.4*. As shown in this figure, the steepness of the ground over which the stream flows, or **stream gradient**, is greater near the headwaters and more gradual at the endpoint. At higher

**Residence Time:**

The average amount of time water spends within a reservoir.

**Stream:**

A conduit through which surface water moves, either constantly or intermittently.

**Stream gradient:**

The slope of the terrain over which a stream flows.

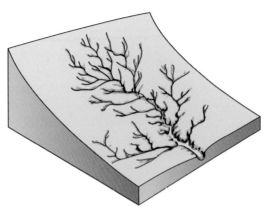

**Figure 30.4**

A typical system of streams. All streams have a headwater and an endpoint. Streams are smaller and more numerous near the headwaters and larger and fewer as they consolidate near the end point.

elevations the tributary streams are smaller and more numerous. The number of tributary streams decreases downstream as they merge into the main channel, which widens and deepens as it carries more and more water.

Eventually, a stream reaches its endpoint. This can be an ocean, a lake, or another stream. The elevation of the endpoint is called **base**

**Base Level:**

The elevation of a stream end point.

**level.** *Figure 30.5a* shows an aerial view of the Provo River. Figure 30.5b shows its elevation profile. The Provo River has its headwaters in the Uinta Mountains at an elevation >10,000 feet and ends at a base-level elevation of 4492 feet in Utah Lake. The base level is the lowest elevation to which the Provo River can erode its channel. If it eroded deeper than 4492 feet, the Provo River would not flow into Utah Lake. Rather, Utah Lake would flow into the Provo River.

The attributes of a flowing stream, like water volume and speed, are interrelated. Water moves more rapidly when flowing down a steeper gradient and also when there is a greater volume flowing. To illustrate speed vs. volume, imagine standing on a bridge over a small mountain stream in late summer when there is only a trickle of water. If you return in the spring when mountain snow is melting, the stream may be a raging torrent. There is not only more water in the spring, but the water is moving much faster even though the gradient at the bridge has not changed. Just as the water moves faster when

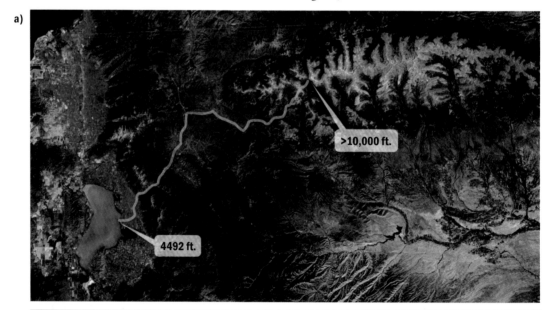

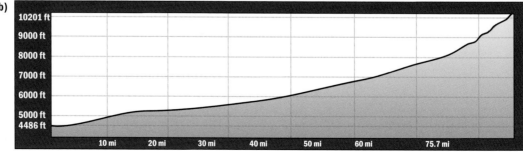

**Figure 30.5**

a) An aerial view of the Provo River from its headwaters in the Uinta Mountains to its base at Utah Lake.

b) A plot of the elevation of the Provo River over the same distance.

you turn up the flow volume on a garden hose, stream velocities must also increase to allow larger flows through their channels.

As the velocity and volume of a stream goes up, the capacity of the stream to carry sediment increases. Thus, the amount of sediment carried by a stream during spring runoff may be enormous compared to the fall.

In any given stream fine-grained sediment is suspended in the water, intermediate-sized particles bounce along the streambed, and larger fragments roll along the bottom. The absolute size of objects in these three categories changes with the water speed. A mountain stream may roll boulders along the bottom in the spring, but only sand grains in the fall. The biggest particles in a streambed move only during the highest flows. So the ability of a stream to erode changes with water speed.

Water within a given stream may deposit sediment, erode the stream bed, or simply transport sediment depending on the place. The slope at which sediment is transported is called the "equilibrium profile." Where the stream gradient is steeper than its equilibrium profile, it will erode. Where it is gentler, it will deposit sediment. Also, as a stream winds back and forth the water within it travels at different speeds. On the interior of a bend water moves more slowly and tends to deposit, making the stream bed shallower. On the outer edge of a bend, water travels more rapidly eroding the channel deeper.

### Erosion

The main cutting agent in eroding water is the sediment itself rolling and bouncing along the river bed. Contact force between the sediment and river bed carves the channel while at the same time the opposite and equal force on the particles abrades and diminishes their size.

As previously mentioned, streams with elevation profiles that are steeper than equilibrium erode downward. The Colorado River has cut the deep, spectacular Grand Canyon into Colorado Plateau bedrock for this reason (*Figure 29.13*). But unlike the Colorado River, most streams do not cut deep canyons. The reason the Colorado River has eroded such a deep canyon is because its base level has rapidly dropped.

Consider the Provo River which has cut a deep canyon, Provo Canyon, through the Wasatch Mountains. Over time, tectonic activity on the Wasatch fault has dropped Utah Valley and Utah Lake (the base level) *relative* to the Wasatch Mountains by about two meters every 1,000 years. The Provo River has adjusted to this drop by downcutting through the rising mountains.

Downcutting is produced by *relative* changes in base level which can happen in five different ways: 1) Utah Valley and the Wasatch Mountains could both be rising, with the mountains rising faster, 2) both could be dropping, with the valley dropping faster, 3) the valley could be dropping and the mountains standing still, 4) the mountains could be rising and the valley standing still, or 5) the valley could be dropping and the mountains rising. All of these five cases cause the valley to drop relative to the mountains. In the case of the Provo River, the rising mountains are most responsible for the changing base level.

### Deposition

Just as a drop in base level causes downcutting, a relative rise in base level causes sediment to be deposited. This is especially true near the endpoints where streams approach base level. As a general rule, sediment will be deposited *wherever* and *whenever* the velocity of water is too slow to carry the sediment in the stream. Such places or circumstances create **alluvial fans**, **deltas**, and **floodplains**. Although different in many ways, all three deposition structures form when flowing streams spread out, lose motion and kinetic energy, and drop their sediment.

**Alluvial fan:**
Sediment and debris at the mouth of a canyon deposited by intermittent water flow.

**Delta:**
Sediment and debris deposited in an ocean or lake at the mouth of a river.

**Floodplains:**
Plains intermittently covered with water from a flooding river.

**Figure 30.6**
An alluvial fan at the mouth of a canyon in Death Valley.

**Figure 30.7**
The Nile River Delta. Notice the triangular shape of the deposition at the river mouth.

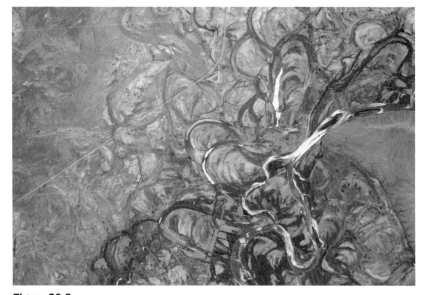

**Figure 30.8**
A floodplain on the Rio Negro River. The river is the silvery ribbon in the middle of the image. The floodplain is clearly marked by where old river channels have been carved on either side of the present path. During flooding, water coursing over the river banks deposits fresh soil making floodplains fertile as well as prone to destruction.

*Figure 30.6* is a classic alluvial fan in Death Valley, California. The stream that cut the narrow canyon is not present in the picture because it flows only during flash floods. In a flash flood water descends as a raging torrent down a steep, narrow canyon following brief but heavy rainfall. The rapidly flowing water transports large masses of loose debris from the canyon walls and floor, abrading the streambed in the process. When the stream exits the canyon at the base level of the valley floor, the unconfined water abruptly spreads out and slows. The slower water cannot carry the sand, cobbles, and boulders further and they drop near the mouth of the canyon. A fan-shaped deposit is constructed over time as the active stream channel wanders back and forth over the surface of the valley next to the canyon mouth.

Alluvial fans form most readily in arid mountainous regions. Mountains provide the steep gradient for rapid flow. Aridity prevents permanent streams from forming which would continually sweep sediment away from the canyon mouth.

Deltas form where perennial streams reach base level in a body of water like the ocean or a lake. Water flowing in the Nile, Mississippi, or Amazon rivers must slow down as it terminates and empties into the relatively static ocean. Because the velocity of water at a river mouth drops to nearly zero, its capacity to carry sediment is essentially eliminated and the material drops to the shallow ocean floor.

*Figure 30.7* is an image of the Nile River Delta. They are called "deltas" because, as shown, they often have a triangular shape like the Greek capital letter delta ($\Delta$). Plants grow abundantly in deltas because of the large quantities of water and nutrients brought by the river system. Deltas are usually agriculturally rich and some of the most desirable places to settle.

Floodplains are flat regions surrounding a river that are periodically flooded and covered anew with fine-grained sediment like silt and clay. Water in a stream just prior to flooding is moving rapidly and therefore carrying a lot of sediment. As this water flows out of the channel, it spreads out as a sheet over the floodplain, slows dramatically, and the sediment settles out.

A floodplain is pictured in *Figure 30.8*. Within the flood plain are now-disconnected loops from the meandering stream channel, which is visible as a silvery ribbon.

Floodplains are more than a geological curiosity. They have shaped the growth of civilization. Floodplains of major streams like the Tigris, Euphrates, and Nile rivers were the birthplaces of early city-states and empires. Regular flooding produced nutrient-rich sediment which, by supporting a large agricultural abundance, made divisions of labor possible, leading to the social institutions of today.

## 30-3  Ice

Glaciers form where winter snowfall exceeds summertime evaporation and melting as takes place near the poles in Antarctica and Greenland or in high mountains like the Alps, Andes, and Himalayas. When a glacier forms, it naturally has two zones. The growth zone, or **zone of accumulation** is where the input of snow exceeds the loss of ice. The shrinking zone or **zone of ablation** occurs where the combined effects of melting, evaporation, sublimation and "calving," exceed winter snow. Calving is where large blocks of ice break off. Icebergs form when glaciers calve into the ocean.

In Chapter 29 we learned that ice satisfies the definition of a mineral. Carrying this further, snowflakes under pressure from the weight of snow above them over time recrystallize into coarse, granular ice called "firn" which compacts further into solid glacial ice. So in a sense, it is also correct to think of glacial ice as a metamorphic rock!

When ice in the zone of accumulation exceeds a certain weight, it begins to flow. Many glaciers, especially **alpine glaciers**, flow downhill. But ice need not be on a slope to flow. Ice will flow from regions of high pressure toward regions of low pressure as well. **Continental glaciers** like the Greenland and Antarctic ice sheets flow over flat bedrock and occasionally may even flow locally uphill. Pressure from greater weight in thicker regions provides an unbalanced force outward toward thinner edges, causing ice to flow toward them. Ice on a steep slope will flow when becoming 20–30 meters thick, whereas 50 meters or more are required to produce flow on flat surfaces.

**Figure 30.9**
Bedrock scoured by moving glacial ice.

Solid ice has both elastic and plastic properties. Ice responds elastically to rapidly applied force. This elasticity makes the ice feel hard when you fall when skating. However, if pressure is applied on ice slowly and constantly, it can deform like a plastic and flow.

Flowing ice will erode, transport, and deposit sediment like a stream does but the pattern of erosion is different. Streams transport smaller sedimentary particles farther than larger particles, whereas glaciers transport particles of various sizes the same distance. Glaciers also present far more pressure on bedrock than a typical stream does. Ice flowing across bedrock on the underside of a glacier can "pluck" pieces of rock from fractures then drag them across the bedrock, flattening and grooving the surface as shown in *Figure 30.9*. These contact forces are quite large where ice is thick and the pressures applied by the ice's weight are substantial. The gaps in the grooves in Figure 30.9 are places where rock was removed by plucking.

In addition to plucked and abraded material embedded within the base, alpine glaciers also carry debris on their surfaces. Alpine glaciers form in geographic and climatic zones that are ideal for the ice wedging described in Chapter 29. Ice wedging dislodges material from valley walls which falls onto the ice and moves with it. All material transported by glaciers is known as **moraine**. The debris of moraines left in the zone of ablation is called **till**.

**Zone of Accumulation:**

The region of a glacier where snow accumulates.

**Zone of Ablation:**

The region of a glacier where snow and ice decrease by melting, sublimation or calving.

**Alpine Glacier:**

A glacier formed in a mountain valley.

**Continental Glacier:**

A glacier covering a large portion of a continent or land mass.

**Moraine:**

Rock and sediment carried by a glacier.

**Till:**

Moraines left in the zone of ablation.

**Figure 30.10**
Terrain in Alaska filled with alpine glaciers.

### Alpine Glaciers

Alpine glaciers are formed in mountainous areas whenever temperatures are low enough and snow fall sufficient for a zone of accumulation to set up. Such zones are at lower elevations in naturally cold places like Alaska and at higher elevations in warmer regions closer to the equator.

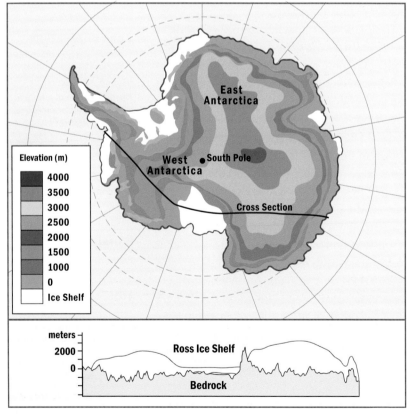

**Figure 30.11**
A map of Antarctica showing the thickness of the continental glacier. The lower part is a profile through the ice at the line of section indicated.

*Figure 30.10* shows terrain dominated by alpine glaciers. Moraines are visible as gray lines within the ice. Glacial erosion produces U-shaped valleys separated by sharp ridges leading to pointed mountain peaks often called "horns" (as in The Matterhorn on the Italian-Swiss border) In general, alpine glaciation produces rugged and scenic mountain topography.

A typical rate of ice flow in an alpine glacier is about 100 m/yr. At this rate ice will move 1 km in a decade meaning it will flow completely through a 10 km long glacier in a century. So a Swiss citizen living near a glacier in the Alps may live to see nearly all of the ice replaced once in his or her lifetime. Although there is only a small amount of ice in alpine glaciers at any instant in time, enormous amounts of ice can move through them over long periods.

### Continental Glaciers

As the name implies, continental glaciers truly are, or can be, continental in scale. Their flow produces a variety of unique erosional and depositional features.

*Figure 30.11* is a map of Antarctica showing the distribution and thickness of ice which in some locations exceeds 3500 meters! Notice from the cross section that much of the Antarctic bedrock surface is below sea level. How can glacial ice accumulate on a surface below sea level?

The answer is that it cannot. The continental elevation was *above* sea level when ice began to accumulate. The weight of the ice has steadily down-warped the lithosphere beneath Antarctica and displaced the underlying asthenosphere. If the ice sheets were to melt, the lithosphere would rebound upward from buoyant forces in the lithosphere. In fact, the lithosphere beneath both Canada and Scandinavia is rising today because their ice sheets have diminished since the last ice age.

Recent ice ages have affected vast portions of North America, Europe, and Asia. *Figure 30.12* shows the extent of the ice sheet in North America during the past ice age. The farthest advance of glaciation, about 18,000 years ago, reached central Illinois, central Indiana, and southern Ohio.

As previously noted, continental ice flowing from the zone of accumulation strips the ground

**Figure 30.12**
A map showing the advance of ice in North America during the last ice age, 18,000 years ago.

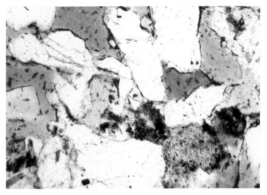

**Figure 30.13**
This photo shows a thin slice through a sandstone from 12,000 feet deep in the Gulf of Mexico. The clear grains of sand are quartz, while the darker grains are mostly clay. The violet-colored regions are the open pores in the rock. It is through these pores where groundwater flows.

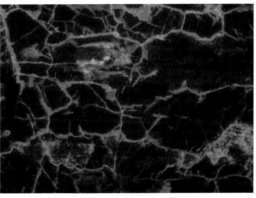

**Figure 30.14**
This is a photo of a piece of granite taken in ultraviolet light after it has been stained with a dye that soaked into the cracks. This interconnected network of cracks provides pathways for groundwater to flow.

of soil and grinds off the upper layers of bedrock. Since they leave rocky tills as they retreat and soil-replenishing chemical weathering rates are low in cold climates, regions where continental glaciers once flowed often have thin soils today. For this reason soils tend to be poorer at higher, colder latitudes.

The residence time of ice in continental ice sheets may be very long. A recent ice core drilled in Antarctica recovered a continuous record of ice from the surface to the base that is 800,000 years old. Such ice records provide detailed information on past polar ice temperatures and atmospheric gas concentrations. These data, in turn, are related to past natural climate variation as discussed in Chapter 31.

## 30-4 Groundwater

Groundwater is liquid water below Earth's surface. A common misconception is that it resides in underground pools or lakes. In reality only a tiny percentage is found in open cavities. Nearly all groundwater resides in the otherwise empty spaces between rock grains, loose sediment and rock fractures. The percentage of empty spaces or "pores" in a rock or sedimentary deposit that water can occupy is called its **porosity**. (See *Figure 30.13*) **Permeability** is a measure of how easily water can flow through this rock or sediment and is related to the interconnectedness of the pores and cracks (*Figure 30.14*). Water flows more freely through rocks of high permeability.

The pores and cracks in rocks near Earth's surface contain a mixture of air and water. Deeper below the surface the rocks at some point become saturated with water, even in desert regions. The depth where saturation begins is called the **water table**. An **aquifer** is saturated material in a water table of sufficient porosity and permeability to supply groundwater to a well or spring. An **aquitard** is material without sufficient permeability to permit flow.

High permeability and high porosity often but not always go hand in hand. Clay has very high porosity—as much as 50%. However, individual clay particles are very small, usually on the order of $10^{-6}$ meters (1 micron) in diameter which creates an abundance of very small pores (*Figure 30.15*). These pores have a lot of surface area compared to the volume of the pore, producing both substantial frictional resistance to

**Porosity:**
The percentage of empty spaces in a rock or that water can occupy.

**Permeability:**
A measure of how easily water can flow through rock or sediment.

**Water table:**
The depth in the ground where rock is saturated with water.

**Aquifer:**
A ground layer saturated with water and having sufficient porosity and permeability to supply groundwater to a well or spring.

**Aquitard:**
A ground layer saturated with water and lacking sufficient porosity and permeability to supply groundwater to a well or spring.

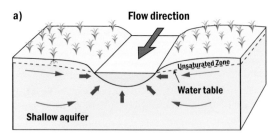

**Figure 30.17**

a) When the water table is above the water level of a stream, water seeps into it creating a gaining stream.

b) When the water table is lower than the water level, water seeps into the ground creating a losing stream.

**Figure 30.15**

An electron microscope image of mixed clay particles. The particle sizes are a millionth of a meter or smaller. The small particle size allows for high porosity but low permeability.

**Recharge:**

Water that soaks into the ground replenishing the groundwater reservoir.

**Discharge:**

Water released from a groundwater reservoir.

**Gaining Stream:**

A stream whose volume of flowing water increases from groundwater discharge along its channel.

**Losing Stream:**

A stream whose volume of flowing water decreases as stream flow is lost to groundwater recharge along its channel.

flow and many places for intermolecular forces to bind water to the clay, holding it in place. Despite its high porosity, clay is almost always an aquitard.

Groundwater, like surface drainage, originates in rain and snow fall. All water that does not run off as drainage, or evaporate or transpire from plants into the air, sinks into the ground as **recharge**. The recharge percolates through the soil into the subsurface to become groundwater, augmenting the existing groundwater reservoir.

In semi-arid regions like Provo, Utah, recharge is about 10% of precipitation.

Groundwater is lost through **discharge**, which occurs naturally at springs, phreatophyte wetlands, and playas (*Figure 30.16*). "Phreatophytes" are plants that draw water directly from a shallow aquifer and release it in transpiration as vapor from their leaves. Playas, often referred to as dry lakebeds, release water to the atmosphere by evaporation directly from the ground.

At long last we are ready to address why the Provo River flows in August. The Provo River, or at least large parts of it, is a **gaining stream** (*Figure 30.17a*). As the Provo River flows through the Heber Valley, the amount of water in the stream increases by about 40% in just a few miles as groundwater discharges directly into its channel. In this sense, the Provo River is a long, thin spring!

Examine the diagram of the gaining stream in Figure 30.17a. The top of the water-filled aquifer, or water table, is higher in elevation than the top of the stream. Therefore the fluid pressure in the aquifer is higher than in the stream. Fluids flow from regions of higher to lower pressure so groundwater migrates into the stream.

And if there are gaining streams, it stands to reasons that there are **losing streams** (Figure 30.17b) where an aquifer is recharged by water seeping from the stream into the ground. In losing streams the water table is lower than the top

**Figure 30.16**

a) Discharge of groundwater directly as a spring, b) through transpiration of plants (as on the lower left of the image) or by evaporation from playas (as in the center).

of the stream and water flows from the stream into the ground (Figure 30.17b).

Very little water that flows in streams has not flowed through the ground first, if only for a short distance. Think of streams you have seen. Even when the flows are high from snow melt or heavy rains, how often have you seen water flowing to the stream as a thin sheet across the ground surface? This seldom happens. Water goes first into the ground and then to the stream, illustrating how ground and surface water systems are intimately interconnected.

Man-made wells are a major source of groundwater discharge. *Figure 30.18* shows the transformation of an aquifer from undeveloped to heavily used. When a well is installed and pumped heavily, water is drawn down around the well faster than it can naturally flow creating a **cone of depression** as shown.

Cones of depression have consequences beyond the physics of groundwater flow. Next to the minor well in Figure 30.18b a major well

has been dug. Suppose the major well is used heavily, perhaps for irrigating crops. If water is extracted from it at a high enough rate the resulting cone of depression will cause the minor well to run dry as shown in Figure 30.18c.

The laws that govern the use of groundwater vary from state to state and are often very complex because the use of groundwater by one individual can influence the availability of this resource to others. Whenever groundwater is used at a rate that is greater than it is naturally replenished, the aquifer is being "mined" and overlapping cones of depression will cause regional water tables to drop.

By similar logic, the pollution of an aquifer by a single entity can ruin this resource for many. Care must be taken to prevent pollutants like oil and chemicals from seeping into an aquifer where they can spread unintentionally throughout the entire system. It is important that we understand natural resources like groundwater so that we can protect and use them properly.

**Cone of Depression:**

A region next to a well or source of discharge where the water table is lowered.

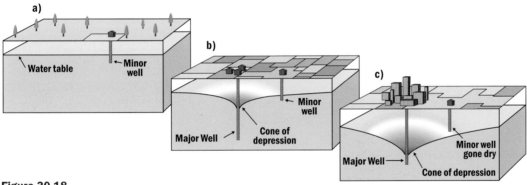

**Figure 30.18**

a) A natural aquifer with a minor well that does not draw more than the aquifer can replenish.

b) A major well is installed that draws water faster than the aquifer can replenish, lowering the water table around it and creating a cone of depression.

c) As the major well continues to draw water at a faster rate, the cone of depression increases to the point that the minor well no longer reaches the aquifer and dries up.

## Chapter Framework

### A. Hydrological cycle
1. Movement of water between reservoirs
2. Driven by heat energy from Sun

### B. Streams
1. Flowing surface water
2. Agent of erosion
   a. *Base level*
3. Agent of deposition
   a. *Alluvial fans, deltas, floodplains*

### C. Ice
1. Continental glaciers
2. Alpine glaciers
3. Zones of accumulation and ablation

### D. Groundwater
1. Found in pores between rock grains
2. Aquifers influenced by recharge and discharge
3. Water tables influenced by wells

## Comprehension

### Matching

a. Alluvial fan
b. Alpine glaciers
c. Aquifer
d. Delta
e. Glacial erosion
f. Ground water
g. Hydrologic cycle
h. Porosity
i. Stream gradient
j. Water table
k. Zone of accumulation

1. ____ Represents the redistribution of water from oceans to continents
2. ____ Steepness of the ground over which a stream flows
3. ____ Type of deposition in arid mountain regions
4. ____ Form where perennial streams reach base level in a body of water
5. ____ Location where the input of snow exceeds the output
6. ____ Glaciers that flow downhill
7. ____ Produces U-shaped valleys
8. ____ Liquid water that occupies empty space between grains or fractures beneath the surface of the earth.
9. ____ Amount of empty space in a rock
10. ____ Rock with significant porosity below the water table
11. ____ The top of a water-filled aquifer

### True/False
1. ____ Regions around the equator receive the most diluted sunlight
2. ____ Glaciers contain the highest percentage of fresh water on the Earth
3. ____ The number of tributaries decreases as you go downstream
4. ____ Alluvial fans are home to an abundant number of plants and animals
5. ____ An aquitard lacks sufficient permeability

### Fill in the Blank
1. _____ is the most important source of fresh water for humans.
2. A _____ denotes anything from a raging river to a small trickle.
3. Where a stream gradient is steeper than its equilibrium profile, it will _____ sediment.
4. Sediment will be _____ whenever the velocity of water is too slow.
5. Aridity is necessary for an _____ _____ because humid climates tend to have permanent streams.
6. In glaciers, when ice exceeds a certain _____, it will begin to flow.

## Analysis

1. The location where melting and evaporation exceeds snowfall is called the
   a) Zone of accumulation
   b) Zone of ablation
   c) Water table
   d) Delta

2. A stream that reaches its endpoint is at its
   a) Gradient
   b) Water table
   c) Base level
   d) Down cut

3. When a stream bends, the water on the outside of the curve has to travel faster and the water on the inside of the curve has to slow down. What will this do to the stream's path?
   a) It will make the bend sharper and more pronounced.
   b) It will make the stream's path straighten out.
   c) It won't change the streams path.

4. At a bend in a river, _____ occurs on the outside of the bend and _____ occurs on the inside of the bend.
   a) erosion . . . deposition
   b) deposition . . . erosion
   c) erosion . . . erosion
   d) deposition . . . deposition

5. Why do rivers cut 'V' shaped valleys?
   a) Because the material in the middle of rivers is softer and erodes more easily.
   b) The rivers don't cause the valleys, they just flow through existing 'V' shaped valleys as they seek their base level.
   c) Because the water in the middle of a stream moves the fastest.
   d) Because the water is coldest in the middle of a stream.
   e) Because the water has the least gravitational potential energy in the middle.

6. What is the primary reason sediment is depos-

ited in large cone-shaped deposits at mountain fronts?

a) because stream valleys widen abruptly at a mountain front

b) because stream valleys narrow abruptly at a mountain front

c) because stream valleys get much steeper at a mountain front

d) because stream valleys get less steep at a mountain front

e) because it rains more at mountain fronts

7. When the gradient is at equilibrium, what does the stream do with sediment?

a) Transports

b) Erodes

c) Deposits

8. Floodplains are flat because

a) They are always flooded

b) They are at the river's base level

c) They are never flooded—levees keep the water out

d) They are made from non-porous rock

e) They are in areas where the river periodically escapes it's banks, slows down and deposits a uniform layer of sediment.

9. How much of the Earth's water is stored in underground aquifers?

a) less than 1%

b) about 5%

c) about 10%

d) about 20%

e) about 50%

10. Clay is porous but not permeable. What happens to ground water when the water table overlaps a layer of clay?

a) Little if any of the ground water will be found in the clay, nor can the ground water move from one side of the clay layer to another.

b) Little if any of the ground water will be found in the clay, but the ground water can easily move from one side of the clay layer to the other.

c) The clay will absorb quite a bit of the ground water, but it will not allow the water to move from one side of the layer to the other.

d) The clay will absorb quite a bit of the ground

water, and it will allow the ground water to easily move from one side to the other.

11. Areas on continents that were recently covered with continental glaciers typically have very thin soil. Why?

a) A layer of ice prevents plant growth, and hence the formation of soil.

b) As the glacier flowed, it picked up and removed all of the soil.

c) The weight of the glacier compacts the soil into metamorphic rock.

d) Very little erosion takes place under glaciers, so no sediment forms.

e) When the glaciers melted, the soil was all washed away.

12. Explain what happens to the velocity of a stream as the amount of water increases.

13. Explain what happens to the velocity of a stream as the gradient changes.

14. Describe how an alluvial fan forms.

15. In an alluvial fan, the material deposited by the stream is sorted by size. The largest rocks are found near the mountains and the sediment gets smaller and finer as you move farther out onto the valley floor. Why?

16. Compare and contrast alpine glaciers and continental glaciers.

17. If we increase the permeability of a rock, what will happen to its porosity?

## Synthesis

1. Explain why the tropics receive a lot of rain in terms of the hydrologic cycle. Why are the deserts of North America and Africa so arid?

2. Why is residence time important to ground-water?

3. Describe the effects of climate, gradient, velocity, etc. on deposition and erosion of sediment.

4. Discuss the impact of dams on the natural erosion and deposition that occurs in streams.

5. Discuss the role of base levels in explaining why the Colorado river cut the Grand Canyon, while the much larger Mississippi River is not in a canyon at all.

6. Discuss the implications of a cone of depression around a large well. Why does one form? What will the long term impact be?

# Earth's Climate

*Climate is what we expect, weather is what we get.*

*Robert A. Heinlein*

## 31

## LEARN

- The five types of climate classifications.

- The factors that affect local climate.

- How Earth's temperature history has been estimated.

- What Milankovich cycles are and how to identify them.

- About the greenhouse effect.

- What evidence exists for climate change.

The return of spring and summer each year reminds us that Earth's relationship with the Sun gives us the seasons, each with its own weather patterns. As seasons change, the weather may be rainy or dry, humid or arid, or hot or cold depending on the time of year. The historic cycle of weather patterns is the **climate**.

Climate of course depends on where you are. The expected weather is not the same for San Francisco, Salt Lake City, Topeka, or New York. Global conditions influence climate greatly: average climates in the tropics will be wetter and warmer than those in places near the north and south poles. But local factors such as terrain, altitude and nearby bodies of water are also influential. In North America, the wettest climates tend to be near the coasts, with the driest climates in the elevated intermountain regions. On the island of Hawaii tall volcanic peaks have created both tropical forests where it rains essentially every day and dry deserts mere miles away where rainfall is sparse.

In this chapter we consider the climates of Earth and the factors that influence them. We

consider how climates can change, how they have changed in the past, and how they are changing today.

## 31-1 Climate Classifications

Climate is a measure of the average seasonal values of many weather conditions including temperature, precipitation, humidity and wind. Of course, weather changes rapidly from day to day and even hour to hour. So we must average over an extended period of time to smooth out these daily variations. If you average weather over several decades, you get an idea of the climate.

Although climate encompasses many factors, a simple and widely used system based on precipitation and temperature was devised in the late 1800s by the German climatologist Wladimir Köppen (1846–1940). Köppen lived before today's extensive system of weather monitoring stations was built. Lacking direct measures of precipitation and temperature for most of the world, he used plant habitats to define cli-

mates and their boundaries since certain types of plants could thrive only in certain types of climates. His original system had five different climate groups which he designated as A through E as follows:

A *Humid Tropical:* Warm places that never experience cold winters. All months have a mean temperature of 18° C (64° F), well above freezing.

B *Dry:* Places where water is always deficient because evaporation and transpiration rates are greater than precipitation rates.

C *Humid mid-latitude with mild winters:* Places with mean temperatures below 18° C (64° F) but above -3° C (27° F).

D *Humid mid-latitude with severe winters:* Places with mean temperatures above 10° C (50° F) but with the coldest monthly averages below -3° C (27° F).

E *Polar:* Places that never experience warm summers. All months have a mean temperature below 10° C (50° F).

**Climate:**

The generally prevailing weather conditions throughout the year when averaged over several years. While weather changes rapidly, climate changes over time scales usually measured in decades.

**Köppen Climate Zones**

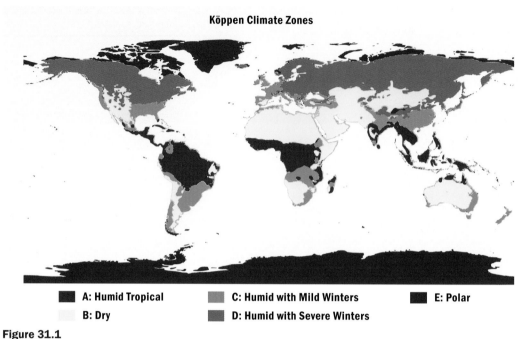

A: Humid Tropical          C: Humid with Mild Winters          E: Polar
B: Dry                     D: Humid with Severe Winters

**Figure 31.1**

The Köppen climate zones. "A" is humid tropical, "B" is dry, "C" is humid with mild winters, "D" is humid with severe winters, and "E" is polar.

*Figure 31.1* shows the distribution of these five classes. Note that the primary criterion for types A, C, D, and E are temperature while for type B is it precipitation. This weakness in the classification has been addressed by dividing the Köppen classes into subtypes that reflect precipitation, temperature and other factors. We will not consider these subdivisions here.

## 31-2 Geographic Factors Affecting Climate

Figure 31.1 illustrates the obvious fact that tropical climates are near the equator and polar climates are near the poles. This obvious trend is because, as mentioned in Chapter 30, the amount of warming sunlight at the equator is considerably more than at higher latitudes. But Figure 31.1 also shows a large variety created by local effects. These local influences include the following:

### Land and Water

As mentioned in Chapter 6, land gains and loses heat faster than water so temperature variations are much greater over land than over oceans or large lakes. As a result, locations near water tend to have milder summers and warmer winters for their latitude while places away from oceans tend to have colder winters and hotter

summers. Seattle, Washington on the coast and Bismark, North Dakota in the middle of the North American continent have similar latitudes but the winters are much colder and the summers much hotter in Bismark.

### Prevailing Winds

The effects of water and land are greatly influenced by the direction of prevailing winds. For example the west coast of the USA has a more moderate climate than the east coast because winds in North America tend to blow west to east. In going this direction the moderating effect of the oceans is more pronounced in the west because wind currents blow air in from it bringing moisture in the process. On the east coast the wind currents blow from the land out to sea and are drier and more extreme in temperature.

### Mountains and Highlands

Mountains promote rainfall. Moisture-laden air striking a mountain range is forced upward to colder layers where the water condenses out as rain or snow. For this reason the windward side of a mountain range may be wet and green while the leeward side is dry and barren.

In Utah, the Salt Lake airport averages 14" of precipitation per year. Just a dozen miles to the east are the Wasatch mountains, where ski resorts may average 50" or more of annual rainfall.

The generally wetter climate in western California contrasts with the drier climate of Nevada because air blowing in from the Pacific Ocean loses its moisture in the Sierra Nevada mountain range. In contrast, Western Europe lacks a mountain barrier so moderate temperatures and higher rainfall characterize that entire region.

### Ocean and Air Currents

Convection currents in the oceans carry warm water to colder regions and cold water to warmer regions, moderating their temperatures. A good example of this is the North Pacific current. This oceanic flow brings warmer water northward toward Alaska making the climates along the western coast of Canada and in the Alaska Panhandle warmer than is typical for their latitudes, and much warmer than the interior of Canada just several hundred miles inland from the coast.

In the atmosphere, the Hadley cells, introduced in Chapter 30, transport moisture from the tropics to the mid latitudes. Because of this mid-latitude climates are wetter than they would be otherwise. Currents can shift and change causing local climates to vary from normal over months and even years (See sidebar on *El Niño and La Niña*)

### Pressure and Temperature

Air flows away from higher pressure zones toward lower pressure zones. At places where high pressure zones are prone to settle over the same land mass, such as in Northern Africa, the flow of moisture from sea to land is inhibited, creating deserts like the Sahara.

Where temperatures are low, precipitation is also low since colder air cannot hold as much water as warmer air. Therefore precipitation is small in the frigid polar regions. Antarctica has the precipitation levels of a desert. It contains vast ice fields only because the small amount of snow that does fall can remain for hundreds of thousands of years without melting.

## EL NIÑO AND LA NIÑA

Often we hear on weather reports about the onset of an "El Niño" or "La Niña" in the Pacific Ocean causing weather to be abnormal. What does that mean?

El Niño or La Niña are opposite phases of what is known as the *El Niño-Southern Oscillation* (ENSO) cycle. The ENSO cycle is a fluctuation in temperature between the ocean and atmosphere in the east-central Equatorial Pacific between Asia and South America. El Niño is the *warm phase* of ENSO while La Niña is the *cold phase*. Each typically lasts 9 to 12 months, but some prolonged events may last for years. El Niño and La Niña events occur on average every two to seven years. Typically, El Niño occurs more frequently than La Niña.

### El Niño

Under normal conditions trade winds blowing east to west push warmer water from South America toward Asia. When these trade winds weaken, the warmer water stays farther to the east keeping the surface water there warmer than normal and preventing deeper, colder water from rising up.

This is called an El Niño or *"The Little Boy"*, or *"Christ Child"* in Spanish. It was originally recognized by fishermen off the coast of South America in the 1600s. The name reflects the fact that the water in which they were fishing became unusually warm around the Christmas season.

During an El Niño there is a large-scale ocean-atmosphere warming across the central and east-central Equatorial Pacific. This causes warmer-than-average temperatures over western and central Canada, and the western and northern United States. The U.S. Gulf Coast and Florida become wetter than average, while the Ohio Valley and the Pacific Northwest become drier. An El Niño can significantly influence weather patterns, ocean conditions, and marine fisheries across large portions of the globe.

### La Niña

Just as trade winds can weaken, they can also strengthen beyond normal and push the warmer surface water ever further west. This allows colder deeper water to circulate up and cool the surface oceans off the west coast of South America and out into the eastern Pacific.

This is called a La Niña or *The Little Girl* in Spanish. La Niña is also sometimes called *El Viejo*, *anti-El Niño*, or simply *"a cold event."* Global climate La Niña impacts tend to be opposite those of El Niño impacts. During a La Niña year, winters are warmer and drier than normal in the Southeast and cooler and wetter than normal in the Northwest.

## 31-3  Climate History

Just as geographic factors influence climate locally, other factors, such as atmospheric composition and solar heating variations, affect climate globally. Over millions of years these changes can be large and can cause the global climate to change significantly.

A few billion years ago, Earth was highly volcanic with a young, emerging atmosphere full of toxic gases. Temperatures were much higher

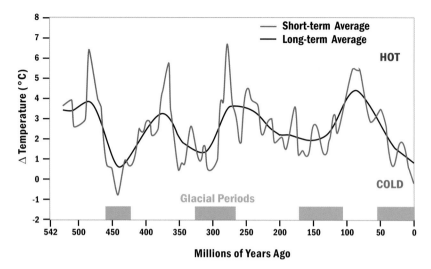

**Figure 31.2**

Estimates of Earth's temperature over the past approximately 540 million years. Earth's temperature has fluctuated considerably over this time. Eras cold enough for glaciers to form are indicated by the blue horizontal bars.

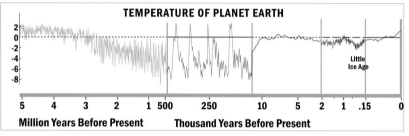

**Figure 31.3**

Estimates of Earth's temperature over the past 5 million years with an emphasis on more recent times. The chart is divided into 5 periods of different resolution, each marked with a vertical line. Earth is currently in a warming period.

then than today. As the earth and entire solar system stabilized, temperatures have cooled.

*Figure 31.2* presents a history of Earth's temperature for the past 540 million years. For nearly all of this period, as life was emerging on Earth, the surface temperature was several degrees warmer than today. Earth's temperature over the last 5 million years, progressively expanded in *Figure 31.3* to show greater detail as we get closer to the present time, shows that Earth's temperature has fallen until several million years ago when it stabilized in a cyclic pattern. But how do we know this?

### Measuring Temperatures

Since about 1850 temperatures across the globe have been recorded at weather stations. For temperatures before that we rely on other means called "temperature proxies." The kind of proxy we use depends on how far back in time we need to go.

For the most recent 1000 years, reliable proxies include the width and characteristics

of tree rings, the chemical abundance in snow, corals, and stalactites, and recorded histories of sea ice melting and crop harvest times. Because these proxies have co-existed for the past 150 years with actual temperature measurements, they can be calibrated directly.

For time periods going back a few hundred thousand years, we use isotope analysis. As discussed in Chapter 25, each chemical element is defined by the number of protons in its nucleus with isotopes of each element being defined by the number of neutrons. Most elements consist of a dominate isotope with traces of less common ones

Having different numbers of neutrons, each isotope of an element has a different mass and changes state at a different temperature. The most common oxygen isotope is $^{16}O$. Water molecules containing the heavier $^{18}O$ isotope condense from air vapor to liquid at higher temperatures than $^{16}O$. Because of this, the ratio of $^{18}O$ to $^{16}O$ in glacial ice is determined by the atmospheric temperature at the time the rain or snow that become the ice condensed out of the atmosphere. So the ratio of oxygen isotopes in ice acts as an atmospheric thermometer.

Every year, snow is deposited onto glaciers. As the snow is compacted over time, ice, particles, and gases from the atmosphere are preserved within it. Antarctica is a dry frozen continent but still has snowy and dry yearly seasons. The dust concentration in new snow is low and looks relatively clear when compacted into ice. But in the dry season when there is less snow, the dust concentration is higher. Dusty snow compacted into ice is darker. So it is possible to measure the passage of years by counting the layers of clear and dark ice.

At the Russian Vostok station in Antarctica, scientists have drilled through the ice sheet to a depth of 3400 meters. They use coring drills that are more like a tube than a regular drill. The outside of the tube cuts through the ice, and the ice in the middle of the tube is pulled out so it can be studied (*Figure 31.4*). From measuring clear and dark banding, the Vostok ice core was found to go back 420,000 years. A similar nearby drilling site names "Epica", sponsored by the European Union, goes back approximately 1 million years. Correlating isotopic abundance with year gives the temperature history of Earth's atmosphere.

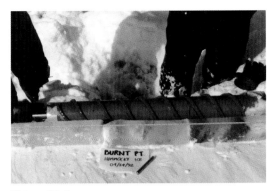

**Figure 31.4**

An example of an ice core drill and sample. Notice the alternating layers of dark and light in the sample. (Photo courtesy of Faye Hicks, University of Alberta.)

Ice cores allow us to study more than just temperature. The dust, ash, radioactive materials, and atmospheric gases trapped within the ice tell us about ancient volcanism, wind patterns, vegetation and precipitation levels as well. All these data are combined to form a coherent model of past climate.

### The Milankovitch Cycles

Since the 1970s, we have known that Earth's climate tends to follow three major cycles of cooling and warming, with periods of about 100,000 years, 41,000 years, and 23,000 years. The longest of these cycles, clearly visible in Figure 31.3, is related to regular changes in the shape of Earth's orbit around the Sun. During one cycle of 100,000 years, Earth's orbit will change from being nearly circular to being slightly elliptical (*Figure 31.5*). The amount that Earth's orbit varies from being circular is called its "eccentricity". When Earth's orbit is circular, there is little variation in the average sunlight received over the course of a year. However, when that orbit becomes a bit elliptical, there is more sunlight received when Earth is close to the Sun than when it is farther away. In the end, this encourages glaciers to develop and expand and causes global temperatures to lower.

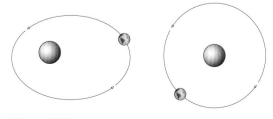

**Figure 31.5**

This figure shows how the shape of Earth's orbit changes during its 100,000 year eccentricity cycle, going from a more elliptical orbit (exaggerated in this drawing) to one that is nearly circular.

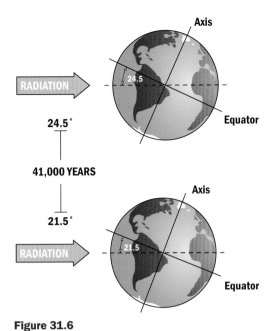

**Figure 31.6**

The axial tilt of Earth toward the Sun changes over a period of 41,000 years. The amount of tilt varies between a low value of 21.5° and a maximum of 24.5°. This change in axial tilt has an effect on Earth's climate.

The second cycle, which has a period of 41,000 years, is related to the tilt of Earth on its axis as it orbits the Sun (*Figure 31.6*). The amount of tilt varies from 24.5° to 21.5° with the current value being 23.5°. As the tilt of Earth's axis decreases, solar energy is more evenly spread across the globe, causing warmer, moister winters with more accumulation of snow and ice, followed by cooler summers when less ice can melt. This triggers an advance of continental glaciers.

The last of the three cycles has a period of about 23,000 years and is related to the wobble of Earth on its axis (*Figure 31.7*). The Earth is not exactly round, the equator bulges slightly. The gravitational force from the Sun pulling on the slightly bulged equator causes the orientation of Earth's rotational axis to change as it spins. This means that over 23,000 years Earth's northern hemisphere tilts toward the Sun at different locations in Earth's orbit. During a cycle the northern hemisphere will change from being tilted towards the Sun when Earth is farthest away from it—producing cooler temperatures and an ice age—to being tilted toward the Sun when Earth is closest to it producing a warmer "interglacial period."

These cycles cause Earth's climate to naturally and regularly become colder and then warmer and then colder again. Collectively they are called the **Milankovitch Cycles** after the

**Milankovitch Cycles:**

The name given to the three cycles in Earth's orbital conditions that influence climate on regular intervals of 100,000-year, 41,000-year, and 23,000-year cycles.

**a)**

PERIODICITY:
23,000 YEARS

**Figure 31.7**

a) As Earth rotates on its axis, it wobbles a bit. The wobble, called precession, has a period of about 23,000 years.

b) Because of this precession, Earth receives different amounts of solar radiation at different times in the 23,000-year cycle. When solar radiation is high, Earth is warm enough to prevent the formation and advance of large continental glaciers, but when solar radiation declines, continental glaciers form and expand.

**Greenhouse Gases:**

Gases in the atmosphere that trap heat and keep Earth warmer than it would otherwise be, just like the glass in a greenhouse traps heat inside the greenhouse. Carbon dioxide, methane, nitrous oxide, and water vapor are the four most important greenhouse gases.

**Greenhouse Effect:**

Short wavelength light from the Sun is transmitted through the atmosphere, warming Earth's surface. Longer wavelength light (also called infrared radiation or "heat") from the Earth is absorbed by greenhouse gases in the atmosphere. This prevents heat from escaping Earth as rapidly as it would without the greenhouse gases, increasing Earth's surface temperature.

**Blackbody Radiation:**

Electromagnetic radiation given off by all objects with a temperature above absolute zero.

**b)**

Present

In 5,750 Years

In 11,500 Years

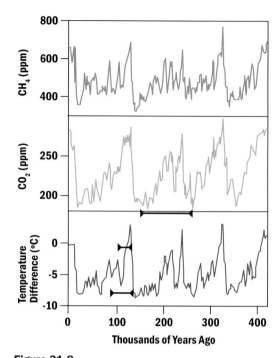

**Figure 31.8**

Measurements of the ancient Antarctic temperature from analysis of the ice taken from the Vostok research station (bottom panel). Atmospheric gases are also trapped in the ice. The top panel shows the concentration of CH4. The middle panel shows the concentration of CO2. Notice how the concentration of these greenhouse gases goes up and down with the temperature. In the bottom panel, horizontal black lines show the 100,000-year, 41,000-year, and 23,000-year Milankovitch cycles.

Serbian astrophysicist who discovered them. Temperature data from the Vostok ice core clearly shows peaks separated by about 100,000 years, the length of the first and most significant Milankovich cycle (*Figure 31.8*). The two other cycles are also present but at much lower levels.

The temperature amplitude of these cycles is affected by the location of Earth's land masses. Antarctica covers the South Pole, while the northern parts of Greenland, North America, Europe, and Asia are near the North Pole. A small temperature drop causes these land masses to be covered with more ice which in turn reflects more sunlight back into space without heating up. As a consequence, the global temperature is lowered further, more snow and ice accumulates, and the temperature drops even more.

This kind of interaction, called a "positive feedback", turns a small temperature change into a larger one. A negative feedback goes against the effect, tending to reduce it. The climate has several feedback mechanisms. Some are positive, and amplify the influence a small temperature change has on the climate. Others are negative, and minimize the influence.

### The Greenhouse Effect

Significant temperature regulators are **greenhouse gases** which are gases in the atmosphere that tend to inhibit energy from leaving Earth, increasing its temperature. These gases include carbon dioxide ($CO_2$), methane ($CH_4$), water vapor ($H_2O$), and nitrous oxide ($N_2O$). Greenhouse gases warm the surface of Earth giving it a temperature well-suited for life. How does this work?

In Chapter 14 we talked about continuous light spectra. The continuous spectrum emitted by a hot dense object has the odd name of **blackbody radiation**. We say a "hot" dense object but all objects with a temperature above absolute zero are hot enough to emit blackbody radiation. In other words, everything in the universe glows to some degree; stars, buildings, trees, people, everything

The peak brightness of blackbody radiation shifts with the temperature of the radiating object—the hotter the object, the bluer the light. Our own bodies with temperatures of 98.6 °F radiate with an infrared energy peak at a wavelength of 10,000 nm—about 20 times longer than visible light. Night vision goggles work by detecting this infrared radiation. A hot stove burner at 500 °F peaks at 700 nm, close to the reddest wavelengths we can see. The Sun at 5400 °C radiates most of its energy at 500 nm, in the visible wavelength range.

Visible and near-ultraviolet light from the Sun travels through the atmosphere down to Earth's surface where much is absorbed depending on what it strikes. Vegetation, water and soil absorb about 70% of this light while snow, clouds and ice reflect the remaining 30% back into space.

Radiation absorbed by Earth is re-radiated back as blackbody radiation. Since Earth has a much lower temperature than the Sun, this radiation peaks at longer, infrared wavelengths. The greenhouse gases allow the predominately short wavelength light from the Sun to pass through but they absorb infrared light coming back up off Earth's surface, as shown in *Figure 31.9*, raising its temperature.

The balance between how much sunlight is absorbed by Earth and how much energy is radiated away again gives it an average global temperature around 15 °C. If the amount of long-wavelength radiation escaping back into space changes, so too does the average temperature of Earth. Greenhouse gases are defined as those that transmit light at short wavelengths, allowing sunlight to reach Earth's surface, but absorb infrared light strongly, slowing down the rate at which heat escapes into space and thus raising Earth's temperature.

As temperatures change, so does the nature of Earth's surface and atmosphere creating both positive and negative feedbacks to the change. For example, wetlands flourish in warmer temperatures. This encourages more bacterial action, which in turn creates more decaying vegetation. The rotting vegetation produces more methane and the climate warms further. This illustrates a positive feedback.

Rising temperatures also produce more water vapor. Although water vapor is a greenhouse gas, a higher water vapor pressure causes more clouds to form. Low lying clouds prevent sunlight from reaching Earth's surface causing the temperature to reduce. This illustrates a negative feedback.

Historic data show that as the temperature changes, the relative abundance of atmospheric

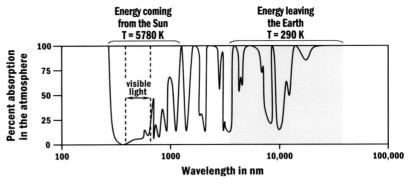

**Figure 31.9**
Absorption of light by Earth's atmosphere. Nitrogen, oxygen, carbon dioxide, and other gases absorb energy as described by the quantum model of the atom and by covalent bonding (Chapters 16 and 23). Energy from the hot Sun (shown in yellow) penetrates the atmosphere and warms Earth's surface. The much cooler Earth radiates thermal energy back at longer wavelengths where greenhouse gases strongly absorb this energy. This absorption prevents Earth's heat from escaping into space, making Earth's surface warmer.

gases also changes. Studies of the Vostok ice core show that when the temperature is high, the concentration of $CO_2$ and $CH_4$ are also high. It appears that a natural warming started by the Milankovitch cycles encourages $CO_2$ and $CH_4$ migration from Earth's surface to the atmosphere, a positive feedback which amplifies the effect.

## 31-4 Climate Change Today

During the last 400,000 years, global temperatures have varied up and down by 4 to 12 degrees Centigrade depending on the latitude. The cold periods have brought ice ages, and the warmer periods are more like today.

Temperatures in the mid-1800s, when pioneers were settling western North America, were a bit lower. At that time Earth was coming out of the "little ice age", a period ranging from about 1300 to 1870 when Europe and North America experienced unusually cold winters. The cause of the little ice age was most likely lower than normal solar radiation and heightened volcanic eruptions putting particles in the atmosphere that block sunlight. Today we rarely see the extremely cold winters that were recorded then.

A study of historical British naval and meteorological records suggests Earth's average temperature has risen by about 0.8 °C since 1850 (*Figure 31.10*). In this time the global sea level has increased by 20 cm and the northern hemispheric snow cover has decreased by 5%.

Over the last 400,000 years, the temperature has correlated strongly with the atmospheric $CO_2$ and $CH_4$ concentrations, and

**Changes in temperature, sea level, and Northern Hemisphere snow cover**

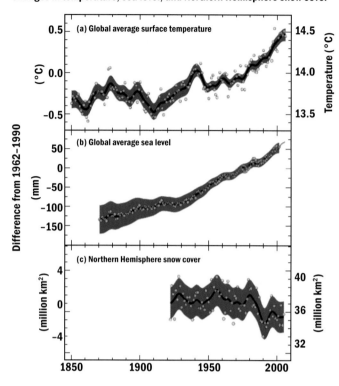

**Figure 31.10**

Data showing the change in Earth's surface temperature, global sea level, and northern hemispheric snow cover since 1850. Earth's surface has warmed by about 0.8 °C in this time. The black lines are the average trend and the blue envelope is the uncertainty in the data. (from the 2007 IPCC Synthesis Report).

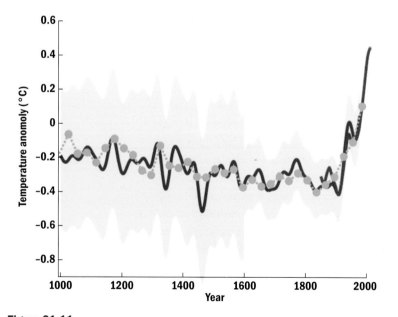

**Figure 31.11**

The average temperature of all landmasses except Africa over the past 1000 years. The blue and red lines and green dots represent three different reconstructions. The shaded blue area represents uncertainty in the values. (From Page 2K Consortium, *Nature Geoscience* 6, 339–346, 2013)

these trends have generally correlated with known solar cycles. However, more recently we have seen trends in both temperature and greenhouse gas concentrations that break from the known solar activity. In the 10,000 years before 1800 A.D. the $CO_2$ concentration rose by about 10 parts per million, for a total increase of about 4%. During just the last 50 years it has increased by 30% from human activities. Fossil fuel exhaust, industrial activity, and agricultural practices have caused this increase in $CO_2$ and in $CH_4$ and $N_2O$ as well. Being greenhouse gases, this should cause Earth's temperature to rise.

*Figure 31.11* shows the average temperature of Earth's land masses over the last 1000 years as inferred by temperature proxies, models, and measurements. The trend is downward until the onset of the industrial revolution in the latter half of the 18th century when it takes a sharp turn upwards creating a shape like a hockey stick. The industrial revolution marked the beginning of the wide-spread burning of fossil fuels that release $CO_2$ into the atmosphere, so the warming correlates with an increase in greenhouse gases as shown in *Figure 31.12*.

The future effect of releasing $CO_2$ into the atmosphere is estimated through computer modeling. These "General Circulation Models" (GCMs) are complex and include the positive and negative feedbacks from how the atmosphere circulates, how the oceans circulate and interact with the atmosphere, how living things produce and consume atmospheric gases, and all the factors affecting climate listed earlier in the chapter.

Because we have records of the temperature and atmospheric gas concentrations of the past, we can test the GCMs by starting them 50 or 100 years ago to see if they can reproduce the known data. Looking back 150 years these models do an excellent job. They can reproduce the warming of the last century as well as other warm and cool periods in the past. They can also account for variability due to temporary effects such as volcanic activity and El Niño and La Niña events (see the side box on El Niño and La Niña). Crucially, the warming of the last several decades is reproduced in the models only if they include all of the greenhouse gases we have produced in recent years together with the feedback mechanisms associated with higher green-

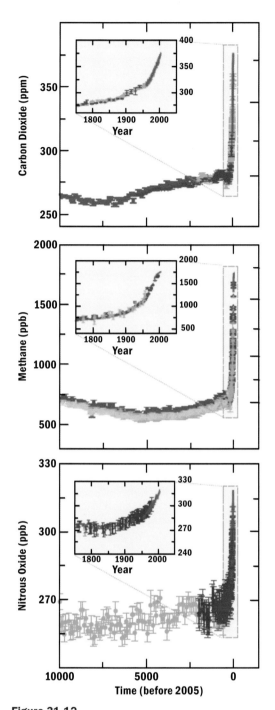

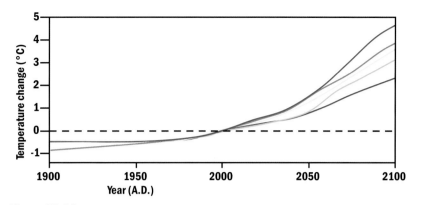

**Figure 31.13**

Predictions of future temperature from Global Circulation Models. Each colored, solid line represents an average of the results of several computer models. Each line describes the rise in temperature based on a different assumption of the amount and rate of greenhouse gas emissions over the next century. All of the models predict that the temperature will rise over the next 100 years, differing only in the amount of the increase.

According to these models, Earth's temperature will rise at a rate of about 0.2 °C per decade for the foreseeable future. In addition to a warmer planet, they predict a rising ocean level, changing rain and weather patterns, increasing areas of desert in some places and vegetation in others, and more frequent and more powerful hurricanes. *Figure 31.13* presents a range of five model predictions based on five different assumptions of the rates and amounts of greenhouse gases emitted over that time period.

The climate is, in a way, a large-scale experiment. We have predictions for what the future will be and we continue to take data and to measure the climate. In the coming years we will know the outcome of the experiment and we will know if the predictions were correct. But being an experiment on the environment in which we live, a vigorous case is being made that greenhouse gas emissions should be curtailed to avoid any even potentially serious, undesirable, and long-term consequences.

The ideas associated with global climate change continue to be examined and tested. As with the development of other scientific models considered in this course, such as the quantum model of the atom, plate tectonics, or the big bang model of cosmology, our developing model for climate change is an illustration of how the scientific process works. Critics and proponents should, do, and will continue to question assumptions, debate results and improve our understanding. Scientists will continue to push the data and calculations to obtain better explanations of the past and better predictions for the future.

**Figure 31.12**

Greenhouse gas concentration in the atmosphere over the past 10,000 years. The inset to each graph shows the greenhouse gas concentrations over the past 250 years. In all cases, the concentrations have dramatically increased since the industrial revolution in the 1800s. This increase is due to human activity. (Graphs from the Intergovernmental Panel on Climate Change.)

house gases. Without this input in the models, they consistently underestimate current global temperatures. Thus, both our knowledge of past climates and our ability to reproduce them using computers is improving. The feeling among climate scientists is that these climate models have become increasingly accurate.

## 31–5 Questions about Global Warming

The public discourse on Earth's temperature is intertwined with discussions on social policies, making it difficult at times to differentiate between them. Here we consider a few questions that have been raised regarding Earth's climate.

### 1. Has the recent rise in temperature been caused by an increase in solar output?

The solar output does change slightly but measurably over several years. Over the past 150 years we have measurements of both the solar output and the global temperature. From 1860 until 1970, the temperature and solar output are correlated. Since 1970, the temperature has continued to rise while the solar output has been relatively stable (see *Figure 31.14*).

### 2. The climate has changed in the past, so why are we concerned about it now?

The desirability of change is a social question. Science helps point out the facts upon which social policy may rest and in this sense is a tool that informs debate. The particular concern today is over the rapid rate of temperature change. If mankind is needlessly causing a rapid change that stresses the environment, the respon-

sible course of action is to minimize the stress and mitigate any harmful effects it may have.

### 3. Why don't all of the experts agree on global warming?

The practice of science is, essentially, a large, ongoing discussion. Scientists are *supposed* to challenge current thinking so that errors can be uncovered, theories refined, and truth more clearly understood. Measuring and predicting climate change is just such a scientific exercise.

To be clear, there is indisputable data showing that the concentrations of greenhouse gases are increasing in our atmosphere which should cause warming. There is overwhelming evidence that there has been a recent warming. Uncertainties in calibrating temperature proxies and in how strong the moderating negative feedback mechanisms are prevent complete agreement in the amount of past heating and in the magnitude of future warming. The Intergovernmental Panel on Climate Change, which is the basis for much of the material presented in this chapter, endeavors to present conclusions held by the majority of climate scientists.

### 4. Hasn't the planet cooled during the last decade?

The rate of warming of Earth's surface from 1998 to 2012 is approximately one-third to one-half the trend over the period from 1951 to 2012. It is likely that this has been caused by volcanic eruptions, a reduction in solar irradiance, and a redistribution of heat within the oceans as through El Niño and La Niña patterns. Even with this reduction in trend, the climate system has very likely continued to accumulate heat since 1998.

From year to year the temperature may go up or down. Computer models of global climate predict that there will be periods of several years with slower warming or even cooling trends. The recent slow-down in warming appears to be part of the normal fluctuations in climate on top of a general warming trend.

### 5. Are the computer models of the climate reliable?

Making an accurate computer model of Earth's temperature is challenging. They are *extrapolations* into the yet-unrealized future, which is the most difficult type of model to accurately create. Even so, all models predict

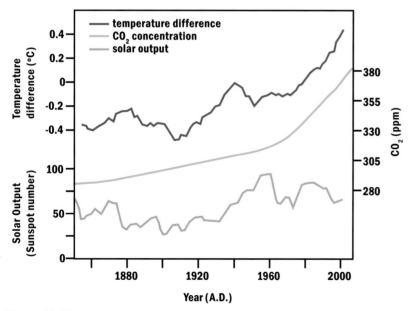

**Figure 31.14**

A comparison of the temperature and CO2 concentration measured on Mauna Loa in Hawaii with the average solar activity. The red and yellow lines (temperature and solar activity) seem to be correlated until about 1970. After this time, the temperature seems to go up as the CO2 concentration goes up. The temperature difference is compared to the average temperature in the 20th century. The solar activity is actually the average sunspot number. The sunspot number shows an 11 year cycle, but that has been averaged out for this graph

Earth's surface will get warmer and none say it will cool. The average climate model underestimated warming by 0.05 °C per decade for 1984 to 1998 and overestimated warming by 0.15 °C per decade for 1998 to 2012. For the period from 1951 to 2012, a longer period that better averages out shorter-term variations, the average models have overestimated the warming trend by about 0.04 °C per decade. As the models are refined with data according to the scientific method, they will continue to become more accurate.

### 6. Didn't climate scientists say we were headed into an ice age in 1970?

Some climate scientists in the 1960s and 1970s thought Earth may be cooling. The majority felt it was more likely to get warmer from an increase in greenhouse gases. Science, properly practiced, encourages diverse points of view and lets these views play out against measurable evidence and well-reasoned hypotheses. Science does not inhibit the expression of any point of view. It *permits* all arguments and *supports* those with the greatest amount of evidence.

### 7. Aren't the glaciers actually growing? How can this happen if there is global warming?

As we have learned in this chapter, climates are greatly affected by local conditions. A few years ago scientists noted that Himalayan mountain glaciers are growing in one particular region. They also appear to be advancing in a few other locations in Greenland and Antarctica. But satellite measurements of the Himalayan mountains from 1962 to 2007 show that the glaciers averaged over the entire region retreated by 20%. One example of a retreating glacier is shown in *Figure 31.15*.

### 8. Are both a colder Earth and a warmer Earth reasons for alarm?

Change is always happening and not all changes are bad. The fossil record shows that the Earth of past, warmer epochs has been conducive to life and satellite image data show that the amount of plant life on Earth increased from 1981 to 2006. Living creatures can adapt and will respond to temperature changes if the changes are slow enough. Again, the rapid rate of temperature rise is a concern and it is prudent for mankind to mitigate harmful effects to the extent that we can.

**Figure 31.15**

On the left is a photograph of Muir Glacier taken on August 13, 1941, by glaciologist William O. Field; on the right, a photograph taken from the same vantage on August 31, 2004, by geologist Bruce F. Molnia of the United States Geological Survey (USGS). According to Molnia, between 1941 and 2004 the glacier retreated more than twelve kilometers (seven miles) and thinned by more than 800 meters (875 yards). Ocean water has filled the valley, replacing the ice of Muir Glacier.

### 9. How can we know what is scientifically correct?

In Chapter 1 we considered the ways in which we gain knowledge. These include authority and intuition as well as reason and sensory data. Since usually only a few people have direct access to the original data of an experiment, the rest of us must rely on the other three methods, particularly authority, to learn about it. Authority in this case mainly means reports on the scientific findings published in peer-reviewed research journals. If a report is peer-reviewed, then it was examined by other experts in the field for accuracy and sound methodology before being published. Non-reviewed sources do not have this same level of authority.

Debate then proceeds by reasoning about the data or conclusions drawn from them as presented in the report. Further investigations are recommended and conducted. In this process scientists, often guided by individual intuition, may choose to give different significance to the various assumptions they reason from. It is helpful to understand the assumptions of the authorities when assessing the correctness of their conclusions.

### References

IPCC, 2014: Climate Change 2014: Synthesis Report. Contribution of Working Groups I, II and III to the Fifth Assessment Report of the Intergovernmental Panel on Climate Change [Core Writing Team, R.K. Pachauri and L.A. Meyer (eds.)]. IPCC, Geneva, Switzerland, 151 pp. http://www.ipcc.ch/report/ar5/syr/

Liu, S., Liu, R. and Liu, Y, "Spatial and temporal variation of global LAI during 1981–2006." Journal of Geographical Sciences, 20, 323–332. (2010)

Mann, M. E., Zhang, Z., Hughes, M. K., Bradley, R. S., Miller, S. K., Rutherford, S., and Ni, F., "Proxy-based reconstructions of hemispheric and global surface temperature variations over the past two millennia," Proc. Nat. Acad. Sci. 105, 13252 (2008)

Page 2K Consortium, D. S. Kaufman corresponding author, Nature Geoscience 6, 339-346, 2013

Veizer, J. "87Sr/86Sr, _13C and _180 evolution of Phanerozoic seawater." Chemical Geology 161: 59–17 (1999).

*Wouldn't it be nice if we could quell the distrust, hatred, violence, and war that we inflict upon ourselves to the point that we might last long enough to fear extinction from global warming?*

Kent Minson

# 31 STUDY GUIDE

## Chapter Framework

### A. Climate classifications
1. Five categories
2. Determined by temperature and precipitation

### B. Geographic factors affecting climate
1. Land and water
2. Winds
3. Mountains and highlands
4. Ocean currents
5. Pressure and wind systems

### C. Climate history
1. Global temperature changes over time
2. Measuring temperatures
3. Milankovitch cycle
4. The greenhouse effect

### D. Climate change today
1. Earth is getting warmer
2. Greenhouse gases are responsible for warming
3. Feedback mechanisms influence the warming rate

### E. Questions about global warming

## Comprehension

### Matching
1. _____ The current temperature, wind, precipitation, and humidity.
2. _____ The weather patterns averaged over several years.
3. _____ A research station in Antarctica where scientists study glacier ice.
4. _____ Methane, carbon dioxide, nitrous oxide, and water vapor are the four most important examples of these.
5. _____ Short-wavelength radiation from the Sun warms Earth's surface, but long-wavelength radiation from the Earth cannot escape into space.
6. _____ 100,000-year, 41,000-year, and 23,000-year patterns in temperature related to the Earth's orbit around the Sun.
7. _____ What scientists call a method used to determine the ancient temperatures.
8. _____ The light given off by all objects due to the temperature of the object.
9. _____ A detailed calculation used to predict the future of the climate.
10. _____ An interaction between systems affected by the climate that can either amplify or reduce climate change.
11. _____ A graph of Northern Hemisphere temperatures showing that the temperature has risen dramatically in the last 100 years.

a. Temperature proxy
b. Greenhouse effect
c. Feedback
d. Blackbody radiation
e. Climate
f. Greenhouse gas
g. Weather
h. Milankovitch cycle
i. Global climate model
j. Vostok
k. Hockey-stick graph

### True/False
1. _____ The Earth's orbit varies with time.
2. _____ The Earth's atmosphere absorbs most of the solar energy that hits the Earth.
3. _____ The amount of solar energy absorbed depends on whether the energy hits snow, dry land, or water.
4. _____ The current climate models don't accurately predict past climate.
5. _____ We depend on indirect temperature measurements, like oxygen isotope ratios, to determine ancient climates.
6. _____ When visible and UV photons hit land, they are absorbed and re-emitted as lower energy infrared photons.
7. _____ Temperature changes over the last 100 years follow past natural variations in climate.

### Fill in the Blank
1. A gas that transmits high energy photons but absorbs a large fraction of infrared photons is called _____.
2. The changes in the amount of solar energy hitting the surface of the Earth due to periodic changes in the Earth's motion about the Sun are called the _____ cycles.
3. Something that varies directly with temperature, like the thickness of tree growth rings and the ratio of oxygen isotopes, that can be used to determine ancient temperatures is called _____.

## Analysis

1. What is the difference between weather and climate?

2. Identify each of the following as a positive or a negative feedback mechanism.
   a) As global temperatures increase, there is more evaporation increasing cloud cover.
   b) As water temperatures increase, the solubility of gases in the water decreases, so the oceans release carbon dioxide.
   c) As surface temperatures increase, the rate of plant growth increases, removing carbon dioxide from the atmosphere.
   d) As surface temperatures increase, the amount of the surface covered with snow and ice decreases.
   e) As surface temperatures increase, decay rates for vegetation increases. Decaying plants produce methane.

3. Identify which of the following factors that influence climate are impacted by human activity and which are purely natural.
   a) The amount of energy the Sun outputs.
   b) The amount of carbon dioxide in the atmosphere.
   c) The amount of water vapor in the atmosphere.
   d) The amount of methane in the atmosphere.

4. Greenhouse gases increase temperature because

a) They are more efficient at absorbing high energy photons and converting them into infrared photons.

b) They transmit high energy photons coming in from the Sun but absorb infrared photons emitted by the ground.

c) They transmit photons that are directed downward, but absorb photons that are directed upward.

d) They prevent convective heat transfer.

e) They block incoming solar radiation.

5. The graph below shows ancient global temperature relative to current averages. There are several repeating patterns in the graph. One period of one of these cycles is highlighted. What is the most likely cause of the highlighted cycle?

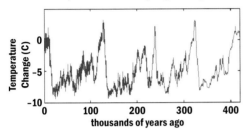

a) The 100,000 year cycle in the eccentricity of the Earth's orbit.

b) The 41,000 year cycle of change in the tilt of the Earth's axis.

c) The 23,000 year precession cycle.

d) The 11 year sunspot cycle.

6. The graph below shows ancient global temperatures relative to current average temperatures. For the past 10,000 years temperatures have been fairly constant. Based on past cycles, what should be happening to the climate?

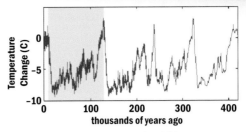

a) Global temperatures should be increasing.

b) Global temperatures should stay the same.

c) Global temperatures should be decreasing.

## Synthesis

1. It has been argued that since we cannot predict the local weather accurately more than a few days in advance, it is ridiculous to think we can predict changes in global climate years in advance. What is wrong with this argument?

2. The three main surfaces on the Earth are water, land, and snow. Explain what happens to energy from the Sun that is incident on each of these surfaces. What feedback mechanisms come into play with each surface? What role does each type of surface play in determining global temperature?

3. Currently the Earth is closest to the Sun during the month of January. This is winter in the northern hemisphere, so the northern axis is tilted away from the Sun. In the past, this configuration in the precession cycle corresponds to times of colder temperatures and an advance of continental glaciers. Why?

4. Currently the Earth's tilt is at 23.5° and is decreasing. What impact should this change have on climate?

# Beyond Earth

# 32

## LEARN

- How we find distances to planets and stars.

- The general structure of the solar system.

- The differences between the terrestrial and Jovian planets.

- The nebular hypothesis explaining the solar system formation.

- What observations support the nebular hypothesis.

The principles discussed so far hold true for experiments done on Earth's surface but what of the heavens? Are the heavens also a realm of the same physical laws that govern Earth? There is no reason to think otherwise, so we confidently assert that any experiment done on Mars will follow the same laws that govern Earth. We *have* conducted experiments on Mars and they verify our thinking but the universe is so vast we cannot hope to visit any but the very, very tiny portion of it that includes Mars and the solar system. Therefore, we rely on the truthfulness of time and position symmetry to enlarge our scope from Earth to the universe itself. In that spirit we apply laws and concepts already presented to understand the planets, stars, and galaxies and why they are the way they are. Ultimately we will contemplate the universe itself to decipher its history and predict its possible future.

## 32-1 The Scale and Scope of the Universe

In Chapter 1, Figure 1.12 shows the contents of the universe organized by size. "Planet" is located at the middle of the figure. The difference in scale between a single proton and a planet like Earth is about the same as the difference in scale between Earth and the universe itself. Don't worry if it is difficult to grasp the enormity of this difference in size. After all, the word "astronomical" means anything too big to quantify.

But we do want to comprehend the universe as best we can and, as the saying goes, if you're going to eat an elephant, do it one bite at a time. So we start our discussion with a quick tour that divides the universe into manageable bites. Numbers quantifying the sizes of these "bites" are presented, but it is more useful here to focus on how objects group together than to memorize their sizes.

### Solar System

We start with familiar territory—our solar system. Earth is one of eight "classic" planets in orbit about the Sun. The planets, the Sun, minor bodies like moons, dwarf planets, asteroids, comets, meteoroids and everything else in orbit about the Sun constitute the solar system. Earth, so significant to us, is merely the fifth largest planet, much smaller than giant Jupiter but larger than tiny Mercury. As large as Jupiter is, its mass, and the entire mass of the planets together is only a tiny fraction of the mass of the Sun. It is the gravitational attraction from the great mass of the Sun that holds the solar system bodies in their orbits.

Earth is 12,756 km across. Our nearest neighbor in the solar system, our Moon, orbits 384,400 km away, a big number but still manageable. We on Earth are 147,000,000 km from the Sun, and the rest of the distances for our solar system are so big that it doesn't make sense to measure with kilometers. A more convenient unit is the time it takes light to travel between the objects. Light takes 0.02 seconds (about

1/10<sup>th</sup> the blink of an eye) to go from one side of Earth to the other, 1.3 seconds to get to Earth from the Moon, and 8 min 20 seconds to get to Earth from the Sun. It takes light about 4 hours 10 minutes to get from the Sun to Neptune, and over half a day to get to the farthest observed dwarf planet. For light traveling from one side of our solar system to the other, the time spent passing planets takes up less than eight eye blinks out of a one day trip. That means that there is a lot of nothing in the solar system.

### Nearest stars

When we step away from our own solar system there is even more empty space. While it takes 8½ minutes for light to get from our own star to Earth, it takes light over 4 years to get to us from the next closest star. Light from the most distant star visible without a telescope takes about 4000 years to get to us. That is why the Sun looks so much larger and brighter than other stars. In reality, our Sun is a relatively small star, but it is just minutes rather than thousands of light years away.

Even though the average distance between stars is huge, there is still a gravitational attraction between them. This attraction decreases with distance, but never goes away. Since it is the only force acting on them, even a small gravitational force clumps them together. The majority of stars are in systems of two or more close companions in orbit around each other. It is common to find clusters of dozens up to millions of stars moving through space together, bound to each other by gravity (*Figure 32.1*). We consider stars in Chapter 33.

**Galaxy:**

A large collection of stars, dust, and gas that is found in a wide variety of sizes ranging from a few million solar masses for a small galaxy to large galaxies with more than a trillion solar masses of material.

### Galaxies

Gravity organizes stars and groups of stars together in systems called **galaxies**. The largest galaxies have a trillion stars and are over a million light years across. Our own galaxy, the Milky Way, contains about 400 billion stars and is about 150,000 light years across.

As you might imagine, gravity binds galaxies into groups and clusters as well. *Figure 32.2* shows a large galaxy which is orbited by a smaller galaxy to the right. Our own Milky Way galaxy has several small galaxies orbiting it. The Milky Way galaxy is part of a "local group" of three large and over 60 small galaxies. The distance across this cluster of galaxies is about 10,000,000 light years. While the jump in size from stars to galaxies was light years to hundreds of thousands of light years, the jump in size from galaxies to clusters of galaxies was only a factor of 100.

### The Universe

The Universe itself is unimaginably huge. For all we know it may be infinite with no end. What we *can* see with the world's biggest tele-

**Figure 32.2**
The spiral galaxy M51 and a smaller companion galaxy, NGC 5195, as seen by the Hubble Space Telescope. Note that the structure in M51 clearly contains glowing gas clouds and dark gas clouds that closely follow the spiral pattern.

**Figure 32.1**
The globular cluster M80 containing several hundred thousand stars. Gravity can organize stars into clusters such as this.

scopes is about 13 billion light years in all directions. This final increase in scale from the local group of galaxies to the edge of vision is a factor of 1,000.

Notice the different structures at different scales. Earth is part of the solar system. The solar system is part of the Milky Way galaxy. The Milky Way is part of a local group of galaxies. And groups of galaxies containing over 100 billion galaxies visible to us, comprise the universe. The gravitational interaction, so weak on small scales, organizes all structures larger than Earth. We talk about galaxies, galaxy clusters, and the rest of the universe in Chapter 34.

## 32-2 Astronomical Distances

Finding distances is a first step toward knowing what the universe looks like and how it works. It is pretty obvious we did not whip out a tape measure and have one person hold it on Saturn while the other read the number. What was actually done is far from obvious. We next consider a few techniques used to measure distances. It turns out that each of the scale steps mentioned above has a different measurement technique that works best in that range.

### Radar Ranging

Here on Earth, air traffic control needs to monitor the location of airplanes flying in the sky where they can't be touched. They do this with radar ranging (*Figure 32.3*). In this technique, a radio signal is beamed towards the plane and a small amount of this signal is reflected back to us. We measure the time between when the signal is sent out and when its reflection returns—like listening for an echo. The radio signal travels at the speed of light. So the distance to the plane is equal to half the "echo" time multiplied by the speed of light.

This same technique is used to measure the distance to nearby objects in space. Because of the large distance the signal has to travel, the radar "echo" is extremely weak, millions of times weaker than the signal that is sent out. If we had to rely on nothing but the echo, we could only measure the distance to our closest neighbors;

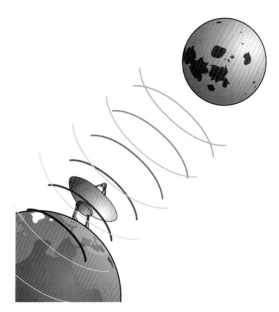

**Figure 32.3**

The technique used for radar ranging measures the time required for a signal to bounce off an object like the Moon and return. It only takes about 2.6 seconds for a signal to travel to the Moon and then return to Earth.

the Moon, Venus, and Mars. Fortunately space probes in orbit about planets can receive a radio pulse and send a much stronger response back to Earth. We've sent space probes as far as Pluto so all the planets and much of the interior solar system has been mapped this way.

Radar ranging is extremely accurate and can provide distances that are precise to a few meters. But it does not work for measuring distances to stars. A pure "echo" signal is too weak to detect for objects farther away than Mars, and our most distant space probes have no hope of reaching the nearest stars. On top of this, stars produce large amounts of electromagnetic radiation at all frequencies and radio waves from the star would drown out any signal we sent. To measure the distance to stars, we must use a different technique.

**Radar Ranging:**

A technique for measuring distance where pulses of microwaves (radar) traveling at the speed of light are sent to a nearby object and the reflected pulse is timed in order to determine the distance.

**Laser Ranging:**

A technique for measuring distance that is similar to radar ranging, but instead of reflecting microwaves, laser light is reflected off a nearby surface and the time for the reflected pulse is observed.

## LASER RANGING

A slightly more efficient variation of radar ranging is **laser ranging**. Astronauts that went to the Moon in the late 1960s and early 1970s left mirrors behind. Using telescopes, scientists aimed powerful lasers at these mirrors. The laser beams reflect from the mirrors on the Moon and were detected again back on Earth. Because the wavelength of these lasers is so much smaller than the wavelength of radio waves, they diffract less. The light reaching the Moon is therefore more concentrated, and the light "echo" is stronger than the radio echo. Laser ranging makes it possible to determine the distance between Earth and the Moon to within a few centimeters.

### Triangulation

A survey method common on Earth and applicable to stars is called **triangulation** because it depends on drawing triangles. If you know two angles and the length of one side of a triangle, you can use trigonometry to calculate the lengths of the other sides. This means you can figure out the distance to something difficult or impossible to reach by measuring a more convenient distance and a couple of angles.

You use triangulation every day. It gives you a sense of depth perception. Your two eyes are set a few centimeters apart in the front of your head. As you grow up, you unconsciously train yourself to estimate distances to objects by comparing the view the brain receives from one eye with the view received by the other eye. The muscles around our eyes move very small amounts to keep each of the two images precisely aligned. Our brains use the angle of our two eyes and the distance between them to tell us the distance to an object. Some people get very good at making these distance estimates. A baseball or ping-pong player judges distances accurately and instantly to hit the ball when it comes to them.

Triangulation can also be used to measure the height reached by the space shuttle (*Figure 32.4*) or to calculate the height of a building or the distance across a river. In the figure, the shuttle is going straight up at an angle of 90 degrees, so if you measure the distance from where you are standing to the launch pad, and the angle from where you are standing to the shuttle, then you can calculate how high the shuttle is. This

**Triangulation:**

A distance measuring technique that involves observing the angle to a distant object from at least two different locations with a known separation. It is then possible to determine the unknown distance by comparing the observed angles.

**Figure 32.4**

The triangulation method can measure a distance that includes a right triangle. In this example, the altitude of the space shuttle can easily be found by knowing the distance from the launch pad and the angle of the shuttle after liftoff. In the right triangle shown in this figure, the tangent of an angle q (theta) is equal to the ratio of y over x, or tan(q)=y/x. The height of the shuttle is y=x tan(q).

technique works the same for a building height or river crossing length.

We apply triangulation to stars by using the distance from Earth to the Sun found by radar ranging techniques. We then form on paper a triangle connecting Earth and the Sun to a nearby star as shown in red or green for the two stars in *Figure 32.5*. The Earth-Sun-star angle is 90 degrees, so the only thing that needs to be found to completely determine the triangle—and get the distance to the star—is the Sun-Earth-star angle marked θ in the figure.

## EARLY ESTIMATES OF ASTRONOMICAL DISTANCES

Approximately 80 years before Eratosthenes, another Alexandrian astronomer named Aristarchus, who believed that Earth moved around the Sun, estimated the size of the Moon. He did this by observing the time required for the Moon to pass through Earth's shadow during a lunar eclipse. He concluded that Earth's diameter is about three times the diameter of the moon. This is fairly close to the actual value of 3.7.

Aristarchus went on to estimate the distance between Earth and the Moon. Using the Moon's estimated size, he looked at how large the Moon appeared in the sky and calculated how far away the Moon must be in order to have that appearance—a kind of triangulation measurement. His estimate of the Earth-Moon distance was accurate to within about 10% of the true distance.

But that's not all! He used these results to estimate the distance between Earth and the Sun, calculating that distance as 20 times the Earth-Moon distance. Unfortunately, his value was about 20 times too small because his measurement of the angles formed by the Earth-Sun-Moon system were too large.

The Moon during a lunar eclipse. The surface is still illuminated by sunlight refracted through Earth's atmosphere.

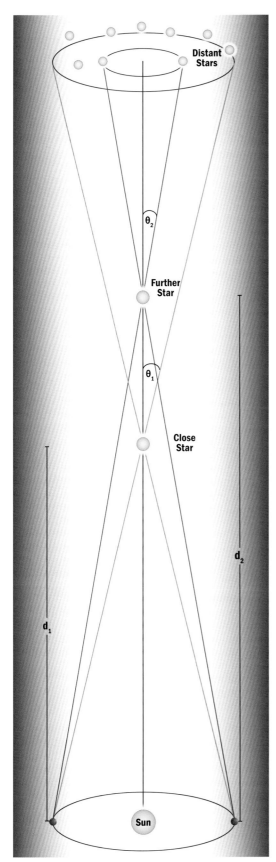

The angle θ is found by first taking a picture of the star against distant background stars. Then a second picture is taken six months later. The nearby star shifts in that time with respect to the very distant ones. The amount of shift is the angle θ. For a nearby star ($\theta_1$ in Figure 32.5) the shift is greater than it is for a more distant star ($\theta_2$ in the same figure). The greater the shift, the closer the object.

Triangulation has limitations. All stars are so far away that even using Earth's orbital diameter as the base results in a very tall and skinny triangle. Even for the star nearest our Sun, the angles differ by just a few seconds of arc (which is 1/3600 of a degree). It was not until the 19th century that telescopes improved enough to measure these tiny angular shifts precisely. In 1838, Friedrich Wilhelm Bessel was the first to do this. He measured the distance to a faint star known as 61 Cygni to be about ten **light years**, or about 95 trillion kilometers.

Turbulence in Earth's atmosphere distorts stellar images, smearing and blurring them and limiting the size of angles that can be measured

**Light Year:**

The distance light travels in a year, approximately ten trillion (1013) kilometers.

**Figure 32.5**

The triangulation method can also measure distances to objects such as stars. Even with a baseline the size of Earth's orbit, the observed angles seen from nearby stars are difficult to measure because they are so small. Note that more distant stars have a smaller apparent motion relative to the background stars.

## THE ROUND EARTH

Aristotle (circa 300 B.C.) recorded that Earth cast a circular shadow on the surface of the Moon. But it was Eratosthenes who first measured Earth's size about 100 years later using trigonometry.

Eratosthenes heard reports from the city of Syene that on the longest day of the year, the noonday Sun would shine directly down the shaft of a well and cast no shadow. He realized that the city where he lived, Alexandria, lay almost due north of Syene. On the longest day of the year, a post driven straight into the ground in Alexandria would cast a shadow. Using trigonometry, Eratosthenes realized that the ratio of the length of the shadow to the height of the post was equal to the ratio of the distance from Syene to Alexandria to the radius of Earth (*Figure 32.6*).

Eratosthenes hired people to help him step off the distance between the two cities. From his measurements he determined the Earth's circumference to be about 42,000 kilometers. This is remarkably close to today's value of 40,000 kilometers.

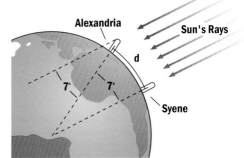

**Figure 32.6**
A representation of Eratosthenes' method for measuring Earth's circumference from the cities of Alexandria and Syene located in Africa.

from Earth's surface. This limits us to finding distances to only about the 1,000 stars closest to the Sun. This is not very far into the Milky Way Galaxy.

Measurements taken above Earth's atmosphere, however, do not have this problem and can determine angles much more accurately. In 1989, a satellite observatory named Hipparcos was launched to perform triangulation above the atmosphere. It contained a small telescope and measured the positions of several hundred thousand stars over a period of several years. This provided distances up to 3,000 light years away for the approximately 120,000 stars nearest our Sun.

Hipparcos was a huge improvement over Earth-based measurements. But it is still only 2% of the diameter of our own Milky Way galaxy. To measure the distances across our galaxy and cluster of galaxies we need a third technique.

### Brightness Distance

Our third technique is again something that you use all the time. When you are driving at night, you judge the distance to an oncoming vehicle by looking at how bright the headlights appear. You know how bright headlights really are, and by comparing that to how much light is hitting your eyes from oncoming traffic, you get a good estimate of how close or far away the vehicle is. We use this same basic method to measure distances to distant stars and galaxies.

Headlights are all about the same brightness making car distance measurements straightforward. The same cannot be said of stars which come in a vast array of sizes and brightness. Fortunately, they also come with "labels" telling astronomers how bright they are. The first label is color. Hotter stars are both bluer and brighter. By measuring how blue a star is and by simultaneously estimating its diameter, we learn how bright it really is. By comparing the true brightness to how bright it appears, we can determine how far away it is. In Chapter 33 we go into more detail about how star brightness varies and how this technique works.

This technique can be used on any star that is resolved in our telescopes. It therefore is useful to determine distances within our own galaxy and the nearest 100 galaxies. Galaxies that are

more distant appear as a blend of starlight. We cannot see the individual stars. To find distances to the edges of the universe, we need one final way of figuring out distance.

### Doppler shift

Back in Chapter 10, we talked about Doppler shift. As a reminder, it is the change in the frequency of a wave when the source and the observer are moving relative to each other. Star light contains the absorption lines of the atoms that make them up. By looking at how much those lines are shifted we can determine how fast the stars are moving relative to Earth. Being able to measure the speed of stars this way is useful in and of itself.

In 1929, Edwin Hubble discovered that when you looked at nearby galaxies, there was a relationship between how fast the galaxy was moving and its size. Assuming average size related to average distance, he hypothesized that Doppler shift gave us the distance; the greater the shift, the greater the distance.

Hubble's first distance estimates were crude and inaccurate because much more needed to be learned about galaxy sizes and speeds. But his idea was correct. Since you only have to be able to collect light from the galaxy as a whole to measure the Doppler shift in the spectrum, this relationship allows us to estimate the distance to any galaxy we can see. We will discuss the details of this technique further in Chapter 34, our chapter on galaxies.

Inside our solar system, the techniques of triangulation and radar ranging have areas of overlap where the distances measured by both techniques can be compared. When we move to nearby stars, triangulation overlaps with the brightness-distance method. At the scale of nearby galaxies, brightness-distance methods overlap Doppler shift. These overlapping techniques verify each other and build what astronomers refer to as the **distance ladder**, the set of techniques which together allow us to more accurately determine increasingly larger distances. The four techniques presented here are fundamental but not the only ones. We will refer again to the distance ladder and a few more distance-finding techniques in the next two chapters.

**Distance Ladder:**
A method used in astronomy where greater and greater distances are determined using many different measuring techniques that overlap to establish a sequence of increasing distances.

## 32-3 The Solar System

In the remainder of this chapter we talk about the realm of the first step on the distance ladder: our own solar system. *Figure 32.7* shows the primary objects in the solar system, and *Table 32.1* summarizes the properties of the Sun and planets. Whether as a youth you were the budding astronaut who could list all of the planets in order from the Sun plus all of the planets' named moons or you were someone whose interest in astronomy only extended to watching *Star Wars* with your friends, you have seen the pictures of the planets before. Rather than focusing on *what* they look like, we're going to turn our attention to *why* they look the way they do, how we know their properties, and what the other planets tell us about how our own planet came to be.

### Mass

Some of the planetary properties in Table 32.1, like the orbital period and radius, can be directly observed. Mass is measured in a more indirect manner. In Section 26.3, we learned that Earth's mass can be calculated from Newton's law of gravitation by measuring gravitational acceleration and Earth's radius.

Finding the mass of the Sun by going there, dropping something and measuring the acceleration isn't possible, but neither is it necessary. A planet in orbit about the Sun undergoes acceleration as was discussed in Chapters 3 and 5. We can use the acceleration of the orbits of the planets to calculate the Sun's mass. From doing so we

Figure 32.7
The primary objects in the solar system. For an idea of relative scale, see Figure 32.9.

| | Orbital Distance (Earth = 1) | Orbital Eccentricity | Orbital Period (years) | Mass (Earth=1) | Diameter (miles) | Rotational Period | Density (g/cm3) | Surface Gravity (g=9.8 m/s) |
|---|---|---|---|---|---|---|---|---|
| Sun | | | | 330,000 | 864,320 | 25.4 days | 1.41 | 28g |
| Mercury | 0.39 | 0.206 | 0.24 | 0.06 | 3005 | 59 days | 5.43 | 0.38g |
| Venus | 0.72 | 0.007 | 0.62 | 0.81 | 7515 | 243 days | 5.20 | 0.90g |
| Earth | 1.0 | 0.017 | 1.0 | 1.0 | 7900 | 23.9 hrs | 5.52 | 1.0g |
| Mars | 1.52 | 0.093 | 1.9 | 0.11 | 4190 | 24.6 hrs | 3.93 | 0.38g |
| Jupiter | 5.2 | 0.048 | 11.9 | 317.8 | 88,580 | 10 hrs | 1.33 | 2.34g |
| Saturn | 9.5 | 0.054 | 29.4 | 95.2 | 74,340 | 10.5 hrs | 0.69 | 1.16g |
| Uranus | 19.2 | 0.047 | 83.7 | 14.5 | 31,635 | 17.2 hrs | 1.29 | 1.15g |
| Neptune | 30.1 | 0.009 | 163.7 | 17.2 | 30,845 | 16 hrs | 1.64 | 1.19g |

**Table 32.1 — Characteristics of the Sun and Planets in our Solar System**

learn that the Sun has 99.8% of the mass of the solar system. All of the rest of the objects in the solar system combined make up the remaining 0.2% of the mass.

All of the planets except Mercury and Venus have moons orbiting around them. The centripetal acceleration of those moons is the gravitational acceleration caused by the planet at that distance. So again using Newton's law of gravity we can calculate the mass of all the planets except Mercury and Venus. We were only able to accurately determine the masses of these two planets after we sent the Mariner space probes into orbit about them in the 1970s. Simply put, we did actually need to go there and 'drop' something (by putting it in orbit) before we could accurately determine their mass.

### Composition

At first glance, composition might seem even more difficult to determine than mass. We've only landed spacecraft on the Moon, Venus, Mars, an asteroid, and a comet. We also have access to meteorites, but that is the extent of our ability to do direct chemical analysis. However, we can get a lot of information from what we see, especially since we're not just looking with visible light but using all of the frequencies in the electromagnetic spectrum.

When you glance at *Figure 32.9*, you see four relatively tiny inner planets and four much larger outer planets. The size information together with the masses lets us calculate the densities and tells us that the inner planets have very different compositions than the outer planets. The density of all the inner planets is about $5 g/cm^3$. A density this high is possible only if they are all made of rock and metal like Earth. Mainly for this reason, Mercury, Venus, Earth and Mars are collectively known as the **terrestrial planets** after the largest rocky planet, Earth.

The outer four planets, on the other hand, all have a density of about $1 g/cm^3$, the same as liquid water on Earth. This tells us that they are composed mostly of the lighter elements, those that most readily form gases and liquids. Jupiter, Saturn, Uranus and Neptune are known as the **Jovian planets** after the largest gas giant planet, Jupiter.

Looking at their images and dividing the planets into "rocky" and "gas" planets is a start. What more information can we get out of their light? Previously we discussed discrete visible and infrared spectra produced by atoms and molecules. We talked about how we can identify atoms and molecules from the frequencies of light that they emit and absorb. The ubiquitous astronomy pictures don't just look pretty; they provide detailed information about the chemical make-up of the objects in the pictures. Many of the images are taken through special filters that only allow emission lines from specific elements through. This allows scientists to identify regions that are rich in hydrogen, oxygen, and other elements or molecules. Colorizing the different emission light taken through these specific filters is often what is meant by a "false color" image.

**Terrestrial Planets:**

The rocky planets, which include Mercury, Venus, Earth, and Mars.

**Jovian Planets:**

The giant gas planets, which include Jupiter, Saturn, Uranus, and Neptune.

## THE MOTION OF THE PLANETS AND KEPLER'S LAW

Claudius Ptolemy (90–168) lived in ancient Greece and following the thinking of his day postulated that Earth stood still and that the Sun, Moon and stars all orbited Earth. This idea survived in Western thought for 1500 years. In the 16th century, a Polish cleric-scientist named Nicholaus Copernicus (1473–1543) developed a model for the solar system in which all of the planets orbited the Sun. Tycho Brahe (1546–1601) devoted his life to measuring the paths that the planets followed across the sky. His detailed notes were studied by his associate Johannes Kepler (1571–1630), who discovered three laws describing the orbital motion of the planets.

Johannes Kepler

1. Planets orbit the Sun in elliptical orbits with the Sun at one focus of the ellipse
2. There is a mathematical relationship between a planet's speed and its distance to the Sun, even though both the speed and distance change during the orbit.
3. Planets farther from the Sun move more slowly than ones that are close to it.

These laws were found by direct observation of each planet's motion, but Kepler could not explain why these laws were true. It wasn't until Sir Isaac Newton (1642–1727) invented calculus and published his Universal Theory of Gravitation that a fundamental force could be used to explain the motion of the planets.

## WHAT IS A PLANET? THE SCIENTIFIC PROCESS IN ACTION

It probably won't surprise you to learn that there are organizations of scientists that regulate the scientific names of things. One of these is the International Astronomical Union, a worldwide organization of astronomers founded in 1919. The IAU holds a General Assembly every three years, during which they do things like standardize the division of the sky into constellations—small areas that enable stars to be more easily designated and named—so that astronomers around the world can avoid confusion and coordinate more effectively.

At the August 2006 General Assembly, the IAU addressed two years of work to distinguish between planets and smaller solar system bodies such as comets and asteroids. The definition proposed by a seven-member Planet

**Figure 32.8**
A NASA illustration of the revised solar system with its eight classical planets (not to scale). In the pursuit of greater knowledge, we must be willing to revise our views of the universe to accommodate new evidence as we discover it.

Definition Committee would have retained Pluto's classification as a planet and added several more objects as planets. However, the proposed definition was amended by the IAU scientists present and voting at the General Assembly's business meeting. The IAU General Assembly ultimately approved a resolution that defines a "planet" within our solar system as a celestial body that a) orbits the Sun, b) has sufficient mass for its self-gravity to overcome rigid body forces in order to assume a nearly round shape, and c) has cleared the neighborhood around its orbital path. Under this definition, Pluto was excluded from the category of planet because it is found in an orbit that is shared with many other similar objects. This resolution left eight "classical planets" in our solar system. A new category of solar system objects was also defined—Plutonian objects, which are dwarf planets that are not satellites and have not cleared the neighborhood around their orbital paths. The IAU determined that all other objects orbiting the Sun should be collectively referred to as "small solar system bodies."

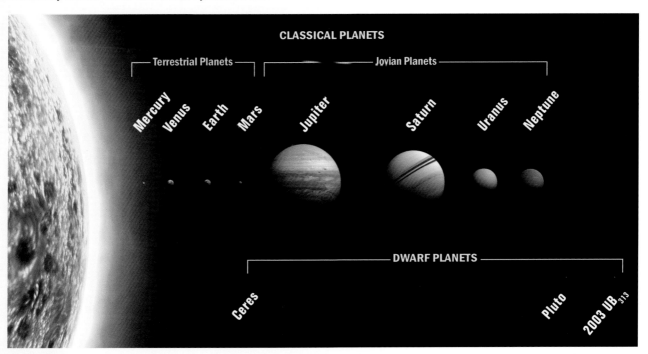

**Figure 32.9**
Illustration from the IAU showing Pluto's reclassification as a "dwarf planet." Although the IAU has voted on the new formal definition of a planet, there are still some scientists who dispute the definition. Pluto's status may change again in the future as scientists continue to debate and new discoveries are made. For now, however, our solar system has only eight planets.

**Nebular Hypothesis:**

The idea that the Sun, the planets, and other objects in the Solar System all formed from a single gigantic cloud of gas and dust. This hypothesis explains the major features and structure of the Solar System.

Spectral analysis is particularly useful in determining atmospheric composition. Analyzing both light reflected from an atmosphere and light from the Sun and stars that gets transmitted through it, gives an accurate idea of what gases are present and what their pressures and temperatures are.

We have learned that the Sun is composed mainly of hydrogen and helium. Mercury has a very thin atmosphere made of gases captured from the Sun. Venus has an atmosphere much thicker than our own that is comprised mostly of carbon dioxide and volcanic aerosol particles like sulfur. Because of a strong greenhouse effect, the surface temperature of Venus is hot enough to melt lead. Mars has a thin atmosphere and is quite cold. Mars also has high wind speeds and global dust storms. These three planets and Earth all have hard surfaces, similar sizes, and are located closest to the Sun.

The Jovian planets all are located farther away. Atmospheric spectral analysis shows them all to be abundant in hydrogen, helium, oxygen, nitrogen, and carbon, the light non-metals. None of them have hard surfaces. Their atmospheres just get more and more dense as you travel into them until the gases transition to liquids. They all very likely have metallic cores.

## 32-4 The Nebular Hypothesis of Solar System Formation

How can we explain the characteristics of the solar system? Any explanation must address these questions:

- Why does the Sun contain almost all of the mass?
- Why are the rocky, high-density, metal-rich terrestrial planets nearer the Sun, while the gaseous, low-density high mass Jovian planets are farther away?
- Why are the terrestrial planets so small and the Jovian planets so large?
- Why do all the planets orbit the Sun in a plane?
- Why are the Sun, meteorites, Moon, Earth, and presumably the other planets all the same age?

The only good explanation is called the **Nebular Hypothesis**. It states that the solar system began 4.6 billion years ago as a slowly rotating giant cloud of gas and dust. Here "gas" means the lighter non-metals that remain in a gaseous state in the cold of space while "dust" means the metals and everything else that coalesces to solid grains in space. Gravity pulled the outer regions

## SOLAR SYSTEM EXPLORATION

The National Aeronautics and Space Act of 1958 established NASA as an aerospace research and development agency to oversee and sponsor missions designed to advance our knowledge and exploration of space. NASA oversees a variety of missions. Over 150 of these missions have flown since NASA's inception, and many future missions are in the planning stages. Some missions are sub-orbital such as the sounding rockets and balloon missions designed to explore our atmosphere, other missions go into orbit around Earth like the Hubble Space Telescope, and a few special missions are sent to explore other planets, like the Cassini mission to Saturn.

The brilliant images of planets you see in this textbook and in the news are usually not taken by telescopes, but by robotic spacecraft. The interplanetary probes we have sent to planets like Mars and Jupiter have greatly increased our understanding of these other worlds. However, for every question they answer, several new questions are raised. New missions are planned to address these questions, and the process of exploration continues. As you view the images in this and the following chapters, remember that the spirit of exploration and discovery is still driving the scientific process, and with each interplanetary mission that NASA sends out, our knowledge of these worlds increases a hundred-fold.

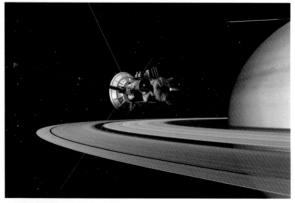

**Figure 32.10**

A NASA illustration of the Cassini Orbiter during the Saturn Orbit Insertion (SOI) maneuver, just after the main engine has begun firing. The spacecraft is moving out of the plane of the page and to the right (firing to reduce its spacecraft velocity with respect to Saturn) and has just crossed the ring plane.

of this cloud into the center which grew rapidly in density. The gravitational potential energy of the gas and dust was converted to kinetic energy, and over time the center became very hot and very dense.

As the cloud collapsed, it began to shape into a hot bulging ball of gas buried at the center of a thinner, flat disk of gas and dust (*Figure 32.11*). The disk flattened by an interaction of gravity with the conservation of angular momentum talked about in Chapter 8. As the slowly rotating giant cloud of gas and dust pulled inward under gravity it rotated faster for the same reason an ice skater rotates more quickly when she pulls in her arms close to her body. The rapid rotation caused a small percentage of the incoming material to remain out in a gravity-flattened disk.

As the disk flattened and became denser, the atoms and molecules collided more frequently. Gas molecules tended to bounce off of each other while the dust grains stuck together forming larger and larger collections. This process, called "accretion", happened continuously over millions of years until the dust grains grew into clumps a few kilometers in diameter. When the clumps were large enough that gravity, rather than random collisions, played a more important role in pulling them together, they became protoplanets. The protoplanets collected more and more material—and each other—until there was only one body, the formed planet, left in the orbit.

Near the center of the disk, closest to where the Sun was forming, the temperatures were fairly high. Only materials with high melting points, those that form metallic and ionic bonds, could stick together to form dust grains. In this volume covalent materials were all gases and didn't accrete. Therefore, the inner planets have high densities and are primarily composed of material with high melting temperatures.

Most of the material in the disk was covalent material: hydrogen and molecules containing hydrogen. Metallic and ionic compounds were only a fraction of a percent of the material in the initial nebula, so the terrestrial planets could not grow to be very large. They never became massive enough to hold onto the gases, like hydrogen, that surrounded them in the disk.

Farther away from the newly formed Sun, the temperatures were low enough that cova-

**Figure 32.11**
An artistic depiction of the solar system in its early formation according to the Nebular Hypothesis. The Sun is surrounded by a swirling disk of material from which planets eventually form by accretion.

lently bonded molecules like water and methane could form ice crystals. These then grew by accretion to become the Jovian planets. Because the nebula from which the solar system was formed contained more of this ice material than metallic or ionic material, the Jovian planets became large. Eventually their mass was great enough to capture hydrogen and helium in their atmospheres through gravitation.

The closest distance to the Sun where water and methane ice formed and mass accumulated is sometimes called the "frost line." Mass condensing here was mainly swallowed up by the Jovian planets, but some of the rockier inner material became the bodies that make up the asteroid belt. Smaller bodies became the meteoroids that occasionally fall to Earth as the accretion process continues.

Once the Sun became sufficiently bright during its early formation, its radiation began to push all lighter, low density material back out into interstellar space, stopping the growth of the planets and preventing any more from forming.

The Nebular Hypothesis was first developed in the 18th century, and has been significantly revised over time as scientists have learned more about the size and structure of the solar system. This model is still being refined as more is understood about the movement of planetary orbits and subtle variations in the size and composition of the outer Jovian planets of Uranus and Neptune and the Pluto-like dwarf planets.

## Chapter Framework

### A. The Scale and Scope of the Universe
1. Solar system
2. Stars
3. Galaxies
4. Universe

### B. Astronomical Distances
1. Radar Ranging
2. Triangulation
3. Brightness Distance
4. Doppler Shift

### C. Characteristics of Our Solar System
1. Mass
2. Composition

### D. The Nebular Hypothesis of Solar System Formation

## Comprehension

### Matching

a. Galaxy

b. Nebular hypothesis

c. Jovian worlds

d. Terrestrial worlds

e. Radar and laser ranging

f. Frost line

g. Spectral analysis

h. Triangulation

1. _____ The point in the disk of material that formed our solar system where temperatures were low enough for water and methane to exist as solids .

2. _____ Method to calculate distance using fundamental principles of geometry by measuring the angle to a star and the diameter of the Earth's orbit.

3. _____ Massive gas planets.

4. _____ The current best description of why the solar system looks the way it does.

5. _____ Mercury, Venus, Earth, and Mars.

6. _____ Large groups of millions to trillions of stars.

7. _____ Allows us to determine the composition of planets.

8. _____ Method that can only measure distance to planets in our solar system.

### True/False

1. _____ Radar and laser ranging can measure distances to the outer reaches of the Galaxy.

2. _____ Earth's density is the largest of all of the planets in our solar system.

3. _____ In order to determine the mass of a planet, we need to land a space probe on it.

4. _____ All of the planets combined only make up 0.2% of the mass of the solar system.

5. _____ The Jovian worlds are much more massive than the terrestrial worlds.

6. _____ Neptune is considered a terrestrial world.

7. _____ Eratosthenes measured Earth's circumference using shadows that the Sun cast.

### Fill in the Blank

1. As the disk of material forming a solar system collapses, its rotational speed _____.

2. Instead of orbiting in a perfect circle, planets actually have _____ orbits.

3. With radar and laser ranging, the signal _____ as the distance to the object being measured increases.

4. The _____ formed by Earth's orbit allows us to measure distance using triangulation to the nearest stars.

5. Earth's atmosphere limits the size of _____ that can be measured in triangulation.

6. Extensions of the _____ allow us to measure distances greater than what triangulation can measure.

7. The process of material sticking together to form larger objects is known as _____.

## Analysis

1. Which of the following is not a characteristic of the Jovian worlds?

   a) A high density, larger than the terrestrial worlds.

   b) Composed mainly of hydrogen, helium, carbon, and nitrogen

   c) Many times more massive than the terrestrial planets

   d) Large internal pressure

   e) All of the above are characteristics

2. What would be the best method to determine the distance to Mars?

   a) Bounce a radio wave off it and time how long it takes to make the round trip

   b) Take pictures of it six months apart and measure how much it has shifted relative to more distant background stars

   c) Use brightness distance relations

   d) Examine its spectrum to see how much it has been shifted toward the red

   e) All of the above would work equally well

3. Which of the following is not a characteristic of *all* the terrestrial worlds?

   a) Densities that are several times denser than water

   b) Composed of rocks similar to those found on Earth

   c) Tectonic plate system

   d) Four planets closest to the Sun in the solar system

   e) All of the above are characteristics of the terrestrial worlds

4. Which of the following characteristics does Pluto *not* have that prevents it from being a classical planet?

a) orbits the Sun

b) has cleared the neighborhood around its orbital path

c) has an average density between the terrestrial worlds and the Jovian worlds

d) has enough mass to form a nearly round shape

5. Which of the following is oldest?

a) The Sun

b) The terrestrial planets

c) The Jovian planets

d) The moon

e) They're all about the same age

6. Radar ranging and laser ranging can measure distance for all of the following except:

a) The Moon

b) Mars

c) Saturn

d) The Sun

7. Which of the following is mentioned as distorting triangulation from Earth's surface?

a) The atmosphere

b) The Moon

c) City lights

d) Overhead airplanes

8. How do we measure the mass of planets?

a) We measure the planet's orbit around the Sun. The length of its year is determined by its mass.

b) We measure the planet's spin. The rate it turns on its axis is determined by its mass.

c) We measure the eccentricity of its orbit. More massive planets will have more eccentric orbits.

d) We only actually know the mass of the planets we've landed on. Once we've landed on

a planet, we can measure the strength of the gravitational force.

e) We observe something orbiting around the planet and use Newton's law of gravitation to calculate the planet's mass.

9. Planets are created in a disk of material surrounding a forming star. What characteristic of the disk determines whether a terrestrial or Jovian planet forms at a given location?

a) The temperature at that position in the disk

b) The amount of hydrogen at that position in the disk

c) The amount of rock and metal at that position in the disk

d) How fast the disk is spinning at that position

e) How dense the disk is at that position

## Synthesis

1. What is a characteristic that most of the planets in our solar system hold in common?

2. What do the common characteristics of the planets in our solar system suggest about the solar system's formation?

3. Why can't radar ranging be used for planets beyond the solar system?

4. With triangulation, what was the solution to overcome atmospheric turbulence?

5. Radar ranging can be used for measuring the distance to nearby planets. Why can't radar ranging be used to measure distances to stars far beyond our Sun?

6. Explain how we can determine the mass of a planet we've never landed a space probe on.

7. Compare and contrast the Jovian planets with the terrestrial planets.

8. Describe the nebular hypothesis of the Solar System. How does this explain the major features and characteristics of the Solar System?

# The Life Cycle of a Star

*Canst thou bind the sweet influences of Pleiades,*
*or loose the bands of Orion?*

*Job 38:31*

# 33

## LEARN

- How protostars form within the interstellar medium.

- The different phases in the life of a typical star.

- How the mass of a star determines the length of each phase in the star's life.

- The three different possible end states of stellar life and how they affect their surroundings.

- What H-R diagrams are and how they are used.

The beauty of a starry night has inspired people since before the dawn of civilization. One of the first songs young children learn is "Twinkle, twinkle little star. How I wonder what you are." Perhaps you still gaze upward in wonder on a dark night at the stars of varying color and brightness grouped across the sky.

If you are looking at the sky from the heart of a large city, you will only see a few of the brightest stars. The rest will be lost in the wash of light from homes, businesses, and streetlights. Away from city lights many more are visible including the faint band of light from the 400 billion more distant stars in our own galaxy, described as a road of milk by the ancient Romans. If the sky is truly dark, as on a moonless camping trip, you can make out the colors of individual stars, see dark areas of dust in the Milky Way, and even see bright fuzzy patches from a few hot clumps of gas where stars are forming.

In this chapter, we are going to try to answer the question from the song and at least partially explain what stars are. By using our understand-

ing of physics and chemistry, we can explain how stars form, how they change with time, and even why they twinkle.

## 33-1 Eyes and Telescopes

When we were trying to determine the nature of atoms, we were able to develop and refine our models by performing experiments on atoms in controlled conditions in laboratories. Stars can't be tested in the same way. We have to rely exclusively on what we can observe.

As with the elements, we start learning of stars by observing the properties of as many as we can. With our unaided eyes, we can see a total of about 6000 stars from Earth, with half or 3000 visible at any given time. That is a start, but compared to the 400,000,000,000 stars in our galaxy alone, it isn't a lot.

Our eyes are amazing light detectors that are suited well for Earth life, but not as well for stars. Eyes control the amount of light that they let in by changing the size of the pupil. At night,

our pupils dilate nearly to a centimeter to let in more light and let us see fainter objects. But one centimeter is still fairly small for objects as faint as stars.

We can improve our vision by using a mirror to concentrate light from a much larger area into our pupils. A telescope mirror 10m across, for example, gathers 1,000,000 times as much light as our pupil can, allowing us to see stars 1,000,000 times fainter.

Telescopes can also collect photons over time periods much longer than the 0.1 seconds for a typical eye. The Hubble Space Telescope created a "deep field" picture by pointing at the same location in the sky for over a month. All of the photons gathered by the telescope during the entire month were added together to form a single image. Long exposure times allow us to see fainter than the eye as well.

For these reasons astronomers today never take research data with their eyes. They always use telescopes equipped with highly sensitive cameras.

## 33-2 The Stellar Life Cycle

We use the familiar terms of "birth," "adult life," "old age," and "death" when discussing the changes that occur between the time a star forms and when it stops radiating. Of course stars are not living organisms and do not live and die in the way these terms are normally used. But they do come into being, evolve through well-defined stages, and go out of existence in events as sudden and definite as death so the terms are appropriate. We speak of these stages together as a star's "life cycle."

From the outset, we have a problem understanding the life cycle. Even the shortest-lived stars last millions of years, much longer than the entire span of recorded human history. How is it then possible to understand how something so long-lived can be born, age, and die?

Fortunately, we do not need to follow individual stars through all their life stages to understand the process. Just as you could learn a great deal about the human life cycle by going to the mall for a few hours and observing humans at various stages of their lives, we observe a large population of stars in the space surrounding us and infer from their various stages of development what the overall process must be.

All stars are at great distances with one significant exception—the Sun. Because of its proximity, this member of the stellar population is the most studied star and has provided much important information about how stars behave in general.

The way stars behave is the result of three fundamental interactions, each of which you have seen earlier. The first is gravity. Stars are massive objects. The Sun, which is a relatively average star, is more than 300,000 times as massive as Earth, or more than 1,000 times as massive as Jupiter. As we learned in Chapter 3, the magnitude of the gravitational interaction depends directly on the amount of mass involved. So gravity pulls the matter in a star strongly toward its center or core.

The second fundamental interaction is the electromagnetic repulsion between the star's atoms. This repulsion creates a pressure which pushes out against gravity. Just as with the fluids studied in Chapter 6, the amount of pressure in turn depends on the density of stellar material. In gases and plasmas, pressure also depends on

temperature. It turns out that nearly all stars are so hot their material is a plasma of charged particles.

The harder gravity compresses a star's plasma, the denser and hotter it becomes. Higher densities and temperatures in turn lead to higher pressures, pushing out. Thus, gravity and electromagnetic repulsion are opposed. The balance between them at any given time determines the state of the star.

Third, the strong nuclear interaction provides the energy source of stars by facilitating the conversion of matter into energy. The nuclear fusion process studied in Chapter 25 is the source of nearly all energy emitted by a star. Through most of a star's existence it provides the heat necessary to keep outward pressure strong enough to counterbalance the attractive force of gravity. The interplay between gravity, electromagnetic repulsion, and the strong nuclear force completely determines a star's life cycle.

## 33-2 Formation of New Stars

The first question to ask when considering how stars form is "what material is available for making them?" Although the space between the stars is a very good vacuum (better than that achievable in any earthly laboratory), it is not completely empty but is filled with a tenuous gas. Analysis of the spectral lines of light emitted by this gas reveals that about 75% of it is the simplest element, hydrogen. Approximately 23% is the second simplest, helium. The remaining 2% is divided among the rest of the elements. So this **interstellar medium** consists mainly of hydrogen and helium, with typical concentrations of only a few atoms per cubic centimeter (see *Figure 33.1*).

As mentioned in the previous chapter, In the cold of space only hydrogen, helium and light nonmetals with very low freezing temperatures like oxygen and neon exist as gases. The other elements exist as small solid grains called dust. In some volumes of space called **molecular clouds** the concentrations of atoms can be billions of times higher than in the typical interstellar medium. The gas here is cold, with temperatures only a few degrees above absolute zero. At these temperatures chemical bonds can form creating molecules, giving these clouds their name. It is in these higher-density molec-

**Interstellar Medium:**

Gas and dust found in the space between stars.

**Molecular Cloud:**

A cold cloud of dust and gas dense enough to form stars.

**Figure 33.1**
A high resolution Hubble Space Telescope view of the Sombrero galaxy. This is a spiral galaxy similar to the Milky Way. Note that the galaxy's disk shows considerable material that blocks the light from stars. This is the interstellar medium from which stars form.

**Protostar:**
An object that will become a star in the early stages of formation before it begins to produce energy from fusion.

ular clouds, held together by the weak mutual gravitational attraction between the molecules, that stars form (*Figure 33.2*).

The birth process begins when something like gravity or radiation pressure creates regions of higher density within the molecular clouds. As the density of the cloud grows, so does its gravitational attraction which leads to even greater density. Soon enough of the cloud collapses at that point to begin to form a star. Typically star formation does not occur as an isolated event. If conditions are right for one star to form, many stars will begin forming at the same time and place, creating a cluster (see *Figure 32.2*).

At this stage conservation of energy plays an important role. The widely separated gas and dust in the molecular cloud has a large amount of gravitational potential energy. As this material falls toward regions of higher density, the gravitational potential energy converts to kinetic energy, just as with falling objects near Earth's surface. As we have seen, temperature is a measure of the average kinetic energy of a gas. Therefore as the gas falls inward, the average kinetic energy increases, the temperature rises, and collisions between the particles become more energetic. They also become more frequent as the density of the gas increases. The warming **protostar** begins to radiate detectable energy, particularly in the infrared region of the

**Figure 33.2**
A young open star cluster, NGC 6611, and star forming region M16, located along the disk of the Milky Way. Also known as the Eagle Nebula, this region of space is known to contain clouds of cold dark gas and glowing emission nebulae.

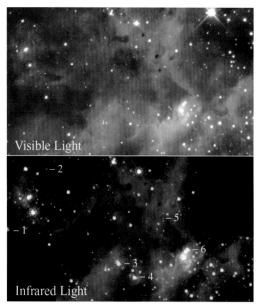

Visible Light

Infrared Light

**Figure 33.3**

Images of the 30 Doradus region secured with the Hubble Space Telescope in both visible light (upper image) and in infrared light (lower image). There are six sources of protostar development marked in the infrared image that are either not seen or are much fainter in the visible light image. This is due to the fact that the infrared light can penetrate the dust and gas that absorbs the visible light.

spectrum (*Figure 33.3*), even though fusion has not yet begun.

The temperatures that are achieved, as well as the time required to achieve them, depend on how much matter falls into the forming protostar. The more mass that is available, the more gravitational potential energy will be available to convert to heat, and the higher the temperature will rise.

The *time* required for the protostar to collapse and form a star, determined using computer models, also depends strongly on the mass available. The greater the mass, the greater the forces involved and the greater the acceleration of the in-falling matter. Therefore, massive protostars condense faster than smaller ones. The time required for a complete collapse ranges from thousands of years when masses are much greater than the Sun, to tens of millions of years for Sun-sized objects, to over a billion years for the smallest stars.

As we saw in Chapter 32, conservation of angular momentum also plays a role in gravitational collapse, causing the collapsing material to form a rotating disk with most of its mass near the center. Such disks have been observed in regions of space where stars are known to be forming, such as the Orion Nebula[1]. The central

**Brown Dwarf:**

A low mass that is too small to sustain fusion reactions in its core.

---
[1] The term "nebula" is Greek for "cloud."

mass is destined to become the new star, with the remaining mass available to form planets, or if there is sufficient mass, other stars.

## 33-3 A Star Is Born

If enough mass is available, the protostar core will reach a "critical" temperature and pressure where collisions between positively-charged hydrogen nuclei become energetic enough to overcome their electrostatic repulsion. The nuclei approach closely enough for the strong nuclear force to dominate and they fuse to form a helium nucleus.[2] By conservation of energy, the decrease in nuclear potential energy creates an increase in kinetic energy. Therefore, the fusion reaction releases heat. When fusion and not gravitational potential energy becomes the energy source, the object ceases to be a protostar and becomes a star.

If the protostar contains less than about 0.1 solar masses, temperatures high enough for fusion are not reached and the resulting object is a **brown dwarf** instead of a star. Brown dwarfs are probably common, but they are difficult to find because, being powered only by gravitational potential energy, they do not emit enough radiation to be easily seen over interstellar distances.

The heat energy released by fusion in the core of the newborn star increases the outward pressure opposing the gravitational collapse. This increased pressure causes the star to expand back out. The expansion reduces the pressure, which reduces the fusion rate, and gravity squeezes the star back in again. After a very short "baby" phase where the star expands and collapses in response to the two opposing forces, the electromagnetic pressure outward and the gravitational force inward reach a state of equilibrium. The net force on the stellar plasma goes to zero, and the star stops collapsing or expanding.

Radiation from the newborn star lights up the nearby gas causing it to glow in emission lines as discussed in Chapter 14. Examples of these glowing clouds include the Eagle Nebula shown in *Figure 33.1*. This radiation also applies pressure outward against the surrounding gas

---
[2] The entire process, called the proton-proton chain, requires 4 total hydrogen to fuse, two of which beta-decay to neutrons.

and dust stopping the star and any associated planets from accumulating any more mass. As more stars form in the nebula, the increasing radiation pressure will dissipate the entire cloud of gas leaving behind a cluster of stars.

## 33-4 Adult Life: Hydrogen Fusion in a Star

After fusion begins in the star's core and equilibrium between gravity and pressure is established, the star enters the "adult" or **main sequence** phase of its life cycle. Main sequence stars have masses ranging from 0.1 to 100 times the solar mass. The small stars are the most common, whereas the largest stars are relatively rare.

Massive stars are hot with surface temperatures over 30,000° K. Low mass stars are cool with surface temperatures of 3 or 4,000° K. This is not surprising since the pressure associated with the temperature has to balance the star's inward gravitational force. The stronger gravitational attraction in massive stars compresses and heats the core more. This results in higher rates of fusion. The greater the fusion rate the more heat is released. This in turn supplies more pressure to balance out the larger gravitational force. Therefore, the more massive the star, the higher the temperature. (*Figure 33.4*).

Temperature determines color. Just as a metal poker heated in a fire first glows dull red, changing to orange, yellow, white, and even blue as it gets hotter, so it is with stars. The outer, light-emitting "surface" of a star is called the

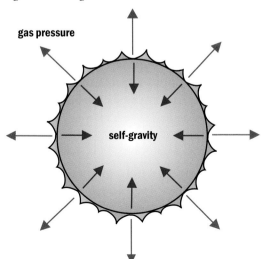

**Figure 33.4**
In a stable star, the inward force of gravity is balanced by outward pressure due to the generation of energy. This type of equilibrium exists in our Sun.

**photosphere**. The temperature of the photosphere determines the color we see. Stars with the coolest photospheres are red. More massive main sequence stars have hotter photospheres and are orange, yellow, or white. The most massive, hottest stars are blue.

Stars are classified into "spectral classes" according to their photospheric temperature. These classes are labeled by different letters of the alphabet, which for historical reasons are ordered from hottest to coolest as O, B, A, F, G, K, M. (A mnemonic for remembering the order is "Oh Be A Fine Girl, Kiss Me"). Our Sun is a quite ordinary G type star.

All stars spend most of their life in the adult/main-sequence phase. Our Sun is a main sequence star as are the vast majority of stars that we observe. We are more likely to catch a star at this stage in its life because it spends so much more time there. This means that we know the most about adult stars.

Interestingly, the more massive stars have the shortest lives. Although larger stars have more hydrogen to fuse, recall they have much higher fusion rates as well. These faster fusion rates mean energy is released more rapidly and the hydrogen available for fusion is consumed more quickly. As a direct consequence, we can place an approximate age on clusters of stars simply be looking at which stars are still in the main sequence stage and which have moved on to "old age." A cluster where the hot blue stars are still present is younger than one where these stars have moved on to the next phase.

The range of stellar lifetimes is enormous. Large, bright, blue, O-type stars exhaust their hydrogen in only a few million years. Smaller, dimmer, yellow, G-type stars like our Sun remain stable for around 10 billion years, but even this is not the record for stellar lifetimes. Small, faint, red M-type stars go through their hydrogen so slowly that they can be stable for as long as a trillion years which is 100 times longer than our Sun or 10,000 times longer than a massive star!

## 33-5 Old Age: The Red Giant Phase

As a main-sequence star ages, hydrogen in the star's core fuses into helium, but the helium does not yet fuse. Being more dense than hydrogen, the helium sinks to the center of the core

**Main Sequence:**

**Photosphere:**
The visible surface of our Sun or stars. The region where visible energy is radiated into space.

where it builds up. Soon fusion stops in the hydrogen-depleted core but continues in a shell surrounding it.

Helium does not immediately fuse because the strength of the electromagnetic interaction is directly proportional to the product of the two interacting charges as explained in Chapter 4. Therefore, of all the elements, hydrogen is easiest to fuse because hydrogen fusion involves pushing together two +1 charges. Helium is harder to fuse because each helium nucleus has a +2 charge and the electromagnetic repulsion that resists fusion in this case is four times greater.

**Red Giant:**

A large, bright, cool star that has exhausted most of the hydrogen fuel in its core.

**Planetary Nebula:**

A glowing shell of gas that has been blown off a red giant star.

**White Dwarf:**

A small star that no longer sustains nuclear fusion and has shrunk to become a dense object about the size of Earth.

The shell of hydrogen-fusing plasma surrounding the core heats up as the denser helium core compresses it in through gravity. Its temperature rises which in turn increases the rate of fusion. The star begins to generate more heat than before.

With more heat being generated, the outward pressure on the outer layers of the star increases and the star expands and grows in size. With expansion, the outer layers cool causing the pressure within them to decrease until a new equilibrium with gravity is reached when the star is much larger than before. In this paradoxical situation, the stellar core is hotter than it was during the mature phase, but the outer parts of the star, including its photosphere, are much larger and cooler. The cooler photosphere is red; hence these expanded stars are called **red giants**.

All stars about half the mass of the Sun and greater will expand to become red giants with outer layers 50 to 100 times their original size. For a star like our Sun, this is enough that the inner planets as far out as Earth would be engulfed (*Figure 33.5*). The red giant star Betelgeuse in the constellation Orion has expanded so far that if it were our Sun it would extend past Jupiter's orbit. Because the brightness of the star depends in part on its size, red giants like Betelgeuse are brighter than average stars.

Stars spend about 90% of their total life as main-sequence core hydrogen burning stars and 10% as red giants. So our Sun, for example, will be a main sequence star for 10 billion years then spend another 1 billion years as a red giant.

Eventually the helium core will become hot enough to fuse helium into carbon and oxygen. When this happens the red giant star drops in brightness and size for a season but eventually returns again to become an even brighter red giant than before.

## 33-6 Impending Death: White Dwarfs, Neutron Stars, and Black Holes

The end state or death of a star, like all the other phases, also depends on its mass. The vast majority of stars, those with masses up to about 8 times the mass of our Sun, fuse their core helium into carbon and oxygen, but do not have sufficient mass to generate high enough temperatures to fuse these into heavier elements. Instead the carbon-oxygen core contracts and heats up creating an interior pressure large enough to completely overcome the gravitational force and drive the outer layers off into space.

We observe these expelled shells of gas glowing with emission spectra. These beautiful objects are called **planetary nebulae** (*Figure 33.6*), not because they were formed from planets, but because as early astronomers turned the newly invented telescope to the heavens these small round nebulae looked like planets.

When the star's outer layers push away, the small, hot core is exposed. These cores are called **white dwarfs**, because they are hot enough to appear white, but are quite small. White dwarfs are approximately the same diameter as Earth and therefore relatively dim. No longer supported by fusion, the core collapses until electrostatic repulsion balances the gravity. From

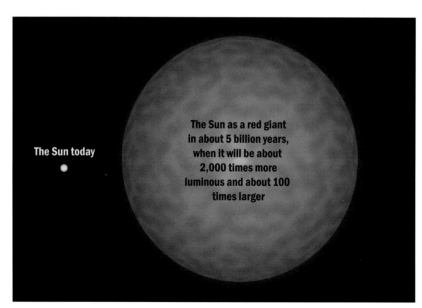

**Figure 33.5**

When a star like our Sun has used most of the hydrogen in its core it changes into a cooler, much larger, and brighter star called a red giant.

The Sun today

The Sun as a red giant in about 5 billion years, when it will be about 2,000 times more luminous and about 100 times larger

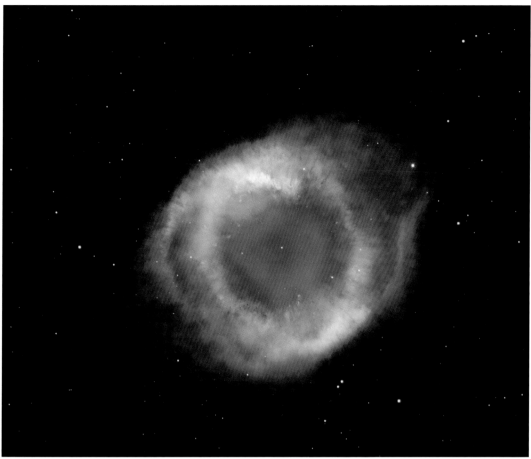

**Figure 33.6**

The Helix Nebula as seen by the Hubble Space Telescope. This object is known as a planetary nebula. The expanding shells of gas visible in the planetary nebula are being expelled by a star similar to our Sun that has already passed through the red giant phase.

the size of the white dwarf and its mass, we can calculate its average density and find it to be about a million times more dense than water. This is expected since the mass of a Sun-sized star is now crammed into a volume only the size of Earth. In about five billion years our Sun will become a red giant and then turn into a white dwarf.

Without fusion to generate more heat, white dwarfs gradually cool over billions of years to become **black dwarfs**, detectable to us only by the gravitational influence they have on other nearby stars.

Heavier stars, between 8 and 25 solar masses, have more spectacular deaths. These stars have enough mass to hold on to their outer layers as the carbon-oxygen core contracts and heats. Eventually core temperatures become high enough to fuse the carbon and oxygen into neon, magnesium, silicon and finally iron.

Each fusion stage is more rapid than the previous one. If a star requires millions of years for hydrogen fusion it will require hundreds of thousands of years for helium fusion, perhaps ten thousand years for carbon-oxygen fusion, a decade or so years for neon fusion and a few days for silicon fusion!

Fusion has a limit as an energy source. Fusion of elements lighter than iron releases energy, but as we saw in Chapter 25, iron has the lowest nuclear potential energy of all the elements. Fusing iron and all elements of larger atomic number cannot release energy, but requires it. Therefore, when a star's core becomes rich in iron, fusion ceases to be an energy source and can no longer provide heat to oppose gravitational collapse. With fusion gone, gravity takes over and the core collapses catastrophically.

The core collapse creates a rebounding shock wave that explosively tears the star apart. The explosion releases more energy in a few weeks than all the energy the star has radiated during the entire length of its mature phase. We see the exploding, suddenly brighter star as a "new" star in the sky. Such exploding stars are

**Black Dwarf:**

The remains of a Sun-sized star that have evolved to a white dwarf and subsequently cooled to where it no longer emits light.

**Supernova:**

A rare celestial phenomenon involving the explosion of most of the material in a star, resulting in an extremely bright, short-lived burst of energy.

**Neutron Star:**

The remnant of a supernova explosion that is composed almost totally of neutrons. It is so dense that the entire mass of our Sun could be contained in a sphere only a few tens of kilometers in diameter.

**Pulsar:**

A variable radio source that is thought to be a rapidly rotating neutron star.

called "**supernovae**," from "super" for "big" and the Latin for "new."

Hundreds of supernovae are detected by large survey telescopes every year. A particularly bright one was observed by Chinese astronomers in 1054 A.D. They noted its position in the sky carefully enough that we can look in the same place today with modern telescopes. At that position is a gas and dust remnant of the explosion called the Crab Nebula, with a tiny, pulsing star at its center (*Figure 33.7*).

The gravitational potential energy released in a core collapse is very large, resulting in very high temperatures. Some of this energy causes iron to fuse with lighter elements during the explosion. It is believed that *all elements heavier than iron are produced in supernova explosions.* In other words, all the elements of the periodic table that are heavier than iron came to be through supernovae. The rebounding shock wave carries this material out into space. Thus,

the death of these large stars "seeds" the interstellar medium with material from which new stars and especially planets can form.

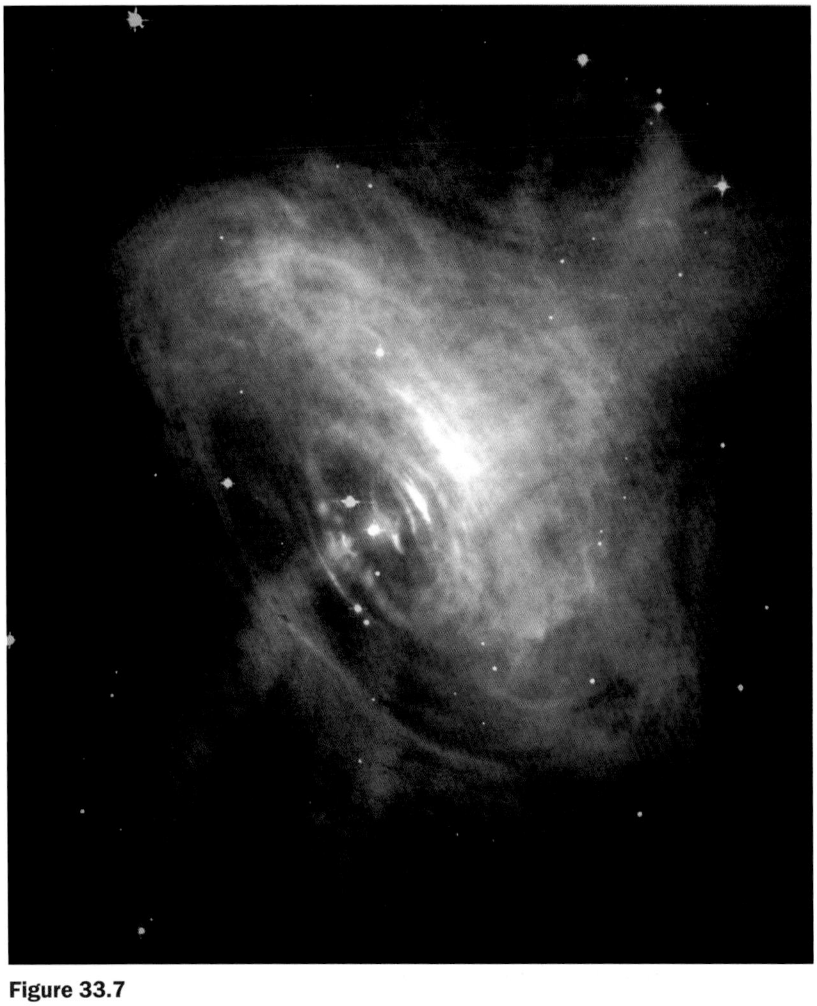

The shock waves from these explosions also compress surrounding molecular gas which encourages high density regions to collapse, beginning anew the process of protostar formation. In fact, our Sun and solar system must have formed from the debris of an earlier explosion, because the solar system is rich in iron and heavier elements. In a sense we owe our lives to the death of an earlier "generation" of stars.

The collapsed core of the star remains intact after the explosion. It is now very small, typically only a few tens of kilometers across. The gravity within it is so strong that it forces electrons and protons to combine by the nuclear weak force, forming neutrons. The resulting stellar core remnant is essentially a giant atomic nucleus of pure neutrons! We call these objects **neutron stars**.

Just like the ice skater going into a spin, the slow rotation of a large star increases as mass falls toward its center. The angular momentum conserved when stellar cores collapse is so large the resulting neutron stars spin rapidly, up to a thousand times per second.

The magnetic field of a spinning neutron star focuses its radiation into beams like those from spinning searchlights. As these beams sweep across our line of sight, we see pulses of light and therefore call them **pulsars**. The pulsing is so regular that when these objects were first discovered some people thought they were artificial signals from space. The neutron star found in the center of the Crab nebula is a pulsar flashing 30 times per second.

The final fate of a massive star, one with more than approximately 25 solar masses, is the most exotic of all. These stars also undergo supernova explosions and seed the surrounding space with heavy elements, but the core that remains after the explosion is more massive and dense than a neutron star—over three or more solar masses within a radius of a few kilometers. With this much mass in so little space, the gravitational forces become so large that nothing, not even the formation of neutrons, can stop the collapse, and velocities greater than the speed of light (which, according to present understanding, are not possible!) would be required for objects to escape. Consequently nothing, not

**Figure 33.7**

The inner regions of the Crab Nebula as seen by the Chandra Observatory and the Hubble Space Telescope. This picture of the famous supernova remnant from 1054 AD combines high energy x-ray data (blue) with visible light (red) images in order to produce an enhanced view. The energetic pulsar at the center of the image is known to flash 30 times each second.

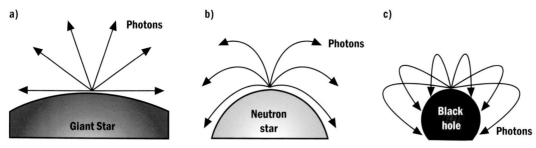

**Figure 33.8**

Formation of a black hole.

a) A supergiant star has relatively weak gravity, causing emitted photons to travel in straight lines.

b) After collapsing into a neutron star, the surface gravity of the star becomes stronger causing the photons to follow curved paths.

c) As the star continues to shrink into a black hole, curved space-time causes photons emitted from a black hole to follow paths that curve back into the hole. The light is bent so far that it can never escape out into space.

even light, can escape from the collapsed massive core, which we call a "**black hole.**"

Another way of picturing what happens is to recall from Chapter 3 that mass causes curvature in space-time, with the curvature increasing as the amount of mass increases. In a black hole, space-time curves back upon itself so that every path in space-time within the hole bends back into the hole; nothing can escape (*Figure 33.8*).

The existence of black holes was originally postulated by the general theory of relativity. This led observational astronomers to look for objects having the predicted behavior. Since then many objects having all of the expected characteristics have been observed and the experimental evidence supporting the existence of these exotic objects is now quite strong.

But if nothing, not even light, can be emitted from black holes, how do we observe them? The signature feature of black holes is their strong gravitational force. Black holes that are gravitationally bound to nearby visible stars are detectable through the motion of the visible companion. In addition, when matter from outside the black hole falls into it, large amounts of radiation are emitted by the accelerating matter (especially if such matter is charged) prior to its falling past detectability. Thus, black holes can be strong sources of high-energy radiation, such as X-rays.

Strong gravitational effects and strong X-ray sources are commonly observed at locations where black holes might be expected to form. In fact, it is believed that supermassive black holes, with masses many millions of times that of our Sun, may lie at the centers of most galaxies, including our own Milky Way. The center of

our galaxy is a strong X-ray emitter because of the black hole there.

## 33-7  Measuring Interstellar Distances

We mentioned at the beginning of this chapter that stars are very far away. In Chapter 32 we saw that distances to nearby stars can be measured using triangulation, with the diameter of Earth's orbit around the Sun as the baseline. This method works for the 120,000 or so stars that are within a few thousand light years. At greater distances, the shift of the target star becomes too small to measure with current technology and triangulation is no longer accurate. For the more distant stars in our galaxy and stars in nearby galaxies we use brightness-distance methods. You now know enough about how stars vary in brightness to explain in more detail how this method works.

Imagine a 100-watt light bulb. It has a well-defined **luminosity**, but how bright it appears to an observer depends on how close the observer is to the bulb. Up close, it can be blinding, but seen from larger distances it looks dimmer and dimmer until at some point it can no longer be seen with the naked eye. The mathematical relationship between the observed brightness of the bulb and the distance is well understood. If we know the luminosity of the bulb (its "wattage"), and measure how bright it appears, it is easy to calculate what the distance between bulb and observer must be.

A similar method works well for measuring the distances to stars. It is easy to measure how bright a star looks in the sky; this is called its **apparent brightness**. We can do this extremely accurately by counting the number of photons

**Black Hole:**

Any object where gravity is so strong that not even light can escape from its surface.

**Luminosity:**

The rate at which energy is radiated from an object.

**Apparent Brightness:**

How bright a star appears to an observer on Earth. It is a measure of the absolute luminosity as affected by distance from the object.

that hit a CCD detector from the star. However, we also need to know the star's "wattage." In technical terms, this is called the **absolute luminosity** of the star, which is the brightness it would have if it were observed from a certain standard distance. Armed with the absolute luminosity and apparent brightness of any star, calculation of the distance is straightforward. But how can we determine the absolute luminosities?

### Main Sequence Stars

One answer lies in a discovery made in the early 1900s simultaneously by two astronomers, Ejnar Hertzsprung from Denmark and Henry Norris Russell from the United States. They each realized that if we know the apparent brightness and the distance to a star, the same mathematical relationship mentioned above for

**Absolute Luminosity:**
The actual amount of energy radiated from an object.

**H-R Diagram:**
A plot of stellar absolute luminosity verses color. Stars fusing hydrogen to helium in their cores lie along the main sequence in these diagrams.

the light bulb can be used in reverse to calculate the star's absolute luminosity. As noted above, for about 120,000 nearby stars, we know the distances from triangulation. Therefore, for these nearby stars, absolute luminosities can be calculated.

Hertzsprung and Russell plotted absolute luminosities for nearby stars vs. the colors of those stars. As noted above, color is related to the temperature of the star's photosphere. In the plot, which is now known as a Hertzsprung-Russell diagram or **H-R diagram**, they found that most stars are grouped along a well-defined region of the graph (*Figure 33.9*). They called the region where most of the stars were located the "main sequence", a term we have already used. Since most stars are adult stars, the term became synonymous with the adult stage in a star's life.

The existence of the main sequence, a well-defined band on the graph, shows that most stars have a regular, predictable relationship between their absolute luminosity and their color. This relationship is better defined if the spectral class of the star and the details of the spectrum of light it emits are considered. These details allow us to separate stars that do not belong on the main sequence from those that do.

We assume that more distant stars have the same color-luminosity relationship as those for which triangulated distances can be determined. With this assumption, we can measure the color of a star then determine its absolute magnitude from an H-R diagram. Next we measure its apparent brightness and calculate its distance. This method works as long as you can see individual main sequence stars. For all the observed stars in our galaxy and even across intergalactic distances to our nearest neighboring galaxies, main sequence stars are bright enough to see.

### Red Giant Stars

When stars turn into bigger, brighter red giants, they are visible at greater distances. But red giants do not have the same tight relationship between color and brightness that we find so useful in main sequence stars. However during specific stages in their evolution, they undergo pulsations which, as it turns out, enable us to identify their absolute luminosity very accurately.

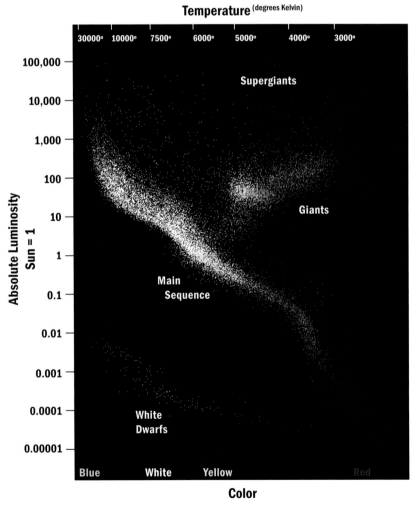

**Temperature** (degrees Kelvin)

**Figure 33.9**
A plot of absolute luminosity versus color for 22,000 nearby stars. This Hertzsprung-Russell diagram shows that most stars fit along the diagonal from upper left to lower right known as the main sequence. Stars that are brighter and redder than the main sequence are giants, and stars that are dimmer and bluer are white dwarves. Note that stellar color, spectral class, and temperature are related. Courtesy Richard Powell.

## DETECTORS

Our eyes detect light using specialized proteins found in the rod and cone cells of the eyes. When a photon of the right energy hits the electrons in the protein, they move to different energy levels and send a signal to the adjacent nerves. There are four different proteins. Each has slightly different molecular orbitals, so each molecule can absorb slightly different frequencies of light in the visible range. The "charge-coupled device" or CCD cameras on telescopes also work by electrons absorbing photons and moving to higher energies, but they are sensitive to a much wider range of frequencies.

CCD arrays are a grid of semi-conductors, each one a single pixel. Rather than jumping to a specific higher energy orbital, the electrons in semi-conductors can jump into the conduction band. Any photon that has more energy than the band gap can be absorbed by an electron. These conduction-band electrons are free to move so they can be collected and counted, giving the number of photons that hit each pixel. Since it doesn't take very much energy to move a semi-conductor's electrons into the conduction band, CCD arrays can be made that can detect photons with energies low into the infra-red range. This means that the cameras on telescopes can "see" from the infra-red well into the x-ray and gamma ray range of the electromagnetic spectrum.

Scientists typically don't want all of the wavelengths jumbled together into a single image. By putting filters and prisms in front of the CCD array, they can control which photons hit the CCD and get counted. True color images are produced using three relatively broad range filters that allow just red, just green, and just blue light through. Narrow range filters allow scientists to identify specific atoms and molecules by only letting light from specific emission lines through. Prisms spread the frequencies out so that each frequency lands on a different part of the CCD, allowing scientists to examine the whole spectrum of the object they are looking at.

On Earth it is impossible to take advantage of the full frequency range because our atmosphere absorbs most of the energy outside of the visible range. Greenhouse gases like water vapor and carbon dioxide absorb all but a few bands of the infra-red light (Figure 31.9). Oxygen and ozone absorb virtually all of the UV photons. The only way to take advantage of the full spectrum is to locate the telescope outside of the Earth's atmosphere. The Hubble Space Telescope is one of several telescopes located above Earth's atmosphere for this reason.

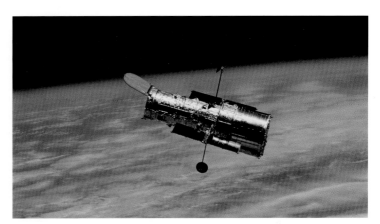

The Hubble Space Telescope

---

While the interior energy source in a red giant is evolving the star goes through a period where perfect equilibrium is not achieved. In this stage gravity collapses the star too tightly, making the pressure inside too high. The star expands until the pressure is too low and gravity makes it shrink too tightly again. As it shrinks and heats, the star gets brighter and bluer. As it expands and cools, the star gets dimmer and redder. The time for this back and forth oscillation is between a few hours and a few months.

More massive stars require greater force to move in and out than low mass stars do. Gravity and pressure can provide these greater forces but it requires more time for each to build up to the higher levels. So, more massive stars pulse with longer periods than less massive stars. As we learned, more massive stars are also more luminous. So there is a natural relation between pulsation period and absolute luminosity: the longer the pulsation period, the more luminous the star.

Similar to the HR diagram, the exact relationship between pulsation period, absolute luminosity and distance was determined using stars close enough that we could measure their distance using triangulation. There are many types of variable stars. But the brightest, best calibrated stars are called **Cepheid variables.** These are the ones most sought for as distance indicators. The distances calculated from their pulsation periods are so critical to cosmology that a key reason for launching the Hubble Space Telescope was to find and measure them in nearby galaxies.

### Type Ia Supernovae

Cepheid variables enable us to find distances out to 10 million light years. To go far-

**Cepheid Variable:**

A pulsating star used to find distances. It has a well-known relation between its pulsation period and absolute luminosity.

**Figure 33.10**

Supernova 1994 D as observed with the Hubble Space Telescope in a spiral galaxy. Notice how the single star in the lower left corner of the picture is as bright as the nucleus of the entire galaxy. A few days before this picture was taken, the supernova was not even visible.

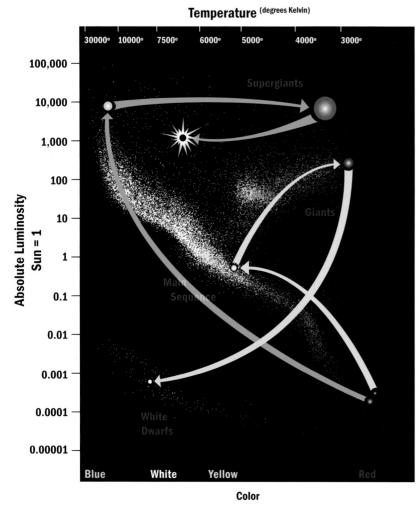

**Figure 33.11**

The life cycle of two stars of different masses as plotted on the Hertzsprung-Russell diagram. Both stars start in the bottom right corner as their coalescing masses create enough pressure to ignite a fusion reaction. The yellow path shows the life cycle of a star similar in size to the Sun. It will move quickly up to the main sequence, where it will spend most of its life cycle before becoming a red giant and then finally shrinking to a white dwarf. The blue path shows the life cycle of a star much more massive than the Sun. It will move even more quickly up to the upper left, having a very high temperature and luminosity as it burns rapidly through its fuel. It will then shift over to a supergiant as it cools, and then begin to drift back across the diagram as it shrinks. However, because of its much larger mass, it will not become a white dwarf, but instead explode as a supernova, throwing off most of its outer material while the remaining core collapses to become a black hole. While the yellow life cycle is about 10 billion years, the blue life cycle of the massive star is only about 11 million years, or about 0.1 percent of the length of the yellow life cycle.

ther we need a brighter star or object. In the 1990s such an object was discovered: type Ia supernovae.

Supernovae are bright enough to be visible 10 billion light years away (*Figure 33.10*). A specific type of supernovae called "type Ia", are actually white dwarf stars that explode in response to matter dumped onto them by a companion star. These supernovae always explode in the same way with a well-determined peak brightness. When we are fortunate enough to discover this type of supernova, we can find the distance to the galaxy that contains it. With this method we can find distances nearly as far as we can see.

To recap, the H-R diagram, variable stars, and type Ia supernovae are all ways to determine the absolute luminosity of a star or event. Once we have that information, we can compare it to the brightness we measure using our telescopes. The ratio of these two brightnesses is used to determine the distance.

### 33-8 H–R Diagrams and the Stellar Life Cycle

While the H-R diagram reveals distances, its greatest triumph is the evidence it provides for our model of the stellar life cycle. The stars on the main sequence, have the exact brightness and colors predicted from nuclear fusion theory. Red giant stars above and to the right of the main sequence perfectly fit our modeling of how main sequence stars evolve. To the left and below the main sequence we find the dimmer and bluer white dwarf stars in the expected locations. (Note how temperature is plotted with hotter to the left and cooler to the right.)

Thus, if we could observe the Sun throughout its life (*Figure 33.11*), we would see it first as a protostar in the red, dim region of the H-R diagram. Relatively quickly it would find its place in the main sequence. Its place is determined by its mass with the most massive stars being hottest, bluest, and brightest and the least massive being coolest, reddest and faintest. The star retains roughly the same color and brightness during its mature, stable phase. Then it brightens and reddens and so moves to the upper right on the diagram as its size and photosphere temperature change. After the outer layers are driven off as a planetary nebula, the remaining small, hot core of the star emerges as a white dwarf.

Figure 33.11 also shows the life of a star much more massive than the Sun. While its movement is similar to the Sun (left-right-left), it is brighter and hotter. Its final state is also significantly different because of its greater mass. *Figure 33.12* gives a flowchart of the stellar life cycle and the possible outcomes based on a star's mass

**Figure 33.12**

The stellar life cycle. Stars begin as cold molecular clouds, which collapse under the influence of gravity to form a protostar. If the mass is sufficient, fusion of hydrogen begins in the star's core and a mature star forms; otherwise, the process ends in a brown dwarf. Eventually a mature star runs low on hydrogen, its core heats, and its outer layers expand to form a red giant. Fusion of elements heavier than hydrogen occurs in the red giant's core. For most stars, this process results in ejection of the outer layers, forming planetary nebulae, with the exposed, leftover core becoming a white dwarf that eventually cools to a black dwarf. More massive stars explode as supernovae, ejecting heavy elements back into space, seeding the creation of new molecular clouds and new generations of stars. Their remaining core material may form a neutron star, or, if it is massive enough, a black hole.

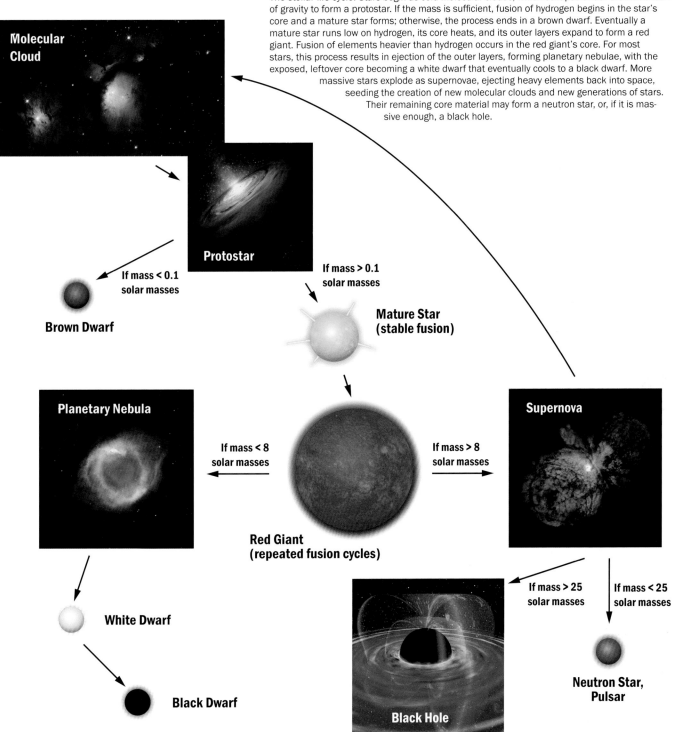

# 33 STUDY GUIDE

## Chapter Framework

**A. Eyes and Telescopes**

**B. The Stellar Life Cycle**

**C. Formation: From Interstellar Medium to Protostar**
1. Composition of molecular clouds
2. Collapse
3. Protostars

**B. Birth**
1. Brown Dwarfs
2. Gravity vs. Pressure
3. Fusion

**C. Adult Life: Hydrogen Fusion in a Star**
1. Rate of fusion
2. Radiation from stars

**D. Old Age: The Star Becomes a Red Giant**
1. Hydrogen-fusion region
2. Red giant phases
3. Planetary nebula

**E. Death: White Dwarfs, Neutron Stars, and Black Holes**
1. Small stars
2. Middle-sized stars
3. Large stars

**F. Astronomical Distances**
1. Triangulation
2. Brightness/Distance
   a. *H-R diagram*
      i. Apparent brightness
      ii. True brightness
   b. *Red giants*
   c. *Supernovae*

**G. HR diagrams and stellar Life Cycle**
1. Plotting the life of a small, Sun-like star
2. Plotting the life of a large star

## Comprehension

a. Interstellar medium

b. Protostar

c. Nuclear fusion

d. Neutron star

e. Pulsar

f. Emission nebula

g. Planetary nebula

h. Photosphere

i. Black hole

j. Molecular cloud

k. White dwarf

l. H- R diagram

m. Red giant

n. Black dwarf

o. Supernova

### Matching

1. _____ Gas that glows from being heated by a nearby hot star.

2. _____ The small hot core that remains after a small star forms a planetary nebula. The star is about the size of Earth at this stage.

3. _____ Remnant of a star composed entirely of neutrons because gravity pulled the electrons into the protons.

4. _____ The final stage of a very massive star that no longer emits light and pinches off the space-time region.

5. _____ The gas that is found in the space between stars.

6. _____ Glowing bubbles of gaseous material that expand out from a small star into space.

7. _____ Cool layer that the star's light comes from.

8. _____ When the star collapses and rebounds creating a massive shock wave that destroys the star.

9. _____ Gas in cool, dark locations of space. The gas emits low-energy radio waves.

10. _____ The name of a white dwarf after it cools and no longer emits energy.

11. _____ Process that provides the energy for a star.

12. _____ Stage during which the star expands to about 50 times its normal size.

13. _____ Neutron star that emits precisely-timed bursts of radio waves and high-energy x-rays.

14. _____ Chart that provides star's luminosity and temperature for a variety of different stars.

15. _____ Beginning phase of a star when gravity begins to condense the surrounding matter.

### True/False

1. _____ Scientists consider the molecular clouds the birthplace of stars.

2. _____ Fusion provides a force that balances the inward force of gravity.

3. _____ For a protostar to form, the force from pressure has to exceed the force of gravity.

4. _____ As the temperature of the star increases, the pressure within the star also increases.

5. _____ The light we see from the Sun comes directly from the center where fusion occurs.

6. _____ The amount of time required for a protostar to collapse depends on the amount of matter in the surrounding region of space.

### Fill in the Blank

1. _____ cannot be directly observed because they don't emit light.

2. Three-fourths of all matter in the Universe is _____.

3. The fundamental interaction of _____ and _____ determines to a large extent the life of a star.

4. The _____ shows plots of luminosity and temperature for a large variety of stars and helps estimate astronomical distances.

5. _____ in the protostar's core marks the time when astronomers begin to refer to the object as a star.

6. We can use the properties of _____ to calibrate an H-R diagram.

7. All brightness-distance calculations are made by comparing a star's _____ brightness and its _____ brightness. Then its distance from us can be calculated.

8. Measurement of Cepheid variable's pulsation periods allow scientists to estimate a star's _____ brightness.

## Analysis

1. The ultimate source of light energy emitted by a protostar is the
   a) conversion of gravitational potential energy to other form(s) of energy that indirectly give rise to light.
   b) nuclear fusion of hydrogen into helium.
   c) nuclear fusion of helium into carbon.
   d) combination of hydrogen and oxygen to form water.
   e) fission of helium into protons and neutrons.

2. Our Sun is now in the state in which it will spend most of its active life. Which of the following best describes the current stage of the Sun?
   a) Protostar
   b) Main sequence star
   c) Red giant star
   d) White dwarf star
   e) Neutron star

3. Our Sun will eventually become a
   a) white dwarf.
   b) neutron star.
   c) black hole.
   d) protostar.
   e) cloud of hydrogen gas.

4. A neutron star is the final stage of what size star?
   a) Small star
   b) Medium star
   c) Large star
   d) Super massive star
   e) Two of the above

5. At what stage does fusion no longer occur in a small star?
   a) Protostar
   b) Middle-life
   c) Neutron star
   d) Main sequence star
   e) White dwarf

6. A type of neutron star that scientists can see because of the radiation it emits is a
   a) pulsar
   b) supernova
   c) black hole
   d) radiator
   e) none of the above

7. Two variable stars, A and B, are seen in a cluster. Star B has a longer pulsation period and appears much brighter than Star A. Which of the following is true?
   a) A has greater luminosity and apparent brightness than B.
   b) A has greater luminosity but less apparent brightness than B.
   c) B has greater luminosity but less apparent brightness than A.
   d) B has greater luminosity and apparent brightness than A.
   e) None of the above are true.

## Synthesis

1. Why do brown dwarfs form?

2. What happens when fusion first begins to occur in a star?

3. How does a neutron star form?

4. What mistake did early astronomers make with triangulation?

5. What are pulsar stars and how do they help us locate neutron stars?

6. Outline the life of a small, medium, and large star. Describe what occurs in each stage of the star's life and the underlying forces responsible for each event in the different stages.

7. Why is hydrogen the first element that fuses in a star?
   a) What force fuses two elements together?
   b) What force needs to be overcome for the elements to fuse?
   c) How does this force that needs to be overcome for fusion compare between hydrogen and the other elements?

8. Why does the amount of matter originally present during the formation of a protostar so greatly affect the different stages that a star goes through?

9. How do astronomers use the H-R diagram to measure distance?

10. Two similar motorcycles travel towards you in the middle of the night. All you know about the two motorcycles is what you observe as they travel towards you. You observe that motorcycle A has a brighter light than motorcycle B. Which of the motorcycles is closer to you?
    a) What does their apparent brightness indicate?
    b) Do you know their true brightness?

# Cosmology: The History of the Universe

*Ten or twenty billion years ago, something happened—the big bang, the event that began our universe. Why it happened is the greatest mystery we know.*

*Carl Sagan*

## 34

## LEARN

- About the Milky Way galaxy and its various parts

- The morphology of galaxies.

- The evidence supporting the big bang model of the universe.

- Important and unanswered questions about the content, expansion, and future of the universe.

On a dark and clear summer night you can gaze upward and see the galaxy in which we reside, the **Milky Way,** as a white cloudy band running mostly north and south. This is the blended light of billions of stars bound by gravity in a disk and orbiting around a mutual center. It appears to us as a stripe circling about us because we are embedded inside the disk.

The Milky Way's disk is full of gas and dust that dims the light from distant stars. If you could somehow see past this obscuring material toward the constellation of Sagittarius, you would get a glimpse of what lies at the galactic center—a giant black hole orbited by huge stars moving at speeds approaching a tenth of the speed of light together with gas clouds being torn apart by the black hole's gravitational pull.

Faintly visible to the naked eye in the constellation of Andromeda is a football-shaped patch three times larger than a full moon. This, the Andromeda galaxy (shown close up on this page and also in Figure 34.2), is a near twin to the Milky Way, bound to it by gravity. This close

neighbor teaches us much about galaxies including our own because, unlike the Milky Way, we can see the Andromeda galaxy from the outside. To understand more clearly what the Milky Way's fundamental parts must be like, we gaze over at the twin.

When first discovered, the Andromeda galaxy and other similar galaxies were thought to be solar systems in the process of forming. This was not a bad hypothesis since they appear flat and centrally condensed as the nebular hypothesis says young solar systems should be. Only after the distance to the Andromeda galaxy was determined did we come to the breathtaking realization that it was not a single star forming less than a light year away but was instead a system of stars as large as the Milky Way spinning far outside of it. This huge misconception illustrates the importance correct distances have in understanding the universe.

The Milky Way and Andromeda galaxies are only two of an estimated 100 billion such systems in the visible universe. Hour-long camera exposures through even small telescopes are always dotted with fuzzy galaxy images. Galaxies are everywhere. They are the main organizational unit of the stars.

## 34–1 The Structure of the Milky Way

It is only in the last 100 years that we have known of galaxies. Hertzsprung and Russell first published their diagram around 1910. With the brightness-distance relation it established, astronomers began to explore the distribution of stars about the Sun. In 1920 Harlow Shapley, using the newly-discovered period-luminosity relation for pulsating stars, found distances to large, ancient clusters of stars called "globular clusters" that orbit out of the Milky Way plane. He made a three-dimensional plot of their locations in space and found that they centered about a point in space in the direction of the constellation Sagittarius, tens of thousands of light years away. Shapley had discovered the location of the center of the galaxy! Contrary to what had been thought up to that time, our Sun was nowhere near the center of the galaxy. Some

**Milky Way:**

The galaxy of over a hundred billion solar masses to which our Sun belongs. As we observe it in the night sky, we see the faint band of light that marks the disk of our Galaxy.

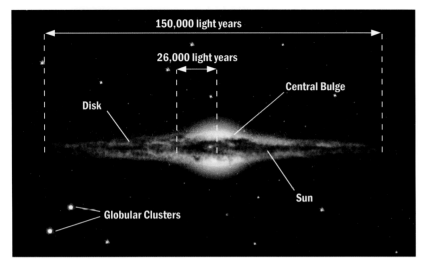

**Figure 34.1**
An artist's conception of the Milky Way. It is clear that the Sun is not in the center of the Galaxy but is located among other stars in the galactic disk.

stars, gas, and dust about 150,000 light years across. The Sun is about one-third of the way out from the center to the edge of the disk, about 26,000 light years from the center.

The general shape of our Galaxy and the location of our Sun is shown in *Figure 34.1*. The Milky Way has arms that curve around in a spiral structure. The Sun is located in a spur off one of the major arms. We are close enough to the galaxy center to appreciate its faint glow but far enough away to not be overwhelmed by light from the many stars there.

## 34-2  A Vast Universe of Galaxies

In 1923, Edwin Hubble used the largest telescope in the world at that time to resolve individual stars in the outer regions of the Andromeda galaxy for the first time (*Figure 34.2*). As stated in the introduction, many thought this was a cloud of gas and dust inside the Milky Way close to the Sun. When Hubble saw individual stars he knew it was not simply

of the most distant clusters Shapley studied were more than 100,000 light years away, suggesting that the galaxy was at least that large.

Distances have been refined since Shapley's pioneering study. We now know the Milky Way is a relatively thin disk-shaped concentration of

**Figure 34.2**
A spectacular photograph of the nearby Andromeda galaxy. Note the two smaller and fainter companion galaxies that are visible in the photograph. The spiral structure and star-forming regions are clearly visible in this photograph. Determining that this was an independent system of stars and not a whirlpool of gas within the Milky Way was a major breakthrough in understanding how matter is organized in our universe.

a luminous cloud of gas but had to be an entire star system in its own right.

Some of the brightest stars Hubble found were Cepheid variable stars. Hubble used these to show that the galaxy was at least a million light years away or at least ten times greater than the distance to the edge of the Milky Way. More refined measurements showed it to be 2.5 million light years distant. With this discovery we knew for the first time that the universe held more than just one star system. When the appropriately named Hubble Space Telescope spent 100 hours in 1995 deeply imaging a location near the Big Dipper, we learned there are more than 100 billion galaxies in the visible universe.

### Galaxy Types

Following the time-honored method of Aristotle, Hubble and others set out to classify galaxies by shape as the first step in understanding how they are made. As illustrated by *Figures 34.3–34.6* all galaxies fall into three general categories: the squashed spherical elliptical galaxies, the disk shaped spiral galaxies, and the amorphous irregular galaxies.

**Elliptical galaxies** are star systems with a three-dimensional elliptical shape like a rugby football. Some elliptical galaxies are small, containing 10 million or so stars. The Andromeda galaxy has two small companions like these which are called dwarf ellipticals. Other elliptical galaxies are gigantic containing nearly 10 trillion stars—fifty times more than the Milky Way. In elliptical galaxies the total angular momentum of all the stars together is very near zero. In other words, each individual star is orbiting about the galaxy with a generally random orientation.

Elliptical galaxies have a dense core of stars at their centers but lack spiral arms or other fine distinctive features. They usually do not contain dust, gas, or star forming regions so no new stars are being formed within them. These galaxies tend to have a red to yellow color (see Figure 34.3) because they are missing the big blue stars. The absence of these short-lived stars means that no new stars have been formed within them for quite some time.

**Spiral galaxies** are what is normally thought of when picturing a galaxy. A spiral galaxy has a bulge in the center, a flattened disk, and a spiral

**Figure 34.3**
A nearby elliptical galaxy in the Virgo cluster. Elliptical galaxies are clearly symmetric, but lack the structure that is evident in spiral galaxies. Also, elliptical galaxies are typically more yellow in color. This indicates an older and cooler generation of stars, along with the general lack of active star-forming regions. There is seldom evidence of dust or gas in elliptical galaxies.

**Figure 34.4**
A nearby spiral galaxy known as M33. Note the numerous emission nebulae that lie along the spiral arms. These are regions of active star formation.

arm structure as shown in *Figure 34.4*. Rather than orbiting randomly, the stars in the disk all orbit around the central core in the same direction and plane.

Our Milky Way galaxy is a spiral galaxy, as are the Andromeda galaxy and Triangulum galaxy, the only other large galaxies in our local neighborhood. Unlike the other two, the Milky Way's central bulge is shaped like a bar, similar to the galaxy shown in *Figure 34.5*. Spiral galaxies are generally of similar size and do not show the same wide variety as elliptical galaxies. A

**Elliptical Galaxy:**

A galaxy with an elliptical shape and little dust or gas.

**Spiral Galaxy:**

A galaxy flattened into a disk shape with a pattern of spiral arms wound about a central nucleus. Spiral galaxies usually include dust, gas, and active regions of star formation.

**Figure 34.5**

The barred spiral galaxy NGC 1300. Except for the bar of material running through the nucleus, barred spiral galaxies are similar in size and structure to regular spiral galaxies.

**Irregular Galaxy:**

A non-symmetric galaxy that does not have a well-defined shape like either the spiral or elliptical galaxies. Irregular galaxies generally include dust, gas, and active star-forming regions.

**Star Cluster:**

A group of stars that formed from the same cloud of material and have been held together in a cluster by gravitational forces. A small open cluster can consist of only a few dozen members while a large globular cluster can contain more than a million individual stars.

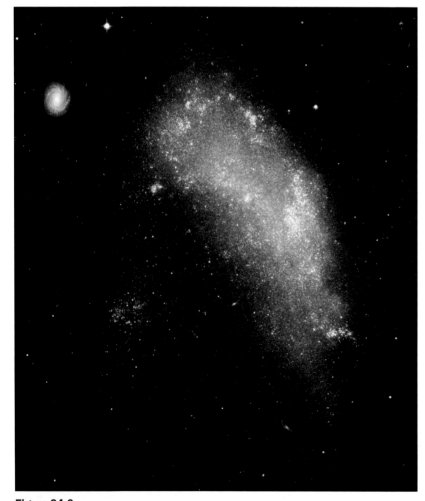

**Figure 34.6**

The irregular galaxy NGC 1427. Irregular galaxies show evidence of recent star formation but lack the structural symmetry that is clearly seen in elliptical and spiral galaxies.

typical spiral galaxy contains 100 billion stars like our Sun.

The central bulges of spiral galaxies are typically composed of old red and yellow stars, like ellipticals. But the disks contain dark dust lanes, bright pink nebula where new stars are forming, and lots of bright blue stars. Unlike ellipticals, star birth continues in spiral galaxies.

**Irregular galaxies** are those that have no obviously regular shape (*Figure 34.6*). We don't see many of these. Approximately 75% of the galaxies in our catalogs are spirals, 20% are ellipticals, and 5% are irregular.[1] They tend to be small and usually contain dust, gas, and active star forming regions as well as young **star clusters**. Two irregular galaxies, the Large Magellanic Cloud and the Small Magellanic Cloud, orbit about The Milky Way. They are visible in the southern hemisphere and derive their names from Magellan who cataloged them in his world-circling voyage.

A type of irregular galaxy that is often termed "peculiar," are those formed by collisions with other galaxies which stretch and distort them (*Figure 34.7*).

Angular momentum plays the major role

---

[1] It is quite probably that there are many more irregular and dwarf elliptical galaxies than listed here that we can't see with our telescopes because they are too faint .

**Figure 33.7**

The Antennae Galaxies were once a spiral (upper) and barred-spiral galaxy (lower) that have passed through each other. The interaction has left both of them with distorted shapes.

**Local Group:**

A small group of about two dozen galaxies that is associated with our Milky Way.

**Galaxy Cluster:**

A group of galaxies that is gravitationally bound together into a cluster, which vary greatly in size. A small cluster may have just a few members, while a large cluster may have several thousand.

in determining which type of galaxy forms. The slower spinning, more massive elliptical galaxies formed earliest and quickest. With little angular momentum and stronger gravity, they collapsed into rounder shapes with stars in randomly oriented plunging orbits. The faster spinning spirals formed later and more slowly. As with the formation of the solar system this spinning flattened them like pizza dough into disks.

### Large-Scale Structure

Galaxies almost never exist in isolation but nearly always have companions. Our Milky Way belongs to a small group of galaxies called the **local group** which contains over 60 members. In addition to the three large spiral galaxies that dominate it, the local group contains several irregular galaxies and the rest of the members are dwarf elliptical galaxies. Larger **galaxy clusters** (*Figure 34.8*) may contain dozens or even thousands of large galaxies. And clusters of galaxies themselves cluster together into

**Figure 34.8**

A distant cluster of galaxies known as Abell 2218. Galaxies are nearly always gravitationally bound to other galaxies in clusters like the one shown here. Clusters of galaxies are almost unimaginably large, with each cluster containing many thousands of galaxies and each galaxy containing hundreds of billions of individual stars.

**Supercluster:**

Clusters of clusters of galaxies.

**Void:**

The space between galaxy superclusters.

**superclusters**. A supercluster can contain tens of thousands of galaxies and can span areas of space over 100 million light years across. The space between superclusters is called a **void**. Galaxy voids have a low population and likely have no galaxies at all in their centers.

## 34-3 An Expanding Universe

When astronomers at the time of Hubble and Shapley first looked at the chemical composition of the blended starlight coming from other galaxies, they noticed something strange. Chemical analysis is done through spectroscopy and looking for emission and absorption lines. But the positions of the lines in the spec-

**Figure 34.9**

This figure shows the Hubble Ultra Deep Field. These are the faintest objects ever observed. Every image visible is of a distant galaxy, each of which contains hundreds of billions of stars. Some of the galaxies visible are more than ten billion light years away from Earth.

tra of every single galaxy, except a few very close neighbors, was shifted towards the red end of the spectrum. Why should that be so?

In Chapter 10 we learned that the wavelength and frequency of a wave changes with the motion of whatever sends or receives it. This, the Doppler Effect, is what causes the whistle from a passing train to drop from high to low when it passes by.

This same effect works for light (*Figure 34.10*). If a light source moves toward us, the

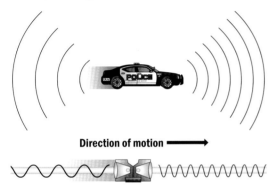

**Direction of motion** ⟶

**Figure 34.10**
An illustration of the Doppler shift for sound and light. As with sound waves, light waves emanating from an object moving relative to an observer will experience a shift in frequency and a corresponding change in wavelength.

waves squeeze together shortening the wavelength. An absorption or emission line in the emitted spectrum would appear to have a shorter or bluer wavelength than if the source were at rest. For sources moving away, the waves appear to stretch out in space. Now spectral lines appear to have a longer wavelength and are shifted toward the red end of the spectrum.

In our own Galaxy, we use the Doppler shift to measure the speed of stars either toward or away from Earth. About half the stars in our galaxy move away from us and the other half move toward us because we are all orbiting the center of our galaxy.

So the fact that essentially all other galaxies—and we have measured more than a million of them over the years—have light that is shifted toward the red end of the spectrum, means that they are traveling away from Earth. This observed fact is called the **cosmological red shift** or just "red shift". Remarkably, the amount of shifting is proportional to how far away the galaxy is located: the farther away it is, the larger the shift.

Interpreting the red shift as a Doppler shift means that the Milky Way is at the center of a

universe in which all galaxies are fleeing from us, an uncomfortably egocentric notion. Why should we be so specially placed and why should galaxies flee from us?

The cosmological red shift, it turns out, is not a traditional Doppler shift. The only good explanation is that the universe is expanding.

The effect of an expansion is illustrated by *Figure 34.11*. This figure represents an expanding space filled with galaxies. As the space goes from its original size (top panel) to a larger size (bottom panel), all galaxies get farther from each other. And the objects that are farthest apart move away from each other the fastest in the process—exactly what is seen in the cosmological red shift.

If the universe is expanding then other galaxies are not really moving away from us in the way that we understand normal motion through space. And we are not at the center of some receding motion. Rather the space itself between us and other galaxies is getting bigger! As the space gets bigger, the light within it is stretched to longer, redder wavelengths. So in an expanding universe every galaxy sees all other galaxy light as red shifted.

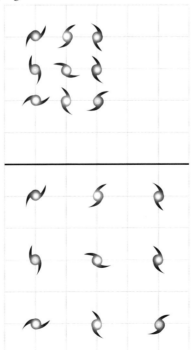

**Figure 34.11**
This figure illustrates that there is no preferred location, or center, within an expanding universe. To demonstrate this fact, choose any one of the nine galaxies as your home and measure the distance to each of the other galaxies before and after expansion. You will find in every case that galaxies that were more distant to start with also appear to move away from you at a greater rate, even though the expansion has been constant.

**Cosmological Red Shift:**
The shifting of galaxy light to the red end of the spectrum caused by the expansion of the universe.

**Figure 34.12**
Can we find the center of the universe? This wonderful sign refers to an astronomical education center located on Vancouver Island in British Columbia, Canada. One could argue that this is the center of the universe as much as any other place you might select.

### Distance and the Cosmological Red Shift

There is one more rung on the distance ladder to be discussed, the cosmological red shift itself, which can be used to find distances to galaxies. The relationship Hubble discovered was between speed and distance. This relation, illustrated in *Figure 34.13*, is called the **Hubble Law** and is simply

$$r = v/H$$

where v is the redshift of a galaxy expressed as a velocity and r is its distance. The value H in this formula is the **Hubble constant**. We measure the recessional velocity from the amount of shift in the lines of a galaxy and divide by this constant to discover its distance.

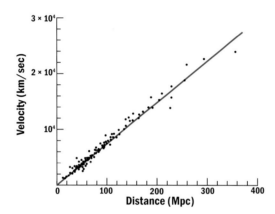

**Figure 34.13**

This plot shows that the speeds with which galaxies recede from Earth are proportional to their distance from us. The observed relation is direct evidence that the universe is expanding.

## 34-4 The Big Bang

With the discovery that the universe is expanding came an interesting hypothesis. An expanding universe has to be smaller in the past that it is today. So if we consider earlier and earlier times, at some point all galaxies had to be in the same place! The hypothesis is that the universe began in the remote past as an unimaginably dense concentration of matter and energy which began expanding in an event called "the big bang".

When did this happen? The Hubble constant, which is given by the slope of the line in Figure 34.13, give the rate at which our universe expands. The reciprocal of this constant in turn gives an approximation for the amount of time since the expansion started. Based on the measured value of the Hubble constant modeled together with how it might have changed with time, that age is now thought to be close to 13.8 billion years. We take this to be the age of the universe itself.

Guided by time symmetry we assume that the laws of nature worked 13.8 billion years ago just like they work today. With this assumption we have put together a **big bang model** that describes how the universe emerged. This model does not explain why a big bang should occur or where the repository of energy was before breaking out in the big bang event. Rather it takes as a given that a big bang occurred and uses known physical and chemical principles to describe how the universe unfolded from there.

According to this model, the big bang event itself was an infusion of pure energy into space. The high energy photons in it converted to and from of matter and antimatter in accordance with the relation of $E=mc^2$. As the universe expanded, processes favored matter remaining while antimatter disappeared and pure energy decreased. When matter emerged, the temperatures were high enough that colliding protons and neutrons could fuse together as discussed in Chapter 25. Soon hydrogen and helium nuclei were created. The universe continued to expand and cool until fusion stopped. Eventually it was cold enough that electrons could stay bound to nuclei to form hydrogen and helium atoms. These collected by pressure waves and gravity into clouds. When these clouds were large enough and temperatures cool enough they contracted chaotically under the force of gravity to form stars and galaxies of stars and gas, ultimately producing the structures we see around us today.

The big bang model was not generally accepted at first. A philosophical debate was enjoined about whether a universe could have a beginning or if it had to have existed forever. Then an unexpected discovery was made which strongly supported the big bang.

### The Cosmic Microwave Background

In the early 1960s, Arno Penzias and Robert Wilson were working with microwave antenna systems at Bell Telephone Laboratories in New Jersey. Their goal was to improve communications with Earth-orbiting satellites. They started out by setting up what was then the most sensitive microwave antenna yet made and were

## CREATION

We can ask, and in some ways have to ask, how did the universe come to be in the first place? Of all questions the physical sciences can address, this one is the most profound. How did the universe come to be? And, for what purpose does it exist?

The big bang theory points to a beginning. Some hypothesize that this beginning sprang from nothing. Others argue that the beginning of our universe is a specific incarnation in a sequence of such events that have always been occurring and will always be occurring. Some argue that the universe began spontaneously from a fluctuation of the sort seen in the random behavior of atoms.

Others argue that the very beginning cannot be a spontaneous event since all events require pre-existing space and time in which to take place.

The truth is we are at our limits of understanding. We know of no way to obtain sensory data from before the big bang, and science, remember, requires both reason and sensory data to be science. We may philosophize about existence before the big bang but without sensory data to refine our thoughts we are not practicing science.

Some outspoken scientists conjecture that there is no god and so he could not create the universe. Others argue that there is a god and that only he could be the creator. Both should remember that science is a tool of learning not a belief system. The scientific method, like trusting in authority and intuition, helps us refine our beliefs, but does not substitute for these other ways of learning.

surprised to find a persistent background signal. It never went away, no matter what they did.

Not far away at Princeton University, some physicists predicted that if the universe had begun with a hot explosive event, all space should still be filled with microwave radiation. When the big bang first occurred, this radiation would have been in the form of high energy photons like gamma rays. But as the universe expanded, the radiation would be red-shifted into the microwave region. Penzias and Wilson measured the microwave signal using their antenna and found that it exactly matched the Princeton prediction for what would be left over from the primordial universe. For this work, Penzias and Wilson received the Nobel Prize.[2]

In Chapter 14, we learned that a continuous spectrum of light is given off by hot bodies. The hotter they are, the bluer their color. So we can determine the temperature of a radiating body by measuring the dominant wavelength of the radiation. The spectrum of the microwave signal is that of a body at a temperature of 2.725 degrees above absolute zero (*Figure 34.14*). In some ways you can say that this is the temperature of the universe itself.

This ever-present signal is called the **cosmic microwave background** (CMB). Since its

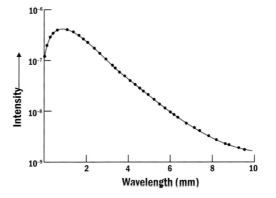

**Figure 34.14**

Data meets theory in these observations from the COBE satellite. The black dots represent actual data points, while the red line is from a theoretical model of how the radiation left over from the creation of the universe should appear today. This figure shows remarkable agreement between theory and observation.

discovery, many careful observations have been made of the CMB. The atmosphere that blankets our Earth blocks the wavelengths where the CMB is the most intense so the best observations of it have been made by satellites. The Cosmic Background Explorer (COBE) satellite showed us that this radiation left over from the big bang can be detected from every direction at the predicted level. Theory says it should have minute variations across the sky.

To test that prediction, NASA launched a more sensitive satellite called the Wilkinson Microwave Anisotropy Probe (WMAP) to measure tiny differences in the microwave back-

**Cosmic Microwave Background:**

A uniform radiant field with an apparent temperature of 2.725 K that is observable in every direction.

---

[2] And the Princeton astrophysicists, led by Robert Dicke, got nothing. Life is not always fair...

**Figure 34.15**

An artist's depiction of WMAP in orbit. Launched on June 30, 2001, WMAP maintains a distant orbit about the second Lagrange Point, or "L2," a gravitational saddle point generated by the combined pull of the Sun and Earth. The L2 Lagrange point is 1 million miles (1.5 km—four times farther than the moon) beyond Earth's orbit and provides an ideal vantage point from which to view deep space free from interference from the Sun, Earth, and moon.

## MEASURING THE CMB

The cosmic microwave background (CMB) has a blackbody temperature of 2.725 degrees Kelvin. An all-sky map of this uniform radiation would look like the top image in *Figure 34.16*. However, data from the COBE satellite in the middle image indicates some small variations in the CMB. The bottom image is the high-resolution observations returned by the WMAP satellite. The blue regions show slightly colder temperatures while yellow and red regions show where the temperature is slightly greater. It is believed that these tiny bumps in the CMB represent density variations in the early universe that are responsible for the formation of the first galaxies and clusters of galaxies. This is a remarkable result, because the largest variations visible in either map are less than 0.0002 Kelvin above or below the smooth background.

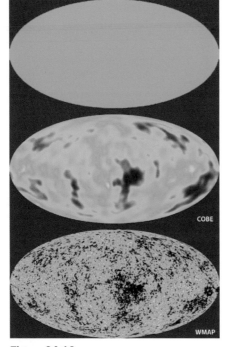

**Figure 34.16**

All-sky maps showing the predicted smooth background of the CMB (top), and the slight measured variations in the CMB by the COBE satellite (middle) and the more precise WMAP satellite (bottom).

ground in different directions in the sky (*Figure 34.15*). The WMAP results, released in 2003, confirmed the COBE data and found the predicted variations. These variations are rich in information and allow us to measure the density, age, geometry, and formation of stars and galaxies during the universe's early history. Maps of the entire sky showing the CMB as seen by COBE and WMAP are in *Figure 34.16*.

### The Abundance of the Elements

As mentioned previously, temperatures in the early universe were high enough that fusion could occur. For a short time the hydrogen fusion cycle—the same one that occurs in a main sequence star—was working throughout our very young, very dense, and very hot universe. This only occurred for a short time, because the universe was expanding and cooling down at an astonishing rate.

A robust prediction emerged from models of how protons and neutrons were created and combined at this stage. Even with the uncertainties of how fast the early big bang expanded and how dense the matter was, it was apparent that 75% of the matter to emerge should be hydrogen and 25% should be helium with a tiny amount of lithium as well.

We learned in the last chapter that helium is also formed as part of the normal life cycle of a star. So finding the "primordial" helium created in the big bang required careful analysis. By studying old, dim, low-mass stars—those that were formed early in the universe and that have burned through their fuel slowly—we determined conclusively that the ratio of hydrogen to helium was as predicted.

Deuterium is an isotope of hydrogen that has one neutron in the nucleus. It is an isotope of hydrogen that should have been created in the primordial nucleosynthesis process. Astronomers have measured this ratio by looking not at stars, but at the material in space in between the stars—the interstellar medium. Once again, this measurement exactly matches the predictions from the big bang model. These measurements of the abundances of the elements are some of the strongest evidence that the big bang hypothesis is correct.

## 34-5 The Fate of the Universe

If the universe began in an enormous infusion of energy then how might it end? Will it expand forever at the current rate or will the expansion rate change with time?

There is a straight-forward relationship between the mass of the universe and expansion. We can understand this by drawing an analogy with a ball thrown into the air. If we don't throw the ball hard enough, it will eventually turn around and fall back down to Earth. If we could launch the ball with just the right velocity (about 25,000 mph), it would barely escape Earth and continue into space, always slowing down the farther away it moved. Or, if we launched the ball with extra energy, it would escape from Earth and travel into space at high speed.

In like manner, if the universe isn't expanding fast enough, the expansion should eventually slow down and turn around, like the ball falling back to Earth. Then all of the galaxies would start accelerating towards each other, and the end of the universe would occur when all of the matter crashes together. Some people jokingly call this the "big crunch" because it would be like the big bang only in reverse. If the expansion rate is just right, the universe will expand to infinitely large distances and end up with zero expansion velocity. And if the expansion rate is even larger, universe will keep expanding forever.

To know which of these possibilities is most likely, we must understand two things: how fast the universe is expanding and the strength of the deceleration force slowing it down. The first item is again the Hubble constant and is well known. To determine the second item, deceleration, we must know the mass of the universe since gravity is the only decelerating force.

We know the mass of stars from the speeds with which they orbit about each other. We also know the mass of gas and dust clouds because the more mass they have, the more they either emit or block light. From knowing these, we can estimate the expected amount of mass in a galaxy.

### Dark Matter

There is a second way to estimate the mass of a galaxy. We can also measure its rotation speed. More massive spiral galaxies have more gravitational force and rotate faster than less massive systems. So just as we determined the mass of the Sun by the orbital speeds of the planets, we can determine the mass of entire galaxies by measuring the rotational speeds of the stars that make them up.

Hundreds of such measurements have made it clear that virtually every galaxy rotates faster than it should based on the mass of its stars, gas, and dust. Some galaxies behave like systems that are 2 or 3 times more massive. Others are more consistent with being several hundred times more massive so the mismatch is not subtle. The unaccounted speeds are best explained by the presence of a form of mass that is adding to the gravity of galaxies. Some galaxies have a lot of this mass, others have little. Since it does not radiate light, it is called **dark matter**. The whole conundrum is called the "missing mass problem."

As noted above galaxies are nearly always found in clusters. We can estimate their mass in yet a third way by measuring how rapidly they orbit about each other. Once again we find that their orbital speeds are too high. Dark matter apparently exists in the centers of galaxy clusters as well.

We do not know what the dark matter might be. We have ruled out traditional mat-

**Dark Matter:**
Unseen matter in galaxies and galaxy clusters that exerts gravity within them.

**Figure 34.17**
M33, also known as the Triangulum Galaxy, as seen from NASA's Spitzer Space Telescope. M33 is a member of our Local Group of galaxies, and is one of the few galaxies that is moving toward the Milky Way. When viewed with Spitzer's infrared eyes, this elegant spiral galaxy sparkles with color and detail. Stars appear as glistening blue gems (many of which are actually foreground stars in our own galaxy), while dust in the spiral disk of the galaxy glows pink and red. This image shows M33 to be surprising large—bigger than its visible-light appearance would suggest. With its ability to detect cold, dark dust, Spitzer can see emissions from cooler material well beyond the visible range of M33's disk. However, observed data on the expansion of the universe indicate large amounts of matter in the universe that we still cannot detect.

ter that does not glow like collections of black holes or giant clouds of dust. These would show their presence in other ways. The most promising explanation is exotic subatomic particles that have mass but no charge and do not participate in the electromagnetic interaction. Such particles are only theoretical at this point. Attempts to discover them are on-going.

Back to our original question: What is the fate of the universe? Accounting for dark matter, we count all the galaxies up and find that there is only approximately 30% of the mass required to stop the universal expansion. But the story is not yet over.

### Dark Energy

In the mid-1990s type Ia supernovae were finally calibrated to sufficient accuracy to independently measure distances more than half way across the universe (Figure 33.10). More significantly, these measurements were assessing the expansion rate of the universe in the past. In other words, when looking 5 billion light years away we are seeing light that was emitted 5 billion years ago. So looking deep into space is also looking back in time and the observed expansion rate of 5 billion years ago can be compared with the expansion rate of today.

The results were totally unexpected. It was found that the universe is expanding faster today than in the past! In our analogy of throwing a ball in the air, we are seeing the ball fly away from our hand faster and faster! For this to happen there has to be some source of energy like from a rocket engine to speed the ball up against the pull of gravity.

Until this discovery, we had been quite confident that the motion of distant galaxies was completely determined by the gravitational interaction. An increasing expansion speed requires an unknown kind of force to push the galaxies faster apart as the distance between them increases. The energy that drives this repulsion has been called **dark energy**.

Remarkably, Albert Einstein anticipated something akin to dark energy in his general theory of relativity. As he used this theory to derive equations describing a space filled with galaxies, he noted that they allowed for a repulsive energy source associated with space itself. No one, including Einstein, believed such an energy, called the **cosmological constant**, was real and it was dismissed until now.

With dark energy we now give our best guess of the fate of the universe. Apparently the universe will expand faster and faster with time until all distant galaxies have fled from our sight and the gravitationally-bound local group of galaxies sits alone in our visible universe. But we must use the word "apparently." We have no idea what dark matter or dark energy are and rest assured that as our knowledge of them continues to evolve, so will our understanding of the future of the universe.

**Figure 34.18**
Spiral galaxy NGC 4319 is 80 million light-years from Earth. The bright object in the upper right is not a neighboring star, but quasar Markarian 205 (Mrk 205). Quasars, once known only as mysterious point-like objects, are now known to be distant galaxies that have extremely bright cores fueled probably by massive black holes. Mrk 205 resides 1 billion light-years from Earth, yet is a relatively nearby quasar. As we continue to seek answers, our understanding of mysteries like dark matter and dark energy may increase, even as our understanding of quasars has increased.

**Dark Energy:**

An energy associated with space that is causing the universal expansion to accelerate faster with time.

**Cosmological Constant:**

A constant introduced into the equations of general relativity by Albert Einstein in an attempt to cancel the predictions of the expanding nature of our Universe.

*A lot of prizes have been awarded for showing the universe is not as simple as we might have thought.*
Stephen W. Hawking

# 34 STUDY GUIDE

A. The structure of the Milky Way

B. A Vast Universe of Galaxies
1. Different kinds of galaxies
2. The structure of the Universe
3. Measuring the distance to galaxies

C. An Expanding Universe
   D. The Big Bang
1. The Cosmic Microwave Background
2. The abundance of the elements

D. The Fate of the Universe
1. Missing mass
2. Missing energy

## Comprehension

### Matching

1. _____ A small group of about two dozen galaxies that is associated with our Milky Way.
2. _____ A group of galaxies that is gravitationally bound together.
3. _____ A group of millions up to trillions of stars with an elliptical shape.
4. _____ A constant introduced by Einstein into his equations in an attempt to cancel the predictions of an expanding Universe.
5. _____ An observed relation between the recessional velocity of a galaxy and the distance to that galaxy.
6. _____ The source of the accelerating expansion of the universe.
7. _____ The galaxy to which our Sun belongs.
8. _____ A simple relation where the actual brightness of stars can be determined by observing the pulsation period of a star.
9. _____ A galaxy flattened into a disk shape with a pattern of spiral arms wound about a central nucleus.
10. _____ Part of the Hubble Law that gives the rate at which our Universe is expanding.
11. _____ A non-symmetric galaxy that does not have a well-defined shape.
12. _____ A cosmological model that indicates that all the mass and energy in the universe originated at a single point in space and time.
13. _____ A group consisting of clusters of clusters of galaxies.
14. _____ The majority of the matter in the universe.

a. Cosmological constant

b. Milky Way

c. Elliptical galaxy

d. Irregular galaxy

e. Period-brightness relation

f. Dark energy

g. Cluster of galaxies

h. Hubble Law

i. Dark matter

j. Spiral galaxy

k. Supercluster

l. Local group

m. Big Bang model

n. Hubble constant

### Fill in the Blank

1. The Big Bang Model helps explain the _____ that accounts for about 25% of a star's mass.
2. When looking at the spectral lines in light from distant galaxies, the lines are shifted towards _____ colors.

## Analysis

1. Which of the following statements correctly explains evidence for the Big Bang?

   a) When we measure how fast galaxies are moving away from us, the more distant the galaxies, the slower they are moving. The microwave background radiation that fills the Universe is left over from the high energy photons that were present shortly after the big bang.

   b) A certain amount of new matter is continually being created in space.

   c) No matter what direction we look, and how far away we look, we see exactly the same types of stars and galaxies.

   d) The heavy elements, like uranium, found on Earth could only have been created in the first few seconds of the Big Bang.

2. Which of the following provides evidence for Dark Matter?

   a) The rotational speed of stars around the center of their galaxies is too fast for the observed mass of the galaxy.

   b) Galaxies are surrounded by large, ancient groups of stars called globular clusters.

   c) Spiral galaxies contain lots of young stars and star forming regions while elliptical galaxies don't.

   d) The cosmic microwave background radiation is nearly uniform in all directions.

   e) Hubble's law shows there is a linear relationship between distance and speed of galaxies.

3. When the spectrum of light from distant galaxies is measured, what is found?

   a) The lines in the spectrum are shifted towards the blue end of the spectrum, with light from the most distant galaxies being shifted by the largest amount.

   b) The lines in the spectrum are shifted towards the blue end of the spectrum, with light from the closest galaxies being shifted by the largest amount.

   c) The lines in the spectrum are shifted towards the red end of the spectrum, with light from the most distant galaxies being shifted by the largest amount.

   d) The lines in the spectrum are shifted towards the red end of the spectrum, with light from the closest galaxies being shifted by the largest amount.

   e) The spectrum has lines in exactly the same place.

4. Which of the following causes some to speculate that our Universe included an era when all mat-

ter had a temperature at least as hot as the core of our Sun?

a) The presence of planets with elliptical orbits in the solar system

b) The helium gas that visibly escapes stars when solar flares occur

c) The relative amounts of hydrogen and helium in interstellar gases and the oldest stars

d) The cosmological red shift.

e) The cosmic microwave background

5. What is the origin of the cosmic microwave background?

a) Gamma rays produced during the Big Bang which were stretched as the universe expanded.

b) Matter in interstellar space that has cooled to 2 degrees above absolute zero.

c) Radio waves produced by Earth orbiting satellites.

d) Black holes found at the center of every galaxy.

e) Dark energy accelerating the expansion of the universe.

6. When you compare images of elliptical and spiral galaxies, elliptical galaxies' stars are a fairly uniform red to yellow color, while spiral galaxies have blueish arms with yellow centers. Why?

a) Elliptical galaxies are found farther away from the Milky Way than spiral galaxies.

b) Elliptical galaxies are moving away from us, and spiral galaxies are moving towards us.

c) Spiral galaxies are rotating and elliptical galaxies are not.

d) New stars are forming in the arms of spiral galaxies, while very little star formation is taking place in elliptical galaxies

e) Elliptical galaxies have bigger dark matter halos than spiral galaxies.

7. What is dark matter?

a) Black Holes

b) Giant clouds of cold dust

c) Brown Dwarfs

d) Hydrogen and helium

e) None of the above

8. What is true about the size of the universe?

a) It is expanding, and the rate it is expanding is increasing.

b) It is expanding, but the rate of expansion is decreasing.

c) It is expanding at a constant rate.

## Synthesis

1. What makes it so difficult to know our location in our Galaxy and what the rest of the Galaxy looks like?

2. List and describe the different types of galaxies.

3. Explain why we cannot assume that our Galaxy is the center of the Universe.

4. What were the accomplishments of COBE and WMAP?

5. How are variable stars used to measure distances?

6. If the Universe's rate of expansion is increasing, why do scientists assume that some unknown force accompanies this type of expansion?

# Looking Backward, Looking Forward

*The most beautiful emotion we have is the mystical. It is the power of all true art and science. He to whom this emotion is a stranger, who can no longer wonder and stand rapt in awe, is as good as dead.*

*Albert Einstein*

# 35

Learning something for the first time has been likened to cutting a path through a jungle with a machete only to look back to see that much of the vegetation has grown back in. Can you relate to this as you pause to consider your experience in this course? If so do not be discouraged. All learning takes time, patience, and repetition.

As you evaluate what you have learned, are you thinking of specific facts, which can quickly fade, or the interconnectedness of ideas, which lasts much longer? The best learning is more than filling your head with facts, although that is part of the process. In an age where information is usually just a mouse click away, the need to memorize has become less significant while the importance of knowing where facts can be found and how to coherently tie them together has become more important. This is a good thing. The less time we must spend memorizing facts, the more time we can spend weaving them into ideas, knowledge and ultimately wisdom.

Our first and overriding objective was to identify and present the most basic scientific

principles. There are many discoveries and ideas to choose from. We sought to present those that best explain the essential and fundamental foundational principles about the physical universe—those that help us understand what it is and how its most significant parts work together.

### 35–1 Looking Back

All things in the universe move, so we started with the laws that describe motion. Newton's laws say that forces cause objects to change their motion by an amount that depends on the force strength and object mass. This, with the law of gravity, was all that was needed to successfully land a man on the moon! Yes, it took millions and millions of hours to refine the details but it did not require additional principles of motion.

We asked where forces came from and considered the four fundamental interactions. We found that the gravitational and electromagnetic interactions act on mass and a property called charge respectively. These have strengths that can be described with simple mathematical formulas. We learned there are two interactions, the nuclear strong and weak, buried inside atomic nuclei. We can describe what these do but do not yet have a force law for them. One might think that we should know something this fundamental by now, but the small size of an atomic nucleus makes these forces hard to explore.

We considered what happens at the fastest speeds possible, those approaching the speed of light. We learned that the laws of Newton need refining at such speeds. An astonishingly simple idea—that the speed of light is an absolute limit and light always travels through the vacuum of space at this speed, means that space and time change with the speed of the person measuring them.

And what of light itself? It transports energy like moving particles or flowing waves do. Attempts to determine which of these two options it is found it to have the properties of both! Neither aspect dominates but each manifests itself when appropriately probed. Light possess a wave-particle dual nature, an inconceivable idea were it not for the rigorous interference and photon counting experiments that so clearly show this to be the case.

While ideas of mass and energy were being refined, the concept that they and other quantities are conserved was a guiding precept. Conservation of energy, mass, charge, momentum, etc. are powerful principles that simplify our understanding of complex interactions. The principle of conservation of energy led to the realization that mass and energy are conserved together via $E = mc^2$. It also led to the realization that the fundamental quantity of entropy or disorder was not conserved but increases with time. This principle allows us to make sense of the way actions in the universe naturally unfold.

Conservation of energy, increasing entropy, and the laws of Newton allowed the molecular model of matter to go from an idea to a rigorous science. Matter being made of aggregates of small particles that obey these principles allows us to understand pressure, temperature, heat flow and states of matte—huge progress in comprehending the building blocks of the world.

Just as the laws of Newton proved inadequate to explain the behavior of very fast-moving objects, they also failed to account for the behavior of the parts that made up the molecules themselves: atoms, electrons, protons, and neutrons. New principles were required to describe sub-atomic motion such as wave-particle duality now applied to matter, the Heisenberg uncertainty principle and the Pauli exclusion principle which likely are true on all length and mass scales, but become significant only on the smallest scales.

Centuries before the atom was properly described, we discovered elements and learned to manipulate them into substances of our choosing. They are diverse with some being metals, some being non-metallic crystals or powders, and some being gases. Order came when it was realized elements could be placed into families of like properties and arranged in a table by increasing mass. This ordering and the diversity of elemental and compound properties were successfully explained by the newly emerged theory of atoms. The concept of electrons residing in standing-wave orbitals was successfully used to understand how elements generate light and create compounds with other elements.

The various types of atomic bonding—ionic, covalent, metallic, and the weaker intermolecular interactions—were explained by how readily atoms exchanged electrons. Exchange is based upon atoms and their electrons spontaneously configuring to minimize energy and maximize entropy. The interplay between these two principles drives chemical reactions that can both release and store energy in new chemical bonds. Without this duality life as we know it would be impossible.

Atomic nuclei follow the same principles of minimizing energy and maximizing entropy. Nuclei susceptible to disruptions from the weak force eject particles in radioactive decay to achieve lower energies. The amount of energy released in this and in fusion or fission can be enormous because of the large magnitude of the strong nuclear force.

Earth is a beautiful arrangement of the elements. Following principles of buoyancy, the densest materials, especially iron and nickel, settled to the core. Lighter silicates floated up to become the crust, water filled the oceans, and gases formed the atmosphere.

The chemical arrangement of elements on Earth is spectacularly diverse. A single building block like the silicate ion is responsible for compounds as different in structure as quartz and asbestos. The principle organic molecules that make up our bodies are just arrangements of carbon, hydrogen, oxygen, and nitrogen. Yet seemingly minor changes in structure give each molecule the stark differences in functionality appropriate for life.

Energy releasing from Earth's interior drives rock formation and change. Earth's crust, floating on plates, is constantly being remade with magnificent mountains, explosive volcanoes, deep trenches, and lush continents. Driven by solar energy, the circulating atmosphere sculpts Earth's surface with the water, ice, and wind of the complex hydrological system. So necessary for life, atmospheric and hydrological evolution reminds us to be responsible stewards of our resources.

As large as Earth is, it dwarfs in comparison with the size of the solar system. Earth formed at the same time and in the same way as all the planets. Their variety reflects the range of temperature, density and chemistry in the different parts of the solar nebula when they formed. The formation process, from dust within a nebula to planets orbiting a star, was governed principally by gravity and conservation of angular momentum.

Our Milky Way galaxy is a system so vast as to be almost incomprehensible. The Sun is only one of hundreds of billions of its stars. The life cycles of these stars are governed by the balance between the contracting pull of gravity, the expanding push of pressure, and the constant interchange of interior kinetic and potential energy. Stars glow by tapping the large nuclear potential energy released from building light elements into heavier ones. This is possible only because of the competition between long-range repulsive electromagnetic forces and short-range attractive nuclear strong forces. Stars die when fuel from fusion is no longer available and gravity forms them into exotic white dwarfs, neutron stars, and black holes.

The universe itself is governed by gravity pulling on its billions of galaxies while a remarkable and unknown force pushes its expansion outward faster and faster with time. The diverse mass of the elements is not all that creates this gravity. Much more of its force comes from the unseen and mysterious dark matter revealed by stellar and galaxian orbits.

The steady cycle between observation and theory was responsible for this journey of knowledge. For example tiny molecules, impossible to examine directly, were first modeled as hard spheres. Chemistry experiments showed that molecules were not hard spheres but were built from the atoms of elements. Electron discharge tube experiments showed that these elemental atoms were in turn composed of positive ions and negative electrons. The Rutherford gold foil experiment showed the positive aspect to be concentrated in a minuscule nucleus. Many, many other experiments refined these models further, teaching us that atoms are comprised of parts with particle and wave properties that lead to bonding, energy distributions, and other properties that make the universe what it is.

### 35-2 Looking to the Future

Knowledge developed through science has brought society to where we are today. Nearly all breakthroughs in technology, engineering, communications, transportations, etc. have had their genesis in physical science discoveries. Where might we go from here?

We have focused largely on the principles derived from the results of carefully posed experiments—those that emerged successfully from thousands of failures. Looking forward, we expect to continue building upon these principles or rules while ironically being especially focused on the *exceptions*. By studying the exceptions, or by studying phenomena for which no rules are yet known, we gain insights into the workings of the physical universe that we do not currently have and progress continues.

Einstein's general theory of relativity has been spectacularly successful at describing how gravity relates to mass. The quantum theories of the atom and subatomic particles have also been similarly successful at describing the emergence of mass on the smallest scales. We believe by Occam's Razor that the two descriptions of mass should "morph" smoothly from the large-length scale of orbits to the small-length scale of atoms.

Models to do this are being proposed, explored, and debated, such as "string theory." We have not discussed the exact structure of particles like electrons because it is not clear what their structure might be. String theory ceases to treat them as points with zero-dimensions and hypothesizes them to have thin one-dimensional structures. A rich, theoretical idea, successful explanations of electromagnetism and quantized gravity have been built on string theory. However, no predictions which can be tested experimentally have yet been advanced. Perhaps soon some will be proposed and experiments will be done to refine the theories.

If we are fortunate string theory or other particle theory will shed light on the dark matter problem since attempts to explain dark matter as a form of known types of matter have all failed. In a coming together of the small and the large, attention is being turned to particles and the notion that there might be a family that does not feel the electromagnetic interaction but does feel and generate gravity. Progress here awaits further experimentation with huge particle accelerators as well as with huge telescopes.

We lamented how difficult it is to understand forces and matter on the smallest scales. But progress is encouraging. The newly emerging field of nanotechnology, which brings together chemists, physicists and material scientists, has found that for structures as small as $10^{-9}$ meters, a nanometer, novel chemical and physical properties become possible. It is on this level that rapid advancements in areas like communications, computer data storage, medicine, cell phone technology, and even sunscreen chemistry are made possible.

Structure on the molecular scale determines chemical reactions. Research is ongoing to create molecular assemblies with structures defined by mankind. If molecules or assemblies of molecules can be created with the proper structures, illnesses, deformities, and physical conditions can be addressed molecule by molecule in ways far more effective and less harmful that is currently possible.

Looking to larger scales, exploration of Earth continues. The simplest plate tectonic models assume that there is a continuous, although slow, movement of the plates. But we know that several factors can lock the plates in place. The locking or stop and go motion of plates on Earth may account for the disparity between the cooling rates of the interior predicted by models and that observed experimentally.

The warming of the atmosphere and its effects on the ecology are being vigorously modeled and measured. The models will continue to be refined making not only better social policy possible but also improving our understanding of heat flow in complex systems and how it affects weather patterns and the adaptability of living things.

Explorations and modeling of the solar system continues. Details in the nebular hypothesis continue to be modified as experiments return surprises. It is not clear exactly how the tiny dust grains first stuck together to form the seeds that grew to be planets. The chemistry of meteorites indicates the solar nebula had temperatures warmer than models predict. In looking at extra-solar planetary systems we have found many large, Jupiter-like gas giants closer to their host star than the nebular hypothesis allows indicating that planetary orbits migrate in and out after the planet is formed.

Dark energy and dark matter are largely unrelated ideas sharing only the word "dark" in their names. But they both have the potential to completely rewrite our understanding of the nature of matter and force. Here exploration has just begun and there is no telling where it might lead.

These are only a small number of the explorations going on. Perhaps others not mentioned will be the ones that bring about the greatest breakthroughs. The journey continues and there is every reason to be excited about what it will bring!

*Science cannot be stopped. Great, interesting, and valuable discoveries
will be made that I have not the imagination to describe—
and I am awaiting them, full of curiosity and enthusiasm.*

—Linus Pauling, Nobel Prize in Chemistry 1954

# Selected Answers

## Chapter 1

### True/False
1. T   3. T   5. F
2. F   4. F

### Fill in the Blank
1. Non-contradiction
2. Charged
3. Atom
4. Theory
5. Molecules

### Matching
1. j   5. o   9. d   13. m
2. k   6. f   10. l   14. a
3. g   7. i   11. c   15. e
4. h   8. n   12. b

### Analysis
1. c

2. b
3. Answers may vary, here is one possibility:
   d. Reason
   e. Authority and Intuition
   f. Authority
   g. Reason and Sensory Data
   h. Sensory Data
   i. Reason and Sensory Data
   j. Reason
11. a. Principle of Non-contradiction
    l. Position Symmetry
    m. Time symmetry
    n. Occam's Razor
    o. Existence
    p. Causality
17. C, B, A, D

18. Position symmetry requires only that the governing laws be the same on Earth and the Moon. However, the numerical predictions of the law can be different.
19. According to the definition of time symmetry the laws of the universe do not change with time.
20. Answers may vary. Essentially a hypothesis is a "first guess" of an experiment you are trying to prove. (For example, Battery A will last longer then battery B.) A theory is a refined and well tested hypothesis over a period of time. A law is a theory tested and verified enough times that it is assumed to always be true. (Like

Newton's First Law of Motion.) A model is what is used to test a phenomenon in the physical world.
21. The diameter of the atom is about 100,000 times the diameter of the nucleus. In size, the atom is to a football field as the nucleus is to the tip of a ballpoint pen.
22. Four light-years, 100,000 light-years, 1,000,000 light-years
23. Gravity is important for anything with mass. Electromagnetic for objects with charge. The strong interaction holds protons and neutrons together. and weak nuclear forces can act on protons, neutrons and electrons.

## Chapter 2

### True/False
1. F   3. F   5. T
2. T   4. T

### Matching
1. a   4. c   7. a
2. b   5. a   8. a
3. b   6. c   9. c

### Fill in the blank
1. Galileo
2. Mass
3. Velocity

4. Velocity

### Analysis
1. b
2. b
3. c
4. See chapter
5. Both answers are no. An object with zero velocity has zero acceleration *only* if it stays still. Any object in uniform motion has zero acceleration.
6. The speed will increase at a constant rate.

7. Net force determines acceleration. Friction counters the force that you apply when pushing on the gas pedal. The faster you go, the bigger the friction, until the two forces balance each other and there is no net force.
8. A book pushing on a table and a table pushing on a book
9. a. Neither, they both experience the same contact force, Newton's 3rd law

j. The chicken experiences the greatest acceleration
11. The environmental forces of friction and gravity. These environmental forces almost always act on objects. For an object to travel in uniform motion another force to balance these forces needs to be present.
12. An increase in force with mass remaining the same increases the acceleration. An increase in mass with the force remaining the same decreases the acceleration.

## Chapter 3

### Matching
1. b   2. c   3. a

### True/False
1. F   3. F   5. F
2. T   4. F

### Fill in the Blank
1. Universal Law of Gravitation
2. Curvature

### Analysis
1. b   3. c   5. b
2. d   4. d
6. The mass of the moon is much less (about 1/100) than the mass of Earth. The gravitational pull on an object (its weight) depends on the mass of the object to which it is attached. Of course the moon is also smaller, so the object is closer to the center.

These factors combine to give the ratio 1/6 from moon vs. earth weight.
7. The gravitational force depends on size and distance. The Sun, in fact, is about 23,000 times as far from us then we are from the center of Earth.
8. a. The baseball's weight is the force of gravity on its mass.
   i. 100 miles above Earth, weight is about 90% of the baseball's weight on Earth's surface.
   j. Moon weight is about 1/6 of earth weight.
   k. Weight would be zero if there are no gravitational forces.
   *The mass is the same at all four locations.*
12. See chapter for definitions

13. a. The two objects experience the same acceleration and, as a result, the same speed at any instance as they fall.
    n. Yes. The weights are not the same (in accordance with the gravitational force law since their masses are different).
    o. Force and mass both help to determine acceleration (Second Law of Motion). In this case, nature conspires so that the ratio of force (weight) to mass is the same for all objects at a particular place. Perhaps a numerical answer would help. Suppose the smaller of the two objects has a mass given by 5 units and a weight given by 50 units. Its acceleration would be force/mass or 50/5 = 10 units. Now suppose a second

object has a mass of 150 units (30 times that of the first). Its weight would also be 30 times that of the first object; that is 30 (50 = 1500 units. Its acceleration would be force/mass or 1500/150 = 10 units, the same as for the smaller object. Notice that this result is predicted by two fundamental laws working together: The Universal Law of Gravitation and the Second Law of Motion.
    p. In part a we stated that the acceleration and velocities of the cannonball and marble are the same. Parts b & c established that because the cannonball has a greater mass, it experiences a greater force pulling it to the earth.
17. One, Gravity.

# Selected Answers

## Chapter 4

### True/False
1. T  3. F  5. T
2. F  4. T

### Fill in the Blank
1. charge, electric current
2. electrons, domains
3. electrons, negativefield lines

### Matching
1. f  4. k  7. l  10. i
2. a  5. g  8. e  11. d
3. c  6. b  9. h  12. j

### Analysis
1. c  2. a  3. b  4. e
5. See chapter

6. See chapter
7. Proton: A tiny, dense particle which caries one positive charge. Electron: A particle with one unit of negative charge and a mass of only 1/1836 times that of a proton.
8. Electrically charged parts that are moving.
9. These forces were thought to be separate until it was discovered that magnetism is simply the electric force of moving charges
10. When the magnetic fields of the domains within the material will align and remain aligned when an external magnetic field is applied.

## Chapter 6

### Matching
1. f  3. d  5. a
2. c  4. b  6. e

### True/False
1. T  3. T  5. F
2. F  4. F  6. T

### Fill in the Blank
1. Depth
2. Convection
3. The displaced liquid, the weight of the floating object
4. Weight

### Analysis
1. b  3. d  5. d
2. d  4. b
6. Pressure= Force/Area. The pressure is the same everywhere at the same depth in a fluid, while the total force depends on the volume of an object placed into the fluid. Everyone and everything on the surface of Earth has 141b/square inch of air pressure, but the force on each object from the air is unique.

7. Convection currents begin with a fluid that has different temperatures within it. If a fluid has different temperatures then it also has different densities. The less dense sections will tend to rise and the more dense sections will tend to sink. A source heats the dense sections while they sink and makes them less dense. Meanwhile, the less dense sections rise and tend to cool and become more dense. Once the rising fluid has become more dense than its surrounding it begins to sink. Likewise, once the fluid that sinks becomes less dense than its surroundings it begins to rise. The fluids follow this pattern of rising and cooling and of sinking and heating creating convection currents.
8. **Pressure depends on depth. Greater depths have greater pressure**

     Pressure equals the weight of the column of fluid directly above it. As depth increases, the weight of the column also increases creating greater pressure.

**Pressure is the same for all points at the same depth**

   Pressure does not depend on surface area or volume. All points at the same depth will have the same amount of pressure on them.

**Pressure at a given depth is independent of direction**

   At any given point, the pressure measured from any direction is the same.

**Pressure is always perpendicular to the surface of a submerged object**

   If there is ever a net sideways force in fluid, the fluid will flow until it balances out. Once balanced out, the fluid only exerts a force perpendicular to the surface of a submerged object.
9. a. bounded
   j. unbounded
   k. bounded
   l. unbounded
   m. unbounded
14. Pressure for a fluid depends on the weight of the column of fluid

above that point. If you are at the same depth, the weight of the column of water above you remains the same regardless of whether you are in the ocean, in a quarry, or in a narrow irrigation pipe.
15. Pressure pushes on the bottom of a submerged object more than on the top of a submerged object. The net upward contact force is buoyancy.
16. Density is just the amount of mass in a certain volume. If an object has less mass than the same volume of fluid, then when it is submerged in fluid, it will displace a mass of fluid greater than its own mass. The buoyant force will be bigger than the gravitational force, and it will rise to the surface. Similarly if it is more dense than the fluid, it weighs more than the volume of fluid it displaces, and will sink.
17. Forces in fluids change with speed and depth. Even when the forces start off unbalanced, they change as the object accelerates until they end up balanced.

## Chapter 7

### Matching
1. c  3. e  5. h  7. g
2. b  4. f  6. a  8. d

### True/False
1. T  6. T
2. T  7. T
3. F  8. T
4. T  9. F
5. F  10. F

### Fill in the Blank
1. contracts, dilates
2. space-time continuum
3. high
4. accelerated, non-accelerated
5. spinning
6. time, space

### Analysis
1. d  2. b  3. f  4. d

5. c  6. a
7. Motion symmetry, speed of light constant for all observers in uniform motion.
8. Time and length are measured relative to a specific observer.
9. Forces and acceleration. The Special Theory of Relativity only applies to inertial frames of reference and therefore cannot

include any situation with an unbalanced force/ acceleration. The General Theory of Relativity applies to non-inertial frames of reference so it can discuss acceleration and forces.
10. Two parallel mirrors spaced far enough apart that a beam of light bounces back and forth once each second (when it is stationary).

## Chapter 8

### Matching
1. c  3. a  5. b
2. d  4. f  6. e

### True/False
1. T  3. F  5. T  7. T
2. T  4. T  6. F  8. F

9. T  10. F  11. F

### Fill in the Blank
1. conserved
2. charge
3. angular momentum
4. quarks
5. momentum

6. mass, velocity
7. direction
8. inside
9. equal, opposite

### Analysis
1. d  2. e  3. d
4. It doesn't change.

5. Mass, charge, fundamental particles, angular momentum, linear momentum, energy
6. Quarks and electron like particles (leptons)
7. The cake lost some water when it transformed into steam, so the

cake weighs slightly less than the batter.

## Chapter 9

### Matching
1. a    5. g    9. j    13. i
2. c    6. e    10. m
3. d    7. f    11. k
4. b    8. h    12. l

### True/False
1. T    5. T
2. F    6. T
3. T
4. F

### Fill in the Blank
1. mass, speed
2. increases
3. hot, cold
4. radiation
5. conduction
6. convection
7. energy, mass, the speed of light

### Analysis
1. c    2. a    3. b    4. d

5. b    6. c    7. c    8. d
9. Anything that stretches or squishes and returns to its original shape
10. Speed of light
11. Mass and energy are really the same thing. If energy changes, so does mass.
12. You can create and destroy mass by turning it into energy and vice versa as long as you don't violate any other rules.

13. See chapter
14. Different chemical potential energies because of the way the two substances arrange the atoms.
15. Some energy is lost to friction with the air and given off as thermal energy and taking away from the gravitational potential and kinetic energies. Eventually it will stop moving as all the energy is transformed.

## Chapter 10

### Matching
1. k    5. f    9. c    13. g
2. l    6. h    10. a    14. e
3. j    7. d    11. m
4. n    8. i    12. b

### True/ False
1. T    3. T    5. F
2. T    4. F    6. F

### Fill in the Blank
1. medium
2. solids
3. Earthquake or seismic
4. wavelength
5. wavespeed
6. longitudinal

### Analysis
1. d    3. b    5. e    7. b
2. e    4. c    6. a    8. d

9. A mechanical wave is when energy vibrates material in its place. The energy travels through the material while the material itself remains in the same place. All mechanical waves travel through a medium that has an equilibrium shape. The wave causes the material to deviate from its equilibrium shape. Eventually the medium returns to its original shape.
10. Glass lenses use or create curved surfaces to preserve the refraction that occurs when light first enters the glass. By changing the curvature of the glass the direction that light travels can be controlled.
11. Forces perpendicular to the direction a wave moves cause shear waves. For example, if you shake a piece of rope up and

down, the wave moves away perpendicular to the motion of your hand. Now imagine trying to shake a liquid, such as water, up and down like a rope. It isn't possible. The bonds between the molecules in a fluid are not strong enough to propagate the energy to their neighboring molecules.
12. Reflection causes a wave to bounce in a different direction than it originally travels. If other waves are behind the reflected wave, they will pass through the same medium at the same time. Waves passing through the medium at the same time may cause constructive or destructive interference depending on how they interact.
13. Frequency and wavelength are inverses of one another. If you

increase one the other decreases. If you decrease one, the other one increases. Regardless of how you change one of the two variables the result remains the same.
14. The two waves need to be identical (That's why a wave and its own reflection work well). They also need to fit into the space perfectly.
15. While both are waves and can diffract, sound waves have much longer wavelengths, so have a much easier time diffracting around macroscopic objects like buildings. For light to diffract appreciably, the opening needs to be the width of a piece of paper or smaller. To see light diffract, try to look at the shadow of a single strand of hair.

## Chapter 11

### Matching I
1. b    3. a    5. a
2. b    4. a    6. a

### Matching II
1. g    3. e    5. a    7. c
2. d    4. b    6. f

### True/False
1. F    2. T    3. F    4. T

### Fill in the Blank
1. 1. two-slit
2. 2. speed of light
3. 3. electromagnetic field
4. 4. detected, measured, observed
5. 5. travels
6. 6. accelerates

### Analysis
1. b    3. a    5. c
2. d    4. a

6. A single-slit, if small enough, causes light to diffract. When two slits close to one another cause a wave of light to diffract, the wave interferes with itself. The interference causes places of constructive and destructive interference. After many photons of light pass through the two slits, the particles of light on the screen begin to exhibit a pattern that shows places of constructive and destructive interference.
7. Radio waves, Microwaves, Infrared radiation, Visible

light (red to blue), Ultraviolet radiation, X-rays, Gamma rays
8. Reflect, Refract, Diffract, Interfere
9. The principle of non-contradictions says that of two contradictory propositions, both cannot be true. The natures of a particle and of a wave are fundamentally different. To say that something is both a particle and a wave is contradictory. From the experiments described, light appears to have both characteristics. To avoid conflict with the principle of non-contradiction, the book doesn't classify light is both a particle and wave. Instead light is neither. Light is light. A

phenomenon in of itself. Thus, this classification avoids directly conflicting with the principle of non-contradiction.
10. For light, with its wave properties, to travel through space it needs some type of medium to travel through. Electromagnetic forces travel through fields. Like electromagnetic forces, scientists believe that light travels through an electromagnetic field.
11. Because the speed of light through space is a constant and the fastest speed possible.
12. The electric and magnetic forces created by the light make charge particles oscillate perpendicular to the direction the light travels.

# Selected Answers

## Chapter 12

**Matching**

| | | | |
|---|---|---|---|
| 1. i | 5. g | 9. o | 13. c |
| 2. n | 6. f | 10. l | 14. m |
| 3. h | 7. b | 11. k | 15. e |
| 4. j | 8. a | 12. d | |

**True/False**

| | | | |
|---|---|---|---|
| 1. T | 3. F | 5. T | 7. F |
| 2. F | 4. F | 6. F | |

**Fill in the Blank**

1. reflects
2. models
3. compression, tension
4. insulator

**Analysis**

1. e      3. d      5. a
2. b      4. c
6. Both have the same density. Density doesn't depend on the total mass.
7. A plasma is an ionized gas. Charged gas particles can move independently. Some examples: the aurora borealis, the bright light associated with lightning, the gas inside a neon light, or a fluorescent light bulb.
8. See image at right.
9. Tap water contains ions from dissolved salts and minerals. Pure water contains only a minuscule concentration of ions and won't carry current.

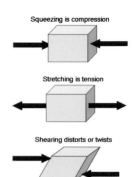

Squeezing is compression

Stretching is tension

Shearing distorts or twists

## Chapter 13

**Matching**

| | |
|---|---|
| 1. e | 5. a |
| 2. d | 6. c |
| 3. f | |
| 4. b | |

**True/False**

| | |
|---|---|
| 1. T | 5. F |
| 2. F | 6. F |
| 3. T | 7. F |
| 4. T | |

**Fill in the Blank**

1. atoms or molecules
2. increases
3. stays the same
4. internal kinetic energy
5. stove, pan
6. gas

**Analysis**

1. b      3. c      5. e      7. a
2. d      4. c      6. b

## Chapter 14

**Matching**

| | | |
|---|---|---|
| 1. a | 3. e | 5. b |
| 2. d | 4. c | |

**True/ False**

| | | |
|---|---|---|
| 1. F | 5. T | 9. T |
| 2. T | 6. T | |
| 3. T | 7. F | |
| 4. F | 8. F | |

**Fill in the Blank**

1. energy
2. electrical
3. elliptical, circular
4. far away from, lots of
5. Bohr

**Analysis**

1. d      2. a      3. c      4. c
5. b
6. a. b, d, c, a
   b. absorption: a, c
      emission: b, d
   c. farthest: absorption
      closest: emission
   d. d
5. These experiments established the electrical nature of the atom. Specifically, from these experiments we learned that the atom contained positively-charged bits charge and mass varied with element and that all atoms contained negatively charged bits that were identical in every atom.

## Chapter 15

**Matching**

| | |
|---|---|
| 1. d | 5. e |
| 2. f | 6. g |
| 3. a | 7. c |
| 4. b | |

**True/False**

| | |
|---|---|
| 1. F | 5. F |
| 2. T | 6. T |
| 3. T | 7. F |
| 4. T | |

**Fill in the Blank**

1. Wave-particle
2. Wavelength
3. Planck's constant
4. Wave
5. Particle

**Analysis**

1. a      3. a      5. c      7. e
2. e      4. b      6. c

## Chapter 16

**Matching**

| | | |
|---|---|---|
| 1. e | 3. c | 5. d |
| 2. f | 4. a | 6. b |

**True/False**

| | |
|---|---|
| 1. T | 5. T |
| 2. T | 6. F |
| 3. F | 7. T |
| 4. F | |

**Fill in the Blank**

1. up, down
2. more
3. shell, orbital shape, spin
4. three

**Analysis**

1. c      3. a, c, d   5. b, c, e
2. e      4. a

**Fill in the Table**

| Shell | Orbital | # of orbitals of this kind | # of electrons in these orbitals |
|---|---|---|---|
| 1 | s | 1 | 2 |
| 2 | s | 1 | 2 |
| 2 | p | 3 | 6 |
| 3 | s | 1 | 2 |
| 3 | p | 3 | 6 |
| 3 | d | 5 | 10 |

## Chapter 17

**Matching**

1. f 6. c
2. a 7. e
3. j 8. h
4. i 9. g
5. d 10. b

**True/False**

1. T 3. T 5. F
2. F 4. T

**Fill in the Blank**

1. metals, non-metals

2. scandium
3. highest, lowest
4. proportions
5. decrease

**Analysis**

1. a 2. c 3. d 4. d

5. Li, Na
   Mg, Ca
   F, Br
   Ne, Ar
   N, As

## Chapter 18

**Matching**

1. e 3. d 5. b
2. c 4. a 6. f

**True/False**

1. T 3. F 5. T
2. F 4. T

**Fill in the Blank**

1. irreversible
2. lower

3. system, surroundings

**Analysis**

1. a 3. c 5. d 7. e
2. c 4. e 6. d
8. The ice in the ice-box naturally changes from a solid to a liquid. As the ice melts, the temperature increases with the increasing entropy. The temperature will never become cooler than 0°

C without increasing disorder elsewhere.
9. As the pressure lowers, the temperature of the refrigerant drops. Since the food reaches a temperature of about –10 °C and heat naturally flows from hotter to colder objects, we can assume that the temperature of the refrigerant reaches a temperature of less than –10 °C during the expansion process.

10. a. The salt solution
    b. Water in the gaseous state
    c. The mixed chamber
4. Aluminum changing between a solid and a liquid state is a reversible process. Aluminum naturally changes from a liquid to a solid as the temperature cools, but to "reverse" this process, heat must be applied, increasing overall entropy.

## Chapter 19

**Matching**

1. d 3. f 5. a
2. e 4. c 6. b

**True/False**

1. T 2. T 3. F 4. F

5. F

**Fill in the Blank**

1. $C_4H_{10}$
2. $C_2H_4O_2$
3. $C_6H_8O_6$

4. $C_8H_{10}O_2N_4$
5. a. 4
   b. 4
   c. 1
   d. hydrocarbon

**Analysis**

1. d

## Chapter 20

**Matching**

1. c 3. e 5. a
2. d 4. b

**True/False**

1. F 3. T 5. F
2. T 4. F

**Fill in the Blank**

1. activation energy
2. catalyst
3. identical

4. uphill
5. decrease
6. equilibrium

**Analysis**

1. a, c, e
2. To the first student: This equation is incorrect because the two sides are not balanced. On the left side, there are 2 hydrogen and 2 oxygen atoms, on the right side, there are 2

hydrogen and only 1 oxygen atom. To the second student: Although the number of molecules matches on each side, the right side forms a compound other than water (the ratio that forms water: 2 hydrogen to 1 oxygen).
3. d
4. a. A favorable entropy change (atoms are mixing and heat is given off in the explosion)

b. Both (states change from a liquid to a liquid and a gas, and energy is given off)
c. favorable entropy change (states stay the same, energy is given off)
d. Both (state changes from a solid and a liquid to only a liquid, atoms increase in movement, and energy is absorbed)

## Chapter 21

**Matching**

1. d 4. e 7. f 10. b
2. i 5. a 8. j
3. c 6. h 9. g

**True/False**

1. F 4. F 7. T
2. T 5. F
3. F 6. T

**Fill in the Blank**

1. wave
2. sizes, energies, valence
3. fluid-like, lubricant

4. band gaps

**Analysis**

1. b 2. c 3. b 4. d

## Chapter 22

**Matching**

1. c 3. b 5. a
2. f 4. e 6. d

**True or False**

1. F 2. F 3. T 4. T

5. T 6. F

**Fill in the Blank**

1. transition metals
2. lowest
3. large, small

4. electrons
5. attractive
6. opposite
7. metal, non-metal

**Analysis**

1. c
2. a. Mg2+
   b. Cl–
   c. Because salts must be electrically neutral and it takes

# Selected Answers

2 Cl– ions to balance a single Mg2+ ion.

d. The overall electronic energy decreases. Energy tends to go downhill.

e. The energy is given off as heat and/or light, which increase the entropy (disorder) of the surroundings.

3. a. shear

---

b. the top one

c. A favorable potential energy situation is when each ion is closest to ions of an opposite charge. In the lower of the two pictures, negative ions are adjacent to negative ions and positive ions next to positive ones.

4. c

---

5. d

6. a. Na and K both form +1 ions
   Mg and Ca both form +2 ions
   Cl and Br form -1 ions
   O and S form -2 ions

   b. only $K_2S$

7. d

8. c

9. A heap of small bits of crystals scatter light; no colors of visible

---

light are absorbed. All colors get reflected back at you and so the crystals appear white.

10. Rubies contain Cr3+ ions, which absorb blue and green photons; sapphires contain Ti4+ and Fe2+ ; the combined effect of the absorption of visible light by these two transition metal ions is to give a blue color.

---

## Chapter 23

### Matching

1. e   4. i   7. c
2. g   5. f   8. d
3. h   6. a   9. b

### True or False

1. T   2. F   3. T   4. F

---

5. F   6. T

### Analysis

1. b
2. c, e, f, g
3. c

---

4. Both C and O are non-metals, so they will form covalent, molecular compounds. The only choice that fits for such compounds is b. As it turns out, both carbon monoxide and carbon dioxide are transparent

---

gases. Answer a describes a compound of metals, answer c is not physically reasonable (because all metals conduct electricity), and answer d describes an ionic material like table salt.

---

## Chapter 24

### Matching

1. h   4. a   7. c
2. b   5. g   8. e
3. f   6. d

---

### True or False

1. T   4. T   7. T   10. F
2. T   5. F   8. F   11. T
3. F   6. T   9. T

---

### Fill in the Blank

1. triglyceride
2. saturated
3. crystalline

---

4. tetrahedron
5. trans-fatty, cis-fatty

### Analysis

1. b   2. c   3. b   4. d

---

## Chapter 25

### Matching

1. d   5. f
2. e   6. b
3. a   7. h
4. g   8. c

---

### True/ False

1. T   5. F
2. T
3. T
4. T

---

### Fill in the Blank

1. less
2. isotopes
3. radioactive decay
4. fusion

---

5. fission
6. element

### Analysis

1. c   3. d   5. c
2. a   4. c   6. d

---

## Chapter 26

### Matching

1. h   5. g   9. d   13. a
2. l   6. k   10. c   14. o
3. n   7. m   11. e   15. j
4. b   8. i   12. f

### True/ False

1. F   2. T   3. F   4. T

### Fill in the Blank

1. seismometer or seismograph
2. Curie temperature
3. focus, epicenter
4. liquid, solid
5. Moho

### Analysis

1. b   3. d   5. b
2. d   4. d

6. The asthenosphere is composed of a soft, plastic, partially-molten

---

mechanical layer in Earth located below the lithosphere. We know the composition through studying seismic waves traveling through Earth's center.

7. The lithosphere, the asthenosphere, the mesosphere, the outer core, and inner core.

8. Iron meteorites are thought to represent the type of material found in Earth's core.

9. Remember the Silly Putty example? Plastic means non-rigid, deformable, and capable of flowing in response to pressure.

10. Compositional layers differ in the kind of material they are made of. They are the crust, mantle, and core. Mechanical layers differ in the behavior of the material. These layers are lithosphere, the asthenosphere,

---

the mesosphere, and the outer and inner core.

11. The inner core is at a higher temperature than the outer core, but it is also under higher pressure. The pressure is so large that, at the prevailing temperatures, the core is solid iron.

12. Earth's interior is differentiated (meaning it has different distinct layers) both mechanically and compositionally. As one goes deeper, the composition and behavior of the material of Earth changes several times.

13. Seismic waves make abrupt changes when traveling through Earth's interior when they encounter an abrupt change in elasticity of the rock and refract. Waves travel in curved paths

---

when the density changes slowly with depth.

14. P-waves are compression waves. They travel the fastest through Earth and so are the first to arrive at any seismic wave detectors. S-waves are shear waves produced by an earthquake. They are slower than P-waves and so arrive later at seismic wave detectors. S-waves cannot travel through the liquid outer core.

15. The focus is the place inside Earth where an earthquake originates and the epicenter is the point on Earth's surface directly above the focus.

16. The process by which the lithosphere ruptures and returns to its normal form after being bent under pressure.

# Chapter 27

## Matching
1. h    4. k    7. b    10. c
2. e    5. a    8. f    11. d
3. i    6. g    9. j

## True/ False
1. F    3. F    5. F    7. T
2. T    4. T    6. F

## Fill in the Blank
1. Paleoclimatic
2. normal, reverse
3. basalt, sediment
4. margins or edges
5. parallel
6. mantle plumes
7. ocean-continental
8. denser, sink

## Analysis
1. c    3. a    5. b    7. a
2. d    4. c    6. b    8. a

9. The continental shelves are those portions of the continents that happen to be below the sea level at this time. They consist of continental rock and are not part of the ocean basin.

10. If the directions of the inherent magnetic fields of ancient lava flows on different continents are measured, it is found that they do not all point towards the same north pole. However, if the continents have rearranged so that their continental shelves fit best, then the magnetic directions all point towards a single location. In answering this question, you should discuss the origin of magnetic fields in rocks, including the concept of the Curie temperature.

11. The parallelism of the Atlantic coastlines and the similarities fossils on different continents.

12. The increasing age of the seafloor rock from the ridges, and the presence of guyots.

13. The supercontinent that broke up at the start of the Mesozoic Era to form the continents we have today.

14. Wegener and his colleagues gave evidences such as the jigsaw fit of the continents, continuity of structural trends, fossils of similar ages and type on different continents, Permian glaciation on multiple continents, and Paleomagnetic evidence.

15. If the continents are assembled into Pangaea, all the glaciation grooves align in a logical and consistent manner.

16. Fold mountain belts come into existence when a continental mass located on a plate boundary becomes involved in a plate convergence—particularly a continent-continent collision. As two continents collide, they do so along a relatively long, narrow collision zone.

17. Answers should include ridge push and slab pull working together to slide a plate towards the trenches and what role basal drive plays, if any. Also include how this results in new ocean floor being created and how the age of the plate increases away from the ridges.

18. Island arcs are always found in association with ocean trenches, but islands chains are formed over hot spots. Trenches are larger than mantle plumes, thus islands arcs tend to be larger.

19. The lithosphere is young and warm and it has hot, low-density asthenosphere welling up beneath it.

# Chapter 28

## Matching
1. f    5. l    9. e    13. j
2. i    6. g    10. h
3. a    7. b    11. k
4. c    8. m    12. d

## True/False
1. F    3. T    5. F
2. F    4. T

## Fill in the Blank
1. uniformitarianism
2. Principle of inclusions
3. unconformity
4. fossils
5. faunal succession

## Analysis
1. d    3. c    5. c    7. c
2. b    4. a    6. b

8. The Geologic Column evolved over a period of many years, before there was a way to determine absolute ages. The periods of the Column were calculated on the basis of the appearance and disappearance of particular fossils in the rock record, but there was no way to know whether the fossils chosen yielded periods of anywhere near uniform length. We now know they didn't.

9. Carbon-14 has a half-life of only 5,730 years—far too short to use for dating anything older than very recent materials (70,000 years old at most). In addition, Carbon-14 measures the time since an object died and stopped replenishing its complement of radioactive carbon, so objects dated in this way must once have been alive.

10. Relative dating compares events according to when they happened. For example, we know that a couple must meet before they can date. They must date before they get engaged and they must get married only after they have been engaged. Absolute dating is an exact date of when events happen. To use the same example: A couple first met in the beginning of January, started dating at the end of January, became engaged in April, and married in July.

11. The same decay curve can be used for all radioactive isotopes because when the time length of the half-life is reached, half of the isotope is decayed. After the time length of the half-life is reached again, half of the remaining isotope has decayed. Therefore, the same decay curve can be used for all radioactive isotopes by simply changing the half-life time along the horizontal axis.

12. Uniformitarianism states that the laws of nature do not change over time. This is essential to understanding the history of Earth because it states that other principles, such as inclusion, cross-cutting relationships, and superposition happen identically today as they did at the foundation of Earth.

13. 1) Principle of Original Horizontality
2) Principle of Superposition
3) Principle of Inclusion
4) Principle of Cross-Cutting Relationships
5) Principle of Faunal Succession

14. Refer to page 327.

15. (Answers may vary) One early method used by James Ussher was to use the genealogy from the Bible. The error with this method is the assumption that Earth was literally created in one week. Other early attempts consist of Lord Kelvin's cooling rates method, calculating the salt accumulation, and the accumulated thickness of sedimentary rock. Problems with these attempts include radioactive decay at Earth's core causes heating, salt has precipitated out of the ocean, and sedimentary rock contains numerous unconformities, respectively.

16. You are measuring how long ago the rock solidified enough to trap the daughter products.

# Chapter 29

## Matching
1. d    4. g    7. f    10. j
2. e    5. b    8. i
3. c    6. a    9. h

## True/False
1. T    3. T    5. T
2. F    4. F

## Fill in the Blank
1. rock cycle
2. magma
3. limestone
4. sedimentary rocks
5. basalt, igneous

## Analysis
1. b    3. a    5. a    7. a
2. b    4. c    6. a

8. Igneous rocks form from molten material (lava if it erupts onto the surface of Earth, magma if it remains below the surface) that cools and crystallizes. Sedimentary rocks consist of debris deposited in layers and cemented together, either by chemicals dissolved in groundwater or by heat and pressure from the weight of overlying layers. Metamorphic rocks are made from igneous, sedimentary, or other metamorphic rocks whose mineral composition is changed by a combination of heat, pressure, and fluids.

9. The size of a crystal in an igneous rock depends on the amount of time the rock had to cool. Crystals grow larger if they have more time to cool (such as those that cool slowly inside the earth). Therefore, igneous rocks with larger crystals cooled slower.

Generally, if the crystals are visible to the naked eye, the rock is plutonic.

10. The two types of igneous rocks are volcanic and plutonic. Volcanic rocks formed on Earth's surface, while plutonic rocks formed beneath Earth's surface.

11. Using radioactive dating techniques on the minerals in a metamorphic rock, we can learn exactly when the metamorphism and foliation occurred.

12. Igneous rock can be eroded at Earth's surface to form sedimentary rock. Sedimentary rock can be heated and recrystallized into metamorphic rock. Metamorphic rock can be melted into magma and resolidified to form igneous rock.

Any of the three rock types can be processed into the other two or into another version of the same type. See Fig. 29.4

13. Because melting is determined by both pressure and temperature, rock in the mantle melts only if it is in the right "zone of melting" with the right pressure and temperature ideal for melting. See Fig. 29.8 and 29.9.

14. The two most important agents of physical weathering is the melting and freezing of water and ice.

15. Clasts must stick together by being buried, compacted, and cemented together by minerals precipitating from ground water into the empty spaces between grains.

## Chapter 30

### Matching

| | | | |
|---|---|---|---|
| 1. g | 4. d | 7. e | 10. c |
| 2. i | 5. k | 8. f | 11. j |
| 3. a | 6. b | 9. h | |

### True/False

| | | |
|---|---|---|
| 1. F | 3. T | 5. T |
| 2. T | 4. F | |

### Fill in the Blank

1. groundwater
2. stream

3. erode
4. deposited
5. alluvial fan
6. weight

### Analysis

| | | | |
|---|---|---|---|
| 1. b | 4. a | 7. a | 10. c |
| 2. c | 5. c | 8. e | 11. b |
| 3. a | 6. d | 9. a | |

12. As the amount of water increases in a stream, the velocity increases.

13. As the down gradient increases, velocity increases, and as the down gradient decreases, velocity decreases.

14. Alluvial fans form in relatively arid mountainous regions. They form when the stream exits the canyon at the base level of the valley floor, and the unconfined water abruptly spreads out, slows, and deposits any sediment that it was transporting.

15. The river slows gradually as it enters the valley, and the size of material it can carry depends on how fast it is moving.

16. Alpine glaciers are formed in a mountain valley, and cover a relatively smaller area. Continental glaciers cover a large portion of a continent or land mass.

17. Increasing the permeability of a rock may also increase its porosity.

## Chapter 31

### Matching

| | | | |
|---|---|---|---|
| 1. g | 4. f | 7. a | 10. c |
| 2. e | 5. b | 8. d | 11. k |
| 3. j | 6. h | 9. i | |

### True/False

| | | | |
|---|---|---|---|
| 1. T | 3. T | 5. T | 7. F |
| 2. F | 4. F | 6. T | |

### Fill in the Blank

1. greenhouse gas
2. Milankovitch cycles
3. Temperature proxy

### Analysis

1. Weather deals with day to day changes, while climate is about long term averages.

2. a. Negative
   b. Positive
   c. Negative
   d. Positive
   e. Positive
6. a. natural
   b. Human influenced, fossil fuel burning

   c. Mostly natural, but irrigation does have a small impact
   d. Human influenced, farming
5. b
6. a
7. c

## Chapter 32

### Matching

| | | | |
|---|---|---|---|
| 1. f | 3. c | 5. d | 7. g |
| 2. h | 4. b | 6. a | 8. e |

### True/False

| | | | |
|---|---|---|---|
| 1. F | 2. T | 3. F | 4. T |
| 5. T | 6. F | 7. T | |

### Fill in the Blank

1. increases
2. elliptical
3. diminishes or weakens
4. baseline
5. angle
6. distance ladder
7. accretion

### Analysis

| | | | |
|---|---|---|---|
| 1. a | 5. e | 9. a | |
| 2. a | 6. d | | |
| 3. c | 7. a | | |
| 4. b | 8. e | | |

## Chapter 33

### Matching

| | | | |
|---|---|---|---|
| 1. f | 5. a | 9. j | 13. e |
| 2. k | 6. g | 10. n | 14. l |
| 3. d | 7. h | 11. c | 15. b |
| 4. i | 8. o | 12. m | |

### True/False

| | | |
|---|---|---|
| 1. T | 3. F | 5. F |
| 2. T | 4. T | 6. T |

### Fill in the Blank

1. Black holes
2. hydrogen
3. gravity, pressure from fusion
4. Hertzsprung-Russell diagram
5. Fusion
6. Nearby stars
7. apparent, true or absolute
8. absolute

### Analysis

| | | | |
|---|---|---|---|
| 1. a | 3. a | 5. e | 7. d |
| 2. b | 4. b | 6. a | |

## Chapter 34

### Matching

| | | | |
|---|---|---|---|
| 1. l | 3. c | 5. h | 7. b |
| 2. g | 4. a | 6. f | 8. e |
| 9. j | 12. m | | |
| 10. n | 13. k | | |
| 11. d | 14. i | | |

### Fill in the Blank

1. helium
2. red

### Analysis

| | | | |
|---|---|---|---|
| 1. b | 3. c | 5. a | 7. e |
| 2. a | 4. c | 6. d | 8. a |

# Glossary

## A

**Absolute Luminosity:** The actual amount of energy radiated from an object.

**Absolute Time:** A numeric or quantitative measure of time.

**Acceleration:** Rate of change of velocity per unit time, or change of velocity divided by the time required for the change.

**Acidic:** Having a pH value less than 7, meaning that the hydronium ion concentration is greater than in pure water.

**Activation Energy:** The difference between the energy of the isolated reactant molecules and energy of the transition state. If the activation energy is added to a set of reactant molecules, it is possible for them to reach the transition state and go on to form products. Reactants with less than the activation energy do not normally form products.

**Activation Entropy:** The difference between the entropy (or disorder) of the isolated reactant molecules and the entropy (or disorder) of the transition state. Frequently, the activation entropy is unfavorable so that colliding molecules do not always react even if they have sufficient energy to react.

**Alloy:** A combination of two or more metals into a single homogeneous substance.

**Alluvial fan:** Sediment and debris at the mouth of a canyon deposited by intermittent water flow.

**Alpha Decay:** The radioactive decay of an atomic nucleus by emission of an alpha particle.

**Alpha Particle:** A positively charged particle that is given off by some radioactive materials including uranium, plutonium, and polonium. Alpha particles are now known to be nuclei of helium atoms.

**Alpine Glacier:** A glacier formed in a mountain valley.

**Alternating Current:** A current of electrons that changes direction of flow.

**Amine Group:** The grouping of $NH_2$ attached to a carbon atom.

**Ammonite:** The name given to the fossil-shell remains of animals that lived in the oceans millions of years ago, but are now extinct. They were squid-like animals whose closest modern-day relatives are the nautilus.

**Amplitude:** The maximum amount that a particle will displace from its normal, undisturbed position when a wave passes through it.

**Amu:** The abbreviation for atomic mass unit. One atomic mass unit = $1.660559 \times 10^{-27}$kg. This is the average mass of the protons and neutrons in a 12C atom. Because protons and neutrons are so small, it is more convenient to measure their mass in units of comparable size.

**Angular Momentum:** Angular momentum is a quantity that measures the amount of rotational motion an object has.

**Anions:** Atoms, or groups of atoms bound together, that have a net negative charge. In an anion, the number of electrons is greater than the number of protons in the atom or group of atoms.

**Anti-Bonding Molecular Orbitals:** Molecular orbitals that have low (or no) electron probability between atomic nuclei in a molecule and high electron density in areas not between the nuclei. When anti-bonding orbitals are occupied by electrons, the resulting electron density in the anti-bonding orbital helps pull the nuclei apart, weakening any chemical bond that may exist between them.

**Antinode:** A location of maximum vibration in a standing wave.

**Apparent Brightness:** How bright a star appears to an observer on Earth. It is a measure of the absolute luminosity as affected by distance from the object.

**Aquifer:** A ground layer saturated with water and having sufficient porosity and permeability to supply groundwater to a well or spring.

**Aquitard:** A ground layer saturated with water and lacking sufficient porosity and permeability to supply groundwater to a well or spring.

**Asthenosphere:** A soft, plastic, partially-molten mechanical layer in Earth located below the lithosphere.

**Atom:** The fundamental unit of an element.

**Atomic Mass Number:** The total number of protons + neutrons in the nucleus of an atom.

**Atomic Matter:** Matter that exists in the solid, liquid, and gaseous states as single atoms.

**Atomic Nuclei:** The positively charged central region of an atom, composed of protons and neutrons.

**Atomic Number:** The number of protons in a nucleus. This number defines an element.

**Atomic Size:** An estimate of the volume occupied by an atom. The number is obtained from the density of the solid state of the element.

**Atomic Theory:** The model that matter is made up of atoms.

**Authority:** An accepted source of expert information or advice.

## B

**Band Gap:** The band gap is the energy difference between the top of the valence band and the bottom of the conduction band in insulators and semiconductors.

**Base Level:** The elevation of a stream end point.

**Basic:** Having a pH value greater than 7, meaning that the hydronium ion concentration is less than in pure water.

**Beta Decay:** The radioactive decay of an atomic nucleus accompanied by emission of a beta particle.

**Big Bang Model:** A cosmological model that indicates that our Universe expanded from a specific moment of creation. It was later realized that this beginning would have to have been very hot.

**Blackbody Radiation:** Electromagnetic radiation given off by all objects with a temperature above absolute zero.

**Black Dwarf:** The remains of a Sun-sized star that have evolved to a white dwarf and subsequently cooled to where it no longer emits light.

**Black Hole:** Any object where gravity is so strong that not even light can escape from its surface.

471

# Glossary

**Blend or Composite:** Solution: A mixture containing two or more compounds, at least one of which is a liquid.

**Bonding Molecular Orbitals:** Molecular orbitals that have high electron probability between atomic nuclei in a molecule. When bonding molecular orbitals are occupied by electrons, the high electron density between the nuclei helps hold the nuclei together, contributing to a bond between the atoms.

**Brown Dwarf:** A low mass that is too small to sustain fusion reactions in its core.

**Brownian Motion:** The constant, irregular motion of very fine particles (such as fine dust or smoke) suspended in a fluid and observed with a microscope. Brownian motion is taken as evidence for molecules, which collide with the observed particles and cause the jittery motion.

**Buoyant Force:** A force pushing upward on objects immersed in a fluid.

## C

**Catalyst:** A chemical whose presence increases the rate of a chemical reaction without being consumed by the reaction. Catalysts make the energy and/or entropy of the transition state more favorable, without affecting the energies or entropies of the initial reactants or final products.

**Cations:** Atoms, or groups of atoms bound together, that have a net positive charge. In a cation, the number of electrons is less than the number of protons in the atom or group of atoms.

**Causality:** Cause must always precede the effect.

**Centripetal:** Toward a center.

**Centripetal Force:** A force sideways to the motion of an object. Centripetal forces cause objects to turn toward the center of a circle.

**Cepheid Variable:** A pulsating star used to find distances. It has a well-known relation between its pulsation period and absolute luminosity.

**Chain Reaction:** A chain reaction is one that is self sustaining or increasing once it has started. Dominoes knocking each other over is a classic example of a chain reaction.

**Chemical Bond:** The attractive force between nuclei and electrons that hold atoms together in molecules or atoms and ions together in network substances.

**Chemical Formula:** Way to represent the kind of atom and its number in a molecule. The chemical formula of a water molecule that contains two hydrogen atoms and one oxygen atom is given by $H_2O$. The subscript to the right of the atomic symbol indicates the number of that kind of atom in the molecule.

**Chemical Potential Energy:** The form of internal energy associated with the physical and chemical states of matter. This is the type of energy stored in a car battery.

**Chemical Properties:** Properties associated with the chemical reactivity of a material. For example, does a substance combine with oxygen or react with water?

**Chemical Weathering:** Breaking down rocks through chemical processes like acidic reactions.

**Chemistry:** Chemistry is the discipline in which atomic interactions are studied.

**Clast:** A grain of rock material weathered from a pre-existing rock.

**Climate:** The generally prevailing weather conditions throughout the year when averaged over several years. While weather changes rapidly, climate changes over time scales usually measured in decades.

**Compound:** Matter that contains two or more atoms in a fixed, definite proportion. New compounds form when the relative proportions of atoms change.

**Compression Force:** A force that is applied in such a way as to compress a material.

**Compression Wave:** A longitudinal wave driven by the force of pressure.

**Conduction:** The transmission of an electric charge or heat through a conducting medium without perceptible motion of the medium itself.

**Conduction Band:** The range of electron energy, higher than that of the valence band, sufficient to make the electrons free to accelerate under the influence of an applied electric field and thus constitute an electric current.

**Conductor:** A material that allows electrons to flow through it.

**Conductors:** Materials that conduct electricity in the solid and liquid state.

**Cone of Depression:** A region next to a well or source of discharge where the water table is lowered.

**Connectivity:** The details of how atoms connect to one another in molecules or extended structures.

**Conserved Quantity:** Unchanging in time. A quantity is "conserved" if the amount of that quantity does not change in time, even though processes may be changing its form.

**Constructive Interference:** When two or more waves passing through the same space at the same time both disturb the medium in the same way so that the resultant amplitude is larger than the amplitude of each individual wave separately.

**Contact Force:** The force arising between objects when they touch. Contact forces are a repulsion caused by the electromagnetic interaction.

**Continental Accretion:** The process by which continents grow. When continents collide with island arcs or with other continents, new material may be added and the continent grows.

**Continental Glacier:** A glacier covering a large portion of a continent or land mass.

**Continental Shields:** The oldest parts of the continents. They represent the roots of very ancient mountains, long since eroded away.

**Continuous Spectrum:** A spectrum in which the colors blend gradually together without noticeably abrupt changes or missing colors.

**Convection:** The process by which energy is moved from one place to another by being stored in matter as internal energy, then moving the matter from one place to another.

**Convergent Plate Boundaries:** Boundaries where two plates are colliding with each other.

**Core:** The deepest or central compositional layer of Earth. It is composed mostly of iron.

**Cosmic Microwave Background:** A uniform radiant field with an apparent temperature of 2.725 K that is observable in every direction.

**Cosmological Constant:** A constant introduced into the equations of general relativity by Albert Einstein in an attempt to cancel the predictions of the expanding nature of our Universe.

**Cosmological Red Shift:** The shifting of galaxy light to the red end of the spectrum caused by the expansion of the universe.

**Coulomb:** The unit of measure for charge; it is named after Charles Augustin de Coulomb, formulator of the Electric Force Law. The amount of electric charge possessed by a single electron or a proton is $1.6 \times 10{-}19$ coulombs.

**Covalent:** Materials characterized by chemical bonds that involve sharing electrons. Typically, the bonds in covalent substances occur between non-metal atoms.

**Covalent Bonding:** Bonding between atoms accomplished by sharing electrons to achieve low-energy arrangement of the electrons between the nuclei.

**Crest:** The part of a wave where the particles are displaced a maximum amount above or in front of their equilibrium position.

**Critical Mass:** The minimum amount of material necessary for each fission to result in one additional fission.

**Crust:** The uppermost compositional layer of Earth. It is very thin and composed of two parts: granitic continental crust and basaltic oceanic crust.

**Crystal:** A solid with a regular repeating arrangement of molecules or ions.

**Curie Temperature:** The temperature above which a metal is no longer magnetized. The Curie temperature is unique for different types of metals.

## D

**Dark Energy:** An energy associated with space that is causing the universal expansion to accelerate faster with time.

**Dark Matter:** Unseen matter in galaxies and galaxy clusters that exerts gravity within them.

**Delocalized Electrons:** Electrons in metallic orbitals are not confined to be near a specific nucleus, but have comparable probabilities of being around many different nuclei.

**Delta:** Sediment and debris deposited in an ocean or lake at the mouth of a river.

**Dense Oxides:** Minerals that form deep in Earth's mantle due to the enormous pressures.

**Density:** An object's mass divided by its volume.

**Destructive Interference:** When two or more waves passing through the same space at the same time both disturb the medium in opposite ways so that the resultant amplitude is smaller than the amplitude of each individual wave separately.

**Diatomic Molecule:** A molecule containing only two atoms of the same kind of element. Hydrogen, nitrogen, oxygen, fluorine, chlorine, bromine, and iodine exist in nature as diatomic molecules.

**Diffraction:** The changing of direction of waves to bend around corners and spread as they encounter obstacles.

**Dipole:** The separation of positive and negative charge in a polar bond or molecule.

**Direct Current:** A steady flow of electrons in one direction, typically through a wire.

**Discharge:** Water released from a groundwater reservoir.

**Discrete Spectrum:** A spectrum of separate and distinct colors in which not all colors are present.

**Dispersion Forces:** Weak intermolecular attraction arising from the formation of temporary dipoles in non-polar molecules. Also known as van der Waals forces.

**Dissolution:** To break apart or dissolve in solution.

**Distance Ladder:** A method used in astronomy where greater and greater distances are determined using many different measuring techniques that overlap to establish a sequence of increasing distances.

**Divergent Plate Boundaries:** Boundaries where two plates are splitting apart from each other.

**Domain:** A small section in a magnet where the magnetic force from all the atoms add together.

**Doppler Effect:** A change in the observed frequency of a wave occurring when the source and observer are in motion relative to each other.

**Double Bond:** A covalent bond involving two pairs of electrons shared between the two bound atoms. In chemical structure drawings, double bonds are represented by double lines. Double bonds usually involve four electrons, two per bond.

## E

**Elastic Potential Energy:** The form of internal energy associated with stretching or compressing material.

**Elastic Rebound:** The point at which stress in Earth's lithosphere is strained to a point where it can bend no further and the lithosphere ruptures and rebounds somewhat like a rubber band that has just been pulled apart.

**Electrical Conductivity:** A measure of the degree to which a substance conducts an electrical current.

**Electrical Potential Energy:** The form of energy associated with the relative positions of charged objects. Objects with opposite charges have maximum electrical potential energy when they are separated by greatest distance, but objects with the same charge have maximum electrical potential energy when they are separated by the least distance. This is the type of energy stored in a lightning cloud.

**Electric Current:** Electric charges flowing through a conductor.

**Electric Force Constant:** A number relating the strength of the electric force to the charges involved and their distance apart.

**Electric Force Law:** The mathematical formula $F = kqQ/d^2$ that describes the strength of the force between two objects of charge Q and q separated between their centers by the distance d.

**Electrolytes:** A chemical compound that ionizes when dissolved in water to produce an electrically conductive medium.

**Electromagnetic Interaction:** The interaction between charged objects that gives rise to the electromagnetic force.

**Electromagnetic Radiation:** Radiation originating in a varying electromagnetic field, such as visible light, radio waves, x-rays, and gamma rays.

**Electromagnetic Spectrum:** The entire range of radiation including, in order of decreasing frequency, cosmic-ray photons, gamma rays, x-rays, ultraviolet radiation, visible light, infrared radiation, microwaves, and radio waves.

**Electron:** An elementary particle in atoms having a negative charge. Electrons are located outside atomic nuclei.

**Electron Configuration Diagram:** An enumeration of how electrons populate atomic orbitals that is consistent with the "lowest-energy filled first" and "exclusion" principles.

# Glossary

**Electronegativity:** A measure of how strongly atoms attract electrons. Both ionization energy (the energy required to remove an electron from a neutral atom) and electron affinity (the energy gained when an electron is added to a neutral atom) contribute to electronegativity. Electronegativity increases from left to right across rows and decreases down columns of the Periodic Table.

**Electron State:** The combination of electron shell, orbital, and spin.

**Electron Volt (eV):** A small amount of energy used to measure energies of particles in atoms and nuclei. It is equal to $1.602 \times 10^{-19}$ Joules.

**Element:** A substance composed of atoms that have an identical number of protons in each nucleus. Elements cannot be reduced to simpler substances by normal chemical means

**Elliptical Galaxy:** A galaxy with an elliptical shape and little dust or gas.

**Emission Spectrum:** An emission spectrum is the set of colors of light given off, or emitted by, an object.

**Entropy:** A quantitative measure of disorder. It increases as the disorder increases. It can be calculated mathematically from the probability of obtaining the system in its current state.

**Enzymes:** Protein molecules that function as catalysts in biochemical reactions.

**Epicenter:** The point on Earth's surface directly above the focus of an earthquake.

**Equilibrium:** The condition where the forward and reverse rates of a chemical reaction are equal, so the system experiences no net change. Equilibrium is also the state of most favorable energy and entropy for a chemical system.

**Eras:** The largest subdivision of geologic time.

**Event:** A happening that occurs at a particular point in space and at a definite time.

**Exclusion Principle:** The rule that two electrons cannot be in exactly the same state in an atom. In other words, no two electrons in the same atom can have exactly the same shell, orbital, and spin values.

**Existence:** The fact or state of having actual or real being.

## F

**Families or Groups of Elements:** Elements that were grouped together because they had very similar chemical properties and are now known to have the same number of valence electrons. An element family occupies a vertical column in the Periodic Table.

**Fats and Oils:** Fats and oils are substances that do not dissolve in water, but can dissolve in hydrocarbon liquids. Fats are solid at room temperature; oils are liquid at room temperature.

**Fatty Acids:** A molecule with a long hydrocarbon tail and an acid group –COOH at the other end.

**Fault:** A break in Earth's lithosphere where rocks on one side of the break have slipped past the rocks on the other side. Faults are created by earthquakes.

**Ferromagnetism:** Metal alloys that are attracted to magnets or are capable of being transformed into permanent magnets are called ferromagnetic.

**Field:** Physical quantity existing at every point in space. Some fields arise from sources and may be thought of as the "influence" of these sources.

**Field Lines:** Lines coming from an object representing the strength of the force. The denser the lines, the stronger the force.

**Fission:** A nuclear reaction in which an atomic nucleus, especially a heavy nucleus such as an isotope of uranium, splits into two fragments of comparable mass, releasing energy.

**Fission-track Dating:** A type of radioactive decay clock that uses the trails or tracks created by uranium fission decay to determine the age of geologic events.

**Floodplains:** plains intermittently covered with water from a flooding river.

**Fluid:** Anything that flows. This refers to gases such as air and liquids such as water.

**Focus:** The place inside Earth where an earthquake originates.

**Foliation:** The structural or chemical arrangement into layers of materials in a rock.

**Force:** A push or pull on an object.

**Freefall:** The act of always falling under the pure influence of gravity.

**Frequency:** The number of wave amplitude crests that pass a particular point in space every second.

**Fusion:** A nuclear reaction in which nuclei combine to form more massive nuclei with the simultaneous release of energy.

## G

**g:** The symbol representing the acceleration caused by gravity. It is equal to 22 mi/hour per second or 32 ft/second per second or 9.8 m/second per second depending on the units.

**Gaining Stream:** A stream whose volume of flowing water increases from groundwater discharge along its channel.

**Galaxy:** A large collection of stars, dust, and gas that is found in a wide variety of sizes ranging from a few million solar masses for a small galaxy to large galaxies with more than a trillion solar masses of material.

**Galaxy Cluster:** A group of galaxies that is gravitationally bound together into a cluster, which vary greatly in size. A small cluster may have just a few members, while a large cluster may have several thousand.

**Galilean Relativity:** The notion that a final speed vector can be computed by directly adding all individual velocity vectors together according to the rules of Euclidean geometry.

**Gas:** A physical state of matter that readily changes both shape and volume to match its container.

**Gedanken Experiment:** A situation of logic contrived to illustrate a particular effect.

**General Theory of Relativity:** Albert Einstein's description of gravity that was published in 1915. This theory explains the relationship between the geometry of space and the flow of time in our Universe.

**Geologic Column:** A chart that shows the subdivisions of geologic time.

**Glossopteris Flora:** An extinct group of seed plants that flourished 250 million years ago. These plants went on to become a dominant part of the flora on the southern part of the supercontinent Pangaea, though they dwindled to extinction after 50 million years.

**Gravitational Constant:** A number relating the strength of the gravitational force to the masses being attracted and their distance apart.

**Gravitational Potential Energy:** The energy stored in an object that has the potential to fall. Near the surface of Earth, the increase of gravitational potential energy of an object that is lifted is given by GPE = weight × height.

**Gravity:** The interaction between anything with mass that gives rise to the gravitational force.

**Greenhouse Effect:** Short wavelength light from the Sun is transmitted through the atmosphere, warming Earth's surface. Longer wavelength light (also called infrared radiation or "heat") from the Earth is absorbed by greenhouse gases in the atmosphere. This prevents heat from escaping Earth as rapidly as it would without the greenhouse gases, increasing Earth's surface temperature.

**Greenhouse Gases:** Gases in the atmosphere that trap heat and keep Earth warmer than it would otherwise be, just like the glass in a greenhouse traps heat inside the greenhouse. Carbon dioxide, methane, nitrous oxide, and water vapor are the four most important greenhouse gases.

# H

**H-R Diagram:** A plot of stellar absolute luminosity verses color. Stars fusing hydrogen to helium in their cores lie along the main sequence in these diagrams.

**Half-life:** The time required for half the nuclei in a sample of a specific isotopic species to undergo radioactive decay.

**Heisenberg Uncertainty Principle:** The product of the uncertainty in an object's position and the uncertainty in its momentum must be greater than or equal to Planck's Constant.

**Hot Spots:** Volcanoes that result from the lithosphere moving over a mantle plume. Hawaii is an example of an island-formed hot spot. As the plate moves over the mantle, a line of volcanic structures (such as the Hawaiian chain of islands) marks the passage. The trail of volcanism is called a hot-spot trail.

**Hubble Constant:** The constant of proportionality, H, in the Hubble Law. It gives the rate at which our Universe is expanding.

**Hubble Law:** The proportionality between the observed recessional velocity of a galaxy and the distance to that galaxy.

**Hydrocarbon Molecules:** Molecules that contain only carbon and hydrogen atoms.

**Hydrocarbons:** Chemical compounds between the elements carbon and hydrogen. The compounds that make up gasoline are examples.

**Hydrogen Bonding:** Interactions between hydrogen atoms bound to oxygen, nitrogen, or fluorine with other oxygen, nitrogen, or fluorine atoms. Hydrogen bonds are among the strongest intermolecular interactions.

**Hydrological Cycle:** The movement of water through the various reservoirs on or near Earth's surface.

**Hypothesis:** A tentative explanation for an observation, phenomenon, or scientific problem that can be tested by further investigation.

# I

**Igneous:** The type of rocks produced when melted material solidifies.

**Inclusion:** Rock, fragment of rock, or fossil enclosed within another rock.

**Inertial Frame of Reference:** A state of motion that is experiencing no acceleration.

**Inner Core:** The lower part of the core that is made of solid iron.

**Insulator:** A material that does not permit electrons to flow through it.

**Interaction:** Any of four fundamental ways in which elementary particles and bodies can influence each other.

**Interference:** The canceling and enhancing effect that occurs when two waves move through the same space at the same time.

**Intermolecular:** Between molecules (as opposed to intramolecular, within molecules).

**Internal Energy:** A name given to energy hidden within matter but manifest by the temperature of the matter, the shape of the matter, the physical state of the matter (solid, liquid, gas), the chemical composition of the matter (i.e., the kind of energy that might be released by burning or explosion of a substance), etc.

**Interstellar Medium:** Gas and dust found in the space between stars.

**Intuition:** The act or faculty of knowing or sensing without the use of rational processes; it involves immediate cognition.

**Ionic Bonding:** Bonding between metals and nonmetals where nonmetals completely gain electrons from metals. Metal atoms lose electrons, forming positive ions. Non-metal atoms gain electrons forming negative ions. In the salt, positive metal ions are surrounded by negative non-metal ions, and vice versa. Because electrostatic forces are strong and long range, each ion experiences attractive interactions with many ions of the other type. The extended interactions give rise to the high melting points.

**Ionic Compound:** A compound formed between a metal and a non-metal. Ionic compounds are crystalline solids at room temperature. They conduct electricity when molten or dissolved in water.

**Ionic Conductors:** Materials that do not conduct electricity in the solid state, but do when molten or dissolved in water.

**Ionization Energy:** The amount of energy needed to completely remove an electron from an atom. The energy needed to remove the first electron from a neutral atom varies periodically with atomic number.

**Iron Meteorites:** Meteorites thought to represent the type of material found in Earth's core.

**Irregular Galaxy:** A non-symmetric galaxy that does not have a well-defined shape like either the spiral or elliptical galaxies. Irregular galaxies generally include dust, gas, and active star-forming regions.

**Irreversible:** An irreversible process is one that goes in only one direction; its effects often cannot be undone. Most processes which occur in nature are irreversible.

**Isotope:** Isotopes of an element have the same number of protons but differing numbers of neutrons. Thus they have differing atomic mass numbers. The number of neutrons can be found by subtracting the atomic number from the atomic mass number. An element's isotope is denoted by writing a superscript on the atomic symbol indicating the amu and a subscript indicating the atomic number, such as $2_1H$ or $3_2He$.

## J

**Jovian Planets:** The giant gas planets, which include Jupiter, Saturn, Uranus, and Neptune.

**Junction:** The interface between two different semiconductor regions in a semiconductor device.

## K

**Kinetic Energy:** The form of energy associated with motion. The kinetic energy of an object in motion is given by KE = ½mass × speed²

## L

**Laser Ranging:** A technique for measuring distance that is similar to radar ranging, but instead of reflecting microwaves, laser light is reflected off a nearby surface and the time for the reflected pulse is observed.

**Law:** A well-tested theory, so firm as to be unquestioned by science.

**Law of Constant Composition:** Substances contain a fixed, definite proportion of elements by mass.

**Law of Gravity:** Expressed by the mathematical formula $F=GmM/d^2$ that describes the strength of the force of gravity between two objects of mass M and m separated between their centers by the distance d.

**Law of Increasing Disorder:** Changes occurring in natural systems always proceed in such a way that the total amount of disorder in the universe is either unchanged or increased. If total disorder is increased, the process is irreversible. Also known as the Second Law of Thermodynamics.

**Length Contraction:** The shortening of an object along its direction of motion as its speed approaches the speed of light, as measured by an observer not moving with the object.

**Lepton:** Electrons and other electron-like particles such as muons.

**Light Year:** The distance light travels in a year, approximately ten trillion (1013) kilometers.

**Linear Island Chains:** A chain of volcanic islands created when an ocean plate moves over a hot spot.

**Linear Momentum:** An object's mass times its velocity. Measures the amount of motion in a straight line.

**Liquid:** A physical state of matter that readily changes shape to match its container but that resists changes in volume.

**Lithosphere:** The uppermost mechanical layer of Earth, which consists of the crust and the outermost part of the mantle that is too cool to be partially molten. It is brittle and is the only layer in which earthquakes can occur.

**Local Group:** A small group of about two dozen galaxies that is associated with our Milky Way.

**Longitudinal Wave:** A wave in which the molecules of the medium vibrate in the same direction as the wave propagates.

**Losing Stream:** A stream whose volume of flowing water decreases as stream flow is lost to groundwater recharge along its channel.

**Low-Velocity Zone:** A region of the upper mantle where seismic waves travel slower than expected.

**Luminosity:** The rate at which energy is radiated from an object.

**Lystrosaurus:** A sturdily built, plant-eating reptile (not a dinosaur). Scientists disagree on whether it spent most of its time in water browsing on plants like a modern hippo, or whether it lived mostly on land. An adult would have been about 3 feet long and weighed about 200 pounds.

## M

**Macroscopic Kinetic Energy:** The kinetic energy possessed by moving objects given by ½mass × (speed)².

**Magma:** Rock in a liquid state.

**Main Group:** The set of metal and non-metal elements designated with A column headings. They have valence electron configurations involving only s and p electrons.

**Main Sequence:**

**Malleability:** The characteristic of substances that allows them to be worked into desirable shapes or drawn out into wires.

**Mantle:** The middle compositional layer of Earth. It is a thick layer made up of peridotite in the upper part and higher density rocks of peridotite composition in the lower part.

**Mantle Plume:** A buoyant mass of hot rock rising through Earth's mantle. As it nears the surface of Earth, some of the plume melts and erupts at the surface forming a "hot spot."

**Mass:** The characteristic of a body which determines how much it accelerates when a force is applied.

**Maxwell's Equations:** A set of four fundamental laws, expressed in mathematical form, that govern electricity and magnetism and their interrelationship. The Electrical Force Law is included in Maxwell's Equations.

**Mechanical Energy:** A name given to the kinetic or potential energy of large, macroscopic objects.

**Mechanical Wave:** A traveling disturbance in material that transports energy.

**Melting Point Line:** A line on a plot of temperature and pressure showing where a substance transitions from solid to liquid.

**Mesosaurus:** A fresh-water dwelling reptile that lived from 300 to 250 million years ago. It had an elongated head and snout with nostrils near its eyes and a flattened tail used for swimming. Typically it would have been about 1.5 feet long.

**Mesosphere:** The mechanical layer between the asthenosphere and the outer core. It is solid, but still plastic and able to flow.

**Metallic Bond:** The chemical bond that binds metal atoms to other metal atoms in forming metal substances.

**Metallic Bonding:** Bonding in metals where large numbers of atoms collectively share electrons.

**Metals:** Elements that are good electrical and thermal conductors and can be hammered into thin sheets or drawn into fine wires.

**Metamorphic:** The type of rocks produced when pre-existing rocks are altered without melting by pressure and heat.

**Metastable:** A mineral that is unstable when subject to temperatures and pressures different from those of its formation, but not liable to spontaneously change.

**Meteorite:** A rock from space that hits Earth's surface.

**Microscopic Kinetic Energy:** The kinetic energy associated with atomic and molecular motions. A stationary object can have microscopic but not macroscopic kinetic energy.

**Milankovitch Cycles:** The name given to the three cycles in Earth's orbital conditions that influence climate on regular intervals of 100,000-year, 41,000-year, and 23,000-year cycles.

**Milky Way:** The galaxy of over a hundred billion solar masses to which our Sun belongs. As we observe it in the night sky, we see the faint band of light that marks the disk of our Galaxy.

**Minerals:** The basic building blocks of rocks.

**Mixture:** Matter that contains multiple substances. Many mixtures can be physically separated into their pure components.

**Model:** A schematic description of a system, theory, or phenomenon that accounts for its known or inferred properties and may be used for further study of its characteristics.

**Modified Solar System Model:** The Bohr model with restricted circular orbits of electrons around a dense nucleus.

**Moho:** The seismic discontinuity at the base of Earth's crust.

**Molecular Cloud:** A cold cloud of dust and gas dense enough to form stars.

**Molecular Ions:** Groups of atoms covalently bound to each other that have a net charge because electrons have been lost or gained to facilitate formation of the covalent bonds. Also called polyatomic ions.

**Molecular Matter:** Matter that exists as molecules in the solid, liquid, and gaseous states.

**Molecular Model:** Also known as the kinetic theory of matter, characteristics of the molecular model are: 1) Matter consists of tiny particles called molecules. 2) Each different kind of matter consists of a different kind of molecule. 3) The molecules in matter are in constant motion. 4) Molecules move and interact in accord with laws of motion, the laws of force and the laws of conservation.

**Molecular Orbitals:** Standing electron probability waves for molecules. These standing wave shapes and sizes are different from those for individual atoms because of the multiple atomic nuclei.

**Molecules:** The tiniest particles of a substance that retain all the physical properties of that substance. They are usually made up of more than one atom.

**Monounsaturated Fats:** Mono = 1 in Greek. Fats containing fatty acids with a single double bond, such as oleic acid.

**Moraine:** Rock and sediment carried by a glacier.

**Morphology:** The form or structure of a material. Asbestos, mica, and quartz all use silicates as a common basic building block. However, these building blocks are connected differently in the three materials. They each have different structures. Consequently, they have extremely different physical properties.

**Mountain Belts:** Regions of the continents where the rocks have been highly deformed by enormous forces. These belts usually lie along the edges of the continents.

# N

**Nebular Hypothesis:** The idea that the Sun, the planets, and other objects in the Solar System all formed from a single gigantic cloud of gas and dust. This hypothesis explains the major features and structure of the Solar System.

**Net Force:** The sum of all the forces present on a body.

**Network or Extended-Bonding Substances:** Substances in which every atom or ion interacts strongly with many neighbors. An extended network of linked atoms or ions form. Distinct molecules or ion pairs do not exist in these materials.

**Neutron:** An uncharged particle in atomic nuclei made up of three quarks.

**Neutron Star:** The remnant of a supernova explosion that is composed almost totally of neutrons. It is so dense that the entire mass of our Sun could be contained in a sphere only a few tens of kilometers in diameter.

**Noble Gases:** Gaseous elements in the rightmost column of the periodic table (helium, neon, argon, krypton, xenon, and radon) that exist in nature as individual atoms. They are quite unreactive and are very unlikely to form chemical compounds.

**Node:** A location of no vibration in a standing wave.

**Non-conductors:** Material which do not conduct electricity in any of their physical states.

**Non-inertial Frame of Reference:** A state of motion that is undergoing an acceleration.

**Non-Metals:** Elements that do not conduct electricity.

**Nuclear Potential Energy:** The energy stored in the nucleus of an atom.

**Nuclear Strong Force Law:** Scientists are still trying to figure out what the equation for the strong force looks like. Compare this with the Electric Force Law equation: $F = kqQ/d^2$.

**Nucleon:** A generic name for either a proton or a neutron.

**Nucleus:** The atomic nucleus is the very dense, positively charged center of the atom.

# O

**Occam's Razor:** The rule that where two or more explanations exist for the same physical phenomenon, we should choose the simplest one that satisfies all of the observations.

**Octet Rule:** An atom will most likely form an ion that has the $ns2np6$ configuration of the closest noble gas atom.

**Opacity:** The opposite of being transparent. Visible light is absorbed by an opaque object.

**Orbital:** A standing wave giving the probability of finding an electron in various locations around the nucleus of an atom.

**Organic Acid:** A molecule that contains the fragment $CO_2H$ attached to another carbon atom.

**Outer Core:** The upper part of the core that is made of liquid iron.

# P

**P-Waves:** Compressional waves produced by an earthquake. They travel the fastest in Earth and so are the first to arrive at seismic wave detectors.

**Paleoclimatology:** The study of ancient climates.

**Paleontologists:** Scientists who study ancient life preserved as fossils in the rocks.

**Pangaea:** Pangaea is the name Alfred Wegener gave to the supercontinent that broke up about 200 million years ago to form the continents we have today.

**Parent & Daughter Isotopes:** The result of radioactive decay, in which one element decays to form another element. The element we start with is called the parent and the new element formed in the decay process is called the daughter.

**Peridotite:** A rock made up mostly of silicon, oxygen, and the transition metals iron and magnesium. It is denser than the basalt and granite that make up Earth's crust.

**Period:** A subdivision of geologic time. Smaller than an era, but still several tens of millions of years long.

**Periodic Law:** The properties of the elements are a periodic function of their atomic masses.

**Periods:** Horizontal rows in the periodic table within which physical and chemical properties change systematically.

**Permeability:** A measure of how easily water can flow through rock or sediment.

**Perpetual Motion Machine:** A perpetual motion machine is something that keeps moving forever without any energy being added.

**pH:** A logarithmic measure of the concentration of hydronium $(H_3O^+)$ ions in water. pH values less than 7 describe acidic solutions, pH = 7 is neutral (that is, the pH of pure water is 7), and pH values greater than 7 indicate the solution is basic.

**Photoelectric Effect:** The ejection of electrons from metals when light is shined on the metal's surface.

**Photon:** A particle of light. It possesses energy, frequency, and wavelength but neither mass nor charge.

**Photosphere:** The visible surface of our Sun or stars. The region where visible energy is radiated into space.

**Physical Properties:** Properties like melting or boiling temperature, density, ionization potential.

**Physical Weathering:** Breaking down rocks through physical processes like freezing and thawing.

**Planck's Constant:** A value when multiplied by the frequency of light, gives the energy of the photon of light at that frequency.

**Planetary Nebula:** A glowing shell of gas that has been blown off a red giant star.

**Plasma:** A physical state of matter characterized by fluid properties in which positive and negative charges move independently.

**Plutonic:** Pertaining to igneous rocks formed beneath Earth's surface.

**Polar:** Bonds or molecules having an unequal distribution of charge (one end being positive, the other negative).

**Polyunsaturated Fats:** Poly = many in Greek. Fats containing fatty acids with many double bonds, such as linolenic or arachidonic acid.

**Porosity:** The percentage of empty spaces in a rock or that water can occupy.

**Position Symmetry:** The laws of the universe are not different at different locations.

**Potential Energy:** Energy that depends on the position of an object or on the positions of an object's constituent parts.

**Potential Energy Surface:** A diagram plotting the total energy of reactants and products as a function of the "completeness" of a chemical reaction. For all but the simplest reactions, these are multidimensional hypersurfaces that are difficult to visualize.

**Pressure:** The total force on an object divided by the area over which the force is applied.

**Principle of Non-contradiction:** Of two contradictory propositions, both cannot be true.

**Probability Curve:** A curve giving the probability of where an object might be detected. The particle is likely to be found where the curve is high and unlikely to be found where the curve is low.

**Probability Wave:** A probability curve that moves in time. At a given moment in time, the places where the wave is high are where the object associated with the wave is most likely to be found.

**Products:** Material(s) produced in a chemical reaction, written on the right-hand side of a chemical equation.

**Protolith:** A pre-existing rock from which other rocks are formed.

**Proton:** A positively charged particle in atomic nuclei made up of three quarks.

**Protostar:** An object that will become a star in the early stages of formation before it begins to produce energy from fusion.

**Pulsar:** A variable radio source that is thought to be a rapidly rotating neutron star.

**Pure Substance:** Chemical matter that has a defined, unchanging chemical composition.

# Q

**Quantum Mechanics:** The branch of physics used to describe the wave properties of light and matter.

**Quantum Model:** The atomic model incorporating the wave aspect of matter.

**Quark:** The elementary particles of which protons and neutrons consist. A proton and a neutron each consist of three quarks.

# R

**Radar Ranging:** A technique for measuring distance where pulses of microwaves (radar) traveling at the speed of light are sent to a nearby object and the reflected pulse is timed in order to determine the distance.

**Radial Shape:** A cross section of what an orbital would look like if it were sliced in two.

**Radiation:** The process by which energy is moved from one place to another in the form of light or related forms such as X-rays, gamma rays, microwaves, etc.

**Radioactive:** A term referring to atoms whose nuclei can spontaneously change under the influence of the weak nuclear force.

**Radioactive Decay:** Spontaneous disintegration of an unstable nucleus accompanied by the emission of ionizing radiation in the form of alpha or beta particles or gamma rays.

**Rate of Reaction:** The speed at which reactants are consumed and products are produced in a chemical reaction per unit time.

**Reactants:** The starting material(s) in a chemical reaction, written on the left-hand side of a chemical equation.

**Reason:** The capacity for logical, rational, and analytic thought—intelligence.

**Recharge:** Water that soaks into the ground replenishing the groundwater reservoir.

**Red Giant:** A large, bright, cool star that has exhausted most of the hydrogen fuel in its core.

**Reflection:** The act of bouncing off a surface.

**Reflectivity:** The characteristic of being capable of or producing reflection.

**Refraction:** The act of changing direction when passing from one medium to another.

**Relative Time:** The determination of the sequence in which events occurred, relative to each other.

**Relativity:** The idea that motion is only defined relative to other objects, which may have their own motion. There is no such thing as an "absolute" motion measured against objects that are absolutely at rest.

**Reservoir:** A place or state where water can reside within the hydrological system.

**Residence Time:** The average amount of time water spends within a reservoir.

**Resistivity:** A measure of the resistance to the flow of electrical current.

**Reversible:** A reversible process goes both forward and backward at the same time. Reversible processes are relatively rare in nature.

**Ridge Push:** Helps move Earth's plates. The ridge is high and has gravitational potential energy that is converted into kinetic energy as the plate moves.

**Rock cycle:** The transformation of igneous, sedimentary and metamorphic rocks from one type to another.

## S

**S-Waves:** Shear waves produced by an earthquake. They are slower than P-waves and so arrive later at seismic wave detectors.

**Salts:** Another name for ionic compounds.

**Saturated Fat:** A triglyceride containing three saturated fatty acid molecules.

**Seafloor Spreading:** The theory that the ocean floor grows on either side as the mid-ocean ridge moves apart. The rift created in this process is filled in with basalt as magma squeezes up into the fractures created by rifting.

**Sedimentary:** The type of rocks created from sediments weathered from other pre-existing rocks.

**Seismic Discontinuity:** A place where the velocities of seismic waves change abruptly.

**Seismic Waves:** Waves produced by earthquakes.

**Seismometer:** Device that measures ground motion.

**Self-ionization:** The reaction of certain neutral molecules (such as water) with other identical molecules to produce cations and anions.

**Semiconductors:** A solid crystalline substance, such as germanium or silicon, that conducts electricity better than insulators, but not as well as metals. Unlike metals, they become better conductors as their temperature increases.

**Sensory Data:** Knowledge obtained through the senses.

**Shadow Zone:** A region of Earth where seismic waves cannot be detected by seismometers.

**Shear Force:** A force that is applied in such a way as to twist or deform a material.

**Shear Wave:** A transverse wave driven by shearing forces between molecules.

**Shell:** A group of orbitals having similar energies and sizes.

**Silicates:** Minerals that contain silicon and oxygen bonded together.

**Single Bond:** A covalent bond involving one pair of electrons shared between the two bound atoms. In chemical structure drawings, single bonds are represented by single lines.

**Slab Pull:** Helps move the tectonic plates. As an oceanic plate becomes old, cold, and dense, it sinks back into the mantle, pulling the rest of the plate along with it.

**Solar System:** The Sun and all planets, comets, asteroids, and other bodies that orbit about it under the pull of gravity.

**Solar System Model:** A model of the atom in which the electrons orbit the small, dense, positively-charged nucleus in elliptical paths. The model was proposed by Rutherford.

**Solid:** A physical state of matter that is characterized by rigidity and resistance to changes in size and shape.

**Solvent:** A material (typically a liquid) in which another material dissolves.

**Spacetime:** Space and time connected together into one continuum by the special theory of relativity.

**Special Theory of Relativity:** The theory of how objects in inertial frames of reference behave at high speeds.

**Spectroscopy:** The study of the brightness and wavelengths of the different frequencies of light emitted by excited atoms and ions.

**Spin:** A characteristic of an electron, giving the direction of its intrinsic magnetic field.

**Spiral Galaxy:** A galaxy flattened into a disk shape with a pattern of spiral arms wound about a central nucleus. Spiral galaxies usually include dust, gas, and active regions of star formation.

**Stable Platform or Covered Shield:** An area of the continent where the old rocks of the shield have been covered by relatively flat-lying sedimentary rocks.

**Standing Wave:** A wave characterized by lack of vibration at certain points, between which areas of maximum vibration occur.

**Star Cluster:** A group of stars that formed from the same cloud of material and have been held together in a cluster by gravitational forces. A small open cluster can consist of only a few dozen members while a large globular cluster can contain more than a million individual stars.

**State of Uniform Motion:** The condition of an object when no unbalanced forces act upon it. A state of motion always refers to being at rest or in uniform motion.

**Stony Achondrites:** Meteorites thought to represent material from small planetary bodies that had differentiated into layers and then were broken up.

**Stony Chondrites:** Meteorites thought to be composed of unprocessed material from the original solar nebula.

**Strata:** A layer of material, often one of several layered upon one another.

**Stream:** A conduit through which surface water moves, either constantly or intermittently.

**Stream gradient:** The slope of the terrain over which a stream flows.

**Strong Nuclear Interaction:** The interaction between nucleons that gives rise to the strong force.

**Structural Trends:** Structural trends are the orientations of major geologic features such as mountain belts, continental shields, stable platforms, and areas of folded and deformed rocks.

**Subduction:** What geologists call the process that occurs at the trenches where old oceanic lithosphere is sinking back into the mantle. The trench area is also called a "subduction zone," and as the plates sink they are said to be subducting.

**Supercluster:** Clusters of clusters of galaxies.

**Supernova:** A rare celestial phenomenon involving the explosion of most of the material in a star, resulting in an extremely bright, short-lived burst of energy.

**Surface Wave:** A wave that travels along the surface of a medium.

# T

**Talus:** A sloping mass of rocky fragments at the base of a cliff.

**Tectonic Plates:** The brittle, rigid but thin outer part of Earth is divided into sections called tectonic plates.

**Tension Force:** A force that is applied in such a way as to stretch a material.

**Terrestrial Planets:** The rocky planets, which include Mercury, Venus, Earth, and Mars.

**Theory:** A set of statements or principles devised to explain a group of facts or phenomena, especially one that has been repeatedly tested or is widely accepted and can be used to make predictions about natural phenomena.

**Thermal Conductivity:** A measure of the degree to which a substance conducts heat. Metals have a high thermal conductivity.

**Thermal Energy:** Total kinetic energy of random motion of molecules in a material.

**Till:** Moraines left in the zone of ablation.

**Time Dilation:** The slowing of a clock as its speed approaches the speed of light as measured by an observer not moving with the clock.

**Time Symmetry:** The laws of the universe do not change with time.

**Trans-fatty Acids:** A non-natural form of unsaturated fatty acids in which H atoms are on opposite sides of the double bond. Cis fatty acids are the natural form. H atoms are on the same side of the double bond.

**Transform Boundaries:** Boundaries where two plates are sliding past each other.

**Transition Metals:** The set of metal elements designated with B column headings. They have valence electron configurations involving d electrons.

**Transition State:** The critical point that separates reactants from products on a potential energy surface. Usually this corresponds to the point on the path from reactants to products where the energy is highest.

**Transverse Wave:** A wave in which the molecules of the medium vibrate at right angles to the direction the wave propagates.

**Triangulation:** A distance measuring technique that involves observing the angle to a distant object from at least two different locations with a known separation. It is then possible to determine the unknown distance by comparing the observed angles.

**Triglyceride:** A large molecule created by reacting three fatty acids with glycerol.

**Trilobites:** A common animal that lived in Earth's oceans during the Paleozoic Era. They are most closely related to the modern Horseshoe Crab.

**Triple Bond:** A covalent bond involving three pairs of electrons shared between the two bound atoms. In chemical structure drawings, triple bonds are represented by triple lines.

**Trough:** The part of a wave where the particles are displaced a maximum amount below or behind their equilibrium position.

# U

**Unbalanced Forces:** The portion of the total force that is unopposed by other forces and so will cause an acceleration. An unbalanced force means that the net force is not zero.

**Unconformity:** A break or gap in the geologic record.

**Uniformitarianism:** The idea that the laws of nature do not change with time. This idea is also called the principle of "Time Symmetry."

**Uniform Motion:** Motion at a constant speed in a straight line.

# V

**Valence Band:** The low energy band of a semiconductor. Unexcited electrons reside here.

**Valence Electrons:** Electrons in the highest-energy, outermost quantum shell of an atom. Valence electrons determine an element's chemical reactivity, as only the valence electrons are involved in chemical reactions.

**Valence Shell:** The outermost, highest-energy set of orbitals in an atom. The arrangement of electrons in the valence shell determines how the atom interacts chemically with other atoms.

**Velocity:** The speed in a particular direction of a moving body.

**Void:** The space between galaxy superclusters.

**Volcanic:** Pertaining to igneous rocks formed on Earth's surface.

**Volcanic Island Arc:** A chain of volcanoes, shaped like an arc, that form at some convergent plate boundaries.

# W

**Water table:** The depth in the ground where rock is saturation with water.

**Wavelength:** The distance between successive similar parts in a repeating wave.

**Wave Speed:** The rate at which a specific wave disturbance travels from point to point.

**Weak Nuclear Interaction:** The interaction between nucleons that gives rise to the weak force.

**Weight:** A measure of the force of gravity pulling on an object.

**White Dwarf:** A small star that no longer sustains nuclear fusion and has shrunk to become a dense object about the size of Earth.

**Work:** The technical name given to the process by which energy is transferred to or from an object by an agent that exerts force on the object and the object moves along the direction of the force.

# Z

**Zone of Ablation:** The region of a glacier where snow and ice decrease by melting, sublimation or calving.

**Zone of Accumulation:** The region of a glacier where snow accumulates.

# Figure Credits

Cover  Kent Minson
Original images courtesy
NASA, Adobe Stock
Contents Splash and other space
images courtesy NASA
Unnumbered historical images courtesy
public domain
End of chapter quote page images
courtesy StockPhotoSecrets

## Chapter 1
Splash  Adobe Stock
1.1   Brent Laker
1.2   Kelli Rane
1.3   BYU
1.4   Kelli Rane
1.5   Adobe Stock
1.6   Chris Henderson
1.7   Adobe Stock
1.8   © 1992 The Harold E. Edgerton Trust.
1.9   Courtesy NASA
1.10  Photos.com
1.11  Chris Henderson, Devin LuBean
1.12  Chris Henderson

## Chapter 2
Splash  Courtesy U.S. Navy
2.1   Chris Henderson
2.2   Adobe Stock
2.3   Chris Henderson, Kent Minson
2.4   Chris Henderson
2.5   Kelli Rane
2.6   Chris Henderson
2.7   Chris Henderson
2.8   Kent Minson
2.9   Courtesy NASA
2.10  Courtesy American Lumberjack Association
Kilogram Courtesy BIPM.org
2.11  Chris Henderson, Kent Minson

## Chapter 3
Splash  Photos.com
3.1   Chris Henderson
3.2   Chris Henderson
3.3   Chris Henderson
3.4   Chris Henderson
3.5   Chris Henderson
3.6   Chris Henderson
3.7   Kent Minson
3.8   Courtesy NASA
3.9   Kent Minson

## Chapter 4
Splash  Photos.com
4.1   Kelli Rane
4.2   Kelli Rane
4.3   Chris Henderson
4.4   Chris Henderson
4.5   Photos.com, Kent Minson, Devin LuBean
4.6   Chris Henderson
4.7   Adobe Stock
4.8   Kelli Rane
4.9   Chris Henderson
4.10  R. V. Coleman and G. G. Scott, Devin LuBean
4.11  Kelli Rane
4.12  Courtesy W. M. Hess
4.13  Photos.com

## Chapter 5
Splash  Adobe Stock

5.1   Chris Henderson
5.2   Chris Henderson
5.3   Courtesy Mark Philbrick and BYU
5.4   Chris Henderson
5.5   Chris Henderson
5.6   Chris Henderson
5.7   Chris Henderson
5.8   Chris Henderson
5.9   Courtesy NASA
5.10  Courtesy NASA
5.11  Photos.com
5.12  Photos.com
5.13  Kent Minson

## Chapter 6
Splash  Photos.com
6.1   Chris Henderson
6.2   Kelli Rane
6.3   Kent Minson
6.4   Chris Henderson
6.5   Chris Henderson
6.6   Chris Henderson
6.7   Chris Henderson
6.8   Chris Henderson
6.9   Chris Henderson
6.10  Chris Henderson
6.11  Chris Henderson
6.12  Kent Minson
6.13  Chris Henderson
6.14  Chris Henderson

## Chapter 7
Splash  Courtesy NASA
7.1   Kent Minson
7.2   Kent Minson. Courtesy NASA
7.3   Photos.com
7.4   Kent Minson
7.5   Kent Minson
7.6   Kent Minson
7.7   Chris Henderson
7.8   Chris Henderson, Kent Minson
7.9   Chris Henderson
7.10  Chris Henderson
7.11  Chris Henderson
7.12  Courtesy SLAC
7.13  Kent Minson
7.14  Chris Henderson

## Chapter 8
Splash  Kent Minson. Modified from Photos.com
8.1   Kelli Rane, Devin LuBean
8.2   Kent Minson
8.3   Courtesy CERN
8.4   Kelli Rane
8.5   Kent Minson
8.6   Kelli Rane, Kent Minson
8.7   Chris Henderson
8.8   Kelli Rane

## Chapter 9
Splash  Courtesy NASA
9.1   Adobe Stock
9.2   Wikimedia
9.3   Kelli Rane
9.4   Chris Henderson
9.5   Adobe Stock, Kent Minson
9.6   Kelli Rane
9.7   Jennifer Berry
9.8   Kent Minson
9.9   Adobe Stock
9.10  Kelli Rane
Table 9.1  Adobe Stock

## Chapter 10
Splash  Photos.com
10.1   Brent Laker
10.2   Kent Minson
10.3   Kelli Rane
10.4   Kelli Rane
10.5   Kent Minson
10.6   Kent Minson
10.7   Kent Minson
10.8   Courtesy AP/Kyodo News
10.9   Annalee Palowski
10.10  Kelli Rane
10.11  Kelli Rane, Devin LuBean
10.12  Kelli Rane
10.13  Kelli Rane
10.14  Chris Henderson
10.15  Kelli Rane
10.16  Kent Minson
10.17  Kelli Rane
10.18  Kelli Rane
10.19  Kent Minson
10.20  Kelli Rane
10.21  Chris Henderson
10.22  Chris Henderson

## Chapter 11
Splash  Adobe Stock
11.1   Kelli Rane
11.2   Kelli Rane
11.3   Kelli Rane
11.4   Kelli Rane
11.5   Kelli Rane
11.6   Kelli Rane
11.7   Kelli Rane
11.8   Kelli Rane, Devin LuBean
11.9   Chris Henderson
11.10  Chris Henderson
11.11  Chris Henderson
11.12  Chris Henderson
11.13  Chris Henderson
11.14  Devin LuBean
11.15  Chris Henderson
11.16  Courtesy *American Journal of Physics*

## Chapter 12
Splash  Adobe Stock
12.1   Chris Henderson
12.2   Courtesy NASA and Adobe Stock
12.3   Kelli Rane
12.4   Chris Henderson
12.5   Chris Henderson, Kelli Rane, Kent Minson
12.6   Kent Minson
12.7   Chris Henderson
12.8   Jennifer Berry
12.9   Chris Henderson

## Chapter 13
Splash  Adobe Stock
13.1   Courtesy of IBM
13.2   Courtesy of IBM
13.3   Chris Henderson
13.4   Kelli Rane
13.5   Chris Henderson
13.6   Chris Henderson
13.7   Chris Henderson
13.8   Chris Henderson
13.9   Kent Minson
13.10  Chris Henderson

## Chapter 14
Splash  Photos.com
14.1   Kelli Rane , Chris Henderson
14.2   Kelli Rane
14.3   Chris Henderson

14.4   Kelli Rane
14.5   Kelli Rane, Kent Minson
14.6   Kelli Rane
14.7   Kelli Rane
14.8   Kelli Rane

## Chapter 15
Splash  Adobe Stock
15.1   Kelli Rane, Kent Minson
15.2   Chris Henderson
15.3   Kent Minson
15.4   Kent Minson
15.5   Courtesy of Hitachi
15.6   Kelli Rane
15.7   Kent Minson
15.8   Kelli Rane
15.9   Courtesy Richard Vanfleet
15.10  Kent Minson
15.11  Kent Minson
15.12  Paul Ehrenfest

## Chapter 16
Splash  Modified from Photos.com
16.1   Kent Minson
16.2   Kent Minson
16.3   Kent Minson
16.4   Kent Minson
16.5   Adobe Stock
16.6   Adobe Stock
16.7   Adobe Stock
16.8   Adobe Stock
16.9   Adobe Stock
16.10  Kent Minson
16.11  Kent Minson
16.12  Kent Minson
16.13  Kent Minson
16.14  Kent Minson
16.15  Kent Minson

## Chapter 17
Splash  Kent Minson
17.1   Kelli Rane
17.2   Kelli Rane
17.3   Greg Allen and Mark Clayton
17.4   Kelli Rane
17.5   Courtesy GSI
17.6   Kent Minson
17.7   Kent Minson
17.8   Kent Minson
17.9   Kent Minson
17.10  Kent Minson
17.11  Kent Minson
17.12  Public Domain

## Chapter 18
Splash  Adobe Stock
18.1   Chris Henderson
18.2   Kelli Rane
18.3   Chris Henderson
18.4   Kelli Rane
18.5   Kelli Rane
18.6   Chris Henderson
18.7   Chris Henderson, Kent Minson
18.8   Kent Minson and Photos.com
18.9   Chris Henderson, Kent Minson
18.10  Copyright Sydney Harris. Reprinted with permission.

## Chapter 19
Splash  Adobe Stock
19.1   Reprinted with permission
19.2   Kent Minson
19.3   Kent Minson, Chris Henderson
19.4   Kent Minson, Kelli Rane. Courtesy Mark Philbrick and

# Figure Credits

BYU
19.5 BYU Chemistry Dept.
19.6 Kent Minson
19.7 Kent Minson
19.8 Tyler K. Meldrum
19.9 Tyler K. Meldrum
19.10 Kelli Rane
19.11 Chris Henderson
19.12 Tyler K. Meldrum. Source: Japanese Spectral Database
19.13 Tyler K. Meldrum. Source: Japanese Spectral Database
19.14 Courtesy Dr. Steven Herron, BYU Department of Chemistry and Biochemistry

## Chapter 20

Splash Photos.com
20.1 Chris Henderson
20.2 Kent Minson
20.3 Kent Minson, Photos.com
20.4 Chris Henderson
20.5 Chris Henderson
20.6 Kent Minson
20.7 Chris Henderson, Kent Minson
20.8 Kelli Rane
20.9 Chris Henderson
20.10 Kent Minson
20.11 Chris Henderson

## Chapter 21

Splash Adobe Stock
21.1 Photos by Jon Hazen. Courtesy of salemoregon.com ©2005.
21.2 Kent Minson
21.3 Kent Minson
21.4 Kent Minson
21.5 Chris Henderson
21.6 Chris Henderson
21.7 Kent Minson
21.8 Kelli Rane
21.9 Kent Minson, Adobe Stock
21.10 Chris Henderson, Kent Minson

## Chapter 22

Splash Kent Minson. Modified from Photos.com
22.1a Courtesy International Crystal.net
22.1b, c Kelli Rane
22.2 Jennifer Berry
22.3 Juliana Boerio-Goates
22.4 Chris Henderson
22.5 Jennifer Berry
22.6 Chris Henderson
22.7 Kelli Rane

## Chapter 23

Splash Adobe Stock
23.1 Kent Minson
23.2 Kent Minson
23.4 Kent Minson
23.5 Kelli Rane
23.6 Kent Minson
23.7 Kent Minson
23.8 Kelli Rane
23.9 Kelli Rane
23.10 Kent Minson
23.11 David Dearden
23.12 David Dearden
23.13 Kent Minson

## Chapter 24

Splash Kelli Rane

24.1 Juliana Boerio-Goates
24.2 Kelli Rane
24.3 Kelli Rane
24.4 Kelli Rane
24.5 BYU Chemistry Dept.
24.6 Kent Minson
24.7 BYU Chemistry Dept.
24.8 Chris Henderson
24.9 Chris Henderson
24.10 Kent Minson
24.11 Tyler K. Meldrum
24.12a,b Kelli Rane
24.12c Kent Minson
24.13 Kent Minson
24.14 Kent Minson
24.15 Juliana Boerio-Goates
24.16 Kelli Rane
24.17 Kelli Rane

## Chapter 25

Splash Courtesy NASA
25.1 Jeanette Lawler and Jennifer Berry (data courtesy NIST)
25.2 Chris Henderson
25.3 Adobe Stock
25.4 Chris Henderson
25.5 Bill Watterson. Reprinted with permission of Andrews McMeel, a Universal Press Syndicate Co.

## Chapter 26

Splash Adobe Stock
26.1 Kelli Rane
26.2a Kelli Rane
26.2b Courtesy NSF and WUSTL
26.2c Courtesy Matteo Chinellato and www.mcomemeteorite.info
26.3 Chris Henderson
26.4 Chris Henderson
26.5 Chris Henderson
26.6 Chris Henderson
26.7 Chris Henderson
26.8 Chris Henderson, Kent Minson
26.9 Chris Henderson
26.10 Kent Minson

## Chapter 27

Splash Crustal Ages of the World's Ocean Floor—Müller, R.D., Roest, W.R., Royer, J.-Y., Gahagan, L.M., and Sclater, J.G., A digital age map of the ocean floor. SIO Reference Series 93–30, Scripps Institution of Oceanography
27.1 Chris Henderson
27.2 Chris Henderson
27.3 Chris Henderson
27.4 Chris Henderson
27.5 © Ken Lucas/ Visuals Unlimited
27.6 Wikimedia Commons under GNU license
27.7 Chris Henderson
27.8 Aaron Saxton
27.9 Chris Henderson
27.10 Courtesy the NGDC
27.11 Courtesy the NGDC
27.12 Chris Henderson
27.13 Kent Minson
27.14 Kelli Rane
27.15 Scott Layton
27.16 BYU Geology Dept.

27.17 Kelli Rane
27.18 Courtesy Peter Swenson
27.19 Kelli Rane
27.20 Kelli Rane
27.21 Kelli Rane
27.22 Kelli Rane
27.23 Courtesy the NGCD
27.24 Courtesy Bart Kowallis
27.25 Chris Henderson, Kelli Rane
27.26 Chris Henderson, Kelli Rane
27.27 Chris Henderson, Kelli Rane

## Chapter 28

Splash Adobe Stock
28.1 Bart Kowallis
28.2 Chris Henderson
28.3 Bart Kowallis
28.4 Jennifer Berry
28.5 Bart Kowallis
28.6 Bart Kowallis
28.7 Bart Kowallis
28.8 BYU Geology Dept.
28.9 Chris Henderson
28.10 Bart Kowallis
28.11 Chris Henderson
28.12 Chris Henderson
28.13 Chris Henderson
28.14 Scott Layton
28.15 Chris Henderson

## Chapter 29

Splash Adobe Stock
29.1 Bart Kowallis
29.2 Kelli Rane
29.3 Kelli Rane
29.4 Annalee Palowski
29.5 BYU Geology Dept.
29.6 Courtesy R. Weller/ Cochise College
29.7 Courtesy R. Weller/ Cochise College
29.8 Kent Minson
29.9 Kent Minson
29.10 Kent Minson
29.11 Annalee Palowski, J. Ward Moody
29.12 Adobe Stock
29.13 BYU Geology Dept.
29.14 J. Ward Moody
29.15 BYU Geology Dept.

## Chapter 30

Splash Adobe Stock
30.1 Chris Henderson
30.2 Annalee Palowski
30.3 Annalee Palowski
30.4 Annalee Palowski
30.5 Annalee Palowski
30.6 BYU Geology Dept.
30.7 Courtesy NASA
30.8 Courtesy NASA
30.9 BYU Geology Dept.
30.10 Courtesy NASA
30.11 Annalee Palowski
30.12 Annalee Palowski
30.13 Bart Kowallis
30.14 Bart Kowallis
30.15 BYU Geology Dept.
30.16 Adobe Stock
30.17 Annalee Palowski
30.18 Annalee Palowski, Kent Minson

## Chapter 31

Splash Courtesy NASA
31.1 Kent Minson

31.2 Annalee Palowski
31.3 Annalee Palowski
31.4 Courtesy Faye Hicks
31.5 Chris Henderson
31.6 Chris Henderson
31.7 Chris Henderson
31.8 Scott Layton
31.9 Scott Layton
31.10 IPCC
31.11 nature.com
31.12 IPCC
31.13 Scott Layton
30.14 Scott Layton
30.15 USGS

## Chapter 32

Splash The first Earthrise as viewed from the Moon by Apollo 8 astronauts. Courtesy NASA.
32.1 NASA
32.2 Hubble Heritage Team, NASA
32.3 Chris Henderson
32.4 Jennifer Berry
32.5 Jennifer Berry
32.6 Chris Henderson
32.7 Courtesy NASA
32.8 Courtesy NASA
32.9 Courtesy NASA
32.10 Courtesy NASA
32.11 Courtesy NASA

## Chapter 33

Splash Courtesy NASA
33.1 Hubble Heritage Team, NASA
33.2 Hubble Space Telescope, NASA
33.3 Hubble Space Telescope, NASA
33.4 Kelli Rane
33.5 Devin LuBean
33.6 Hubble Space Telescope, NASA
33.7 Courtesy CXC, HST, NASA
33.8 Kent Minson
33.9 Courtesy Richard Powell
33.10 Hubble Space Telescope, NASA
33.11 Kent Minson
33.12 Aaron Saxton

## Chapter 34

Splash Gravitational lenses seen by the Hubble Space Telescope in a distant cluster of galaxies known as Abell 1689. Courtesy NASA.
34.1 Kent Minson
34.2 Robert Gendler
34.3 Robert Gendler
34.4 Robert Gendler
34.5 Hubble Space Telescope, NASA
34.6 Hubble Space Telescope, NASA
34.7 Hubble Space Telescope, NASA
34.8 Courtesy STScI, HST, NASA
34.9 Courtesy STScI, HST, ESA, NASA
34.10 Chris Henderson, Kent Minson
34.11 Kelli Rane
34.12 Michael Joner
34.13 Kelli Rane
34.14 Kelli Rane
34.15 Courtesy NASA
34.16 Courtesy NASA/ WMAP Science Team
34.17 NASA
34.18 Hubble Space Telescrope, NASA

## Chapter 34

Splash Photos.com

# Index

# Periodic Table of Elements

**Legend:**

- Atomic Number
- Symbol
- Atomic Weight
- Name

Example:
36 — Kr — 83.798 — Krypton

- ■ Metals
- ■ Non-metals
- ■ Synthesized (do not occur naturally)

| 1A | 2A | 3B | 4B | 5B | 6B | 7B | 8B | 8B | 8B | 1B | 2B | 3A | 4A | 5A | 6A | 7A | 8A |
|---|---|---|---|---|---|---|---|---|---|---|---|---|---|---|---|---|---|
| 1 **H** 1.00794 Hydrogen | | | | | | | | | | | | | | | | 1 **H** 1.00794 Hydrogen | 2 **He** 4.0026 Helium |
| 3 **Li** 6.941 Lithium | 4 **Be** 9.0122 Beryllium | | | | | | | | | | | 5 **B** 10.811 Boron | 6 **C** 12.0107 Carbon | 7 **N** 14.0067 Nitrogen | 8 **O** 15.9994 Oxygen | 9 **F** 18.9984 Fluorine | 10 **Ne** 20.1797 Neon |
| 11 **Na** 22.9897 Sodium | 12 **Mg** 24.3050 Magnesium | | | | | | | | | | | 13 **Al** 26.9815 Aluminum | 14 **Si** 28.0855 Silicon | 15 **P** 30.9738 Phosphorus | 16 **S** 32.065 Sulfur | 17 **Cl** 35.453 Chlorine | 18 **Ar** 39.948 Argon |
| 19 **K** 39.0983 Potassium | 20 **Ca** 40.078 Calcium | 21 **Sc** 44.9559 Scandium | 22 **Ti** 47.867 Titanium | 23 **V** 50.9415 Vanadium | 24 **Cr** 51.9961 Chromium | 25 **Mn** 54.9380 Manganese | 26 **Fe** 55.845 Iron | 27 **Co** 58.9332 Cobalt | 28 **Ni** 58.6934 Nickel | 29 **Cu** 63.546 Copper | 30 **Zn** 65.38 Zinc | 31 **Ga** 69.723 Gallium | 32 **Ge** 72.64 Germanium | 33 **As** 74.9216 Arsenic | 34 **Se** 78.96 Selenium | 35 **Br** 79.904 Bromine | 36 **Kr** 83.798 Krypton |
| 37 **Rb** 85.4678 Rubidium | 38 **Sr** 87.62 Strontium | 39 **Y** 88.9059 Yttrium | 40 **Zr** 91.224 Zirconium | 41 **Nb** 92.9064 Niobium | 42 **Mo** 95.96 Molybdenum | 43 **Tc** 97.9072 Technetium | 44 **Ru** 101.07 Ruthenium | 45 **Rh** 102.9055 Rhodium | 46 **Pd** 106.42 Palladium | 47 **Ag** 107.8682 Silver | 48 **Cd** 112.411 Cadmium | 49 **In** 114.818 Indium | 50 **Sn** 118.710 Tin | 51 **Sb** 121.760 Antimony | 52 **Te** 127.60 Tellurium | 53 **I** 126.9045 Iodine | 54 **Xe** 131.293 Xenon |
| 55 **Cs** 132.9055 Cesium | 56 **Ba** 137.327 Barium | La-Lu Lanthanide series | 72 **Hf** 178.49 Hafnium | 73 **Ta** 180.9479 Tantalum | 74 **W** 183.84 Tungsten | 75 **Re** 186.207 Rhenium | 76 **Os** 190.23 Osmium | 77 **Ir** 192.217 Iridium | 78 **Pt** 195.084 Platinum | 79 **Au** 196.9666 Gold | 80 **Hg** 200.59 Mercury | 81 **Tl** 204.3833 Thallium | 82 **Pb** 207.2 Lead | 83 **Bi** 208.9804 Bismuth | 84 **Po** 208.9824 Potonium | 85 **At** 209.9871 Astatine | 86 **Rn** 222.176 Radon |
| 87 **Fr** 223 Francium | 88 **Ra** 226 Radium | Ac-Lr Actinide series | 104 **Rf** 261 Rutherfordium | 105 **Db** 262 Dubnium | 106 **Sg** 266 Seaborgium | 107 **Bh** 264 Bhorium | 108 **Hs** 269 Hassium | 109 **Mt** 268 Meitnerium | 110 **Ds** 271 Darmstadtium | 111 **Rg** 272 Roentgenium | 112 **Cn** 285 Copernicium | 113 **Nh** 286 Nihonium | 114 **Fl** 289 Flerovium | 115 **Mc** 289 Moscovium | 116 **Lv** 293 Livermorium | 117 **Ts** 294 Tennessine | 118 **Og** 294 Oganesson |

**Lanthanide series:**

| 57 **La** 138.9055 Lanthanum | 58 **Ce** 140.116 Cerium | 59 **Pr** 140.9 Praseodymium | 60 **Nd** 144.242 Neodymium | 61 **Pm** 145 Promethium | 62 **Sm** 150.36 Samarium | 63 **Eu** 151.964 Europium | 64 **Gd** 157.25 Gadolinium | 65 **Tb** 158.9254 Terbium | 66 **Dy** 162.5 Dysprosium | 67 **Ho** 164.9303 Holmium | 68 **Er** 167.259 Erbium | 69 **Tm** 168.9342 Thulium | 70 **Yb** 173.054 Ytterbium | 71 **Lu** 174.9668 Lutetium |
|---|---|---|---|---|---|---|---|---|---|---|---|---|---|---|

**Actinide series:**

| 89 **Ac** 227 Actinium | 90 **Th** 232.0381 Thorium | 91 **Pa** 231.0359 Protactinium | 92 **U** 238.0289 Uranium | 93 **Np** 237 Neptunium | 94 **Pu** 244 Plutonium | 95 **Am** 243 Americium | 96 **Cm** 247 Curium | 97 **Bk** 247 Berkelium | 98 **Cf** 251 Californium | 99 **Es** 252 Einsteinium | 100 **Fm** 257 Fermium | 101 **Md** 258 Mendelevium | 102 **No** 259 Nobelium | 103 **Lr** 262 Lawrencium |
|---|---|---|---|---|---|---|---|---|---|---|---|---|---|---|